Schizophrenia
Part Two
Biological Aspects

REPRINTED FROM

Schizophrenia

SECOND EDITION

EDITED BY
STEVEN R. HIRSCH
DANIEL R. WEINBERGER

Blackwell
Publishing

9600 Garsington Road, Oxford OX4 2DQ, UK

ISBN 1-4051-1413-4

Printed and bound in Denmark by
Narayana Press, Odder

Contents

11 The secondary schizophrenias

T.M. Hyde and S.W. Lewis

Schizophrenia is a behavioural disorder that is a diagnosis of exclusion. There are no established laboratory tests, neuroimaging studies, electrophysiological paradigms or neuropsychological testing batteries that can explicitly confirm this disorder to the exclusion of phenocopies. This was explicitly recognized by Kraepelin and Bleuler, and particularly by Schneider, as a caveat in the delineation of his first-rank symptoms.

The existence of a disparate range of brain disorders that can, uncommonly, give rise to schizophrenia-like symptomatology presents psychiatry with a problem and an opportunity. On the one hand, it poses nosological dilemmas about the limits of the definition of schizophrenia; on the other, it provides insights into the biological mechanisms underlying the generation of schizophrenic symptoms.

This chapter first outlines the nosological challenges and how recent classification systems have dealt with these, distinguishing secondary schizophrenia-like psychoses arising from defined neuropathological processes and those secondary to cerebral complications of systemic illness. Secondly, it attempts to estimate the prevalence of such secondary schizophrenias in relation to schizophrenia in general. Thirdly, it examines the evidence for symptomatic differences between secondary and primary schizophrenia and discusses their clinical diagnosis. Finally, the chapter reviews broadly which specific brain diseases seem to present a particularly increased risk of schizophrenic symptoms.

Terminology and classification

In the past, schizophrenia has belonged to a class of disorders conventionally known as 'functional psychoses' and this was the terminology that held sway in ICD-9 (World Health Organization 1978). Although the ICD-9 had several disadvantages, most particularly the absence of clearly defined reliable operational diagnostic criteria, one potential advantage was the adherence to a descriptive pattern of phenomenological definition. Thus, the term 'organic', as opposed to 'functional', was not intended to imply an organic aetiology, but specifically to describe a set of symptoms of cognitive impairment such as disorientation, reduced level of consciousness and impairments of memory. This allowed schizophrenia secondary to coarse brain disease to be classed under the rubric of schizophrenia, with appropriate subdiagnosis according to the pathology of the causative agent or disease. In DSM-III and DSM-IIIR, the term 'organic' was redefined in an important way, so as to imply an organic aetiology, rather than to describe particular symptoms in the mental state. Thus, separate categories of 'organic mental disorders' were introduced. Cases of psychosis without cognitive impairment, but in the presence of 'evidence from the history, physical examination or laboratory tests of a specific organic factor judged to be aetiologically related', were now called 'organic delusional syndrome' or 'organic hallucinosis', depending on the predominant symptoms. Nevertheless, in DSM-III it was acknowledged that symptoms in these 'organic' mental disorders could be 'essentially identical with schizophrenia'. This convention put the diagnostician in the problematic position of having to rename a syndrome whenever a likely organic cause became apparent (Lewis *et al.* 1987).

In so far as all behavioural disorders have a biological component, the differentiation between *schizophrenia-like* symptoms arising from a definite cause and those with an obscure aetiology is an inherently dissatisfying process. As we better define the biological basis of psychosis in schizophrenia, the aetiology of these pathological processes will become apparent. As it now stands, in a sense, schizophrenia is a term reserved for those 'idiopathic' cases of chronic psychosis.

Potential problems with the term 'organic' are exemplified by treatment of the term in the ICD-10 (World Health Organization 1992), particularly in the section on 'Other organic mental disorders' (F06). It is worthwhile examining this in a little detail so as to advance the argument that the term organic should be abandoned as a descriptor for schizophrenias caused by coarse brain disease. The ICD-10 use of the term organic introduces a paradox that is referred to in the text thus: 'use of the term organic does not imply that conditions elsewhere in this classification are non-organic'. Moreover, the criteria put forward in ICD-10 by which to identify disorders such as organic schizophrenia-like disorder are not strictly logical. One of the two requirements to justify a diagnosis is 'a temporal relationship (weeks or a few months) between the development of the underlying disease and the onset of the syndrome'. In reality, this time-scale limits inclusion to what are essentially precipitating factors rather than true causes which, as will be discussed later in the chapter, seem often to take several years before generating schizophrenia-like symptoms. A further limitation of the notion of splitting off 'organic' schizophrenias from schizophrenia in general is that our knowledge base as to the epidemiology of the first group, and of the relationship in general between the two groups, is very limited. The greatest difficulty in confidently diagnosing a case of organic schizophrenia-like disorder is in the attribution of the symptoms to a particular organic cause. This is seldom simple, particularly because there may be little time congruence between onset of the physical disorder and onset of the schizophrenic symptoms. It is this difficulty in attribution that seems to have led to the comparatively poor interrater reliability reported in recent field trials of ICD-10 for these organic categories, as compared with their 'functional' counterparts (Sartorius *et al.* 1993).

Spitzer *et al.* (1992) argued cogently for retiring the term 'organic mental disorders'. In this review we shall follow their lead. They asserted that the term 'organic' has insoluble problems attached to it and for this reason another term should be chosen. They considered the term 'symptomatic', but noted that this can be ambiguous and proposed that the term 'secondary' should be used instead. Secondary disorders should be distinguished from substance-induced disorders and are recognized if they are caused by medical disorders that are classified outside the mental disorder section of the ICD. Schizophrenic symptoms can thus be categorized in any individual case to being primary, or secondary 'to a non-psychiatric medical disorder', or substance-induced.

The DSM-IV (American Psychiatric Association 1994) has adopted this approach, which harks back to the phenomenological basis of classification in ICD-9. Sensibly, the introduction to the organizational plan in DSM-IV states that 'the term organic mental disorder is no longer used in DSM-IV because it incorrectly implies that the other mental disorders in the manual do not have a biologic basis.' Thus, schizophrenic symptoms secondary to a non-psychiatric medical disorder are now headed under the section 293.8 'psychotic disorder due to a general medical condition'.

Secondary schizophrenias can be thought of as falling into two categories:

1 Where the psychotic symptoms arise from the cerebral involvement of a systemic illness known to affect the brain. This is the category headed 293.8 in DSM-IV.

2 Where schizophrenic symptoms arise in the context of a demonstrable, often clinically unsuspected, neuropathologically defined disorder that is not part of an ongoing systemic disease process.

This latter area has become considerably more important since the advent of high-resolution neuroimaging techniques in the past 20 years. In the DSM-IV, this category is subsumed into the general class of psychotic disorders due to a general medical condition. This is paradoxical because many of these disorders are restricted to the central nervous system, such as neoplasms and cerebrovascular disease.

In reviewing the literature regarding the association between psychosis and coarse brain disease, another problem frequently arises. Over the decades, the term psychosis has been applied to a wide variety of signs and symptoms. Defined criteria for primary schizophrenia have only been commonly agreed upon in the past 30 years. Even within this period, the criteria have been significantly modified. The details of case reports must be scrutinized carefully. For example, a problem arises in differentiating disorders with prominent psychotic features from delirium. Most reserve the term delirium for an agitated confusional state, with prominent sensory illusions and misperceptions. In fact, there is significant overlap between the clinical signs and symptoms of delirium, primary schizophrenia and the secondary schizophrenias. A relatively abrupt onset and short time course helps differentiate delirium from the other two entities when reported in the literature. Frequently, however, many so-called secondary schizophrenias are actually delirious states, such as the encephalopathy associated with sepsis in the elderly.

How common are secondary schizophrenias?

Given the disputes over definition and diagnosis, it is not surprising that there is little known about the detailed epidemiology of secondary schizophrenia. One difficulty in estimating prevalence is the problem of definition: how confident can one be that the well-defined brain disease is truly responsible for the presenting schizophrenic symptoms? A second difficulty is that the closer one looks, the more likely it is that structural pathology will be revealed. The widespread availability of high-resolution brain imaging techniques has shown that unsuspected cerebral lesions occur in a small but significant number of patients with schizophrenic symptoms. Most structural brain imaging research in psychosis has concentrated rather on minor quantitative changes involving widened fluid spaces and reduced volume of particular structures in the medial temporal lobe. These minor quantitative changes would not usually be reported as abnormal by most clinical radiologists. However, there are a handful of reports in the literature of gross focal brain lesions in schizophrenia.

Three larger imaging studies using X-ray-based computerized tomography (CT) enable an estimate to be made of the prevalence of such unequivocal focal lesions in schizophrenia. Owens *et al.* (1980) in their series of 136 schizophrenic patients found 'unsuspected intracranial pathology' as a focal finding on CT in 12 cases (9%), after excluding lesions resulting from leucotomy. This was a relatively elderly sample: five of these 12 cases were

Table 11.1 Laterality, locus and nature of focal lesions found on computerized tomography in 13 of 228 schizophrenic patients. (From Lewis 1990.)

Site	Number	Nature of lesion
Right-sided		
Frontal	1	Low attenuation
Parietal	3	Calcified mass (1)
		Porencephalic cyst (1)
		Low attenuation (1)
Temporal	1	Old abscess cavity
Left-sided		
Frontoparietal	1	Low attenuation
Temporal	3	Arachnoid cyst (2)
		Calcification (1)
Occipitotemporal	1	Arachnoid cyst
Midline	1	Septal cyst
Bilateral	2	Occipital low attenuation (1)
		Parasagittal calcification (1)

aged over 65. Lewis (1990) examined a series of 228 Maudsley Hospital patients who met Research Diagnostic Criteria (RDC) for schizophrenia and who had been consecutively scanned for clinical reasons. Patients with a history of epilepsy or intracranial surgery, or who were aged over 65 at the time of scan, were excluded. The original scan reports were examined and the films of those not unequivocally normal were reappraised by a neuroradiologist blind to the original report. In 41 patients the scan showed a definite intracranial abnormality. This was in the nature of enlarged fluid spaces in 28 cases, but in 13 patients (6%) there was a discrete focal lesion. These lesions varied widely in location and probable pathology (Table 11.1), although left temporal and right parietal regions were most commonly implicated.

The third study (S. Lewis & M. Reveley, unpublished data) was an attempt to examine a geographically defined sample of schizophrenic patients, ascertained as part of a large multidisciplinary survey (Brugha *et al.* 1988). All Camberwell residents who, on a particular census day, were aged between 18 and 65 and were in regular contact with any psychiatric day service were approached. Of 120 eligible people, 83 consented to CT and psychiatric interview. Fifty of these met RDC for schizophrenia or schizoaffective disorder. In four of these 50 patients (8%) were found clinically unsuspected focal lesions: low density in the right caudate head; a left occipital–temporal porencephalic cyst; low-density regions in the right parietal lobe; and agenesis of the corpus callosum (see below). None of 50 matched healthy volunteers showed focal pathology on CT.

Given the differences in the nature of the patient samples, these three studies are in rough agreement about the prevalence of unexpected focal abnormalities on CT: between 6% and 9%. One magnetic resonance imaging (MRI) study has also examined the issue of the prevalence of focal abnormalities in schizophrenia. Given the higher resolution of MRI technology, one might predict a higher lesion detection rate than with CT. O'Callaghan *et al.* (1992) scanned 47 patients under the age of 65 meeting DSM-III criteria for schizophrenia, with 25 matched controls. Four patients (9%) were revealed to have unsuspected lesions of a neurodevelopmental type: one partial agenesis of the corpus callosum; two cases of marked asymmetric dilatation of the left lateral ventricle (one with an associated porencephalic cyst); and one cerebellar hypoplasia.

The only epidemiologically sound and well-executed study to report prevalence figures for secondary schizophrenias of the type produced by systemic physical illness is the study by Johnstone *et al.* (1987). The study examined a sample of 328 consecutive patients presenting with a first episode of schizophrenia between the age of 15 and 70 years. Patients were screened clinically, without routine diagnostic neuroimaging, for the presence of organic illnesses that the authors judged were 'of definite or possible aetiological significance'. Thirteen patients fell into the category of substance-induced schizophrenia, including one patient who was judged to have developed schizophrenia-like symptoms secondary to treatment with steroids. Nine patients (3%) were regarded as falling into the category of schizophrenia secondary to non-psychiatric medical disorders. These comprised three cases of tertiary syphilis, two cases of neurosarcoidosis, one case of multisystem autoimmune disease including systemic lupus erythematosus, one case of carcinoma of the bronchus with a secondary right parietal and frontal brain infarction, one of cerebral cysticercosis and one of chronic thyrotoxicosis. In these cases, neurological signs were the exception rather than the rule and a history of epilepsy was noted in only one case. Over half of the cases had migrated from developing countries and had presumably been at increased risk of untreated infections and other disorders. No case had a family history of schizophrenia. Two additional aspects of their data that were not specifically commented on by the authors were the relatively late age at onset of these nine cases (range 29–59 years) and, curiously, that all nine cases were female.

Inferring cause and effect

The establishment of a cause–effect relationship between a particular organic disease or lesion and schizophrenic symptoms in clinical practice can be very difficult. Table 11.2 gives general criteria by which observations are used in disease models to support the existence of a causal relationship. As can be seen, in the case of secondary schizophrenias several of these criteria are difficult to fulfil. Neurodevelopmental formulations of aetiology in schizophrenia generally are relatively recent, but mean that the temporality criterion can be difficult to demonstrate if the cause arises many years before the schizophrenic symptoms. None the less, there are clear instances in the literature of cause being attributed where it is by no means clear that the lesion predated the schizophrenia. For example, several old

Table 11.2 General criteria to support causal relationships used in disease models.

Criterion	Observation	Comments regarding schizophrenia
Temporality	Cause precedes effect	Cause may be several years earlier
		Problems with cross-sectional surveys of schizophrenic patients: temporality must be inferred
Consistency	Repeatedly observed	Many observations are anecdotal, single-case reports
Strength	Large relative risk	Relative risk difficult to establish because associations are often rare; best established for epilepsy
Dose–response	Larger exposure to cause associated with larger effect	May not hold for schizophrenia where specific subtle lesion may be important
Reversibility	Reduced exposure to cause associated with reduced effect	Not shown
Specificity	One cause leads to one effect	Several different causes with no clear common pathology; each cause can have different neuropsychiatric effects
Analogy	Similar exposure gives known effects	Closest analogy probably epilepsy; variety of causes, latent period, pleiomorphic behavioural syndrome
Biological plausibility	Makes sense	Neurodevelopmental model facilitates understanding of mechanisms; but what about non-neurodevelopmental causes?

postmortem studies disclosed brain tumours in schizophrenic patients without evidence that the tumour predated the psychiatric symptoms (Davison & Bagley 1969). In addition to the problems noted in Table 11.2, there are other difficulties in many cases. In some instances both the physical disease and the schizophrenic symptoms may result from another underlying cause. Epilepsy might be the best example of this, where both the symptoms of epilepsy – itself a syndrome – and schizophrenia may arise from some underlying brain disease, rather than epilepsy causing schizophrenia directly. Drug treatments of the physical disorder can also predispose to psychotic symptomatology; e.g. steroids and amphetamines (in the case of narcolepsy). A further possible confounding factor is that some aspect of preschizophrenic personality might predispose to health-endangering behaviours, e.g. head injury. Despite all these caveats, a number of different physical disorders have, down the years, been linked to the emergence of secondary schizophrenia.

The co-occurrence of schizophrenia-like symptoms and organic brain disease

In 1969 Kenneth Davison and Christopher Bagley published an extensive review of the world literature, backed with some 800 references, of the co-occurrence of schizophrenia-like symptoms and organic disease. This review remains a landmark in the field. It took as its starting point the operational criteria for schizophrenia of the 1957 WHO Committee, which were adapted slightly by Davison and Bagley so that their case material included cases which today would broadly be headed under the rubric of schizophrenia and paranoid psychosis. Criteria also included the absence of impaired consciousness and the absence of prominent affective symptoms. The authors concluded that the occurrence of schizophrenia-like symptoms exceeded chance expectation in many organic central nervous system disorders and that, where a discrete lesion was present, those in the temporal lobe and diencephalon seemed to be particularly significant.

Davison and Bagley reviewed the evidence for the association between schizophrenia and a large range of individual central nervous system disorders. Epilepsy was statistically associated with schizophrenia-like psychosis, particularly where a temporal lobe lesion existed. Head injury was also a risk factor for psychosis, again with a possible association with temporal lobe lesions. Severe closed head injury with diffuse cerebral damage was related to early development of psychotic symptoms. Encephalitic disorders, cerebral syphilis, Wilson's disease, Huntington's disease, Friedreich's ataxia, vitamin B_{12} deficiency, subarachnoid haemorrhage and cerebral tumour also seemed to be associated with an increased risk of schizophrenia-like symptoms. They found much less evidence to implicate other central nervous system disorders such as multiple sclerosis, motor neurone disease and Parkinson's disease.

Not surprisingly, 20 years later, a few of Davison and Bagley's conclusions might be amended. For example, their association between narcolepsy and psychosis most likely reflects a side-effect of amphetamines used in treatment, rather than the disease itself. The correlation between cerebral tumour and schizophrenia-like symptoms is weak. Many such instances could be better explained as chance association, unless the tumours were of the type whose natural history was very longstanding, such as hamartomas of the temporal lobe. Conversely, new evidence for these and other disorders being associated is now available, and is reviewed below.

Epilepsy

Estimates of the incidence of schizophrenic symptoms in temporal lobe epilepsy vary widely (reviewed in Hyde & Weinberger 1997), and are obviously sensitive to artefacts of ascertainment. Roberts *et al.* (1990) reported that 25 out of his consecutive autopsy series of 249 cases (10%) had a lifetime history of psychotic symptoms. Trimble (1988) estimated that patients with epilepsy were at three- to ninefold increased risk of schizophrenia-like psychoses.

The definitive case series of 69 patients by Slater and Beard (1963) noted that classical Schneiderian 'positive' symptoms were predominant, often without negative symptoms. Additionally, psychoses frequently arose in the context of a normal premorbid personality, without a family history of schizophrenia. An association between medial temporal lobe, particularly dominant temporal lobe, epilepsy and Schneiderian symptoms does seem to exist. Flor-Henry's initial report (1969) about laterality actually contained 19 cases of left and 12 cases of right temporal lobe involvement (most cases had bilateral involvement), a similar proportion to Slater and Beard's original series (36 left, 32 right). The 10 independent series to examine the laterality issue do show a trend towards left-sided predominance, as reviewed by Trimble (1990). None the less, the observation that about one-sixth of patients with schizophrenic psychoses of epilepsy had only right temporal lobe involvement detracts from the hypothesis that left temporal involvement is necessary: involvement of either side may be sufficient.

In temporal lobe epilepsy with psychosis, neurodevelopmental lesions in the temporal lobe such as hamartomas, rather than the early acquired lesion of mesial temporal sclerosis, are overrepresented. Taylor (1975) compared a series of 47 temporal lobectomy patients with hamartomas and focal dysplasias in the resected temporal lobe with 41 patients with mesial temporal sclerosis. Of the former group 23% had histories of psychosis, compared with 5% in the latter group: psychosis was particularly common in left-handed females. Roberts *et al.* (1990) noted that in 16 of 249 cases schizophrenic symptoms were present preoperatively; in a further nine they emerged postoperatively. Schizophrenic symptoms were more commonly found in those epilepsies associated with lesions originating *in utero* or perinatally, which were physiologically active at a relatively early age, as inferred from a comparatively early age at first seizure. The medial temporal lobe was most often involved. An unusual neurodevelopmental tumour, the ganglioglioma (also known as the dysembryoplastic neuroepithelioma, or DNET), was specially associated with heightened risk of psychosis, especially after surgical resection (Andermann *et al.* 1999). The reason for this association is unclear.

Two competing hypotheses attempt to explain the association between epilepsy and schizophrenic symptoms. Either both sets of symptoms arise from a common underlying cerebral pathology, usually in the temporal lobe, or, less plausably, the schizophrenic symptoms arise out of a process of progressive facilitation of subthreshold electrical activity ('kindling'). The relationship between the timing of seizures and the emergence of schizophrenic symptoms can vary. Classically, the schizophrenic symptoms emerge as interictal phenomena, although occasionally schizophreniform symptoms are part of a postictal psychosis or even an ictal phenomenon during partial complex seizures (Mace 1993). The scalp EEG usually shows no change during interictal schizophrenic psychosis, which argues against the notion of kindling being an important mechanism. Stevens (1992) has advanced a third, neurodevelopmental explanation of the link between epilepsy and schizophrenia, proposing that abnormal neuronal regeneration and connectivity develops in adolescence in some individuals with epilepsy that predisposes to schizophrenic symptoms. Many cases of partial complex seizures develop in late childhood and early adolescence (Mendez *et al.* 1993). Importantly, most cases of schizophrenia develop slightly later, in late adolescence and early adulthood. The overlap in the timing of the appearance of seizures and psychosis is congruent with the notion of neurodevelopmental pathology. More refined electrophysiological studies, perhaps using magnetoencephalography, may be the most promising avenue to explore the anatomical and physiological links between schizophrenic symptoms and epilepsy (Mace 1993).

Cerebral trauma

Head injury is a ubiquitous experience, but in its more severe forms causes lasting pathological change. The most comprehensive psychiatric study of brain-injured patients is the national Finnish cohort of war veterans described by Achté *et al.* (1969, 1991). Of these, 762 (7.6%) were described as having psychotic disorders, although systematic evaluation was lacking. Delusional disorder appeared to be the most common form of psychosis (Achté *et al.* 1991). In his earlier report, Achté *et al.* (1969) found that temporal lobe injury was the site most frequently associated with the subsequent development of psychosis. Gualtieri and Cox (1991) estimated that traumatic brain injury increases risk of psychosis by two- to fivefold. Many years often elapse between the head injury and the emergence of psychotic symptoms. Buckley *et al.* (1993) ascertained three cases of schizophrenia and two cases of schizoaffective disorder in whom the psychosis followed a severe head injury (loss of consciousness greater than 4 h). MRI showed no abnormality in the two schizoaffective patients. Left temporal gliosis and/or atrophy was consistently found in the three schizophrenic patients. Psychosis followed injury at intervals of 1, 7 and 19 years in these patients. Risk factors for psychosis following traumatic brain injury include pre-existing neurological disorders, head injury earlier than adolescence and male gender (Fujii & Ahmed 2001).

Once again, especially with a history of closed head injury in childhood, it is unclear if the head injury is causative or an unrelated comorbidity. Any time a significant head injury occurs prior to the time period of greatest liability towards the development of primary schizophrenia, its role in the production of chronic psychosis is questionable. However, in the initial Achté *et al.* (1969) study, paranoid and schizophrenic psychoses occurred in 4.1% of the patients, a much higher percentage than would have been expected by chance alone.

Cases where psychosis arises in patients with patterns of acquired brain injury, through trauma or vascular damage, can lead to hypotheses about the possible nature of functional brain abnormalities crucial to schizophrenia. A small number of case reports suggest that, given a specific pattern of brain injury in adult life, schizophrenia can result. Burke *et al.* (1999) described a schizophrenic illness arising in a case 8 years after a left frontal infarct at age 16. Pang and Lewis (1996) described a case of combined injury to left temporal and ablation of left dorsolateral frontal cortex in a 23-year-old man which appeared to 'convert' pre-existing bipolar disorder to chronic schizophrenia. G.E. Jaskiw and J.F. Kenny (submitted) reported schizophrenia arising in a 34-year-old man 1 year after combined injury to left anterior temporal lobe and frontal cortex. It is known that combined lesions of mesial temporal and prefrontal cortex in the rat lead to increased dopaminergic transmission in the ventral striatum of the rat (Lipska *et al.* 1994) and this may be the mechanism at work in these cases.

Cerebrovascular disease

There is a time-honoured saying in clinical neurology that neuroanatomy is learned 'one stroke at a time'. In the unusual circumstances where psychosis develops after a stroke, traditional clinical–pathological correlations coupled with modern neuroimaging techniques may elucidate the neuroanatomy of psychosis. Miller *et al.* (1991) assessed 24 consecutively ascertained patients with 'late-life psychosis', defined as DSM-IIIR schizophrenia, schizophreniform or delusional disorder, or unspecified psychosis of at least 4 weeks' duration, beginning over the age of 45. MRI scans were obtained to rule out structural lesions, and compared with a series of 72 healthy controls. A known history of neurological disease was an exclusion criterion in all subjects. Unsuspected cortical or subcortical white matter infarcts were seen in 25% of the patients, compared with 6% of controls. The largest regional difference between patients and controls was in the temporal lobe. Another two patients showed radiological changes suggesting dementia: one a cerebellar tumour and one post-traumatic brain injury. Delusions and hallucinations occur in early Alzheimer's disease in about 50% of cases (Chen *et al.* 1991). Moreover, ischaemic cerebrovascular disease occurs in the same age range as Alzheimer's disease and can be a comorbid condition. More often than not, Alzheimer's disease probably underlies the psychotic symptoms. Autopsy is usually the only way to definitively differentiate these processes, unless the psychotic symptoms occur in close relation to the timing of the stroke. Again, this is a fertile area for research into the pathogenesis of psychotic symptoms (Zubenko *et al.* 1991).

A number of case reports suggest that schizophreniform symptoms can appear as a result of cerebral infarction, even in patients where comorbid Alzheimer's disease is unlikely. Miller *et al.* (1989) described five cases of subfrontal white matter infarction leading to psychosis. Ischaemic subfrontal damage also appears to lead to psychosis in young adults. Hall and Young (1992) described an acute schizophreniform psychosis with blunted affect, thought disorder and auditory hallucinations in a 23-year-old man, attributed to a ruptured cerebral aneurysm in the left frontal lobe. Case reports such as this need to be viewed critically, however, as schizophrenia arises with great frequency in this age range. Bouckoms *et al.* (1986) described a delusional disorder appearing shortly after subarachnoid haemorrhage in a 66-year-old woman, associated with significant impairment of frontal lobe function on neuropsychological testing. Price and Mesulam (1985) presented five cases of right hemispheric infarction with primary psychiatric manifestations. However, only one was a convincing association between infarction and psychosis. In the others, the infarction could not be clearly identified by CT scan, the time between infarction and the appearance of psychosis was extremely delayed, or the psychiatric symptoms were atypical for a psychotic disorder. Levine and Finklestein (1982) described eight cases of hallucinations often accompanied by delusional thoughts, following either intracerebral haemorrhage, infarction or cerebral contusion. Applying more rigorous criteria, four of these cases occurred between the ages of 35 and 65 years of age, making it unlikely that comorbid primary schizophrenia or Alzheimer's disease was confounding their analysis. In all cases, the lesions were localized to the right temporoparietooccipital region.

Demyelinating diseases

Multiple sclerosis (MS) has been associated with a variety of psychiatric sequelae, most commonly affective syndromes. Stevens (1988) noted superficial epidemiological similarities between MS and schizophrenia, proposing that both disorders might have a similar immunological cause. However, MS and schizophrenia have markedly different clinical profiles, and the neuropathological substrate of MS has nothing in common with that of schizophrenia. Moreover, Davison and Bagley (1969) proffered that there was little evidence for increased risk of schizophrenic symptoms in MS. However, recent reports suggest that schizophrenia can arise secondary to MS, but only in rare cases. Temporal lobe demyelination may be the mediating link (Ron & Logsdail 1989). Feinstein *et al.* (1992) compared MRI findings in 10 psychotic and 10 non-psychotic MS patients: the psychotic patients tended to show more lesions around the temporal horns bilaterally, a similar finding to Reischies *et al.* (1988) and Honer *et al.* (1987). Feinstein *et al.* noted that the symptoms of schizophrenia began relatively late (mean age 36) in their sample, although were typical of schizophrenia thereafter, and postulated that long-standing strategically placed lesions were crucial in the development of psychosis. However, both MS and schizophrenia often begin in the third decade of life, and coincidence should not be confused with causality.

Schizophrenic symptoms have also been noted in rarer demyelinating syndromes (Neumann *et al.* 1988). Schilder's disease is a progressive usually fatal demyelinating disease of children and adolescents which is sporadic and probably related to MS. Occasional reports with schizophrenic symptoms exist (Davison & Bagley 1969; Ramani 1981). A review of reported cases (Ramani 1981) confirmed primary frontal lobe involvement in those cases presenting with psychoses.

Metachromatic leucodystrophy (MLD) is a rare autosomal recessive demyelinating disorder with a particularly strong association with psychosis. Deficiency of arylsulphatase-A is the basic biochemical defect, which leads to progressive demyelination. The inheritance shows incomplete penetrance and the extent of arylsulphatase-A deficiency seems to dictate age at onset. Hyde *et al.* (1992) reviewed the published case reports on MLD, 129 definite cases, and noted that when the onset occurred in adolescence or early adulthood (10–30 years) hallucinations or delusions occurred in over 50% of cases and a clinical diagnosis of primary schizophrenia was made in 35%. Complex auditory hallucinations typical of schizophrenia were commonly reported and other motor as well as negative symptoms also occurred. Hyde *et al.* (1992) argued that the high frequency of schizophrenic symptoms seen in MLD reflected its neuropathological origins in the periventricular frontal white matter. Progressive extension posteriorly heralds the appearance of more formal neurological signs. These observations led to the authors' hypothesis that dysfunctional subcortical pathways linking frontal cortex with normal functioning temporolimbic cortex are crucial to the production of schizophrenic symptoms.

Arylsulphatase-A abnormalities in the absence of clinical MLD have occasionally been reported in schizophrenic samples (Manowitz *et al.* 1981). Adrenoleucodystrophy (ALD) is a separate group of disorders, the main subtype of which involves an X-linked deficit in the breakdown of very-long-chain fatty acids. Three cases have been described with schizophrenic symptoms (Kitchin *et al.* 1987).

Metabolic and autoimmune disorders

Metabolic disorders rarely induce psychotic symptoms; more commonly, such disorders are associated with depression or delirium. For example, thyroid-related psychoses are most usually affectively based (Davis 1989). Hyperparathyroidism, usually an adenoma leading to hypercalcaemia, often causes psychiatric symptoms, although again convincing schizophrenic symptoms seem to be rare (Johnson 1975; Alarcon & Franceschini 1984; Ebel *et al.* 1992). Organic mental states with delirium or depressive symptoms are more commonly seen (Gatewood *et al.* 1975). Vitamin B_{12} deficiency can present with mental changes, although psychosis is unusual. Zucker *et al.* (1981) reviewed the literature and found only 15 cases of 'B_{12} psychosis' responding to B_{12} replacement: most of these were depressive disorders. B_{12} deficiency may more often be an effect, rather than a cause, of schizophrenic symptoms.

It has been recognized only relatively recently that cerebral systemic lupus erythematosus (SLE) can give schizophrenia-like symptoms (MacNeil *et al.* 1976). Attributing causation in individual cases can be difficult: SLE is common, with variable course and symptoms and its first-line treatment, steroids, can produce psychotic symptoms. Additionally, cerebral involvement more often produces seizures and delirium rather than pure psychotic symptoms. Childhood Sydenham's chorea, an immunologically mediated complication of rheumatic fever with probable basal ganglia involvement, may predispose to later schizophrenia (Wilcox & Nasrallah 1986). Paraneoplastic encephalopathies are uncommon poorly understood complications of non-central nervous system tumours, possibly mediated by tumour-directed antibodies. They can, rarely, cause schizophrenic symptoms, seemingly mediated by limbic inflammation (Van Sweden & Van Peteghem 1986).

Encephalitis and other infections of the central nervous system

Wilson (1976) reported three cases of viral encephalitis presenting as psychosis. Limbic encephalitis is most often associated with psychotic symptoms. Many viruses are known to cause limbic encephalitis (Glaser & Pincus 1969; Damasio & Hoesen 1985). In a review of 22 cases, Torrey (1986) noted reports of a variety of neuropathic viruses causing encephalitis leading to psychotic symptoms: Epstein–Barr, cytomegalovirus, rubella, herpes simplex and measles. Nunn *et al.* (1986) reported four cases of adulttype arising in children after viral encephalitic illnesses of varying pathology: rubella, measles, varicella and herpes simplex. Psychosis in Epstein–Barr virus infection is unusual (Leavell *et al.* 1986) and most commonly depressive in form (Rubin 1978; White & Lewis 1987).

Subacute sclerosing panencephalitis (SSPE) is a rare presentation of measles infection of the central nervous system, secondary to an aberrant form of the virus. It presents as a progressive neurological disorder (Koehler & Jakumeit 1976), with a clinical onset usually in early adult life or before, although often years after the initial measles infection. Two case histories are typical: symptoms of schizophrenia (Duncalf *et al.* 1989) or delusional disorder (dysmorphophobia: Salib 1988) presenting in young adults, with the emergence of rapidly progressive neurological signs several months later and death within a year. A report of schizophreniform psychosis more directly following measles infection (Stoler *et al.* 1987) was criticized for failing conclusively to demonstrate brain involvement with the virus (McCune 1987). Sporadic reports of schizophrenia in other infective and inflammatory conditions exist. *Borrelia* encephalitis (neuro-Lyme disease) is a recently described cause of schizophrenic symptoms which apparently responds to antibiotic therapy (Barnett *et al.* 1991). Neurocysticercosis results from invasion of the central nervous system with *Taenia solium* larvae, producing cysts, nodules, fibrosis and hydrocephaly. Schizophrenia-like complications are apparently not uncommon, although this contention deserves more research (Tavares *et al.* 1993). Childhood encephalitis has emerged as a clear-cut but rare risk factor for adult schizophrenia, conferring a fivefold relative risk in epidemiological cohort studies.

Psychotic symptoms can arise in the context of HIV infection, usually AIDS (McDaniel *et al.* 1997). Harris *et al.* (1991) reviewed the literature, as well as the histories of a cohort of 124 HIV-infected patients followed up for 6 years, for new-onset psychosis, after excluding cases where psychotic symptoms arose out of substance abuse or delirium. Psychotic symptoms usually took the form of acute-onset delusions, hallucinations and bizarre behaviour, most often in the context of a mood disturbance, particularly mania or hypomania. Typical schizophrenic symptoms in clear consciousness were rarely described. In a follow-up report, Sewell *et al.* (1994) examined the characteristics of psychosis in HIV-infected individuals. In addition to hallucinations and delusions, the majority of patients had substantial mood symptoms. The psychotic patients also had high rates of previous substance abuse. The pathogenesis of psychosis in the setting of HIV infection has yet to be established.

Sex chromosome abnormalities

Minimal evidence links sex chromosome abnormalities with schizophrenia-like disorders. The first report linked an XXXY genotype to schizophrenia (Money & Hirsch 1963). Most of the reports are single case studies. For example, Turner's syndrome (45 XO) has been associated with schizophrenia in about 10 cases. However, studies with large sample sizes (Nielsen & Stradiot 1987) have not disclosed an increased incidence of schizophrenia in Turner's syndrome: two cases in 968 female schizophrenic patients (Kaplan & Cotton 1968); or one case in 3558 (Akesson & O'Landers 1969), with a likely incidence rate for Turner's being 0.01% of live female births. The coincidence is so low that Bamrah and MacKay (1989) speculated that Turner's syndrome was actually protective against schizophrenia. The issue is complicated by the heterogeneity of Turner's: only half of cases are 45 XO, the rest being mosaics or having a structurally abnormal X chromosome (Fishbain 1990).

There is little evidence associating more unusual sex chromosome abnormalities with schizophrenia-like syndromes. Other sex chromosome abnormalities reported with schizophrenia include an XX male (Muller & Endres 1987) and an XO/XY mosaic with basal ganglia calcification (Deckert *et al.* 1992). Schizophrenia has been described in Noonan's syndrome (Turner's phenotype with normal karyotype: Krishna *et al.* 1977) and in 47 XYY males (Faber & Abrams 1975; Dorus *et al.* 1977). Of 20 psychotic males with Klinefelter's syndrome (47 XXY) described by Sorensen and Nielsen (1977), five fulfil criteria for schizophrenia. The authors surprisingly concluded that this was insufficient evidence for genuine association. XXXY associations have also been reported. More recently, DeLisi *et al.* (1994) found that the XXX and XXY karyotypes are more common in the schizophrenic population. In his review of the area, Propping (1983) considered that the Klinefelter karyotype and the XXX karyotype were the two sex chromosomal abnormalities that had the strongest association with schizophrenia. From the data available, Propping estimated that for both XXY and XXX the risk of schizophrenia was increased threefold. DeLisi *et al.* (1991) concurred with this conclusion, citing it as evidence for possible linkage of schizophrenia to the X chromosome.

Associations with Mendelian disorders

Propping's (1983) review discussed possible associations between a variety of Mendelian disorders and schizophrenia. Table 11.3 summarizes Propping's conclusions, dividing such disorders into probable and possible associations with increased risk of schizophrenia. Linkage and association studies have been undertaken at many laboratories and clinical centres around the world to identify candidate genes or chromosomal regions conferring an increased risk for schizophrenia or some of its biological components, such as abnormal frontal lobe function on neuropsychological testing batteries (Risch 1990; Egan *et al.* 2000).

The association of Huntington's disease with an increased risk of schizophrenia is well established. Huntington's disease, an autosomal dominant disorder with complete penetrance, localized to chromosome 4, is the first major neurological disorder with a well-characterized genetic defect (Gusella *et al.* 1983). Schizophrenic symptoms were reported in 5–11% of Huntington's patients in those six series each comprising at least 50 cases reviewed in Hyde *et al.* (1992). The reviews by Davison (1983) and Naarding *et al.* (2001) quote similar prevalence figures. Weinberger (1987) noted the age-related risk of psychosis in Huntington's disease, suggesting that psychosis most often appears in the third decade of life, like primary schizophrenia itself. However, developmental changes in the central nervous system immediately before or around this time of life may predispose towards the appearance of psychotic symptoms from a variety of causes, not just genetic abnormalities.

Acute intermittent porphyria is an autosomal dominant disorder of porphyrin metabolism resulting from a deficiency of the enzyme porphobilinogen deaminase. Acute intermittent porphyria may present with episodic psychiatric symptoms. Additionally, psychotropic medications may precipitate or exacerbate an acute attack. Psychiatric symptoms include

Table 11.3 Inherited disorders with an increased risk of schizophrenia. (Adapted from Propping 1983.)

Highly probable
Acute intermittent porphyria
Familial basal ganglia calcification
Huntington's disease
Metachromatic leucodystrophy
Porphyria variegata
Velocardiofacial syndrome
Possible
Congenital adrenal hyperplasia
Erythropoietic porphyria
Fabry's disease
Familial ataxia/spinocerebellar degeneration
Gaucher's disease, adult type
G6PD deficiency
Haemochromatosis
Homocystinuria
Hyperasparaginaemia
Ichthyosis vulgaris
Kartaneger's syndrome
Kufs disease
Laurence–Moon–Biedl syndrome
Niemann–Pick type C disease
Oculocutaneous albinism
Phenylketonuria
Sex chromosome anuoploides
Wilson's disease

G6PD, glucose-6-phosphate dehydrogenase.

psychosis, depression, anxiety and/or delirium. Tishler *et al.* (1985) screened 3867 psychiatric inpatients for acute intermittent porphyria and found a prevalence of 0.21%, higher than the general population. Most of the patients had symptoms of agitated psychosis, apathy or depression, with neuropsychological impairment. In rare cases, acute intermittent porphyria may cause a transient schizophrenia-like state; however, most of the attacks are of relatively short duration. Unlike schizophrenia, with treatment, many individuals with porphyria are relatively normal between acute attacks. The link between the acute intermittent porphyria and psychosis has fuelled recent searches for linkage of schizophrenia to chromosome 11, home of both the D_2 receptor and porphobilinogen deaminase gene. Nevertheless, at least in one study, no linkage has been established (Moises *et al.* 1991). This is not surprising given the rarity of acute intermittent porphyria even in the general psychiatric population.

It is likely that the alleged association between Wilson's disease (hepatolenticular degeneration) and schizophrenic symptoms has been overemphasized. Wilson's disease is an autosomal recessive disease of copper transport linked to chromosome 13 (Frydman *et al.* 1985). Although Wilson's original series included two patients with schizophrenic symptoms, the 520 case reports up to 1959 included only eight convincing cases (Davison & Bagley 1969). Dening (1985) and Dening and Berrios (1989) reviewed psychiatric symptomatology in a series of 195 cases. Hallucinations occurred in only two cases, delusions in three. Personality and mood disorders are much more common.

Homocystinuria is an autosomal recessive disorder characterized by an abnormality in methionine metabolism. It is often caused by a defect in the gene for methylenetetrahydrofolate reductase, an essential enzyme in folate metabolism. The gene is located on chromosome 1p36.3 (Gaughan *et al.* 2000). Homocystinuria is often associated with mental retardation, seizures and an increased risk of stroke. While some have associated homocystinuria with schizophrenia, literature reviews do not substantiate this assertion, except in unusual cases (Bracken & Coll 1985; Abbott *et al.* 1987; Regland *et al.* 1997). Interestingly, the increase in schizophrenia in cohorts exposed to famine in early gestation in the Dutch 'hunger winter' of 1944–45 has been attributed to folate deficiency. In these cases, it is believed that folate deficiency produced subtle abnormalities of cerebral development, which did not become manifest until early adulthood (Susser *et al.* 1996).

Niemann–Pick type C disease is an autosomal recessive disorder starting in adolescence or early adulthood. Vertical gaze abnormalities, ataxia and extrapyramidal signs predominate. Cataplexy and seizures often appear as the disease evolves. Psychosis may be the initial manifestation of the disease in some cases, leading to the misdiagnosis of primary schizophrenia (Turpin *et al.* 1991). The diagnosis is made by bone marrow biopsy, which reveals sea-blue histiocytes.

Oculocutaneous albinism is an unusual genetic disorder. Cosegregation of schizophrenia and oculocutaneous albinism has been described repeatedly (Baron 1976; Clarke & Buckley 1989); interestingly, neurodevelopmental abnormalities, particularly of projections to the visual association cortex, occur in albinism (Clarke & Buckley 1989). A common biochemical defect may underlie the pigmentary and psychiatric manifestations of this disorder. How the genetic defect in this form of albinism translates into neurodevelopmental abnormalities remains to be explained.

A variety of genetic disorders have been linked to schizophrenia in selected pedigrees. Although these may be chance associations, it is possible that the specific genetic defect may have protean manifestations. In most cases, the psychotic symptoms begin during the traditional window of vulnerability to schizophrenia, in the late second and third decades of life. Two families in which the autosomal dominant connective tissue disorder Marfan's syndrome cosegregated with schizophrenia have been described (Sirota *et al.* 1990), plus one additional case (Romano & Linares 1987). Two autosomal recessive syndromes causing progressive sensorineural deafness and blindness have been described in large pedigrees cosegregating with schizophrenia: Usher's syndrome (Sharp *et al.* 1993). A family with multiple instances of the X-linked Alport's syndrome and psychosis has been described (Shields *et al.* 1990). Recent interest has also focused on the risk of psychoses in families affected by Wolfram syndrome, an autosomal recessive disorder characterized by juvenile-onset diabetes mellitus and progressive bilateral optic nerve atrophy (Swift *et al.* 1990). Tuberous sclerosis is an unusual autosomal dominant disorder characterized by the development of slow-growing hamartomatous tumours in many organs, including the brain. This disorder has been linked to genetic defects on chromosomes 9 and 16 (Jones *et al.* 1997). Schizophrenia-like symptoms have been reported and seem to be linked with tumours affecting the medial temporal lobe (Heckert *et al.* 1972). Bilateral calcification in the temporal lobe was probably the mediating link in a patient with psychotic symptoms in the context of a long-standing autosomal illness, lipoid proteinosis (Emsley & Paster 1985). Better understanding of the precise genetic defect in each of these disorders, and the impact of the defect upon the development and integrity of the central nervous system, might offer intriguing clues into the neurobiology of schizophrenia.

Two unusual genetically based neurodevelopmental disorders have attracted attention as being associated with a schizophrenia-like phenotype. Each involves a disturbance of neuronal migration and is potentially informative about the pathogenesis of schizophrenia. Kallman's syndrome is characterized by anosmia with hypogonadism. The anosmia is a result of a neurodevelopmental failure in the olfactory tracts. The hypogonadism is a result of low hypothalamic secretion of gonadotrophic-releasing hormone. The X-linked subtype is caused by a mutation at Xp22.3; autosomal subtype also exists. Parallels between Kallmann's syndrome and schizophrenia have been drawn in the literature (Cowen & Green 1993), because patients with schizophrenia have relative anosmia and reduced fertility. However, O'Neill *et al.* (1999) found no mutations of the relevant gene (*KAL-X*) in nine schizophrenic patients with Kallmann-type symptoms. The authors concluded that such a mutation rarely, if ever, causes schizophrenia. The first recorded case of DSM-IV schizophrenia arising in a young man with a history of Kallmann's syndrome has recently been described (N. Nuttall, S. Sandhu, J. Stirling, D. Craufurd & S.W. Lewis, submitted). The parallels between the phenotype of Kallman's syndrome and schizophrenia are weak. Schizophrenic subjects do not have obvious pathology in the olfactory tracts or hypogonadism. Their reduced reproductive rate may be more aptly ascribed to their deficits in social function, rather than gonadal dysfunction. It is not surprising that O'Neill *et al.* found no mutations in the relevant gene. The description of a single individual with Kallmann's syndrome and schizophrenia is most likely serendipitous.

Velocardiofacial syndrome (VCFS) is a genetic disorder characterized by craniofacial structural abnormalities, cardiac defects and learning disabilities. In addition, children and adolescents with VCFS have smaller cerebellar, pontine, temporal lobe and hippocampal volumes than normal controls (Eliez *et al.* 2001a,b). VCFS is usually associated with deletion mutations of chromosome 22q11, the same region which includes the gene for catechol-O-methyl transferase (COMT), an enzyme involved in the metabolism of dopamine. VCFS is associated with high rates of schizophrenia. Fluorescence *in situ* hybridization is the best technique to identify the deletion mutations and confirm the diagnosis of VCFS (Larson & Butler 1995). The largest series examined to date was 50 cases in the UK ascertained mainly through clinical genetic services (Murphy *et al.* 1999). Of these, 15 had a history of a psychotic disorder, and 12 of these met DSM-IV criteria for schizophrenia (24%). In samples of subjects with schizophrenia and clinical features suggestive of VCFS, raised rates of 22q11 deletions have been found (Bassett *et al.* 1998). Interestingly, although the genetic defect and the dysmorphic changes are present from birth, psychotic symptoms do not develop until early adulthood. This illustrates the principle that psychosis only appears in an age-specific window of vulnerability, suggesting an interaction between genetic defects and the natural biology of human brain maturation. Clearly, the discovery of the exact genetic defect leading to psychosis in VCFS is paramount in understanding this syndrome. The role of COMT in the induction of psychosis in VCFS remains speculative at this time.

Tumours and other space-occupying lesions

Routine non-invasive imaging in the clinical assessment of schizophrenia, as well as prospective research, has led to increasing numbers of case reports of more or less unusual cerebral lesions in schizophrenia (Lewis 1989). In most cases these are clinically unsuspected, in that there was no history of neurological symptoms nor neurological signs on examination. Such lesions have been described in many parts of the brain and are of different pathologies. Some lesions are likely to be coincidental. Lesions falling into this category include the small cerebral infarcts and white matter abnormalities on MRI that are seen predominantly in older patients, and which are also seen in normal controls. If numerous, these are often linked to a history of cerebrovascular disease. A retrospective study of 731 psychiatric patients referred for MRI found that patients with psychotic symptoms had the lowest frequency of MRI-identified pathology (Wahlund *et al.* 1992).

Very rarely, unsuspected slow-growing cerebral tumours can present with schizophrenic symptoms. In the series reported by Malamud (1967), these symptoms were most common in tumours affecting the temporal lobe and cingulate gyrus. Frontal tumours have less frequently been implicated (Andy *et al.* 1981). A more extensive review was published by Lisanby *et al.* (1998). They noted that psychosis associated with brain tumour is more common above 50 years of age, although they fail to mention that brain tumours themselves are more common above this age. In their review, like Malamud, tumours located in the temporal lobe are more commonly associated with psychotic symptoms. Given the preponderance of evidence implicating the temporal lobe in the pathophysiology of primary schizophrenia, this localization is not surprising.

When reviewing case reports, there often is difficulty ascribing psychotic symptoms directly to the effects of the tumour itself on adjacent brain structures. For example, a suprasellar germinoma presented with a complex constellation of psychiatric symptoms, including psychosis (Mordecai *et al.* 2000). While the tumour involved the frontal lobes, basal ganglia and brainstem, areas implicated in the pathophysiology of psychosis, it had other profound effects. There were marked disturbances in the neuroendocrine axis. Additionally, there may have been a component of reactive depression. In summary, while tumours may be associated with schizophrenia-like presentations, this is a rare phenomenon, and the presentation may be secondary to remote effects from the tumour. A more intri-guing case involved a 26-year-old woman with a 7-year history of auditory hallucinations and paranoia. After resection of meningioma located in the antrum of the right lateral ventricle with extension into the corpus callosum and periventricular white matter, the patient's psychosis completely remitted (Lisanby *et al.* 1998). The complete remission off medication suggests that the tumour was definitively the aetiology of her psychosis.

Occult brain lesions found in association with schizophrenia are often those that can be classified as neurodevelopmental anomalies of one type or another. These include aqueduct stenosis (Reveley & Reveley 1983), arachnoid cysts (Lanczik *et al.* 1989), porencephalic cysts (O'Callaghan *et al.* 1992) and cerebrovascular malformations including congenital arteriovenous malformations in the temporal lobe (Vaillant 1965) and the midline great vein of Galen (Remington & Jeffries 1984). Despite cases of familial basal ganglia calcification being reported in association with schizophrenia (Propping 1983), two large studies have found no association in general between basal ganglia calcification and schizophrenia in large samples of psychiatric patients (Casanova *et al.* 1990; Philpot & Lewis 1990).

Probably the most intriguing subclass of neurodevelopmental lesions reported in association with schizophrenia is midline anomalies associated with the septum pellucidum and adjacent corpus callosum. The first case description of complete agenesis of the corpus callosum (Lewis *et al.* 1987) has been followed by further cases of callosal agenesis, usually involving partial agenesis of the anterior part of the corpus callosum (Velek *et al.* 1988; Swayze *et al.* 1990; O'Callaghan *et al.* 1992). In so far as the corpus callosum is concerned, abnormalities in the projections of the frontal lobes, which have been implicated in the pathophysiology of schizophrenia by neuroimaging, neuropsychological and neuropathological studies, may produce a phenotypic copy of schizophrenia.

In addition to abnormalities of the corpus callosum, other midline malformations have been associated with schizophrenia. An initial CT report of six cases of developmental cavum septum pellucidum (Lewis & Mezey 1985) has been complemented by a combined MRI and postmortem study reporting a surprisingly high prevalence of varying degrees of this anomaly in schizophrenic patients compared with controls (DeGreef *et al.* 1992). Congenital absence of the septum pellucidum has also been described in schizophrenia (George *et al.* 1989). Midline pathology common in schizophrenic subjects includes non-specific abnormalities of the septum pellucidum, cavum vergae, cavum septum pellucidum and agenesis of the corpus callosum (Scott *et al.* 1993). These abnormalities are more common in women than men. More work is needed in this area. It is unclear whether such neurodevelopmental lesions are in some way directly conferring an increased risk of schizophrenia or whether they are merely signals of a more general neurodevelopmental brain abnormality, whose critical site of action is actually elsewhere. In any event, these lesions usually develop *in utero*, and are relatively 'silent' for several decades before the onset of schizophrenia-like symptoms. This lag reinforces the notion that there is a crucial interface between a static pathological lesion and normal maturational brain processes in the production of psychosis.

Phenomenology of primary vs. secondary schizophrenia

Both brain imaging and clinical studies point to a prevalence rate of 5–8% for psychoses of likely identifiable organic aetiology amongst series of relatively unselected patients. If this is the case, is it possible to distinguish the minority of organic cases on clinical grounds alone?

The short answer is no, in that there is a large overlap in presenting symptoms between functional and organic psychoses. Nevertheless, several studies have compared symptom profiles in the two groups and some general differences do emerge. In their review of the literature, Davison and Bagley (1969) compared rates of individual psychotic symptoms in 150 reported cases of various organic schizophrenia-like psychoses with a series of 475 patients with functional schizophrenia reported by other authors. Of 14 clinical features compared, seven occurred significantly less frequently in the organic group: flat or incongruous affect; passivity feelings; thought disorder; auditory hallucinations; tactile hallucinations; schizoid premorbid personality; and family history of schizophrenia.

Catatonic symptoms were reported more frequently in organic cases. Of the organic group 64% showed Schneiderian first-rank symptoms, although this feature was not recorded in the control group. These results are intriguing, although they represent a retrospective survey of a varied collection of different case reports.

Cutting (1987) compared the Present State Examination (PSE)-rated symptomatology of 74 cases of organic psychosis with 74 cases of RDC acute schizophrenia, all prospectively interviewed. Like Davison and Bagley, he found auditory hallucinations to be less common in the organic group. Delusions were also less frequently found, although simple persecutory delusions were actually more common in the organic group. Contrary to the findings of Davison and Bagley, Schneiderian symptoms were rare in the organic group (3%). Thought disorder and visual hallucinations were more common. Cutting also noted a difference in the content of the phenomenology. Whereas delusions of the first rank were unusual in organic cases, in nearly one-half of the deluded organic patients, two delusional themes were patent: either belief of imminent misadventure to others, or bizarre occurrences in the immediate vicinity. Few non-organic schizophrenic patients showed these features. Cutting offers possible explanations for these organic themes as being delusional elaborations of deficits of perception, or memory. In the area of perceptual disturbance, the mistaken identity of other people was another theme found more commonly in the organic group.

In the study of Johnstone *et al.* (1988), PSE-rated symptomatology was compared between 23 cases of so-called organic psychosis and 92 non-organic psychoses matched for age, sex and ethnicity conforming to DSM-III criteria for schizophrenia, mania and psychotic depression. The authors found considerable overlap in symptoms. Comparing the organic and schizophrenic (n = 43) groups, nuclear (first rank) schizophrenic symptoms tended to be less frequent in the organic group (50% vs. 74%, $P < 0.06$). Visual hallucinations were more common in the organic group only if consciousness was clouded.

In the series of RDC schizophrenia patients under 65 referred to above, Lewis (1987) compared clinical features of those 41 patients with unequivocally abnormal CT scans to features in the 166 with a normal CT scan. Those with abnormal CT had significantly less evidence of a family history of schizophrenia in first-degree relatives, were more likely to have demonstrated formal thought disorder and more often had EEG abnormalities. Clinical presentation also seemed more atypical in the abnormal scan group, in that these patients were significantly more likely to have received alternative prior hospital diagnoses and a longer interval had intervened before a diagnosis of schizophrenia was made.

Feinstein and Ron (1990) examined the symptomatology in a series of 53 schizophrenic patients ascertained retrospectively, in whom psychotic symptoms arose secondary to overt brain disease. Symptom patterns were compared with normative data derived from the international pilot study of schizophrenia. The only individual symptom difference was an excess of visual hallucinations in the secondary schizophrenia group. Feinstein and Ron (1990) noted a relatively old age at onset (mean of 34 years) and a family history of schizophrenia in first-degree relatives was present in three of 53 cases. A wide variety of organic disease was represented. Overall, 50% of cases had epilepsy, reflecting a referral bias compared with the more representative series of Johnstone *et al.* (1987).

Individual cases included frontal meningioma, cerebral lymphoma, tuberous sclerosis, multiple sclerosis, Huntington's disease, encephalitis, cerebral abscess and hyperparathyroidism. Three cases of schizophrenic symptoms arising after neurosurgical operation were also included. The authors noted the wide variability in brain regions involved with, in particular, no consistent lateralized temporal pathology.

Velocardiofacial syndrome appears to be the organic disorder which confers one of the highest risk for the development of schizophrenia. In their series of VCFS cases, Murphy *et al.* (1999) compared the clinical characteristics of those with schizophrenia to a large series of schizophrenic cases without VCFS. The VCFS schizophrenic patients had a later age at onset and less negative symptoms than those with primary schizophrenia.

Table 11.4 Secondary schizophrenias: suggested screening procedures.

Physical investigations
First line
Neurological history and examination
Full blood count and differential
Erythrocyte sedimentation rate
Electrolytes
Syphilis serology
Thyroid function tests
Liver function panel
Electroencephalography
Urinary drug screen
Second line
Autoantibody titres
Magnetic resonance imaging of the brain
Serum calcium
HIV antibody titres
Arylsulphatase-A levels
Copper and ceruloplasmin levels
Karyotype
Cerebrospinal fluid analyses

Excluding secondary schizophrenia in practice: physical investigations

Table 11.4 outlines first- and second-line physical investigations which should be considered in new cases of psychosis, including schizophrenia. Of the first-line investigations, some may dispute the need always for syphilis serology and EEG. However, tertiary syphilis still occasionally presents as a psychosis in clinical practice. The EEG is performed to exclude the generalized slowing indicative of diffuse brain disease, or the focal paroxysmal spike-and-wave discharges of an epileptic focus.

The second-line investigations are dependent on other abnormal findings (autoantibodies if raised erythroctye sedimentation rate, chromosome studies if developmental delays or unusual body morphology). In particular, CT or MRI scan is probably only warranted in clinical practice if there are neurological symptoms in the history (e.g. epilepsy), or neurological signs on examination, or with an abnormal EEG.

Conclusions

Clinically unsuspected, usually neurodevelopmental, brain lesions of aetiological relevance occur in 5–10% of schizophrenic illness. Males seem to predominate. There is no indication that the discovery of such a lesion influences treatment in any specific way. The more classical variants of secondary schizophrenias are those psychotic disorders arising in the context of systemic physical disease. The best evidence available is that these account for about 3% of newly presenting schizophrenias. Clinically, it is important to detect this subtype, because recognition and treatment of the primary disorder are needed. The existence of secondary schizophrenias offers several potential avenues to illuminate the cause of primary schizophrenia. The observation of neurodevelopmental lesions was one of the building blocks of the neurodevelopmental model of schizophrenia. Association with Mendelian disorders is currently of interest in the search for candidate chromosomes or chromosomal regions predisposing to primary schizophrenia.

Those disorders which remain unexplained are adult-onset physical disorders which produce secondary schizophrenic symptoms, although the notion of a developmental window may prove important in understanding the onset of these disorders.

References

Abbott, M.H., Folstein, S.E., Abbey, H. & Pyeritz, R.E. (1987) Psychiatric manifestations of homocystinuria due to cystathionine beta-synthase deficiency: prevalence, natural history, and relationship to neurologicl impairmnet and vitamin B_6-reponsiveness. *American Journal of Medical Genetics* **26**, 959–969.

Achté, K.A., Hillbom, E. & Aalberg, V. (1969) Psychosis following war brain injuries. *Acta Psychiatrica Scandinavica* **45**, 1–18.

Achté, K., Jarho, L., Kyykka, T. & Vesterinen, E. (1991) Paranoid disorders following war brain damage. *Psychopathology* **24**, 309–315.

Akesson, H.O. & O'Landers, S. (1969) Frequency of negative sex chromatin among women in mental hospitals. *Human Heredity* **19**, 43–47.

Alarcon, R.D. & Franceschini, J.A. (1984) Hyperparathyroidism and paranoid psychosis case report and review of the literature. *British Journal of Psychiatry* **145**, 477–486.

American Psychiatric Association (1994) *Diagnostic and Statistical Manual of Mental Disorders*, 4th edn. American Psychiatric Association, Washington, DC.

Andermann, L.F., Savard, G., Meencke, H.J. *et al.* (1999) Psychosis after resection of ganglioglioma or DNET: evidence for an association. *Epilepsia* **40**, 83–87.

Andy, O.J., Webster, J.S. & Carranza, J. (1981) Frontal lobe lesions and behavior. *Southern Medical Journal* **74**, 968–972.

Bamrah, J.S. & MacKay, M.E. (1989) Chronic psychosis in Turner's syndrome. *British Journal of Psychiatry* **155**, 857–859.

Barnett, W., Sigmund, D., Roelcke, U. & Mundt, C. (1991) Endogenous-like paranoid–hallucinatory syndrome due to borrelia encephalitis. *Nervenarzt* **45**, 445–447.

Baron, M. (1976) Albinism and schizophreniform psychosis: a pedigree study. *American Journal of Psychiatry* **133**, 1070–1073.

Bassett, A.S., Hodgkinson, K., Chow, E.W. *et al.* (1998) 22q11 Deletion syndrome in adults with schizophrenia. *American Journal of Human Genetics* **81**, 328–337.

Bouckoms, A., Martuza, R. & Henderson, M. (1986) Capgras syndrome with subarachnoid hemorrhage. *Journal of Nervous and Mental Disease* **174**, 484–488.

Bracken, P. & Coll, P. (1985) Homocystinuria and schziophrenia: literature review and case report. *Journal of Nervous and Mental Disease* **173**, 51–55.

Brugha, T.S., Wing, J.K., Brewin, L.R. *et al.* (1988) The problems of people in long-term psychiatric care: an introduction to the Camberwell High Contact Survey. *Psychological Medicine* **18**, 457–468.

Buckley, P., Stack, J.P., Madigan, C. *et al.* (1993) Magnetic resonance imaging of schizophrenia-like psychoses associated with cerebral trauma: clinicopathological correlates. *American Journal of Psychiatry* **150**, 146–148.

Burke, J.G., Dersun, S.M. & Reveley, M.A. (1999) Refractory symptomatic schizophrenia resulting from frontal lobe lesion: response to clozapine. *Journal of Psychiatry and Neuroscience* **24**, 456–461.

Casanova, M.F., Prasad, C.N., Waldman, I. *et al.* (1990) No difference in basal ganglia mineralization between schizophrenic and non-schizophrenic patients: a quantitative CT study. *Biological Psychiatry* **27**, 138–142.

Chen, J., Stern, Y., Sano, M. & Mayeux, R. (1991) Cumulative risks of developing extrapyramidal signs, psychosis, or myoclonus in the course of Alzheimer's disease. *Archives of Neurology* **48**, 1141–1143.

Clarke, D.J. & Buckley, M. (1989) Familial association of albinism and schizophrenia. *British Journal of Psychiatry* **155**, 551–553.

Cowen, M.A. & Green, M. (1993) The Kallmann's syndrome variant (KSV) model of the schizophrenias. *Schizophrenia Research* **9**, 1–10.

Cutting, J. (1987) The phenomenology of acute organic psychosis: comparison with acute schizophrenia. *British Journal of Psychiatry* **151**, 324–332.

Damasio, A.R. & Van Hoesen, G.W. (1985) The limbic system and the localisation of herpes simplex encephalitis. *Journal of Neurology, Neurosurgery and Psychiatry* **48**, 297–301.

Davis, A.T. (1989) Psychotic states associated with disorders of thyroid function. *International Journal of Psychiatry in Medicine* **19**, 47–56.

Davison, K. (1983) Schizophrenia-like psychoses associated with organic cerebral disorders: a review. *Psychiatric Developments* **1**, 1–34.

Davison, K. & Bagley, C.R. (1969) Schizophrenia-like psychoses associated with organic disorders of the central nervous system. In: *Current Problems in Neuropsychiatry: Schizophrenia, Epilepsy, the Temporal Lobe* (ed. R. Herrington). Special Publication No. 4, British Journal of Psychiatry, London.

Deckert, J., Strik, W.K. & Fritze, J. (1992) Organic schizophrenic syndrome associated with symmetrical basal ganglia sclerosis and XO/XY-mosaic. *Biological Psychiatry* **31**, 401–403.

DeGreef, G., Bogerts, B., Falkai, P. *et al.* (1992) Increased prevalence of the cavum septum pellucidum in magnetic resonance scans and post-mortem brains of schizophrenic patients. *Psychiatry Research* **45**, 1–13.

DeLisi, L.E., Crow, T.J., Davies, K.E. *et al.* (1991) No genetic linkage detected for schizophrenia to Xq27–q28. *British Journal of Psychiatry* **158**, 630–634.

DeLisi, L.E., Friedrich, U., Wahlstrom, J. *et al.* (1994) Schizophrenia and sex chromosome anomalies. *Schizophrenia Bulletin* **20**, 495–505.

Dening, T.R. (1985) Psychiatric aspects of Wilson's disease. *British Journal of Psychiatry* **147**, 677–682.

Dening, T.R. & Berrios, G.E. (1989) Wilson's disease: psychiatric symptoms in 195 cases. *Archives of General Psychiatry* **46**, 1126–1134.

Dorus, E., Dorus, W. & Telfer, M.A. (1977) Paranoid schizophrenia in a 47,XYY male. *American Journal of Psychiatry* **134**, 687–689.

Duncalf, C.M., Kent, J.N., Harbord, M. & Hicks, E.P. (1989) Subacute sclerosing panencephalitis presenting as schizophreniform psychosis. *British Journal of Psychiatry* **155**, 557–559.

Ebel, H., Schlegel, U. & Klosterkotter, J. (1992) Chronic schizophreniform psychoses in primary hyperparathyroidism. *Nervenarzt* **63**, 180–183.

Egan, M.F., Goldberg, T.E., Gscheidle, T. *et al.* (2000) Relative risk of attention deficits in siblings of patients with schizophrenia. *American Journal of Psychiatry* **157**, 1309–1316.

Eliez, S., Schmitt, J.E., White, C.D., Wellis, V.G. & Reiss, A.L. (2001a) A quantitative MRI study of posterior fossa development in velocardiofacial syndrome. *Biological Psychiatry* **49**, 540–546.

Eliez, S., Blasey, C.M., Schmitt, J.E. *et al.* (2001b) Velocardiofacial syndrome: are structural changes in the temporal and mesial temporal regions related to schizophrenia? *American Journal of Psychiatry* **158**, 447–453.

Emsley, R.A. & Paster, L. (1985) Lipoid proteinosis presenting with neuropsychiatric manifestations. *Journal of Neurology, Neurosurgery and Psychiatry* **48**, 1290–1292.

Faber, R. & Abrams, R. (1975) Schizophrenia in a 47,XYY male. *British Journal of Psychiatry* **127**, 401–403.

Feinstein, A. & Ron, M.A. (1990) Psychosis associated with demonstrable brain disease. *Psychological Medicine* **20**, 793–803.

Feinstein, A., du Boulay, G. & Ron, M.A. (1992) Psychotic illness in multiple sclerosis: a clinical and magnetic resonance imaging study. *British Journal of Psychiatry* **161**, 680–685.

Fishbain, D.A. (1990) Chronic psychoses in Turner's syndrome. *British Journal of Psychiatry* **156**, 745–746.

Flor-Henry, P. (1969) Psychosis and temporal lobe epilepsy. *Epilepsia* **10**, 363–395.

Frydman, M., Bonne-Tamir, B., Farber, L.A. *et al.* (1985) Assignment of the gene for Wilson disease to chromosome 13: linkage to the esterase D locus. *Proceedings of the National Academy of Sciences of the USA* **82**, 1819–1821.

Fujii, D.E. & Ahmed, I. (2001) Risk factors in psychosis secondary to traumatic brain injury. *Journal of Neuropsychiatry and Clinical Neurosciences* **13**, 61–69.

Gatewood, J.W., Organ, C.H. & Mead, B.T. (1975) Mental changes associated with hyperparathyroidsm. *American Journal of Psychiatry* **132**, 129–132.

Gaughan, D.J., Barbaux, S., Kluijtmans, L.A. & Whitehead, A.S. (2000) The human and mouse methylenetetrahydrofolate reductase (MTHFR) genes: genomic organization, mRNA structure and linkage to the *CLCN6* gene. *Gene* **257**, 279–289.

George, M.S., Scott, T., Kellner, C.H. & Malcolm, R. (1989) Abnormalities of the septum pellucidum in schizophrenia. *Journal of Neuropsychiatry and Clinical Neurosciences* **1**, 385–390.

Glaser, G.H. & Pincus, J.H. (1969) Limbic encephalitis. *Journal of Nervous and Mental Disease* **149**, 59–67.

Gualtieri, T. & Cox, D.R. (1991) The delayed neurobehavioural sequelae of traumatic brain injury. *Brain Injury* **5**, 219–232.

Gusella, J.F., Wexler, N.S., Conneally, P.M. *et al.* (1983) A polymorphic DNA marker genetically linked to Huntington's disease. *Nature* **306**, 234–238.

Hall, D.P. & Young, S.A. (1992) Frontal lobe cerebral aneurysm rupture presenting as psychosis. *Journal of Neurology, Neurosurgery and Psychiatry* **55**, 1207–1208.

Harris, M.J., Jeste, D.V., Gleghorn, A. & Sewell, D.D. (1991) New-onset psychosis in HIV-infected patients. *Journal of Clinical Psychiatry* **52**, 369–376.

Heckert, E.E., Wald, A. & Romero, O. (1972) Tuberous sclerosis and schizophrenia. *Diseases of the Nervous System* **33**, 439–445.

Honer, W.G., Hurwitz, T., Li, D.K.B., Palmer, M. & Paty, D.W. (1987) Temporal lobe involvement in multiple sclerosis patients with psychiatric disorders. *Archives of Neurology* **44**, 187–190.

Hyde, T.M. & Weinberger, D.R. (1997) Seizures and schizophrenia. *Schizophrenia Bulletin* **23**, 611–622.

Hyde, T.M., Ziegler, J.C. & Weinberger, D.R. (1992) Psychiatric disturbances in metachromatic leukodystrophy: insights into the neurobiology of psychosis. *Archives of Neurology* **49**, 401–406.

Johnson, J. (1975) Schizophrenia and Cushing's syndrome cured by adrenalectomy. *Psychological Medicine* **5**, 165–168.

Johnstone, E.C., Owens, D.G., Frith, C.D. & Crow, T.J. (1987) The relative stability of positive and negative features in chronic schizophrenia. *British Journal of Psychiatry* **150**, 60–64.

Johnstone, E.C., Cooling, N.J., Frith, C.D., Crow, T.J. & Owens, D.G. (1988) Phenomenology of organic and functional psychoses and the overlap between them. *British Journal of Psychiatry* **153**, 770–776.

Jones, A.C., Daniells, C.E., Snell, R.G. *et al.* (1997) Molecular genetic and phenotypic analysis reveals differences between TSC1 and TSC2 associated familial and sporadic tuberous sclerosis. *Human Molecular Genetics* **6**, 2155–2161.

Kaplan, A.R. & Cotton, J.E. (1968) Chromosomal abnormalities in female schizophrenics. *Journal of Nervous and Mental Diseases* **147**, 402–417.

Kitchin, W., Cohen-Cole, S.A. & Mickel, S.F. (1987) Adrenoleukodystrophy: frequency of presentation as a psychiatric disorder. *Society of Biological Psychiatry* **22**, 1375–1387.

Koehler, K. & Jakumeit, U. (1976) Subacute sclerosing panencephalitis presenting as Leonhard's speech-prompt catatonia. *British Journal of Psychiatry* **129**, 29–31.

Krishna, N.R., Abrams, R., Taylor, M.A. & Behar, D. (1977) Schizophrenia in a 46,XY male with the Noonan syndrome. *British Journal of Psychiatry* **130**, 570–572.

Lanczik, M., Fritze, J., Classen, W., Ihl, R. & Maurer, K. (1989) Schizophrenia-like psychosis associated with an arachnoid cyst visualized by mapping of EEG and P300. *Psychiatry Research* **29**, 421–423.

Larson, R.S. & Butler, M.G. (1995) Use of fluorescence *in situ* hybridization (FISH) in the diagnosis fo DiGeorge sequence and related diseases. *Diagnostic and Molecular Pathology* **4**, 274–278.

Leavell, R., Ray, C.G., Ferry, P.C. & Minnich, L.L. (1986) Unusual acute neurologic presentations with Epstein–Barr virus infection. *Archives of Neurology* **43**, 186–188.

Levine, D.N. & Finklestein, S. (1982) Delayed psychosis after right temporoparietal stroke or trauma: relation to epilepsy. *Neurology* **32**, 267–273.

Lewis, S.W. (1987) *Schizophrenia with and without intracranial abnormalities on CT scan*. M. Phil thesis, University of London.

Lewis, S.W. (1989) Congenital risk factors for schizophrenia. *Psychological Medicine* **19**, 5–13.

Lewis, S.W. (1990) Computed tomography in schizophrenia fifteen years on. *British Journal of Psychiatry* **157** (Suppl. 9), 16–24.

Lewis, S.W. & Mezey, G.C. (1985) Clinical correlates of septum pellucidum cavities: an unusual association with psychosis. *Psychological Medicine* **15**, 43–54.

Lewis, S.W., Reveley, A.M., Reveley, M.A., Chitkara, B. & Murray, R.M. (1987) The familial–sporadic distinction in schizophrenia research. *British Journal of Psychiatry* **151**, 306–313.

Lipska, B.K., Jaskiw, G.E. & Weinberger, D.R. (1994) The effects of combined prefrontal cortical and hippocampal damage on dopamine-related behaviors in rats. *Pharmacological Biochemistry and Behavior* **48**, 1053–1057.

Lisanby, S.H., Kohler, C., Swanson, C.L. & Gur, R.E. (1998) Psychosis secondary to brain tumor. *Seminars in Clinical Neuropsychiatry* **3**, 12–22.

McCune, N. (1987) Schizophreniform episode following measles infection. *British Journal of Psychiatry* **151**, 558–559.

McDaniel, J.S., Purcell, D.W. & Farber, E.W. (1997) Severe mental illness and HIV-related medical and neuropsychiatric sequelae. *Clinical Psychology Review* **17**, 311–325.

Mace, C.J. (1993) Epilepsy and schizophrenia. *British Journal of Psychiatry* **163**, 439–445.

MacNeil, A., Grennan, D.M., Ward, D. & Dick, W.C. (1976) Psychiatric problems in systemic lupus erythematosus. *British Journal of Psychiatry* **128**, 442–445.

Malamud, N. (1967) Psychiatric disorder with intracranial tumours of limbic system. *Archives of Neurology* **18**, 113–123.

Manowitz, P., Goldstein, L. & Nora, R. (1981) An arylsulfatase-A variant in schizophrenic patients: preliminary report. *Biological Psychiatry* **16**, 1107–1113.

Mendez, M.F., Grau, R., Doss, R.C. & Taylor, J.L. (1993) Schizophrenia in epilepsy: seizure and psychosis variables. *Neurology* **43**, 1073–1077.

Miller, B.L., Lesser, I.M., Boone, K. *et al.* (1989). Brain white-matter lesions and psychosis. *British Journal of Psychiatry* **155**, 73–78.

Miller, B.L., Lesser, I.M., Boone, B.K. *et al.* (1991) Brain lesions and cognitive function in late-life psychosis. *British Journal of Psychiatry* **158**, 76–82.

Moises, H.W., Gelernter, J., Giuffra, L.A. *et al.* (1991) No linkage between D_2 dopamine receptor gene region and schizophrenia. *Archives of General Psychiatry* **48**, 643–647.

Money, J. & Hirsch, S.R. (1963) Chromosome anomalies, mental deficiency and schizophrenia. *Archives of General Psychiatry* **7**, 242–251.

Mordecai, D., Shaw, R.J., Fisher, P.G. *et al.* (2000) Case study: suprasellar germinoma presenting with psychotic and obsessive–compulsive symptoms. *Journal of the American Academy of Child and Adolescent Psychiatry* **39**, 116–119.

Muller, N. & Endres, M. (1987) An XX male with schizophrenia: a case of personality development and illness similar to that in XXY males. *Journal of Clinical Psychiatry* **48**, 379–380.

Murphy, K.C., Jones, L.A. & Owen, M.J. (1999) High rates of schizophrenia in adults with velocardiofacial syndrome. *Archives of General Psychiatry* **56**, 940–945.

Naarding, P., Kremer, H.P.H. & Zitman, F.G. (2001) Huntington's disease: a review of the literature on prevalence and treatment of neuropsychiatric phenomena. *European Psychiatry* **16**, 439–445.

Neumann, P.E., Mehler, M.F., Horoupian, D.S. & Merriam, A.E. (1988) Atypical psychosis with disseminated subpial demyelination. *Archives of Neurology* **45**, 634–636.

Nielsen, J. & Stradiot, M. (1987) Transcultural study of Turner's syndrome. *Clinical Genetics* **32**, 260–270.

Nunn, K.P., Lask, B. & Cohen, M. (1986) Viruses, neurodevelopmental disorder and childhood psychoses. *Journal of Child Psychology and Psychiatry* **27**, 55–64.

O'Callaghan, E., Buckley, P., Redmond, O. *et al.* (1992) Abnormalities of cerebral structure on MRI: interpretation in relation to the neurodevelopmental hypothesis. *Journal of the Royal Society of Medicine* **85**, 227–231.

O'Neill, M., Brewer, W., Thornley, C. *et al.* (1999) Kallmann syndrome gene (*KAL-X*) is not mutated in schizophrenia. *American Journal of Medical Genetics* **88**, 34–37.

Owens, D.G.C., Johnstone, E.C., Bydder, G.M. *et al.* (1980) Unsuspected organic disease in chronic schizophrenia demonstrated by computed tomography. *Journal of Neurology, Neurosurgery and Psychiatry* **43**, 1065–1069.

Pang, A. & Lewis, S.W. (1996) Bipolar affective disorder minus left prefrontal cortex equals schizophrenia. *British Journal of Psychiatry* **168**, 647–650.

Philpot, M. & Lewis, S.W. (1990) Psychopathology of basal ganglia calcification. *Behaviourial Neurology* **2**, 227–234.

Price, B.H. & Mesulam, M.M. (1985) Psychiatric manifestations of right hemispheric infarctions. *Journal of Nervous and Mental Disease* **173**, 610–614.

Propping, P. (1983) Genetic disorders presenting as schizophrenia: Karl Bonhoffers early view of the psychoses in the light of medical genetics. *Human Genetics* **65**, 1–10.

Ramani, S.V. (1981) Psychosis associated with frontal lobe lesions in Schilder's cerebral sclerosis: a case report with CT scan evidence. *Journal of Clinical Psychiatry* **42**, 250–252.

Regland, B., Germgard, T., Gottfries, C.G., Grenfeldt, B. & Koch-Schmidt, A.C. (1997) Homozygous thermolabile methylenetetrahydrofolate reductase in schizophrenia-like psychosis. *Journal of Neural Transmission* **104**, 931–941.

Reischies, F.M., Baum, K., Brau, H. *et al.* (1988) Cerebral magnetic resonance imaging findings in multiple sclerosis: relation to disturbance of affect, drive and cognition. *Archives of Neurology* **45**, 1114–1116.

Remington, G. & Jeffries, J.J. (1984) The role of cerebral arteriovenous malformations in psychiatric disturbances: case report. *Journal of Clinical Psychiatry* **45**, 226–229.

Reveley, A.M. & Reveley, M.A. (1983) Aqueduct stenosis and schizophrenia. *Journal of Neurology, Neurosurgery and Psychiatry* **46**, 18–22.

Risch, N. (1990) Genetic linkage and complex diseases, with special reference to psychiatric disorders. *Genetics Epidemiology* **7**, 17–45.

Roberts, C.W., Dane, D.J., Bauton, C. & Crow, T.J. (1990) A 'mock-up' of schizophrenia: temporal lobe epilepsy and schizophrenia-like psychosis. *Biological Psychiatry* **1990**, 127–143.

Romano, J. & Linares, R.L. (1987) Marfan syndrome and schizophrenia: a case report. *Archives of General Psychiatry* **44**, 190–192.

Ron, M.A. & Logsdail, S.J. (1989) Psychiatric morbidity in multiple sclerosis: a clinical and MRI study. *Psychological Medicine* **19**, 887–895.

Rubin, R.L. (1978) Adolescent infectious mononucleosis with psychosis. *Journal of Clinical Psychiatry* **39**, 773–775.

Salib, E.A. (1988) SSPE presenting as a schizophrenia-like state with bizarre dysmorphophic features. *British Journal of Psychiatry* **152**, 709–710.

Sartorius, N., Kaelber, C.T., Cooper, J.E. *et al.* (1993) Progress toward achieving a common language in psychiatry: results from the field trials accompanying the clinical guidelines of mental and behaviourial disorders in ICD-10. *Archives of General Psychiatry* **50**, 115–124.

Scott, T.F., Price, T.R., George, M.S., Brillman, J. & Rothfus, W. (1993) Midline cerebral malformations and schizophrenia. *Journal of Neuropsychiatry and Clinical Neuroscience* **5**, 287–293.

Sewell, D.D., Jeste, D.V., Atkinson, J.H. *et al.* (1994) HIV-associated psychosis: a study of 20 cases. San Diego HIV Neurobehavioral Research Center Groups. *American Journal of Psychiatry* **151**, 237–242.

Sharp, C.W., Muir, W.J., Blackwood, D.H. *et al.* (1993) Schizophrenia: a neuropsychiatric phenotype of the Usher syndrome type 3 allele. *Schizophrenia Research* **9**, 125.

Shields, G.W., Pataki, C. & DeLisi, E. (1990) A family with Alport syndrome and psychosis. *Schizophrenia Research* **3**, 235–239.

Sirota, P., Frydman, M. & Sirota, L. (1990) Schizophrenia and Marfan syndrome. *British Journal of Psychiatry* **157**, 433–436.

Slater, E. & Beard, A.W. (1963) The schizophrenia-like psychoses of epilepsy. *British Journal of Psychiatry* **109**, 95–112.

Sorensen, K. & Nielsen, J. (1977) Twenty psychotic males with Klinefelter's syndrome. *Acta Psychiatrica Scandinavica* **56**, 249–255.

Spitzer, R.H., First, M.B., Williams, J.B.W. *et al.* (1992) Now is the time to retire the term 'organic mental disorders'. *American Journal of Psychiatry* **149**, 240–244.

Stevens, J.R. (1988) Schizophrenia and multiple sclerosis. *Schizophrenia Bulletin* **14**, 231–241.

Stevens, J.R. (1992) Abnormal reinnervation as a basis for schizophrenia: a hypothesis. *Archives of General Psychiatry* **49**, 235–243.

Stoler, M., Meshulam, B., Zoldan, J. & Sirota, P. (1987) Schizophreniform episode following measles infection. *British Journal of Psychiatry* **150**, 861–862.

Susser, E., Neugebauer, R., Hoek, H.W. *et al.* (1996) Schizophrenia after prenatal famine. *Archives of General Psychiatry* **53**, 25–31.

Swayze, V.W., Andreasen, N.C., Ehrhardt, J.C. *et al.* (1990) Developmental abnormalities of the corpus callosum in schizophrenia. *Archives of Neurology* **47**, 805–808.

Swift, R.G., Sadler, D.B. & Swift, M. (1990) Psychiatric findings in Wolfram syndrome homozygotes. *Lancet* **336**, 667–669.

Tavares, A.R., Pinto, D.C., Lemow, A. & Nascimento, E. (1993) Lesion localization in schizophrenia-like disorder associated with neurocysticerosis. *Schizophrenia Research* **9**, 111.

Taylor, D. (1975) Factors influencing the occurrence of schizophrenia-like psychoses in temporal lobe epilepsy. *Psychological Medicine* **1**, 247–253.

Tishler, P.V., Woodward, B., O'Connor, J. *et al.* (1985) High prevalence of intermittent acute porphyria in a psychiatric patient population. *American Journal of Psychiatry* **142**, 1430–1436.

Torrey, E.F. (1986) Functional psychosis and viral encephalitis. *Integrated Psychiatry* **4**, 224–236.

Trimble, M.R. (1988) *Biological Psychiatry*. John Wiley, Chichester.

Trimble, M.R. (1990) First-rank symptoms of Schneider: a new perspective? *British Journal of Psychiatry* **156**, 195–200.

Turpin, J.C., Masson, M. & Baumann, N. (1991) Clinical aspects of Niemann–Pick type C disease in the adult. *Developmental Neuroscience* **13**, 304–306.

Vaillant, G. (1965) Schizophrenia in a woman with temporal lobe arteriovenous malformations. *British Journal of Psychiatry* **111**, 307–308.

Van Sweden, B. & Van Peteghem, P. (1986) Psychopathology in paraneoplastic encephalopathy: an electroclinical observation. *Journal of Clinical Psychiatry* **47**, 267–268.

Velek, M., White, L.E. Jr, Williams, J.P., Stafford, R.L. & Marco, L.A. (1988) Psychosis in a case of corpus callosum agenesis. *Alabama Medicine* **58**, 27–29.

Wahlund, L.-O., Agartz, I., Säaf, J., Wetterberg, L. & Marions, O. (1992) MRI in psychiatry: 731 cases. *Psychiatry Research* **45**, 139–140.

Weinberger, D.R. (1987) Implications of normal brain development for pathogenesis of schizophrenia. *Archives of General Psychiatry* **44**, 660–669.

White, P.D. & Lewis, S.W. (1987) Delusional depression following infectious mononucleosis. *British Medical Journal* **295**, 297–298.

Wilcox, J.A. & Nasrallah, H.A. (1986) Sydenham's chorea and psychosis. *Neuropsychobiology* **15**, 13–14.

Wilson, L.G. (1976) Viral encephalopathy mimicking functional psychosis. *American Journal of Psychiatry* **133**, 165–170.

World Health Organization (1978) *The ICD-9 Classification of Mental and Behaviourial Disorders*. WHO, Geneva.

World Health Organization (1992) *The ICD-10 Classification of Mental and Behaviourial Disorders*. WHO, Geneva.

Zubenko, G.S., Moossy, J., Martinez, A.J. *et al.* (1991) Neuropathologic and neurochemical correlates of psychosis in primary dementia. *Archives of Neurology* **48**, 619–624.

Zucker, D.K., Livingston, R.L., Nakra, R. & Clayton, P.J. (1981) B_{12} deficiency and psychiatric disorders: case report and literature review. *Biological Psychiatry* **16**, 197–205.

12 The epidemiological horizon

A. Jablensky

Establishing the epidemiological 'signature' of a disease – its frequency in specified populations, geographical spread and spatial distribution, temporal variation, and associations with comorbid conditions and risk factors – is an essential step towards unravelling its causes and a prerequisite for its ultimate prevention and control. In a number of instances, the epidemiological mapping of a syndrome has revealed patterns suggestive of possible causation and narrowed down the search area for subsequent clinical and laboratory research. The classic examples of successful application of the epidemiological method include pellagra, rubella encephalopathy, the fetal alcohol syndrome and kuru. Attempts to apply this approach to the study of schizophrenia have not met with comparable success although epidemiological investigations into the schizophrenic disorders have been conducted for over a century. A principal source of difficulty is the nature of the disease concept of schizophrenia itself. The attributes defining schizophrenia are primarily inferential and depend critically on self-reported subjective experience; the underlying structural and functional pathology remains hypothetical and there is no objective diagnostic test or easily measurable biological marker that could provide a secure anchor point for epidemiological field research. As pointed out by Jaspers (1963), the disease concept of schizophrenia is 'an idea in Kant's sense', i.e. a guiding methodological principle helping to organize knowledge which should not be mistaken for a tangible piece of empirical reality.

Notwithstanding occasional proposals to scuttle the very concept of schizophrenia because of its elusive nature, there is an increasing acceptance of the notion that schizophrenia is, in a genetic sense, one of the *complex* diseases – characterized by a non-Mendelian pattern of transmission, polygenic or oligogenic basis, incomplete penetrance, possible non-allelic heterogeneity, and a significant non-genetic contribution to its phenotypic expression. Advancing the understanding of the neurobiology of such a complex disorder with ill-defined phenotype boundaries requires an epidemiological horizon for the planning and interpretation of genetic, neuropathological and neurophysiological research. No less important is the demand for an epidemiological resource that would aid clinicians in making evidence-based diagnostic and treatment decisions. In reviewing the existing vast and often inconsistent epidemiological information about schizophrenia, it is therefore essential to identify findings that are replicable and likely to be valid, despite the variation in concepts and research methods that still confound the field. The present chapter surveys a broad range of topics which add up to a composite epidemiological picture of a complex disease. Special attention is given to findings reported in the last few years and to the epidemiological implications of recent clinical and biological research.

Sources of variation in the epidemiology of schizophrenia related to the method of investigation

The measurement of the prevalence, incidence and morbid risk of schizophrenia depends critically on: (i) the capacity to identify in a given population all affected individuals (or the great majority of them); and (ii) the availability of a diagnostic system which will select 'true' cases corresponding to established clinical concepts. The first prerequisite refers to the sensitivity of the case finding and the second to the specificity of disease category allocation needed to minimize false-positive diagnoses.

Case finding

The majority of case finding designs fall into three groups:
1 case detection in clinical populations;
2 population surveys: door-to-door or representative samples; and
3 birth cohort studies.

Cases in treatment contact

At any given time, psychiatric hospital or outpatient populations contain substantial percentages of persons with the diagnosis of schizophrenia. This provides a relatively easy access to cases for epidemiological investigation. However, the probability of being in treatment depends on nosocomial factors such as availability and accessibility of services, their location and the rate of their utilization by population groups. Hospital samples rarely are representative of all the persons with a given disorder. The age and sex distribution, marital state, socioeconomic status, ethnicity and severity of illness in hospital samples often differ from those characterizing the larger pool of people in the community exhibiting the disorder of interest. The extent of the selection bias affecting clinical populations may vary widely from one setting to another (e.g. in a developing country compared with an industrialized country) and between different points in time.

Under the rare circumstances of stable social conditions, adequate service provision, and lack of major changes in legislation, admission policies and treatment philosophy, the presumption that the great majority of people with schizophrenic disorders eventually get admitted to hospital (Ødegaard 1952) may be justified. At present, such conditions hardly obtain anywhere. As a general trend, mental health care is moving away from the hospital into the community. It has been shown that an increasing number of patients with schizophrenia are being managed on an outpatient basis without admission to hospital. Over 50% of first-episode patients with schizophrenia in Nottingham, UK, are not admitted within 3 months of their first contact with a primary care facility (Harrison *et al.* 1991). Therefore, epidemiological case finding for schizophrenia that is restricted to hospital admissions is liable to be methodologically flawed.

The deficiencies of case finding through hospitals can be overcome by extending the case detection network to community mental health services, general practitioners, private providers and charity organizations. An example of such extension of case finding into the community is provided by a recent Australian national prevalence survey of psychoses (Jablensky *et al.* 2000) in which the great majority (82%) of cases were identified through non-hospital services and agencies. Another approach to case finding is by using psychiatric case registers, where such facilities exist. Registers collate data from multiple sources, including outpatient and rehabilitation services. The cumulative nature of the data and the capacity for record linkage to other databases make registers highly effective tools for many types of epidemiological research. However, the advantages of the case registers do not offset the problem that an unknown number of persons with schizophrenia never contact the psychiatric services. The proportion of people with schizophrenia who never consult has been estimated at about 17% in the USA (Link & Dohrenwend 1980). There is no evidence that persons with schizophrenia who are not in contact with the mental health services are treated by other agencies such as general practitioners or private psychiatrists. In both Denmark (Munk-Jørgensen & Mortensen 1992) and the UK (Bamrah *et al.* 1991), the number of patients with schizophrenia managed solely by general practitioners was found to be negligible, although it may have increased during the last decade.

Short of a door-to-door community survey, no standard method of estimating the 'hidden' schizophrenic morbidity is available. The presence of such latent morbidity needs to be taken into account in the planning of epidemiological surveys of schizophrenia. Its size is likely to be increasing as a result of diverse reasons including the spread of alternative treatments, the existence of cult or religious groups providing niches to people with unconventional beliefs and the marginalization of the destitute and homeless in the big cities.

Door-to-door and sample surveys

The field survey method has produced some of the most robust epidemiological data on schizophrenia. An early version of the survey method was used by Brugger (1931) in his investigations of the prevalence of psychoses in Thuringia and Bavaria. The method was applied with great success by Scandinavian investigators in the 1930s to 1960s (Strömgren 1938; Sjögren 1948; Bremer 1951; Essen-Möller *et al.* 1956; Hagnell 1966; Bøjholm & Strömgren 1989). In the majority of these studies, a single investigator, or a small group of researchers, interviewed and diagnosed nearly every member of a well-defined community, usually of a small size. Several of the Scandinavian studies were prospective and the original population was re-examined after intervals of 10 or more years. While the completeness of case finding and thoroughness of assessment are probably unsurpassed, the representativeness of results obtained from selected small communities is problematic.

A viable substitute for the complete census of a population is the sample survey in which a probability sample is drawn and interviewed to establish point or lifetime prevalence. Examples include the National Institute of Mental Health (NIMH) Epidemiological Catchment Area (ECA) study in which some 20 000 persons at five sites in the USA were interviewed (Robins & Regier 1991); the National Comorbidity Survey (Kessler *et al.*

1994) based on a national probability sample of 5877 US residents; and the Australian National Mental Health Survey (Andrews *et al.* 2001), in which a national probability sample of 10 641 adults was interviewed. A remarkable feature of these major surveys is that all three used a common method of case detection and diagnosis, based on versions of the same generic diagnostic instrument (administered by lay interviewers). However, because all three were designed as general mental morbidity surveys, the numbers of identified cases of schizophrenia were too small for epidemiological and clinical analysis. In the instance of the Australian survey, a separate in-depth study of 'low-prevalence' disorders, including schizophrenia and other psychoses, was conducted on a stratified sample of 980 cases drawn from a census of 3800 individuals found to be screen-positive for psychosis (Jablensky *et al.* 2000).

Birth cohorts

The birth cohort study can be a particularly effective method for determining incidence and morbid risk because its results produce a 'natural' morbidity and mortality life table. The method was first applied to the major psychoses by Klemperer (1933), who took from the birth registers a random sample of 1000 individuals born in Germany in 1881–90 and attempted to trace them as adults in their fourth decade of life. Because of the high cohort attrition levels that typically affect mobile populations, he succeeded in tracing only 44% and in interviewing a total of 271 probands or key informants. However, there are examples of remarkable success when the method is applied to 'captive' populations such as island inhabitants. Fremming (1947) in Denmark, Helgason (1964) and Helgason and Magnusson (1989) in Iceland were able to trace 92–99% of the members of birth cohorts and to estimate the lifetime morbid risk for schizophrenia. More recent examples of successful use of the method include the search for developmental precursors of adult schizophrenia using prospectively collected data from the UK 1946 birth cohort of the National Survey of Health and Development (NSHD; $n = 5362$; Jones *et al.* 1994; Cannon *et al.* 1996); the UK 1958 birth cohort of the National Child Development Study (NCDS; $n = 15\,398$; Done *et al.* 1994); and the North Finland 1966 birth cohort ($n = 11\,017$; Isohanni *et al.* 1998; Jones *et al.* 1998). Samples from two birth cohorts in the USA, the National Collaborative Perinatal Project 1959–66 ($n = 9236$; Cannon *et al.* 2000) and the Child Health and Development Study 1960–67 ($n = 19\,044$; Susser *et al.* 2000), have recently been drawn for follow-up studies focusing on prenatal, perinatal and early childhood influences on the development of schizophrenia. Birth cohort samples of this kind are eminently suited for the testing of hypotheses about risk factors, especially if the original data collection included biological samples such as frozen blood or placenta specimens. However, their main limitation stems from: (i) the long 'latency' period before follow-up studies can generate schizophrenia incidence data; and (ii) the relatively small yield of cases of schizophrenia (81 cases by age 43 in the NSHD; 45 cases by age 23 in the NCDS; 76 cases by age 28 in the Finnish cohort study). The latter factor restricts the range of data analyses because of limited statistical power.

Variants of the cohort design include follow-up studies of individuals who had undergone some kind of assessment at a specified age. Examples are a Swedish study including 50 087 men given a psychological examination as army conscripts at age 18–20 during 1969–70 and followed up through the national psychiatric case register until 1983 (Malmberg *et al.* 1998), and a similar Israeli study based on a preconscription cognitive and behavioural assessment during 1985–91 of 9724 male adolescents aged 16–17 and a follow-up through the psychiatric case register (Davidson *et al.* 1999). Follow-up studies of cohorts defined by a particular maternal exposure at a given time, e.g. the offspring of pregnant women exposed to acute undernutrition during the 1945 Dutch 'hunger winter' (Susser & Lin 1992), the stress of the 5-day *blitzkrieg* against Holland in 1940 (van Os & Selten 1998), radiation from the Nagasaki A-bomb in 1945 (Imamura *et al.* 1999), or prenatal rubella (Brown *et al.* 2001) provide further examples of rich research opportunities using cohort data.

Diagnosis

Diagnostic concepts have a critical role in the epidemiology of schizophrenia because: (i) a proportion of the variation in results of individual studies is caused by variation in diagnostic concepts and practices; (ii) the diagnostic classification of cases may not be comparable across studies; and (iii) in any particular study the diagnosis of schizophrenia may include or exclude conditions of uncertain nosological status such as acute schizophreniform episodes, schizoaffective disorders or other 'spectrum' disorders. In addition, the question of how and by whom the diagnosis was made is an important qualifier of the reported results.

Diagnosis-related bias is usually difficult to detect in past epidemiological research. Until the late 1960s, diagnostic rules were seldom explicitly stated and the description of assessment methods often lacked sufficient detail. As demonstrated by the US–UK diagnostic study (Cooper *et al.* 1972), concepts of schizophrenia in two different psychiatric cultures diverged to an extent that practically invalidated the comparisons. The World Health Organization (WHO) International Pilot Study of Schizophrenia (IPSS; World Health Organization 1973, 1979) examined the diagnostic variation across nine countries by applying a computerized reference classification, CATEGO (Wing *et al.* 1974), in addition to the clinical diagnoses made locally by psychiatrists. It transpired, reassuringly, that psychiatrists in the majority of settings were using similar diagnostic concepts of schizophrenia, broadly corresponding to the Kraepelin–Bleuler tradition. In most settings the core diagnostic concept of schizophrenia does not seem to have undergone major changes over time. In a reanalysis of Kraepelin's original cases from 1908, Jablensky *et al.* (1993) demonstrated that clinical data on dementia praecox and manic-depressive psychosis collected early this century could be coded and analysed in terms of CATEGO syndromes and that the agreement between the 1908 diagnosis of dementia praecox and the CATEGO classification of the same cases was 88.6%.

Since 1980, the comparability of epidemiological data on schizophrenia over time has been affected by the adoption of operational diagnostic criteria such as the Research Diagnostic Criteria (RDC), DSM-III, DSM-IIIR and DSM-IV. The introduction of such criteria has helped to resolve some old, and to create some new, diagnostic problems with epidemiological implications. Brockington *et al.* (1978) applied 10 different definitions of schizophrenia to the same clinical material and obtained an 11-fold difference in the frequency of the disorder, depending on the criteria chosen. Similarly, Stephens *et al.* (1982), using nine diagnostic systems, established that only 7% of the cases were diagnosed as schizophrenic by all systems. The DSM-III requirement of 6 months' prior duration of symptoms and an upper age limit at 45 for a first diagnosis of schizophrenia excluded from the incidence estimates as many as two-thirds of the cases which met the ICD-9 glossary definition of the disorder. ICD-10, which requires only 4 weeks' symptom duration, agrees well with DSM-IIIR and DSM-IV on the classification of 'core' cases of schizophrenia but the classifications may produce discrepant results in atypical or milder cases (Jablensky *et al.* 1999). Such differences may be relatively unimportant for clinical practice but are likely to result in serious bias in epidemiological and genetic studies. The inclusion of the 6 months' symptom duration criterion in the DSM classification aims to increase the homogeneity of patient samples and to minimize the false-positive diagnoses. However, this is not an unequivocal advantage for epidemiology. The application of restrictive diagnostic criteria at the case finding stage of surveys is likely to exclude potential 'true' cases that fall short of meeting the full set of criteria on initial examination. As a rule, initial overinclusion of false-positives is less damaging than exclusion of false-negatives in two-stage surveys because, once properly assessed at the second stage, false-positives can be eliminated from data analysis. In contrast, erroneously rejected cases are unlikely ever to be retrieved. Until the aetiology of schizophrenia is elucidated, or a validating pathognomonic lesion is established, the decision as to what constitutes 'true' schizophrenia will remain arbitrary. With regard to epidemiological studies, less restrictive criteria are preferable to strict exclusion rules because they allow for a broader spectrum of outcomes at the endpoint of observation. This greater variation at endpoint should help to identify outcome-based subgroups and to relate their characteristics to the initial symptoms and to various risk factors.

Investigators

Epidemiological studies of schizophrenia vary with regard to how and by whom potential cases are identified and diagnosed. Many of the earlier European studies had been carried out by a single investigator (usually a psychiatrist) or by a small group of researchers. This had the advantage of diagnostic consistency, although systematic bias could not be excluded. Clinician-led studies are less common in current research, where multicentre collaborative designs, large samples and cost considerations limit the use of such strategies. Lay interviewers or professionals other than psychiatrists are increasingly involved in case finding and interviewing, and the clinicians' role is often restricted to a diagnostic review of cases. The effects of interviewer-related variation (e.g. professional vs. lay interviewers) have only been studied in a limited way (Robins 1989). However, there is an increasing concern that lay interviewers using structured diagnostic interviews in community surveys are liable to commit response errors, especially regarding the rating of symptom severity (Regier *et al.* 1998).

Instruments

Instruments used in epidemiological research into the psychotic disorders differ with regard to purpose and scope, sources of data, output format and user. At a basic conceptual level, the most widely used current diagnostic instruments fall into three categories.

The first category comprises tools designed for screening for psychosis as part of two-phase surveys. At present, there is no generally agreed validated set of screening criteria that could serve as a 'gold standard' in case finding for schizophrenia. Based on a reanalysis of ECA data, Eaton *et al.* (1991) have suggested that a combination of DSM-III criterion A and 16 items from the Diagnostic Interview Schedule (DIS; Robins *et al.* 1988) might be capable of identifying two-thirds of the psychotic cases in a community survey, and that the addition of a single question about past psychiatric hospitalization could increase the 'hit' rate to nearly 90%. However, such a screening device is yet to be tested. A psychosis screening questionnaire (PSQ) developed for use by lay interviewers (Bebbington & Nayani 1995) has been shown to perform with a satisfactory positive predictive value of 91.2% and negative predictive value of 98.4%.

The second category of assessment tools includes fully structured interviews, such as the NIMH DIS (Robins *et al.* 1981) and the related WHO–Alcohol, Drug Abuse, and Mental Health Administration (ADAMHA) Composite International Diagnostic Interview (CIDI; Robins *et al.* 1988). Both have been designed to match specifically the diagnostic criteria of DSM-IIIR and ICD-10. These instruments were designed for use by non-psychiatric interviewers and clinical judgement is not required in their administration and scoring.

The third category includes semistructured interview schedules such as the Present State Examination (PSE; Wing *et al.* 1974) and the Schedules for Clinical Assessment in Neuropsychiatry (SCAN; Wing *et al.* 1990, 1998), which cover a very broad range of psychopathology and require clinical judgement for their administration and scoring. The data elicited by the SCAN can be processed by computer diagnostic algorithms providing ICD-10, DSM-IIIR and DSM-IV diagnoses.

Each type of instrument has both advantages and disadvantages. The main advantage of the DIS/CIDI is that it can be used by lay interviewers who have received brief (2 week) training. It has been shown as capable of achieving high interrater reliability and of generating standard diagnoses in a single-stage survey design. However, the range of psychopathology covered by DIS/CIDI and other similar instruments is restricted to the diagnostic system with which such instruments are interlocked. A major disadvantage is that their clinical validity, in terms of sensitivity and specificity in diagnosing schizophrenia, is questionable. The PSE-SCAN type of interview, on the other hand, allows a great amount of descriptive information to be collected and processed in alternative ways. Both the reliability and validity of the PSE are to a large extent a function of the training and skills of the interviewer. The main disadvantages of the PSE-SCAN system are that the interview is time-demanding, and that making a proper diagnosis often requires collateral information that may only be obtainable in a clinical setting. However, it should be noted that an abbreviated survey version of SCAN, which partly overcomes these limitations, is already available (Brugha *et al.* 1999).

Measures of morbidity

Depending on the type of cases included in the numerator and the time period covered, different aspects of morbidity are captured by indices of prevalence, incidence and morbid risk (disease expectancy). However, problems often arise in relation to the denominator (i.e. the population base from which the cases are recruited). Using as a denominator the total population size (all age groups) is appropriate when 'burden of disease' or service needs are being estimated. The total population is not an appropriate base when the objective is to measure incidence because the probabilities of disease onsets are not evenly distributed over the life span. The denominator therefore should reflect the pooled risks of developing schizophrenia within a given population and exclude age groups for which the risk equals or approximates zero. Three methods can be used to achieve this, depending on the design of the study. First, age correction can be applied, setting the lower limit for schizophrenia risk at 15 years. The upper limit is often set at age 54, but there is no reason why it could not be higher. Secondly, when determining cumulative incidence (morbid risk) in cohort studies, both the numerator and the denominator need to be adjusted by weighting each affected person in the numerator for average life expectancy at the age of ascertainment (or at the age at death for patients who had died prior to survey), as well as by adjusting the denominator for persons who had died as unaffected prior to the survey. Weinberg's abridged method of estimating person-years of exposure (*Bezugsziffer*, BZ) to the risk of disease (Weinberg 1925; Reid 1960) is still widely used. Thirdly, to enable comparisons of rates, the denominator may need to be recalculated to a standard population by direct or indirect standardization.

Although relatively simple statistical methods are available for standardization and adjustment, they have been inconsistently applied in schizophrenia research. Lack of proper standardization of morbidity measures introduces uncontrolled variation and may compromise the validity of comparisons across different studies. In the last decade, the epidemiological analysis of schizophrenia has been showing a trend towards increased use of statistical procedures that are currently standard in the epidemiology of other non-communicable diseases, such as relative risk, incidence ratios, multivariate regression, proportional hazards models, survival analysis, etc. This signals a gradual transition from descriptive to analytical or risk factor epidemiology of the disorder.

Descriptive epidemiology of schizophrenia

The descriptive epidemiology of schizophrenia still contains gaps but the contours of the overall picture have been laid down and enable some tentative conclusions.

Prevalence

The prevalence of a disorder is defined as the number of cases (per 1000 persons at risk) present in a population at a given time or over a defined period. Point prevalence refers to cases which are active (i.e. symptomatic) on a given date, or within a brief interval, with a census date as midpoint. Because cases in remission will usually be missed in a point prevalence survey, the assessment of the present mental state in census or birth cohort studies needs to be supplemented with information about past episodes of the disorder. This results in a lifetime prevalence index, or proportion of survivors affected (PSA). In disorders tending towards a continuous course, such as schizophrenia, point and lifetime prevalence estimates are closely similar or identical. The index of period prevalence, i.e. the number of cases per 1000 population that are active during a specified period (e.g. 6 months or 1 year) is less useful because it confounds point prevalence with incidence.

An overview of selected prevalence studies of schizophrenia spanning a period of some 60 years is given in Table 12.1. The studies differ in their methodology but have in common a high intensity of case finding (many of them were census investigations). Several studies included repeat surveys in which the original population was re-examined at some later time (the resulting follow-up prevalence figures are indicated in the table by an arrow).

The majority of the studies have produced prevalence figures in the range 1.4–4.6 per 1000 population at risk. Considering the many possible sources of variation, this range is fairly narrow. However, similar prevalence figures may mask important differences in incidence rates between populations with different mortality experiences, age structures and migration rates. Crude prevalence figures are difficult to interpret in the absence of such background demographic data. Therefore, it is unwarranted to assume that the modal prevalence rate emerging from the studies listed in Table 12.1, i.e. 1.4–4.6 per 1000, is the unqualified, 'true' rate of schizophrenia in those populations.

Table 12.1 Selected prevalence studies of schizophrenia.

Study	Country	Population	Method	Prevalence per 1000 population at risk
Surveys in developed countries				
Brugger (1931)	Germany	Area in Thuringia ($n = 37\,561$); age 10+	Census	2.4 (point)
Strömgren (1938); Bøjholm & Strömgren (1989)	Denmark	Island population ($n = 50\,000$)	Repeat census	3.9 → 3.3 (point)
Lemkau *et al.* (1943)	USA	Household sample	Census	2.9 (point)
Essen-Möller *et al.* (1956); Hagnell (1966)	Sweden	Community in southern Sweden	Repeat census	6.7 → 4.5 (point)
Crocetti *et al.* (1971)	Croatia	Sample of 9201 households	Census	5.9 (point)
Rotstein (1977)	Russia	Population sample ($n = 35\,590$)	Census	3.8 (lifetime)
Robins & Regier (1991)	USA	Aggregated data across five ECA sites	Sample survey	7.0 (point) 15.0 (lifetime)
Kendler & Walsh (1995)	Ireland	Roscommon County ($n = 32\,775$)	Register-based family study	Lifetime: 5.4 (males) 4.3 (females)
Jeffreys *et al.* (1997)	UK	London health district ($n = 112\,127$)	Census; interviews of a sample ($n = 172$)	5.1 (point)
Jablensky *et al.* (2000)	Australia	Four urban areas ($n = 1\,084\,978$)	Census; interviews of a sample ($n = 980$)	3.1–5.9 (point)* 3.9–6.9 (1 year)†
Surveys in developing countries				
Rin & Lin (1962); Lin *et al.* (1989)	Taiwan	Population sample	Repeat census	2.1 → 1.4 (point)
Bash & Bash-Liechti (1969)	Iran	Rural area ($n = 11\,585$)	Census	2.1 (point)
Dube & Kumar (1972)	India	Four areas in Agra ($n = 29\,468$)	Census	2.6 (point)
ICMR (1988)	India	Rural area ($n = 46\,380$)	Census	2.2 (point)
Padmavathi *et al.* (1987)	India	Urban ($n = 101\,229$)	Census	2.5 (point)
Salan (1992)	Indonesia	Slum area in West Jakarta ($n = 100\,107$)	Two-stage survey: (a) key informants (b) interview	1.4 (point)
Lee *et al.* (1990)	Korea	Urban and rural	Census	Lifetime: 3.0 (urban) 4.0 (rural)
Chen *et al.* (1993)	Hong Kong	Community sample ($n = 7229$)	DIS interviews	Lifetime: 1.2 (males) 1.3 (females)
Waldo (1999)	Kosrae (Micronesia)	Island population ($n = 5500$)	Key informants and clinic records; some interviews	6.8 (point), age 15+
Kebede & Alem (1999)	Ethiopia	District ($n = 227\,135$) south of Addis Ababa; mixed urban and rural	Two-stage survey: (a) door-to-door and key informants (b) SCAN interviews	7.1 (point), age 15–49

*All psychoses.
†Schizophrenia and other non-affective psychoses.

Incidence

The incidence rate of schizophrenia (annual number of new cases in a defined population per 1000 individuals at risk) is of greater interest than prevalence because its variation is far more sensitive to the effects of causal and risk factors. The estimation of incidence depends critically on the capacity to pinpoint disease onset or inception. There is no agreed definition of inception of schizophrenia and the idea of onset as some kind of a point event raises fundamental difficulties. Because the timing of the 'true' onset of the still hypothetical neural dysfunction that underlies schizophrenia is unknown, investigators have to operate with proxy events. The social onset (appearance of conspicuous behavioural abnormalities leading to consultation, admission or other action) rarely coincides with the onset of the earliest symptoms enabling a diagnosis of the disorder; the diagnostic symptoms are in many cases preceded by a prodromal subclinical phase of varying duration. Precursors of schizophrenia including developmental delays, cognitive abnormalities and behavioural oddities may appear very early in life but, at present, such developmental precursors cannot serve as reference points for dating onset (such precursors can only be identified *post hoc*). Thus, any point on the continuum spanning the prodromal phase, the appearance of psychotic symptoms and the social onset could be arbitrarily designated as the beginning of a schizophrenic illness. This continuum may extend over 2–6 years (Häfner *et al.* 1993) and inconsistencies in the ascertainment of the onset in individual cases may result in unreliable incidence estimates within or across studies. It is clearly important for epidemiology to design and agree on a procedure that ensures consistency in defining onset, e.g. as the point in time when the disorder becomes diagnosable according to specified criteria. A convention addressing this problem has not yet been adopted in incidence studies of schizophrenia. In many studies, the first hospital admission is still being used as an index of onset. This is difficult to sustain in view of the wide variation across individuals, settings and time as regards the time lag between first appearance of symptoms and first admission. A better approximation to the time of onset is provided by the first contact, i.e. the point at which some 'helping agency' is contacted by an individual with incipient psychotic illness. The majority of first contacts are ambulatory and often precede admission to hospital by many months. In a number of instances hospitalization may not take place at all. A version of this method was used in the WHO 10-country study (Jablensky *et al.* 1992) in which case finding targeted prospectively over 2 years first contacts with a variety of services, including many non-medical ones.

Table 12.2 presents the essential features of 11 incidence studies of schizophrenia. Leaving aside the rates based on the RDC or DSM-III definition of schizophrenia, the first admission and first contact rates range from 0.17 to 0.54 per 1000 population per year, i.e. show a threefold difference. There is a very close concordance among the Scandinavian rates (0.20–0.27 per 1000), which is probably because of the nearly complete enumeration of the cases, uniform diagnostic practices and accurate denominator data. Some of the lowest rates in Table 12.2 originate from studies involving non-European populations, e.g. Hindu and Moslem Indians in Mauritius (0.14 and 0.09 per 1000), as well as indigenous people in Taiwan (0.17 per 1000). Because the Mauritius data are on first hospital admissions, the low rates may have resulted from a nosocomial threshold. This does not apply to the Taiwan data, which were collected in a community survey. Two recent studies employing a polydiagnostic (International Classification of Diseases (ICD), RDC and DSM-III) classification illustrate the impact of the restrictive diagnostic criteria which, compared with ICD-9, leads to a threefold drop in the incidence rate for the same population.

To date, the only study that has generated directly comparable incidence data for different populations by using identical case finding and diagnostic procedures prospectively and simultaneously in 12 catchment areas is the WHO 10-country investigation (Sartorius *et al.* 1986; Jablensky *et al.* 1992). Incidence estimates in the WHO study were based on first-in-lifetime contacts with 'helping agencies' in the area (including traditional healers in the developing countries) which were screened and monitored over a 2-year period. Potential cases and key informants were interviewed using standardized instruments, and the onset of psychotic symptoms diagnostic of schizophrenia was ascertained for the majority of the patients (1022 out of the total 1379). For 86% of the 1022 patients the first appearance of diagnostic symptoms of schizophrenia was within a year of the first contact and therefore the first-contact rate could serve as a reasonable approximation to the onset rate. The rates for eight catchment areas are shown in Table 12.3.

The differences between the rates for broadly (ICD-9) defined schizophrenia were significant ($P < 0.001$, two-tailed test) while those for the narrow, or 'nuclear', schizophrenia syndrome were not significant. No consistent differences were found between cases meeting the broad clinical criteria and the cases classified by the computer algorithm CATEGO as 'nuclear' schizophrenia (class S +) with regard to the course and outcome of the disorder or the type of onset (acute or insidious). Therefore, the similar incidence rates across the study areas do not imply that schizophrenia is homogeneous with regard to its prognosis in those populations, nor is there a reason to assume that the cases meeting the narrow S + criteria are in any sense phenotypically 'purer' expressions of schizophrenia, in contrast to cases meeting the broader clinical criteria but not S + 0. The salient aspect of the WHO findings is not the lack of statistically significant differences in the rates of CATEGO S + schizophrenia, but rather the narrow range of variation (0.16–0.42 per 1000) in the incidence of schizophrenia when standard case definitions, case finding procedures and assessment methods are used across very different populations. In recent years, replications of the design and methods of the WHO have been carried out with very similar results by investigators in India, the Caribbean and the UK (Table 12.3).

Table 12.2 Selected incidence studies of schizophrenia.

Study	Country	Population	Method	Annual rate per 1000
Surveys in industrialized countries				
Ødegaard (1946a)	Norway	Total population	First admissions 1926–35 ($n = 14231$)	0.24
Helgason (1964)	Iceland	Total population	First admissions 1966–67 ($n = 2388$)	0.27
Häfner & Reimann (1970)	Germany	City of Mannheim ($n = 330000$)	Case register	0.54
Lieberman (1974)	Russia	Moscow district ($n = 248000$)	Follow-back of prevalent cases	0.20 (male) 0.19 (female)
Castle *et al.* (1991)	UK	London (Camberwell)	Case register	0.25 (ICD) 0.17 (RDC) 0.08 (DSM-III)
Nicole *et al.* (1992)	Canada	Area in Quebec ($n = 338300$)	First admissions	0.31 (ICD) 0.09 (DSM-III)
McNaught *et al.* (1997)	UK	London health district ($n = 112127$)	2 censuses, 5 years apart	0.21 (DSM-IIIR)
Brewin *et al.* (1997)	UK	Nottingham	2 cohorts of first contacts (1978–80 and 1992–94)	0.25 → 0.29 (all psychoses) 0.14 → 0.09 (ICD-10 schizophrenia)
Surveys in developing countries				
Raman & Murphy (1972)	Mauritius	Total population ($n = 257000$)	First admissions	0.24 (Africans) 0.14 (Indian Hindus) 0.09 (Indian Moslems)
Lin *et al.* (1989)	Taiwan	3 communities ($n = 39024$)	Household survey	0.17
Rajkumar *et al.* (1993)	India	Area in Madras ($n = 43097$)	Door-to-door survey and key informants	0.41
Hickling & Rodgers-Johnson (1995)	Jamaica	Total population ($n = 2.46$ million)	First contacts	0.24 ('broad') 0.21 ('restrictive')
Mahy *et al.* (1999)	Barbados	Total population ($n = 262000$)	First contacts	0.32 ('broad') 0.28 ('restrictive')

First-episode psychosis

The increased interest in the early detection and treatment of first episodes of psychosis has been bolstered by the hypothesis that the course and outcome of the early stages of a schizophrenic illness may have a pathoplastic effect on its subsequent course. More specifically, it has been proposed that excitotoxic neurotransmitter release and neuroendocrine stress responses during an early episode of manifest psychosis may induce irreversible changes in the connectivity between neural networks (Lieberman 1999). As an extension of this hypothesis, it has been suggested that a behavioural or pharmacological intervention prior to the onset of psychotic symptoms might delay or, in some cases, prevent the onset of schizophrenia (McGorry *et al.* 1996). Some evidence has been presented that a longer period between the first onset of psychotic symptoms and the initiation of treatment (duration of untreated psychosis, or DUP) correlates with increased time to remission and poor response to treatment (Loebel *et al.* 1992), but several other studies have failed to replicate this effect. None of the hypotheses referred to above have been properly tested, yet some studies focusing on the earliest manifestations of psychosis have highlighted novel phenomena, such as a preonset deterioration in cognitive performance which then remains static (Goldberg *et al.* 1993), early

Table 12.3 Annual incidence rates per 1000 population at risk, age 15–54, for a 'broad' and a 'narrow' case definition of schizophrenia (WHO 10-country study).

Country	Area	'Broad' definition (ICD-9)			'Restrictive' definition (CATEGO S +)		
		Male	Female	Both sexes	Male	Female	Both sexes
Denmark	Aarhus	0.18	0.13	0.16	0.09	0.05	0.07
India	Chandigarh (rural area)	0.37	0.48	0.42	0.13	0.09	0.11
	Chandigarh (urban area)	0.34	0.35	0.35	0.08	0.11	0.09
Ireland	Dublin	0.23	0.21	0.22	0.10	0.08	0.09
Japan	Nagasaki	0.23	0.18	0.20	0.11	0.09	0.10
Russia	Moscow	0.25	0.31	0.28	0.03	0.03	0.02
UK	Nottingham	0.28	0.15	0.22	0.17	0.12	0.14
USA	Honolulu	0.18	0.14	0.16	0.10	0.08	0.09

co-occurrence of both 'positive' and 'negative' symptoms (Gupta *et al.* 1997a), significant decline in social functioning (Häfner *et al.* 1999), and a general malleability of dysfunction through appropriate behavioural interventions and low-dose time-limited pharmacological treatment (Szymanski *et al.* 1996). All this suggests that clinical research bridging the gap between epidemiological investigations of risk factors or antecedents of disease and individual pathways to psychotic illness may contribute importantly to the understanding and management of the early course of schizophrenia.

Morbid risk (disease expectancy)

Morbid risk is the probability (expressed as a percentage) that an individual born into a particular population or group will develop the disease if he/she survives through the entire period of risk for that disease (15–54 in the instance of schizophrenia). If age- and sex-specific incidence rates are available, lifetime disease expectancy can be estimated directly by summing up the rates across the age groups within the period of risk. An indirect approximation to disease expectancy can be obtained from census data using the so-called abridged method of Weinberg (1925):

$$P = \frac{A}{B - \left(B_0 + \frac{1}{2} B_m\right)},$$

where P is disease expectancy (%), A the number of prevalent cases, B the total population surveyed, B_0 persons who have not yet entered the risk period and B_m persons within the risk period.

A modification of Weinberg's method, proposed by Strömgren (1935) and by Bøjholm and Strömgren (1989), weights the numerator for the excess mortality observed among schizophrenic patients. Whether estimated directly from age-specific incidence rates, or indirectly from prevalence data, disease expectancy enables a more reliable comparison of the occurrence of schizophrenia in different populations than the prevalence or incidence rates. Notwithstanding different methods of data collection, the figures suggest considerable consistency of the disease expectancy of schizophrenia across populations and over time. Excluding the northern Swedish isolate and a few other 'outliers', the highest risk ratio (highest–lowest morbid risk) is about 5.0; for the WHO 10-country study it is 2.9 (ICD-9 schizophrenia) and 2.0 (CATEGO S +). Most studies have produced morbid risk estimates in the range 0.50–1.60. Therefore, the often quoted 'rule of thumb' that the morbid risk for schizophrenia is about 1% seems to be consistent with the evidence.

Populations and groups with high and low rates of schizophrenia

The question of whether significant differences exist among populations in the 'true' rate of schizophrenia (Torrey 1987) has no simple answer. Depending on the population size or samples being compared, statistically significant differences are bound to occur. Whether such differences are epidemiologically meaningful is open to interpretation. Because many confounding factors and selection bias can inflate or deflate the incidence and morbid risk estimates, comparisons of schizophrenia rates across populations should be interpreted with caution, taking into account the methods applied and the demography of the populations concerned. For example, it would be a mistake to interpret the sevenfold difference in the estimated population incidence of schizophrenia reported from two of the ECA study sites as evidence of large variation in the incidence of schizophrenia in the USA (Tien & Eaton 1992). The high rates reported from the ECA study in the USA (Robins & Regier 1991), coupled with a 13-fold difference in the rates for age group 18–24 across the sites, remain unexplained. Above all, inconsistencies in the administration of the diagnostic instrument by lay interviewers are likely to have affected the diagnostic classification of cases. In the National Comorbidity Survey (NCS), diagnoses of 'non-affective psychosis' by computer algorithm based on CIDI (a derivative of the DIS) were found to agree poorly with clinicians' diagnoses based on telephone reinterviews, and to result in discrepant estimates of the lifetime prevalence of both 'narrowly' and 'broadly' defined non-affective psychotic illness (Kendler *et al.* 1996a). A different problem is highlighted by a recent incidence study based on a 1959–67 birth cohort in Alameda County, CA, USA (Bresnahan *et al.* 2000). The study reported unusually high rates for males aged 15–29 but, because of the wide confidence intervals, the authors could not rule out the possibility that the high male rates may have resulted from chance.

With such methodological caveats, true 'outlier' populations nevertheless do exist. Very high rates (2–3 times the national or regional rate) have been reported for population isolates, such as an area in northern Sweden (Böök *et al.* 1978) and several areas in Finland (Hovatta *et al.* 1999). High rates have also been described in an area in Croatia, characterized by a high level of emigration during the nineteenth and early twentieth century (Crocetti *et al.* 1971). Certain migrant populations, e.g. the African-Caribbeans in the UK (Harrison *et al.* 1997), and the Surinamese in the Netherlands (Selten *et al.* 1997), have been reported to have an unusually high prevalence of schizophrenia, exceeding 5–7 times the average rate in the general population of the host country, as well as the rate in the country of origin.

At the other extreme, a virtual absence of schizophrenia and a moderate or high rate of depression have been observed among the Hutterites in South Dakota, a Protestant sect whose members live in closely knit endogamous communities, largely sheltered from the outside world (Eaton & Weil 1955; Torrey 1995; Nimgaonkar *et al.* 2000). Negative selection for schizoid individuals who fail to adjust to the communal lifestyle and eventually migrate without leaving progeny has been suggested, but not definitively proven, as an explanation. Low rates have also been reported for certain Pacific Island populations (Rin & Lin 1962) but uncertainties about the completeness of case finding makes the interpretation of such reports problematic. Two surveys in Taiwan (see Table 12.2), separated by 15 years during which major social changes took place, found that the prevalence of schizophrenia decreased from 2.1 to 1.4 per 1000. In both surveys, the aboriginal Taiwanese had significantly lower rates than the mainland Chinese who had migrated to the island after World War II.

The general conclusion is that according to the great majority of studies, the prevalence and incidence rates of schizophrenia are similar across populations. However, a small number of populations have been identified that clearly deviate from this central tendency. The magnitude of these deviations is modest compared with the differences observed across populations with regard to other multifactorial diseases such as diabetes, ischaemic heart disease or cancer, where 10- to 30-fold differences in prevalence across populations are not uncommon. Such 'outlier' population groups with high or low incidence of schizophrenia are of considerable interest as potentially informative settings for the search for susceptibility genes, as well as for studies of culture–gene interactions over multiple generations.

Secular trends in the incidence and prevalence of schizophrenia

The rarity of descriptions of schizophrenia in the medical literature before the eighteenth century has led to speculation that the condition had not existed (Torrey 1980), or was rare (Hare 1983), until the industrial revolution. The earliest references to psychotic states clearly matching the clinical picture of schizophrenia can be found in Pinel (1803) and Haslam (1809). Examination of the nineteenth century asylum statistics suggests that 'monomaniac insanity', 'delusional insanity' and 'ordinary dementia' (i.e. the diagnostic groups likely to contain schizophrenic patients in the pre-Kraepelinian era) composed between 5.3% and 18.9% of all institutionalized patients (Jablensky 1986). The records of the Munich University Psychiatric Clinic under the direction of Kraepelin in 1908 indicate that in the course of a year dementia praecox accounted for only 9.1% of the first admissions among men and for 7.3% among women (Jablensky *et al.* 1993). It is likely that during much of the nineteenth century schizophrenia was less conspicuous than it is today, because of the much higher prevalence of organic brain diseases such as general paresis. The hypothesis that schizophrenia is of recent origin is not plausible, considering the genetics of the disorder and its similar rates of occurrence in diverse populations. However, it is possible that the number of people diagnosed and hospitalized as schizophrenic increased rapidly during the early decades of the twentieth century. Whether the increase was real (e.g. resulting from a decreasing mortality, rising incidence, or both) or spurious (increased use of the diagnosis, social pressure to institutionalize the mentally ill) remains unclear.

The question of whether long-term trends in the incidence of schizophrenia can be detected has attracted interest following reports since 1985 indicating a 40% or more reduction in the first admissions with a diagnosis of schizophrenia in Denmark, UK and New Zealand over the last three decades. A decline in the hospitalization rate for schizophrenia was first reported by Weeke and Strömgren (1978), who noted that the national census of hospitalized patients with schizophrenia in Denmark had dropped from 6200 in 1957 to 4500 in 1972. The more recent data can be summed up as follows: (i) a trend of diminishing administrative incidence rates (both first hospital admissions and first contacts with a psychiatric case register) has been demonstrated but the data are inconsistent as regards the age- and sex-specific rate reduction; (ii) this trend has been found in large national databases, e.g. in Denmark, Scotland, England and Wales, but has not been consistently replicated at local or regional level: two case registers have identified a downward trend (Eagles *et al.* 1988; de Alarcon *et al.* 1992), another two have shown increases (Castle *et al.* 1991; Bamrah *et al.* 1991), and one has reported no change (Harrison *et al.* 1991); (iii) studies in which research diagnoses (RDC, DSM-III or CATEGO) were made (Bamrah *et al.* 1991; Castle *et al.* 1991) have shown no decline in rates; (iv) in the areas where reduction of schizophrenia has been reported, there have been during the same period concomitant reductions in the total number of beds and first admissions; (v) in several areas increases have been reported in the mortality of schizophrenic patients (Munk-Jørgensen & Mortensen 1992), in the diagnoses of paranoid and reactive psychoses or borderline states on first admission (Munk-Jørgensen 1986; Der *et al.* 1990; Harrison *et al.* 1991) and in the delay between first outpatient contact and first hospital admission (Harrison *et al.* 1991). Although a trend of diminishing rates of schizophrenia cannot be excluded, the combined effect of several factors could explain the observed changes: variations in the definition of first admission or first contact; changes in diagnostic practices over time; changes in the treatment modalities and settings; increases in the mortality of schizophrenic patients; and changes in the age composition of the populations concerned. An increasing reluctance to make a diagnosis of schizophrenia on first admission has been noted among Danish psychiatrists (Munk-Jørgensen 1986) and the same may be occurring in the diagnostic practice in other countries. The reported size of the compensatory increase of other diagnoses on first admission is sufficient to account for the drop in schizophrenia diagnoses. In addition, the time lag in the diagnosis of schizophrenia, which in many instances amounts to years after the first service contact, may artificially depress the first admission rates for the most recent years of the observation period. The gradual 'disappearance' of schizophrenia therefore is a rather unlikely hypothesis.

Comorbid association with other diseases

The concept of comorbidity refers to the simultaneous presence in an individual of two or more nosologically different disorders which may be either coincident or causally related. In schizophrenia, comorbidity comprises: (i) relatively common medical problems and diseases that tend to occur among schizophrenic patients more frequently as a consequence of dysfunctional behaviour, poor self-care or medical neglect; and (ii) specific disorders that may have a putative pathogenetic relationship with schizophrenia itself.

Physical disease is common among patients with schizophrenia but is rarely diagnosed. Between 46% and 80% of inpatients, and between 20% and 43% of outpatients with schizophrenia, have been found in different surveys to have concurrent medical illnesses. In 46% of the patients a physical illness was thought to aggravate the mental state, and in 7% it was life-threatening (Adler & Griffith 1991). In a study of acute admissions of patients with schizophrenia, 10% were found to be dehydrated, 33% had hypokalaemia and 66% had elevated serum muscle enzymes (Hatta *et al.* 1999). Schizophrenic patients have a dramatically increased risk of poisoning with psychotropic drugs (50-fold for men and 20-fold for women, according to Mäkikirö *et al.* 1998). In addition to a generally increased susceptibility to infection, especially pulmonary tuberculosis prior to hospitalization (Baldwin 1979), schizophrenic patients have higher than expected rates of diabetes, arteriosclerotic disease and myocardial infarction (Saugstad & Ødegaard 1979), middle ear disease (Mason & Winton 1995), irritable bowel syndrome (Gupta *et al.* 1997b), some rare genetic or idiopathic disorders such as acute intermittent porphyria (Crimlisk 1997) and HIV (5–7% estimated prevalence in patients with schizophrenia in the USA; Sewell 1996). This heavy burden of medical morbidity remains largely under-recognized because schizophrenic patients with comorbid conditions are usually excluded from research studies (Jeste *et al.* 1996).

'Negative' comorbidity (i.e. a lower than expected rate of occurrence of diseases) has been demonstrated for rheumatoid arthritis (Österberg 1978; Eaton *et al.* 1992), although a recent record linkage study (Lauerma *et al.* 1998) failed to replicate this. Several population-based record linkage studies have shown that schizophrenic patients have a significantly lower incidence of cancer, compared with the general population (Dupont *et al.* 1986; Mortensen 1994; Lawrence *et al.* 2000a). The lower rates are particularly pronounced for lung cancer in male patients. There is no obvious explanation for this finding but some protective effect of long-term neuroleptic medication has been suggested (Mortensen 1987).

Numerous studies have reported a significantly increased frequency of dysmorphic features and minor physical anomalies, including high-steepled palate, malformed ears, epicanthus, single palmar crease and finger and toe abnormalities, which may result from deviations in fetal development during the first gestational trimester (Murphy & Owen 1996; Ismail *et al.* 1998). A variety of rare organic brain disorders and anomalies have been described to occur in association with schizophrenia, including basal ganglia calcification (Francis & Freeman 1984; Flint & Goldstein 1992), aqueductus Sylvii stenosis (Reveley & Reveley 1983; Roberts *et al.* 1983; O'Flaithbheartaigh *et al.* 1994), cerebral hemiatrophy (Puri *et al.* 1994; Honer *et al.* 1996), corpus callosum agenesis (Lewis *et al.* 1988), schizencephaly (Alexander *et al.* 1997), septal cysts (Lewis & Mezey 1985), acute intermittent porphyria (Propping 1983), coeliac disease (Dohan 1966), and Marfan syndrome (Sirota *et al.* 1990). Most of these associations have been observed in single case studies; epidemiological evidence of a higher than chance co-occurrence with schizophrenia has so far only been provided for epilepsy (Bruton *et al.* 1994; Bredkaer *et al.* 1998) and metachromatic leukodystrophy (Hyde *et al.* 1992).

Comorbidity with substance use

Substance abuse is by far the most common comorbid problem among schizophrenic patients (Strakowski *et al.* 1993; Rosenthal 1998) and involves alcohol, stimulants, anxiolytics, hallucinogens, antiparkinsonian drugs, as well as caffeine and tobacco. In the WHO 10-country study (Jablensky *et al.* 1992), a history of alcohol use in the year preceding the first contact was elicited in 57% of the male patients, and in three of the study areas drug abuse (mainly cannabis and cocaine) was reported by 24–41% of the patients. Cannabis abuse exacerbates the symptoms, may precipitate relapse (Linszen *et al.* 1994) and was a significant predictor of poor 2-year outcome in the WHO study. Heavy cannabis use prior to the manifest onset of psychotic symptoms has been consistently reported in over 60% of patients with a first episode of schizophrenia (Allebeck *et al.* 1993; Silver & Abboud 1994). In a recent Australian prevalence study of psychoses (Jablensky *et al.* 2000), 38.7% of the male patients and 17.0% of the female patients with schizophrenia had a comorbid lifetime diagnosis of substance abuse or dependence. The prevalence of cigarette smoking among schizophrenia patients was 73.2% in males and 56.3% in females (compared with 27.3% and 20.3%, respectively, in the general population).

The interactions between the pharmacological effects of drugs of abuse and the neurocognitive deficits that are thought to be intrinsic to schizophrenia remain little understood (Tracy *et al.* 1995). Recent research on the interactions between the nicotinic receptor and the glutamatergic and dopaminergic systems has led to the hypothesis that smoking in schizophrenic patients might be an attempt at self-medication reinforced by the modulatory and short-term normalizing effect of nicotine on neurocognitive deficits such as defective sensory gating (Dalack *et al.* 1998). Endogenous cannabinoids, which downregulate gamma-aminobutyric acid (GABA) release in hippocampal neurones (Wilson & Nicoll 2001), have been found elevated in schizophrenia patients independent of recency of cannabis use, suggesting an abnormality in cannabinoid receptors and signalling (Leweke *et al.* 1999). However, the question of whether excessive cannabis use can precipitate or advance the onset of a schizophrenic illness in vulnerable individuals, or is a self-medication phenomenon analogous to nicotine abuse and secondary to a developing psychosis, has not been unequivocally answered. Studies using small samples suggest that, among acutely psychotic patients, cannabis users are more likely to have a higher familial risk of schizophrenia than non-users (McGuire *et al.* 1995). In a recent study using an epidemiological design, the prevalence of cannabis use in a relatively large sample of first-episode patients ($n = 232$) was 13%, twice that found among matched normal controls. Approximately equal proportions among the early psychosis patients had been using cannabis for several years prior to the onset of symptoms, had started using it concurrently with the development of psychosis and had initiated cannabis use following the onset of schizophrenia (Hambrecht & Häfner 2000). Thus, analysis of the temporal sequence of cannabis use and psychosis onset appears unlikely to help resolve the causality issue without recourse to biological vulnerability markers, such as polymorphisms in the cannabinoid receptor type 1 (*CNR1*) gene that may characterize a particular 'cannabis-sensitive' subset of schizophrenia patients (Krebs *et al.* 2002).

Mortality

Excess mortality among schizophrenic patients has been documented by epidemiological studies on large cohorts. National case register data for Norway indicate that while the total mortality of psychiatric patients decreased between 1926–41 and 1950–74, the relative mortality of patients with schizophrenia remained unchanged at a level more than twice that of the general population (Ødegaard 1946a). Results from more recent cohort and record linkage studies in European countries and North America suggest that the excess mortality of people with schizophrenia is not decreasing and may, indeed, be increasing (Lawrence *et al.* 2000b; Ösby *et al.* 2000). Successive Danish national cohorts (Mortensen & Juel 1993) show an alarming trend of increasing mortality in first-admission patients with schizophrenia. The 5-year cumulated standard mortality ratio (SMR) increased from 530 (males) and 227 (females) in 1971–73 to 779 (males) and 452 (females) in 1980–82. Particularly striking was the SMR of 164 for male schizophrenics in the first year after the diagnosis was made. A meta-analysis of 18 studies (Brown 1997) resulted in a crude mortality rate of 189 deaths per 10 000 population per year and a 10-year survival rate of 81%. Current SMRs for patients with schizophrenia are of the order of 260–300, which corresponds to more than 20% reduction in life expectancy compared with the general population (S. Brown *et al.* 2000). SMRs as high as 376 (men) and 314 (women) have been observed among homeless people with schizophrenia (Babidge *et al.* 2001). The significantly higher mortality among males, as compared with females, is almost entirely explained by excess suicides and accidents. Unnatural causes apart, there is a nearly fivefold increase (SMR 468) of 'avoidable' natural deaths, caused by hypertension, cerebrovascular disease and smoking-related disease (S. Brown *et al.* 2000). The phenomenon of 'sudden unexplained death' among schizophrenic patients (Appleby *et al.* 2000) may be related to cardiotoxic effects of antipsychotic drugs, especially in patients receiving more than one antipsychotic concurrently (Waddington *et al.* 1998). The single most common cause of death among schizophrenic patients at present is suicide (aggregated SMR 960 in males and 680 in females) which accounts, on average, for 28% of the excess mortality in schizophrenia (Mortensen & Juel 1993). The actual mortality as a result of suicide is likely to be higher because a proportion of the deaths classified as accidental or of undetermined cause are probably suicides. Thus, the suicide rate in schizophrenic patients is at least equal to, or may be higher than, the suicide rate in major depression. Several risk factors have been suggested as relatively specific to schizophrenic suicide: being young and male, experiencing a chronic disabling illness with multiple relapses and remissions, realistic awareness of the deteriorating course of the condition, comorbid substance use and loss of faith in treatment (Caldwell & Gottesman 1990). Data from Scotland (Geddes & Juszczak 1995) point to a trend of an increasing suicide rate in schizophrenic patients, mostly within the first year after discharge. This trend seems to parallel the significant reductions in the number of psychiatric beds. Whether this new wave of increasing suicide mortality can be attributed to the transition from hospital to community management of schizophrenia remains to be established.

Fertility

The low fertility of men and women diagnosed with schizophrenia has been extensively documented by Essen-Möller (1935), Larson and Nyman (1973) and Ødegaard (1980). The average number of children fathered by schizophrenic men was 0.9 in Sweden, and the average number of live births over the entire reproductive period of women treated for schizophrenia in Norway during 1936–75 was 1.8, compared with 2.2 for the general female population. Similar results have been reported from Germany (Hilger *et al.* 1983) and Australia (McGrath *et al.* 1999). Yet this phenomenon does not seem to be either universal or consistent over time. According to the WHO 10-country study (Jablensky *et al.* 1992), the fertility of women with schizophrenia in India did not differ from that of women in the general population within the same age groups and geographical areas. An increase in the fertility of women with schizophrenia has been observed in recent decades (Nimgaonkar *et al.* 1997) and is likely to be sustained as a result of the deinstitutionalization of the mentally ill. Although men with schizophrenia continue to be reproductively disadvantaged, at least two studies (Lane *et al.* 1995; Waddington & Youssef 1996) have found a higher than average fertility among married schizophrenic men. The results of studies which have examined the fertility of biological relatives of probands with schizophrenia suggest that clinically asymptomatic parents and siblings of patients have higher than average fertility (Fañanás & Bertranpetit 1995; Srinivasan & Padmavati 1997). Such findings are sometimes invoked to explain the maintenance of a stable incidence of schizophrenia in populations despite the reduced fertility of affected probands.

Analytical epidemiology of schizophrenia: risk factors and antecedents

Risk factors influence the probability of occurrence of a disease or its outcome without necessarily being direct causes. Because the strongest proof of causation is the experiment, the identification of risk factors that are modifiable by intervention and may result in a reduced incidence or a better outcome is the ultimate aim of risk factor epidemiology. This is still a remote aim in schizophrenia but current research is beginning to address the issue. The epidemiological classification of initiating pathogenetic and interacting risk factors (Khoury *et al.* 1993) is not readily applicable to schizophrenia, as the role of many putative risk factors is still insufficiently understood. A provisional grouping of such factors into familial, sociodemographic, pre-, peri- and early postnatal, neurodevelopmental and heurocognitive variables may be more appropriate to the present state of knowledge (Table 12.4).

Age and sex

There is abundant evidence that schizophrenia may have its onset at almost any age – in childhood as well as past middle age – although the vast majority of onsets fall within the interval of 15–54 years of age. Neither childhood-onset schizophrenia (onset before age 12) nor late-onset schizophrenia (onset after age 50) present with any clinical features or risk factors that are qualitatively distinct from those characterizing schizophrenia arising in young adults (Brodaty *et al.* 1999; Nicolson & Rapoport 1999; Palmer *et al.* 2001), with the possible exception of psychotic disorganization symptoms being more likely to characterize early-onset cases and systematized paranoid delusions being predominant in late-onset cases (Häfner *et al.* 2001). With regard to age at onset, schizophrenia appears to be a continuum, where variation is consistent with a model incorporating random developmental effects and environmental experiences unique to the individual (Kendler *et al.* 1996b).

Onsets in men peak steeply in the age group 20–24; thereafter the rate of inception remains more or less constant at a lower level. In women, a less prominent peak in the age group 20–24 is followed by an increase in incidence in age groups older than 35. While the age-specific incidence up to the mid-thirties is significantly higher in men, the male–female ratio becomes inverted with age, reaching 1 : 1.9 for onsets after age 40 and 1 : 4 or even 1 : 6 for onsets after age 60. Scandinavian population-based studies which have followed up cohorts at risk into a very old age (over 85) reported a higher cumulated lifetime risk in women, compared with men (Helgason & Magnusson 1989). In the WHO 10-country study (Jablensky *et al.* 1992), the cumulated risks for males and females up to age 54 were approximately equal.

An earlier age at onset in men than in women has been reported in over 50 studies (Häfner *et al.* 1998) and such observations have stimulated theorizing and empirical studies into a possible protective effect of oestrogen via reduction of the sensitivity of the D_2 receptor in the brain (Häfner *et al.* 1998). Data from the WHO 10-country study (Jablensky & Cole 1997) show that age at onset is influenced by multiple interacting factors including sex, premorbid personality traits, family history of psychosis and marital status. The unconfounding of such interactions resulted in a significant attenuation of the effect of sex on age at onset. Thus, the observed sex difference in age at onset is unlikely to be an invariant biological characteristic of the disease. Within families with two or more affected members with schizophrenia, no significant differences in age at onset have been found between male and female siblings (DeLisi *et al.* 1987; Albus & Maier 1995) and, in some populations, e.g. India, the male–female difference in the frequency of onsets in the younger age groups is attenuated or even inverted (Murthy *et al.* 1998).

There is therefore no unequivocal evidence of consistent sex differences in the symptoms of schizophrenia, including the frequency of positive and negative symptoms. Although sex differences have been described in relation to premorbid adjustment (better premorbid functioning in women), occurrence of brain abnormalities (more frequent in men), course (a higher percentage of remitting illness episodes and shorter hospital stay in women) and outcome (higher survival rate in the community, less

Table 12.4 Risk factors and antecedents of schizophrenia.

Risk factor or antecedent	Estimated effect size (odds ratio or relative risk)	Reference
Familial (family member with schizophrenia)		
Biological parent	7.0–10.0	Mortensen *et al.* (1999)
Two parents	29.0	Kringlen *et al.* 1978)
Monozygotic twin	40.8	Cardno *et al.* (1999)
Dizygotic twin	5.3	Cardno *et al.* (1999)
Non-twin sibling	7.3	Gottesman *et al.* (1987)
Second-degree relative	1.6–2.8	Gottesman *et al.* (1987)
Social and demographic		
Low socioeconomic status	3.0	Eaton (1974)
Single marital status	3.9	van Os *et al.* (2000)
Stressful life events	1.5	
Migrant/minority status (e.g. African-Caribbeans in UK)	>7.0	Harrison *et al.* (1997)
Urban birth	2.1–4.2	Mortensen *et al.* (1999) Eaton *et al.* (2000)
Winter birth	1.1	Mortensen *et al.* (1999)
Prenatal, perinatal and early postnatal		
Obstetric complications ('non-optimality' summary score)	4.6	Hultman *et al.* (1997)
Maternal respiratory infection, second trimester	2.1	A.S. Brown *et al.* (2000)
Birth weight < 2000 g	3.0	Byrne *et al.* (2000)
Birth weight < 2500 g	2.9	Wahlbeck *et al.* (2001)
Severe malnutrition during pregnancy	2.6	Susser & Lin (1992)
Gestation < 37 weeks	2.5	Ichiki *et al.* (2000)
Perinatal hypoxic brain damage	4.6–6.9	Zornberg *et al.* (2000) Jones *et al.* (1998)
Neurodevelopmental and neurocognitive		
Early CNS infection	4.8	Rantakallio *et al.* (1997)
Epilepsy	11.1	Mäkikyrö *et al.* (1998)
Low IQ (< 74)	8.6	David *et al.* (1997)
Difficulty in maintaining close personal relationships	30.7	Malmberg *et al.* (1998)
Preference for solitary play, age 4–6	2.1	Jones *et al.* (1994)
Speech and educational problems, age < 12	2.8	Jones *et al.* (1994)
Low score on Continuous Performance Test	3.3	Egan *et al.* (2000)

disability in women), such differences are consistent with normal sexual dimorphism in brain development (Noupoulos *et al.* 2000), as well as with learned gender-assigned social roles, and do not invoke the need for a sex-specific aetiological factor.

Genetic risk

The contribution of genetic liability to the aetiology of schizophrenia is one of the few firmly established facts about the disorder. As pointed out by Shields (1977), 'no environmental indicator predicts a raised risk of schizophrenia in small or moderate-sized samples of persons not already known to be genetically related to a schizophrenic'. The genetic epidemiology of schizophrenia is underpinned by heritability estimates from twin, adoptive and family studies which have been consistently at 0.80 or higher (Cardno *et al.* 1999). Because the concordance rate in monozygotic twins (MZ) does not exceed 50%, it is widely assumed that environmental factors also contribute to its pathogenesis, but no single environmental variable has yet been demonstrated to be either necessary or sufficient for causation. Three models of the joint effects of genotype and environment have been proposed (Kendler & Eaves 1986):

1 the effects of predisposing genes and environmental factors are additive and increase the risk of disease in a linear fashion;

2 genes control the sensitivity of the brain to environmental insults; and

3 genes influence the likelihood of an individual's exposure to environmental pathogens, e.g. by fostering certain personality traits.

Attempts to identify major genetic loci by linkage analysis of multiply affected pedigrees or of affected sib pairs have produced inconsistent results. Few of the positive linkage findings have stood the test of replication (DeLisi & Crow 1999). Similarly, numerous association studies have been beset with problems of type I or II error brought about by population stratification, diagnostic misclassification and questionable biological plausibility of the candidate genes. The majority of investigators today share the view that schizophrenia is one of the genetically complex disorders, characterized by oligo- or polygenic inheritance, likely locus heterogeneity, incomplete penetrance and high population frequency of the disease-causing alleles (Hyman *et al.* 1999). The relationship between genotype and phenotype in schizophrenia is likely to be mediated by complex causal pathways involving gene–gene and gene–environment interactions, 'programmable' neural substrate and stochastic events. Under such circumstances, the gene effects might be too weak to be detectable through the clinical diagnostic phenotype in any but very large samples (Lander & Schork 1994).

In view of such constraints, alternative clinical and epidemiological strategies have been proposed in order to circumvent the need for excessively large pooled samples (such samples may be confounded by latent population differences and by variations in ascertainment methods and diagnostic assessment). One such strategy aims at resolving the locus heterogeneity problem through search and investigation of genetically homogeneous populations in which schizophrenia segregates in multiply affected family groups of common ancestry – as is the case in isolates or rare sporadic lineages. Schizophrenia in such families is more likely to be linked to a small number of predisposing loci, some of which may be of moderate to strong effect, detectable by screening for alleles shared among affected individuals originating from common ancestors. To date, this strategy has produced mixed results, indicating that multiple susceptibility loci operate even in isolated populations (Hovatta *et al.* 1999). However, at least one study has detected linkage to a major susceptibility locus (Brzustowicz *et al.* 2000).

Another strategy proceeds from the assumption that the ICD-10 or DSM-IV clinical diagnoses of schizophrenia and its 'spectrum' satellites, such as schizotypal disorder, schizoaffective disorder and other non-affective psychosis, may not represent relevant phenotypes for genetic research. Because of the multiple pathways that lead from genotype to phenotype, and from structural brain abnormalities to behavioural expression, the observable clinical phenotypes are likely to be heavily confounded with 'downstream' epigenetic events that make it hard for the currently available methods of genetic analysis to detect the primary genetic defect. This has led to an exploration of alternative 'correlated' phenotypes (or 'endophenotypes'), such as neurocognitive abnormalities or temperament and character traits that are known to be associated with schizophrenia and may be expressed in both affected individuals and their asymptomatic biological relatives. Correlated phenotypes have the advantage of higher penetrance and more clearly definable patterns of inheritance. There have been promising attempts to detect genetic linkage using neurobehavioural markers (Freedman *et al.* 2000).

A genetic epidemiological criterion for the gain in power to detect linkage by using correlated phenotypes, regardless of the mode of transmission, is the magnitude of the risk (or prevalence) ratio (λ_s) between the prevalence of the trait or abnormality in the first-degree relatives of affected probands and its prevalence in the general population (Risch 1997). To increase the power to detect linkage, λ_s, for a 'correlated' phenotype should be well in excess of the risk ratio for clinically manifest schizophrenia (usually estimated at 10.0). A number of neurocognitive and personality traits, associated with schizophrenia, appear to meet this criterion (Faraone *et al.* 1995) and therefore should be explored as candidate phenotypes. A prerequisite for the application of this approach is the establishment of population prevalences for such phenotypes in epidemiological samples. A step in this direction has been made recently with regard to a measure of attention dysfunction (Chen *et al.* 1998).

Children at high genetic risk

Studies of children born to parents diagnosed with schizophrenia (mothers, in the majority of studies) have highlighted a range of early developmental abnormalities that could be markers of increased risk of adult schizophrenia. Studies in the USA (Fish 1977; Goldstein 1987; Erlenmeyer-Kimling *et al.* 1997), Denmark (Schulsinger *et al.* 1984), Sweden (McNeil & Kaij 1987) and Israel (Mirsky *et al.* 1995) have examined in prospective case–control designs a total of 230 high-risk (HR) children of schizophrenic parent(s), 248 children of parents with other psychiatric disorders and 392 control children born to parents with no psychiatric disorder. In reviewing the data, Fish *et al.* (1992) proposed a syndrome of 'pandysmaturation' (PDM), defined as a transient retardation of motor and visual development, an abnormal pattern of functional test scores on cross-sectional developmental examinations, and a retardation of skeletal growth. PDM could be a marker of a neurointegrative defect and a precursor of schizotypal traits. PDM may develop *in utero* and in such cases it is associated with low birth weight, but obstetric complications do not lead to PDM in the absence of genetic risk. The schizophrenic parent effect has been identified as the only 'robust and direct predictor of adult psychiatric outcomes' in another HR study in which 18% of the offspring of schizophrenic parent(s) had developed schizophrenic illnesses after 19 years of follow-up, compared with 7% psychosis in the offspring of parent(s) with affective disorders and 2% in the control group (Erlenmeyer-Kimling *et al.* 1991). The PDM syndrome remains as a promising developmental marker of high risk for schizophrenia because it is relatively specific to the biological offspring of parent(s) with schizophrenia. However, it is not known if PDM can be reliably diagnosed in large samples. Furthermore, it is not known how frequently it occurs in non-HR subjects, and whether its causation is primarily genetic or environmental (e.g. resulting from parenting disrupted by psychosis). Further research could clarify these issues and explore the potential use of PDM as an intermediate phenotype for genetic research.

Individuals at high genetic risk who develop schizophrenia as adults are more likely to manifest: (i) neurocognitive deficits; and (ii) difficulties in social interaction during childhood and adolescence, compared with individuals at high risk who do not develop schizophrenia. Thus, in the Israeli High-Risk Study cohort, poor scores on attention tasks obtained in childhood were associated with schizophrenia spectrum disorders at ages 26 and 32 (Mirsky *et al.* 1995). In a reanalysis of the Copenhagen High-Risk Study (Cannon *et al.* 1990), in which 207 children of schizophrenic women and 104 controls had been assessed at age 15 and reassessed 10 years later, poor social competence, passivity and social isolation in adolescence predicted predominantly negative symptoms, while overactive behaviour and aggressiveness predicted positive symptoms in the 15 high-risk subjects who developed schizophrenia by age 25 (Cannon *et al.* 1990). In addition to genetic risk, a possible role of non-genetic factors was suggested in this study by the increased incidence of perinatal complications and enlarged third ventricle in the negative symptom subgroup, and of a history of an unstable early rearing environment in the positive symptom subgroup.

Obstetric complications

Maternal obstetric complications (OC), a focus of research since the 1960s (Lane & Albee 1966; Stabenau & Pollin 1967; Mednick 1970), are widely cited as an established risk factor in schizophrenia (Cannon 1997). Several explanatory models have been proposed:

1 Severe OC, such as perinatal hypoxia and a resulting hippocampal damage, can prepare the ground for adult schizophrenia even if genetic liability is weak or absent.

2 Genetic predisposition sensitizes the developing brain to lesions resulting from randomly occurring less severe OC.

3 Genetic predisposition to schizophrenia leads to abnormal fetal development which in turn causes OC.

4 Maternal constitutional factors, partially influenced by genes, such as small physique or proneness to risk behaviour (drug use, smoking during pregnancy), increase the risk of OC and fetal brain damage.

The testing of these hypotheses presupposes epidemiological and clinical samples, as well as animal models (Bernstein *et al.* 1999; Mallard *et al.* 1999). A total of 34 studies and databases have been examined by Geddes and Lawrie (1995) and by Verdoux *et al.* (1997) using meta-analysis techniques and a comprehensive review has been published by McNeil *et al.* (2000). Although significant associations have been found between complications of pregnancy and adult schizophrenia, the effects observed are inconsistent and indicate significant interstudy heterogeneity. A large number of published case–control studies, reporting positive findings of an association between OC and schizophrenia, are of small sample size and have used parental interviews as the source of OC data. OC histories based on maternal recall have been shown to have methodological limitations (Cantor-Graae *et al.* 1998). For these reasons, the standards for this type of research should involve:

1 birth cohorts or large populations samples;

2 prospectively recorded pregnancy and birth data; and

3 use of standardized scales enabling comparisons of data across studies.

While a number of studies in the last decade have met the first two criteria, there is still no generally adopted framework for summarizing, analysing and reporting OC data; this limits the interpretation of findings.

Positive findings that have emerged from population-based studies with prospectively collected OC data include:

1 perinatal brain injury involving hypoxia (Jones *et al.* 1998; Cannon *et al.* 2000; Zornberg *et al.* 2000);

2 low birth weight (Jones *et al.* 1998; Ichiki *et al.* 2000; Wahlbeck *et al.* 2001);

3 gestation < 37 weeks and/or small for gestational age (Jones *et al.* 1998; Hultman *et al.* 1999; Ichiki *et al.* 2000; Wahlbeck *et al.* 2001);

4 low maternal body mass index (Sacker *et al.* 1995; Wahlbeck *et al.* 2001); and

5 combinations of the above, plus specific OC events, such as bleeding and placentation abnormalities (Jones *et al.* 1988; Hultman *et al.* 1999).

Although all of the above epidemiological studies report significant associations between one or more OC risk factor and subsequent schizophrenia, no obvious pattern or hierarchy of causal pathways can be inferred from these studies, nor is it possible to conclude whether the effects of individual OCs are additive or interactive. The interpretation of the OC findings is further complicated by the fact that at least two recent population-based studies have failed to identify any significant associations with schizophrenia (Byrne *et al.* 2000; Kendell *et al.* 2000). It is difficult to answer conclusively the question about possible interactions between familial risk of schizophrenia and the effects of OCs on the manifestation of the disease in adult life. Studies on monozygotic twins discordant for schizophrenia (Cantor-Graae *et al.* 1994; Torrey *et al.* 1994) found a significant intratwin pair effect for minor physical anomalies in the cotwin who subsequently developed schizophrenia but not for OCs, including birth weight. A recent linkage study between the Danish twin resister and the psychiatric case register reported a significantly greater rate of first admissions for schizophrenia in members of dizygotic, but not monozygotic, twin pairs when compared with the general population (Kläning 1999). Because maternal age, physique, parity, as well as a maternal genetic factor, are all known to influence dizygotic twinning but have no effect on monozygotic twinning, assessment of OCs in dizygotes may offer an additional paradigm for studies aiming to disentangle the complex relationships between OCs and genetic liability in schizophrenia.

Overall, the many inconsistencies among the findings of individual studies evoke a critical appraisal of the whole field (Crow 2000) and caution against an unqualified acceptance of OC as a proven risk factor in schizophrenia. To clarify their role should remain an important priority for epidemiological research.

Maternal influenza and other pre- and postnatal infections

In utero exposure to influenza has been implicated as a risk factor since a report that an increased proportion of adult schizophrenia in Helsinki was associated with presumed second trimester *in utero* exposure to the 1957 A2 influenza epidemic (Mednick *et al.* 1988). Over 40 studies have subsequently attempted to replicate the putative link between maternal influenza and schizophrenia, using designs ranging from interviews with mothers of probands with schizophrenia to complex statistical analyses of large databases linking the incidence of schizophrenia in birth cohorts to measures of mortality or morbidity associated with documented influenza epidemics. Putative ascertainment of influenza on the basis of retrospective recall has been shown to result in 70% false-positive self-diagnosis when questionnaire responses were correlated with individual serological findings (Elder *et al.* 1996). Reports from studies utilizing this method are unlikely to be valid. Several studies correlating schizophrenia incidence in population databases with influenza epidemics (Barr *et al.* 1990; Sham *et al.* 1992; Adams *et al.* 1993; Takei *et al.* 1994; Kunugi *et al.* 1995) have produced results supporting the original Finnish findings. However, as argued by Crow (1994), statistical overanalysis may have resulted in false-positive findings. More recently, negative results have been reported from an increasing number of studies based on large epidemiological samples, some from populations previously implicated in the reports on positive findings (Grech *et al.* 1997; Morgan *et al.* 1997; Battle *et al.* 1999; Selten *et al.* 1999a; Mino *et al.* 2000). While all of the population-based studies were 'ecological' in design (in the sense that information on actual individual exposure was not available), the only two studies to date (Crow & Done 1992; Cannon *et al.* 1996) in which data on actually infected pregnant women were accessed by the investigators found no increase in the risk of schizophrenia among the offspring. These negative results are consistent with the failure of studies using polymerase chain reaction to detect influenza virus-specific nucleic acid sequences in brain tissue or cerebrospinal fluid from patients with schizophrenia (Sierra-Honigmann *et al.* 1995; Taller *et al.* 1996). The balance of evidence therefore does not support the hypothesis of a significant contribution of *in utero* exposure to influenza to the aetiology of schizophrenia.

The more general issue of pre- or postnatal exposure to infection as a risk factor has not been laid to rest. A recent analysis of data from a well-documented birth cohort (A.S. Brown *et al.* 2000) suggests that second trimester exposure to respiratory infections (including tuberculosis, influenza, pneumonia and upper respiratory tract infections) may be associated with increased incidence of schizophrenia spectrum disorders in the offspring. In a follow-up study of the children of a cohort of women clinically and serologically documented with prenatal rubella, Brown *et al.* (2001) reported increased risk of schizophrenia spectrum disorders. Postnatal central nervous system infections in children followed up to age 14 in the North Finland 1966 birth cohort was associated with a significant odds ratio of 4.8 for subsequent schizophrenia (Rantakallio *et al.* 1997). An association between Borna disease virus and both schizophrenia and affective disorders has been suggested by several serological studies but this line of investigation is still in an early stage (Taieb *et al.* 2001). The extent to which such research is capable of discovering true causal contributions to schizophrenia, in the absence of a more advanced pathogenetic understanding of the role of genetic factors, remains debatable (DeLisi 1996).

Other prenatal exposures

A variety of other prenatal exposures have been explored in 'opportunistic' epidemiological studies making use of documented historic cohorts. Fetal vulnerability to acute maternal starvation during the first trimester, with an increased subsequent risk of schizophrenia, has been suggested by a study of the offspring of Dutch women exposed to severe wartime famine in 1944–45. Severe food deprivation (<4200 kJ/day) during the first trimester was associated with an increased relative risk of 2.6 for narrowly defined schizophrenia in female offspring (Susser & Lin 1992) and a relative risk of 2.0 for schizotypal personality disorder (Hoek *et al.* 1996). Another Dutch study has attempted to evaluate the effect of maternal stress on the risk of schizophrenia in the offspring, using the five day German *blitzkrieg* against the Netherlands in May 1940 as a proxy measure of stress exposure during pregnancy. A small but statistically significant increase in RR (risk ratio 1.28) was found for first trimester exposure (van Os & Selten 1998). Another Dutch stress exposure study (the 1953 flood catastrophe in the south-west of the Netherlands; Selten *et al.* 1999b) failed to find a significant association between maternal stress and non affective psychoses in the offspring. The lifetime prevalence of schizophrenia among 1867 people prenatally exposed to the 1945 atomic bomb explosion over Nagasaki was examined by Imamura *et al.* (1999) and found to be 0.96%, i.e. not different from the expected rate in non-exposed populations.

The early rearing environment

Support for an effect of the early rearing environment on the risk of developing schizophrenia comes from a recent study of a Finnish sample of 179 adopted-away children of schizophrenic parents (a high-risk group) and a matched control sample of adoptees at no increased genetic risk (Tienari 1991; Wahlberg *et al.* 1997). Psychosis or severe personality disorder was diagnosed in 34 out of 121 HR subjects followed up for 5–7 years after the initial assessment, compared with 24 out of 150 controls. While the rates of adult psychosis or severe personality disorder were significantly higher in the HR group compared with the control group, the difference was entirely attributable to the subset of HR children who grew up in dysfunctional adoptive families – a result consistent with the model of genetic control of the sensitivity to the environment.

Premorbid traits and social impairment

Schizoid (Kretschmer 1936) or schizotypal (Meehl 1962) premorbid traits have been thought to express a predisposition to schizophrenia. Estimates of the frequency of schizotypal personality disorder among siblings of schizophrenic patients are of the order of 17% (Kendler *et al.* 1984; Baron *et al.* 1985) but epidemiological data on its occurrence in the general population are lacking. The association between early schizoid or schizotypal traits and the risk of adult schizophrenia is not restricted to HR populations, such as offspring of schizophrenic parents. Evidence of early developmental peculiarities in children who develop schizophrenia as adults has been provided by prospectively collected data on a national birth cohort in the UK (Jones *et al.* 1994). Preschizophrenic children had an excess (odd ratios 2.1–5.8) of speech and educational problems, social anxiety and preference for solitary play. The Swedish cohort study of 50 087 men conscripted into the army at age 18–20 and followed up over 15 years (Malmberg *et al.* 1998) found that poor social adjustment during childhood and adolescence was significantly more common among the 195 individuals who subsequently developed schizophrenia than among the rest of the cohort. Positive scores on four variables (having fewer than two friends, preference for socializing in small groups, feeling excessively sensitive and not having a steady girlfriend) were strongly associated with schizophrenia in later life but, because a high proportion of the cohort scored positive on at least one item, the predictive value of this set of variables was negligible. Similar results (deficits in social functioning and organizational ability, as well as low test scores on all measures) were reported from the Israeli conscript study (Davidson *et al.* 1999).

On balance, there is converging evidence that a cluster of behavioural traits broadly similar to adult schizoid or schizotypal personality traits and to some of the negative symptoms of schizophrenia can be detected during childhood and adolescence in a proportion of the people who develop schizophrenia in adult life. However, there is no conclusive evidence on the extent to which such traits are genetically or environmentally determined.

Premorbid intelligence (IQ)

The association between mental retardation and schizophrenia was first highlighted by Kraepelin (1919), who estimated that about 7% of the cases of dementia praecox evolved on the basis of intellectual impairment and introduced the term *Pfropfschizophrenie* (engrafted schizophrenia) for a subtype characterized by early onset, negativism and stereotypies. A deficit in intellectual performance antedating by many years the onset of schizophrenia was described by Lane and Albee (1964). More recently, the concept has been revived and partially validated (Doody *et al.* 1998; Sanderson *et al.* 2001) in a study which identified a comorbid pattern of mild learning disability, neurological symptoms and schizophrenia-like psychosis segregating in multiply affected families with high rates of chromosomal abnormalities. Independently of the notion of a discrete subtype of schizophrenia characterized by intellectual impairment, a strong relationship between low IQ and risk of schizophrenia has been demonstrated in the Swedish (David *et al.* 1997) and the Israeli conscript studies (Davidson *et al.* 1999). After controlling for confounding effects in the Swedish cohort, the risk of schizophrenia increased linearly with the decrement of IQ (compared with an IQ > 126 as the baseline, the odds ratio for schizophrenia increased from 3.5 for IQ 90–95 to 8.6 for IQ < 74). The prevalence of borderline intellectual disability among patients with psychoses has been estimated at 18% (Hassiotis *et al.* 1999).

The relationship between low IQ and risk of schizophrenia is among the most robust findings in the risk factor epidemiology of the disorder and merits further study with a view to its genetic determinants and pathogenetic implications.

Neurocognitive and neurophysiological markers

Cognitive impairment in the domains of attention control, verbal memory, spatial working memory and executive function – all compromising the ability to select task-relevant response strategies and to recruit appropriate neural circuits (Gold & Weinberger 1995) – represent a stable core feature of schizophrenia and are relatively independent of the symptom dimension. Specific deficits in sustained attention (Cornblatt & Keilp 1994; Egan *et al.* 2000), verbal fluency (Chen *et al.* 2000), event-related brain potentials (Freedman *et al.* 1996; Frangou *et al.* 1997; Javitt *et al.* 1997; Michie *et al.* 2000) and saccadic eye movement control (Clementz *et al.* 1994) have been found in clinical and laboratory research to be common in schizophrenic patients and in a proportion of their clinically normal biological relatives, but rare in control subjects drawn from the general population. Their sensitivity and specificity as risk predictors in schizophrenia needs to be investigated in larger population samples. Family and field studies employing the Continuous Performance Test (CPT) suggest that versions of this task involving an increased processing load (engaging working memory) may be a particularly sensitive measure of sustained attention as one of the core deficits characterizing schizophrenia. In a proportion of the clinically asymptomatic first-degree relatives of probands with schizophrenia, CPT performance is within the range of the affected probands. Estimates of relative risk for CPT as a neurocognitive trait vary in different studies between a low $\lambda_s = 2.1–3.3$ (Egan *et al.* 2000) and a high $\lambda_s = 15–30$ (Chen *et al.* 1998). In the latter study, the heritability of CPT performance has been estimated at 0.48–0.62. Should CPT and other neurocognitive variables be further validated by epidemiological studies as biological markers of schizophrenia, the power of risk prediction at the level of the individual may increase substantially.

Social class

Since the 1930s, numerous studies in North America and Europe have consistently found that the economically disadvantaged social groups contribute disproportionately to the first admission rate for schizophrenia. Two explanatory hypotheses, of social causation ('breeder') and of social selection ('drift'), were originally proposed (Mischler & Scotch 1983). According to the social causation theory, the socioeconomic adversity characteristic of lower class living conditions could precipitate psychosis in genetically vulnerable individuals who have a constricted capacity to cope with complex or stressful situations. In the 1960s this theory was considered refuted by a single study which found that the social class distribution of schizophrenic patients' fathers did not deviate from that of the general population, and that the excess of low socioeconomic status among schizophrenic patients was mainly attributable to individuals who had drifted down the occupational and social scale prior to the onset of psychosis (Goldberg & Morrison 1963) – a tendency that has been confirmed in more recent prospective studies focusing on the prodromal period (Häfner *et al.* 1999). Generally, aetiological research in schizophrenia in the last decades has tended to ignore 'macrosocial' risk factors. However, the possibility remains that social stratification and socioeconomic status are important in the causation of schizophrenia but the effect manifests in ways that do not conform to the earlier theories. An example of this is the finding, reported from the North Finland 1966 birth cohort (Mäkikirö *et al.* 1997), that the cumulative incidence of early-onset schizophrenia was significantly higher among individuals whose fathers had attained status and achievement, placing them into the highest social class. Upward occupational mobility in fathers was found to be associated with acculturation stress and high levels of psychopathology which might exacerbate latent predisposition to psychosis in the offspring. However, this remains speculative and more refined research tools may be needed to tackle the issue.

Urban birth

The nineteenth century hypothesis that urban environments increase the risk of psychosis (Freeman 1994) has been revived in recent years. The 'urban drift', resulting in a higher density of cases of psychosis in inner city areas, has been extensively documented since the 1930s (Faris & Dunham 1939) and was mainly interpreted in socioeconomic and behavioural terms (availability of cheap accommodation, attraction of an anonymous lifestyle). Recently, the focus has shifted towards presumed exposure to physicochemical and infectious risk factors. In a reanalysis of archival material (the US 1880 census data on 'insanity'), Torrey *et al.* (1997a) found that urban residence was associated with an odds ratio of 1.66 for psychosis and semiurban residence with an odds ratio of 1.46, when completely rural counties were used as the baseline for comparisons. The authors speculate that the greater likelihood of infectious and toxic insults on the brain (e.g. lead exposure) in urban settings might be part of the explanation.

The crucial distinction between urban birth and urban residence was introduced in the epidemiological literature only in the 1960s (Astrup & Ødegaard 1961). Marcelis *et al.* (1999) analysed by place of birth all first admissions for schizophrenia and other psychoses in the Netherlands between 1942 and 1978. A graded measure to urban exposure was found, suggesting a linear relationship between urban birth and moderate but statistically significant increases in the incidence of schizophrenia, affective psychoses and other psychoses, with the effect size increasing in successive birth cohorts. In two record linkage studies across the Danish civil registration system, the medical birth register and the national psychiatric case register, Mortensen *et al.* (1999) and Eaton *et al.* (2000) calculated an RR = 2.4–4.2 for schizophrenia prevalence of those born in the capital Copenhagen as compared with rural births. In terms of population attributable risk, urban birth accounted for 34.6% of all cases of schizophrenia in Denmark – in contrast to history of schizophrenia in a first-degree relative which, with RR = 9.3, accounted for only 5.5% of the cases. The presumed urban birth risk factor was not mediated by obstetric complications.

In interpreting these findings, it is important to take into consideration that genetic predisposition to schizophrenia may remain unexpressed in gene carriers; therefore the comparison of risks attributable to familial occurrence of schizophrenia and place of birth is problematic. Moreover, the nature of the suspected 'urban risk factor' remains cryptic and the possibility that it is a proxy for multiple interacting factors, including selective urban–rural and rural–urban migration of individuals varying in their 'load' of schizophrenia predisposing genes, cannot be excluded. As pointed out by Verheij *et al.* (1998) in a study of urban–rural variations in general health status in the Netherlands, migration processes may cause spurious findings in cross-sectional research into the relation between urbanicity and health. Therefore, the existence of an 'urban risk factor' for schizophrenia remains unproven.

Season of birth

Seasonality of schizophrenic births was first described by Tramer (1929). The current interest in the phenomenon dates back to the 1960s (Barry & Barry 1961). A 5–8% excess of schizophrenic births in winter–spring has been reported by a large number of studies (reviewed by Bradbury & Miller 1985; Torrey *et al.* 1997b). The effect seems to be present in the northern but not in the southern hemisphere, where studies (reviewed by McGrath & Welham 1999) have failed to demonstrate a consistent seasonal effect. Seasonality fluctuations of births are not specific to schizophrenia and have been described in bipolar affective disorder, autism, attention deficit disorder, alcoholism, stillbirths, diabetes, Alzheimer's disease and Down's syndrome. Many of the studies are methodologically vulnerable with regard to sample size, sampling bias or statistical analysis. Furthermore, the evidence for a seasonal factor associated with the risk for schizophrenia and operating at birth has been weakened, although not invalidated, by the argument that it could be an artefact of the so-called age-incidence and age-prevalence effect (Dalen 1975; Lewis & Griffin 1981): because the risk of onset of schizophrenia rises rapidly from age 15 onwards, 'older' individuals born in the early months of each calender year will have a higher rate of onset of schizophrenia than 'younger' individuals born late in the same year. Nevertheless, a relative excess of winter births among people with schizophrenia still seems to be a valid and robust finding. Kendell and Adams (1991) calculated year-to-year and month-to-month variation in schizophrenic births between 1914 and 1960 for all patients admitted to hospitals in Scotland since 1963 ($n = 13\,661$). A Poisson distribution fitted to the data indicated a significant deviation from the expected chance fluctuations. This deviation, entirely limited to the months February–May, in which the rates of schizophrenic births increased by 7%, needs discussion. Similar findings were reported by Mortensen *et al.* (1999) on the basis of a large Danish cohort.

Notwithstanding the fact that seasonality of schizophrenia births has been extensively documented and cannot be explained away as a statistical artefact, the understanding of its underlying causes has hardly progressed since the phenomenon was first described. Various explanations have been proposed. According to the procreational habits hypothesis, parents of schizophrenic patients are more likely to have a seasonal pattern of sexual activity and conception, with a peak in the summer months (Hare & Price 1968). Some evidence consistent with this hypothesis (a slight winter–spring excess of births of both patients and their unaffected siblings) has been reported by Suvisaari *et al.* (2001). Other theories include 'seasonal ovopathy' involving increased risk of chromosomal anomalies because of delayed ovulation (Pallast *et al.* 1994). A range of noxious influences capable of causing fetal damage have also been proposed, including seasonal viral infections, extremes of temperature, seasonal variation in nutrition or vitamin levels, exposure to insecticides and birth trauma. None have yet been identified and it is unlikely that the problem will be resolved by further studies of the effect itself. Seasonality of births is likely to be a distant echo of the impact of such risk factors that will remain hidden, although their nature may not be entirely novel and surprising. Therefore, a reversal of the strategy may be more productive: instead of focusing on seasonality of births, research should systematically examine risk factors known to disrupt normal fetal brain development for seasonal effects in their operation.

Marital status

Marital status is a strong predictor of psychiatric hospitalization (Jarman *et al.* 1992). In schizophrenia, it is significantly associated with measures of incidence, age at onset, and course and outcome. Single men and, to a lesser degree, single women tend to be over-represented among first admissions or first contacts (68% and 39%, respectively, in the WHO 10-country study; Jablensky *et al.* 1992). Riecher-Rössler *et al.* (1992) found a 12-fold higher first admission rate for single men when compared with married men, and a 3.3 times higher rate for single women when compared with married women. Being single was associated with 50-fold higher odds of developing schizophrenia in males and 15-fold higher odds in women during the 1-year follow-up of the Epidemiological Catchment Area study (Tien & Eaton 1992). This is not sufficient to prove that being single is an independent antecedent risk factor (or that being married is a protective risk modifier) because both overt schizophrenia and preschizophrenic traits and impairments reduce the chances of getting married. Schizophrenic patients living in a stable marital or other partnership may be a positively selected group with a milder form of the disease (Ødegaard 1946b). Evidence that being married (or living with a partner) can delay the onset of schizophrenia in males, and thus act as a risk modifier, was obtained from the WHO 10-country study after unconfounding the effects of gender, premorbid personality traits, family history of psychosis and marital status on age at onset. (Jablensky & Cole 1997). An interaction between single marital status and a neighbourhood environment characterized by a high degree of social isolation was significantly associated with incidence of schizophrenia in a recent Dutch study (van Os *et al.* 2000).

Migrant status and ethnic minorities

Since the publication of the first report on an increased morbidity of psychoses among African-Caribbean immigrants to the UK (Hemsi 1967), an increasing number of studies have pointed to exceptionally high incidence rates of schizophrenia (about 6.0 per 10 000) in the African-Caribbean population in the UK (Bhugra *et al.* 1997; Harrison *et al.* 1997). This excess morbidity is not restricted to recent immigrants and is, in fact, higher in the British-born second generation of migrants. Similar findings of nearly fourfold excess over the general population rate have been reported for the Dutch Antillean and Surinamese immigrants in Holland (Selten *et al.* 1997). In spite of much research effort focusing on this phenomenon, its causes remain almost entirely obscure. Little evidence has been presented to support suggestions that these psychotic illnesses might be better explained as acute transient psychoses or drug-induced psychoses. It seems that neither the psychopathology nor the course and outcome of these disorders presents any atypical features that would sufficiently set them apart from ICD-10 or DSM-IIIR schizophrenia (Harrison *et al.* 1999; Hutchinson *et al.* 1999), although one report (Hickling *et al.* 1999) indicated poor diagnostic agreement ($\kappa = 0.45$) between a Jamaican psychiatrist and a group of British psychiatrists assessing the same cases. Incidence studies in the Caribbean (Hickling & Rodgers-Johnson 1995; Bhugra *et al.* 1999) do not indicate any excess schizophrenia morbidity in the indigenous populations from which migrants are recruited. Explanations in terms of biological risk factors, such as an increased incidence of obstetric complications or maternal influenza, have so far found no support (Hutchinson *et al.* 1997; Selten *et al.* 1998). Hypotheses involving psychosocial risk factors, such as lack of a supportive community structure, acculturation stress, demoralization cause by racial discrimination and blocked opportunities for upward social mobility, have been proposed (Bhugra *et al.* 1999) but none has yet been adequately tested. A potentially important finding in need of replication is the significant increase of schizophrenia among the siblings of second-generation African-Caribbean schizophrenic probands, compared with the incidence of schizophrenia in the siblings of white patients (Hutchinson *et al.* 1996). 'Horizontal' increases in the morbid risk usually suggest that environmental factors may be modifying (increasing) the penetrance of the predisposition to disease in gene carriers. Although psychosocial stress is most likely a factor affecting the majority of African-Caribbeans in the UK, there is at present no plausible mechanism linking such stress selectively to schizophrenia. Unexplored gene–environment interactions, involving various infectious, nutritional or toxic environmental factors, remain a possibility.

Prospects for epidemiology in the search for the causes of schizophrenia

After nearly a century of epidemiological research, essential questions about the nature and causes of schizophrenia still remain unanswered. Nevertheless, important insights into this complex disorder have been gained from population-based studies. Two major conclusions stand out. First, the clinical syndrome of schizophrenia is robust and can be identified reliably in diverse populations. This suggests that a common pathophysiology and underlying genetic predisposition are likely to underlie the spectrum of manifestations of schizophrenia. On balance, the evidence suggests that no major differences in incidence and disease risk can be found across populations at the level of large population aggregates. However, the study of 'atypical' populations, such as genetic isolates or minority groups, may be capable of detecting unusual variations in the incidence of schizophrenia that could provide novel clues to the aetiology and pathogenesis of the disorder. Notwithstanding the difficulties currently accompanying the genetic dissection of complex disorders, novel methods of genetic analysis will eventually identify genomic regions and loci predisposing to schizophrenia. The majority are likely to be of small effect, although one cannot rule out the possibility that genes of moderate or even major effects will also be found, especially in relation to the neurophysiological abnormalities associated with schizophrenia. Clarifying the function of such genes will be a complex task. Part of the solution is likely to be found in the domain of epidemiology because establishing their population frequency and associations with a variety of phenotypic expressions, including personality traits, is a prerequisite for understanding their causal role.

The second conclusion is that no single environmental risk factor of major effect on the incidence of schizophrenia has yet been discovered. Further studies using large samples are required to evaluate potential risk factors, antecedents and predictors for which the present evidence is inconclusive. Assuming that the methodological pitfalls of risk factor epidemiology (such as the 'ecological fallacy') can be avoided, and that a number of environmental variables of small to moderate effect will eventually be identified as risk factors, epidemiology will usefully complement genetic research that implicates multiple genes of small to moderate effect. Current epidemiological research is making use of large existing databases such as cumulative case registers or birth cohorts to test hypotheses about risk factors in case–control designs. Methods and models of genetic epidemiology are increasingly being integrated within population-based studies. These trends predict an important role for epidemiology in the coming era of molecular biology of mental disorders. The complementarity between genetics and epidemiology will provide tools for unravelling the gene–environment interactions that are likely to be the key to the aetiology of schizophrenia. The molecular epidemiology of schizophrenia may be the next major chapter in the search for its causes and cures.

References

Adams, W., Kendell, R.E., Hare, E.H. & Munk-Jørgensen, P. (1993) Epidemiological evidence that maternal influenza contributes to the aetiology of schizophrenia. *British Journal of Psychiatry* **163**, 522–534.

Adler, L.E. & Griffith, J.M. (1991) Concurrent medical illness in the schizophrenic patient: epidemiology, diagnosis and management. *Schizophrenia Research* **4**, 91–107.

de Alarcon, J., Seagroatt, V., Sellar, C. & Goldacre, M. (1992) Evidence for decline in schizophrenia [Abstract]. *Schizophrenia Research* **6**, 100–101.

Albus, M. & Maier, W. (1995) Lack of gender differences in age at onset in familial schizophrenia. *Schizophrenia Research* **18**, 51–57.

Alexander, R.C., Patkar, A.A., Lapointe, J.S., Flynn, S.W. & Honer, W.G. (1997) Schizencephaly associated with psychosis. *Journal of Neurology, Neurosurgery and Psychiatry* **63**, 373–375.

Allebeck, P., Adamsson, C., Engström, A. & Rydberg, U. (1993) Cannabis and schizophrenia: a longitudinal study of cases treated in Stockholm County. *Acta Psychiatrica Scandinavica* **88**, 21–24.

Andrews, G., Henderson, S. & Hall, W. (2001) Prevalence, comorbidity, disability and service utilisation: overview of the Australian National Mental Health Survey. *British Journal of Psychiatry* **178**, 145–153.

Appleby, L., Thomas, S., Ferrier, N. *et al.* (2000) Sudden unexplained death in psychiatric in-patients. *British Journal of Psychiatry* **176**, 405–406.

Astrup, C. & Ødegaard, Ø. (1961) Internal migration and mental illness in Norway. *Psychiatric Quarterly* **34**, 116–130.

Babidge, N.C., Buhrich, N. & Butler, T. (2001) Mortality among homeless people with schizophrenia in Sydney, Australia: a 10-year follow-up. *Acta Psychiatrica Scandinavica* **103**, 105–110.

Baldwin, J.A. (1979) Schizophrenia and physical disease. *Psychological Medicine* **9**, 611–618.

Bamrah, J.S., Freeman, H.L. & Goldberg, D.P. (1991) Epidemiology of schizophrenia in Salford, 1974–84. *British Journal of Psychiatry* **159**, 802–810.

Baron, M., Gruen, R., Asnis, L. & Lord, S. (1985) Familial transmission of schizotypal and borderline personality disorders. *American Journal of Psychiatry* **142**, 927–934.

Barr, C.E., Mednick, S.A. & Munk-Jorgensen, P. (1990) Exposure to influenza epidemics during gestation and adult schizophrenia. *Archives of General Psychiatry* **47**, 869–874.

Barry, H. & Barry, H. Jr (1961) Season of birth: an epidemiological study in psychiatry. *Archives of General Psychiatry* **5**, 100–108.

Bash, K.W. & Bash-Liechti, J. (1969) Psychiatrische Epidemiologie in Iran. In: *Perspektiven der heutigen Psychiatrie* (ed. H.E. Ehrhard), pp. 313–320. Gerhards, Frankfurt.

Battle, Y.L., Martin, B.C., Dorfman, J.H. & Miller, L.S. (1999) Seasonality and infectious disease in schizophrenia: the birth hypothesis revisited. *Journal of Psychiatric Research* **33**, 501–509.

Bebbington, P. & Nayani, T. (1995) The Psychosis Screening Questionnaire. *International Journal of Methods in Psychiatric Research* **5**, 11–19.

Bernstein, H.G., Grecksch, G., Becker, A., Hollt, V. & Bogerts, B. (1999) Cellular changes in rat brain areas associated with neonatal hippocampal damage. *Neuroreport* **10**, 2307–2311.

Bhugra, D., Hilwig, M., Hossein, B. *et al.* (1997) Incidence and outcome of schizophrenia in Whites, African-Caribbeans and Asians in London. *Psychological Medicine* **27**, 791–798.

Bhugra, D., Mallett, R. & Leff, J. (1999) Schizophrenia and African-Caribbeans: a conceptual model of aetiology. *International Review of Psychiatry* **11**, 145–152.

Bøjholm, S. & Strömgren, E. (1989) Prevalence of schizophrenia on the island of Bornholm in 1935 and in 1983. *Acta Psychiatrica Scandinavica* **79** (Suppl. 348), 157–166.

Böök, J.A., Wetterberg, L. & Modrzewska, K. (1978) Schizophrenia in a North Swedish geographical isolate, 1900–77: epidemiology, genetics and biochemistry. *Clinical Genetics* **14**, 373–394.

Bradbury, T.N. & Miller, G.A. (1985) Season of birth in schizophrenia: a review of the evidence, methodology and etiology. *Psychological Bulletin* **98**, 569–594.

Bredkær, S., Mortensen, P.B. & Parnas, J. (1998) Epilepsy and non-organic non-affective psychosis: national epidemiologic study. *British Journal of Psychiatry* **172**, 235–238.

Bremer, J. (1951) A social-psychiatric investigation of a small community in Northern Norway. *Acta Psychiatrica et Neurologica Scandinavica Supplement* **62**.

Bresnahan, M.A., Brown, A.S., Schaefer, C.A. *et al.* (2000) Incidence and cumulative risk of treated schizophrenia in the Prenatal Determinants of Schizophrenia study. *Schizophrenia Bulletin* **26**, 297–308.

Brewin, J., Cantwell, R., Dalkin, T. *et al.* (1997) Incidence of schizophrenia in Nottingham. *British Journal of Psychiatry* **171**, 140–144.

Brockington, I.F., Kendell, R.E. & Leff, J.P. (1978) Definitions of schizophrenia: concordance and prediction of outcome. *Psychological Medicine* **8**, 387–398.

Brodaty, H., Sachdev, P., Rose, N., Rylands, K. & Prenter, L. (1999) Schizophrenia with onset after age 50 years. I. Phenomenology and risk factors. *British Journal of Psychiatry* **175**, 410–415.

Brown, A.S., Schaefer, C.A., Wyatt, R.J. *et al.* (2000) Maternal exposure to respiratory infections and adult schizophrenia spectrum disorders: a prospective birth cohort study. *Schizophrenia Bulletin* **26**, 287–295.

Brown, A.S., Cohen, P., Harkavy-Friedman, J. *et al.* (2001) Prenatal rubella, premorbid abnormalities, and adult schizophrenia. *Biological Psychiatry* **49**, 473–486.

Brown, S. (1997) Excess mortality of schizophrenia. *British Journal of Psychiatry* **171**, 502–508.

Brown, S., Inskip, H. & Barraclough, B. (2000) Causes of the excess mortality of schizophrenia. *British Journal of Psychiatry* **177**, 212–217.

Brugger, C. (1931) Versuch einer Geisteskrankenzählung in Thüringen. *Zeitschrift für die gesamte Neurologie und Psychiatrie* **133**, 252–390.

Brugha, T.S., Nienhuis, F., Bagchi, D., Smith, J. & Meltzer, H. (1999) The survey form of SCAN: the feasibility of using experienced lay survey interviewers to administer a semi-structured systematic clinical assessment of psychotic and non-psychotic disorders. *Psychological Medicine* **29**, 703–711.

Bruton, C.J., Stevens, J.R. & Frith, C.D. (1994) Epilepsy, psychosis and schizophrenia. *Neurology* **44**, 34–42.

Brzustowicz, L.M., Hodgkinson, K.A., Chow, E.W., Honer, W.G. & Bassett, A.S. (2000) Location of a major susceptibility locus for familial schizophrenia on chromosome 1q21–q22. *Science* **288**, 678–682.

Byrne, M., Browne, R., Mulryan, N. *et al.* (2000) Labour and delivery complications and schizophrenia. *British Journal of Psychiatry* **176**, 531–536.

Cannon, M., Cotter, D., Coffey, V.P. *et al.* (1996) Prenatal exposure to the 1957 influenza epidemic and adult schizophrenia: a follow-up study. *British Journal of Psychiatry* **168**, 368–371.

Caldwell, C.B. & Gottesman, I.I. (1990) Schizophrenics kill themselves too: a review of risk factors for suicide. *Schizophrenia Bulletin* **16**, 571–589.

Cannon, T.D. (1997) On the nature and mechanisms of obstetric influences in schizophrenia: a review and synthesis of epidemiologic studies. *International Review of Psychiatry* **9**, 387–397.

Cannon, T.D., Mednick, S.A. & Parnas, J. (1990) Antecedents of predominantly negative- and predominantly positive-symptom schizophrenia in a high-risk population. *Archives of General Psychiatry* **47**, 622–632.

Cannon, T.D., Rosso, I.M., Hollister, J.M. *et al.* (2000) A prospective cohort study of genetic and perinatal influences in the etiology of schizophrenia. *Schizophrenia Bulletin* **26**, 351–366.

Cantor-Graae, E., McNeil, T.F., Fuller Torrey, E. *et al.* (1994) Link between pregnancy complications and minor physical anomalies in monozygotic twins discordant for schizophrenia. *American Journal of Psychiatry* **151**, 1188–1193.

Cantor-Graae, E., Cardenal, S., Ismail, B. & McNeil, T.F. (1998) Recall of obstetric events by mothers of schizophrenic patients. *Psychological Medicine* **28**, 1239–1243.

Cardno, A.G., Marshall, E.J., Coid, B. *et al.* (1999) Heritability estimates for psychotic disorders: the Maudsley twin psychosis series. *Archives of General Psychiatry* **56**, 162–168.

Castle, D., Der Wessely, S.G. & Murray, R.M. (1991) The incidence of operationally defined schizophrenia in Camberwell, 1965–84. *British Journal of Psychiatry* **159**, 790–794.

Chen, C.N., Wong, J., Lee, N. *et al.* (1993) The Shatin community mental health survey in Hong Kong. II. Major findings. *Archives of General Psychiatry* **50**, 125–133.

Chen, W.J., Liu, S.K., Chang, C.J. *et al.* (1998) Sustained attention deficit and schizotypal personality features in non-psychotic relatives of schizophrenic patients. *American Journal of Psychiatry* **155**, 1214–1220.

Chen, Y.L.R., Chen, Y.H.E. & Lieh, M.F. (2000) Semantic verbal fluency deficit as a familial trait marker in schizophrenia. *Psychiatry Research* **95**, 133–148.

Clementz, B.A., McDowell, J.E. & Zisook, S. (1994) Saccadic system functioning among schizophrenia patients and their first-degree biological relatives. *Journal of Abnormal Psychology* **103**, 277–287.

Cooper, J.E., Kendell, R.E., Gurland, B.J. *et al.* (1972) *Psychiatric Diagnosis in New York and London*. Oxford University Press, London.

Cornblatt, B.A. & Keilp, J.G. (1994) Impaired attention, genetics, and the pathophysiology of schizophrenia. *Schizophrenia Bulletin* **20**, 31–46.

Crimlisk, H.L. (1997) The little imitator: porphyria – a neuropsychiatric disorder. *Journal of Neurology, Neurosurgery and Psychiatry* **62**, 319–328.

Crocetti, G.J., Lemkau, P.V., Kulcar, Z. & Kesic, B. (1971) Selected aspect of the epidemiology of psychoses in Croatia, Yugoslavia. II. The cluster sample and the results of the pilot survey. *American Journal of Epidemiology* **94**, 126–134.

Crow, T.J. (1994) Prenatal exposure to influenza as a cause of schizophrenia. *British Journal of Psychiatry* **164**, 588–592.

Crow, T.J. (2000) Do obstetric complications really cause psychosis? Why it matters: invited commentary. *British Journal of Psychiatry* **176**, 527–529.

Crow, T.J. & Done, D.J. (1992) Prenatal exposure to influenza does not cause schizophrenia. *British Journal of Psychiatry* **161**, 390–393.

Dalack, G.W., Healy, D.J. & Meador-Woodruff, J.H. (1998) Nicotine dependence in schizophrenia: clinical phenomena and laboratory findings. *American Journal of Psychiatry* **155**, 1490–1501.

Dalen, P. (1975) *Season of Birth: A Study of Schizophrenia and Other Mental Disorders*. North Holland, Amsterdam.

David, A.S., Malmberg, A., Brandt, L., Allebeck, P. & Lewis, G. (1997) IQ and risk for schizophrenia: a population-based cohort study. *Psychological Medicine* **27**, 1311–1323.

Davidson, M., Reichenberg, A., Rabinowitz, J. *et al.* (1999) Behavioral and intellectual markers for schizophrenia in apparently healthy male adolescents. *American Journal of Psychiatry* **156**, 1328–1335.

DeLisi, L.E. (1996) Is there a viral or immune dysfunction etiology to schizophrenia? Re-evaluation a decade later. *Schizophrenia Research* **22**, 1–4.

DeLisi, L.E. & Crow, T.J. (1999) Chromosome Workshops 1998: current state of psychiatric linkage. *American Journal of Medical Genetics* **88**, 215–218.

DeLisi, L.E., Goldin, L.R., Maxwell, M.E., Kazuba, D.M. & Gershon, E.S. (1987) Clinical features of illness in siblings with schizophrenia or schizoaffective disorder. *Archives of General Psychiatry* **44**, 891–896.

Der, G., Gupta, S. & Murray, R.M. (1990) Is schizophrenia disappearing? *Lancet* **335**, 513–516.

Dohan, F.C. (1966) Cereals and schizophrenia: data and hypothesis. *Acta Psychiatrica Scandinavica* **42**, 125–152.

Done, D.J., Crow, T.J., Johnstone, E.C. & Sacker, A. (1994) Childhood antecedents of schizophrenia and affective illness: social adjustment at ages 7 and 11. *British Medical Journal* **309**, 699–703.

Doody, G.A., Johnstone, E.C., Sanderson, T.L., Cunningham Owens, D.G. & Muir, W.J. (1998) 'Pfropfschizophrenie' revisited: schizophrenia in people with mild learning disability. *British Journal of Psychiatry* **173**, 145–153.

Dube, K.C. & Kumar, N. (1972) An epidemiological study of schizophrenia. *Journal of Biosocial Science* **4**, 187–195.

Dupont, A., Jensen, O.M., Stromgren, E. & Jablensky, A. (1986) Incidence of cancer in patients diagnosed as schizophrenic in Denmark. In: *Psychiatric Case Registers in Public Health* (eds S.H. ten Horn, R. Giel & W. Gulbinat), pp. 229–239. Elsevier, Amsterdam.

Eagles, J.M., Hunter, D. & McCance, C. (1988) Decline in the diagnosis of schizophrenia among first contacts with psychiatric services in north-east Scotland, 1969–84. *British Journal of Psychiatry* **152**, 793–798.

Eaton, W.W. (1974) Residence, social class, and schizophrenia. *Journal of Health and Social Behavior* **15**, 289–299.

Eaton, J.W. & Weil, R.Y. (1955) *Culture and Mental Disorders*. Free Press, Glencoe, IL.

Eaton, W.W., Romanoski, A., Anthony, J.C. & Nestadt, G. (1991) Screening for psychosis in the general population with a self-report interview. *Journal of Nervous and Mental Disease* **179**, 689–693.

Eaton, W.W., Hayward, C. & Ram, R. (1992) Schizophrenia and rheumatoid arthritis: a review. *Schizophrenia Research* **6**, 181–192.

Eaton, W.W., Mortensen, P.B. & Frydenberg, M. (2000) Obstetric factors, urbanization and psychosis. *Schizophrenia Research* **43**, 117–123.

Egan, M.F., Goldberg, T.E., Gscheidle, T. *et al.* (2000) Relative risk of attention deficits in siblings of patients with schizophrenia. *American Journal of Psychiatry* **157**, 1309–1316.

Elder, A.G., O'Donnell, B., McCruden, E.A.B., Symington, I.S. & Carman, W.F. (1996) Incidence and recall of influenza in a cohort of Glasgow healthcare workers during the 1993–94 epidemic: results of serum testing and questionnaire. *British Medical Journal* **313**, 1241–1242.

Erlenmeyer-Kimling, L., Rock, D., Squires-Wheeler, E., Roberts, S. & Yang, J. (1991) Early life precursors of psychiatric outcomes in adulthood of subjects at risk for schizophrenia or affective disorders. *Psychiatry Research* **39**, 239–256.

Erlenmeyer-Kimling, L., Adamo, U.H., Rock, D. *et al.* (1997) The New York High-Risk project: prevalence and comorbidity of Axis I disorders in offspring of schizophrenic patients at 25-year follow-up. *Archives of General Psychiatry* **54**, 1096–1102.

Essen-Möller, E. (1935) Untersuchungen über die Fruchtbarkeit gewisser Gruppen von Geisteskranken. *Acta Psychiatrica et Neurologica Scandinavica Supplement* **8**.

Essen-Möller, E., Larsson, H., Uddenberg, C.E. & White, G. (1956) Individual traits and morbidity in a Swedish rural population. *Acta Psychiatrica et Neurologica Scandinavica Supplement* **100**.

Fañanás, L. & Bertranpetit, J. (1995) Reproductive rates in families of schizophrenic patients in a case–control study. *Acta Psychiatrica Scandinavica* **91**, 202–204.

Faraone, S.V., Kremen, W.S., Lyons, M.J. *et al.* (1995) Diagnostic accuracy and linkage analysis: how useful are schizophrenia spectrum phenotypes? *American Journal of Psychiatry* **152**, 1286–1290.

Faris, R.E.L. & Dunham, H.W. (1939) *Mental Disorders in Urban Areas*. University of Chicago Press, Chicago.

Fish, B. (1977) Neurobiologic antecedents of schizophrenia in children: evidence for an inherited, congenital neurointegrative defect. *Archives of General Psychiatry* **34**, 1297–1313.

Fish, B., Marcus, J., Hans, S.L., Auerbach, J.G. & Perdue, S. (1992) Infants at risk for schizophrenia: sequelae of a genetic neurointegrative defect. *Archives of General Psychiatry* **49**, 221–235.

Flint, J. & Goldstein, L.H. (1992) Familial calcifraction fo the basal ganglia: a case report and reivew of the literature. *Psychological Medicine* **22**, 581–595.

Francis, A. & Freeman, H. (1984) Psychiatric abnormality and brain calcification over four generations. *Journal of Nervous and Mental Disease* **172**, 166–170.

Frangou, S., Sharma, T., Alarcon, G. *et al.* (1997) The Maudsley Family Study. II. Endogenous event-related potentials in familial schizophrenia. *Schizophrenia Research* **23**, 45–53.

Freedman, R., Adler, L.E., Myles-Worsley, M. *et al.* (1996) Inhibitory gating of an evoked response to repeated auditory stimuli in schizophrenic and normal subjects. *Archives of General Psychiatry* **53**, 1114–1121.

Freedman, R., Adams, C.E., Adler, L.E. *et al.* (2000) Inhibitory neurophysiological deficit as a phenotype for genetic investigation of schizophrenia. *American Journal of Medical Genetics* **97**, 58–64.

Freeman, H. (1994) Schizophrenia and city residence. *British Journal of Psychiatry* **164** (Suppl. 23), 39–50.

Fremming, K.H. (1947) Sygdomsrisikoen for sindslidelser og andre sjaelige abnormtilstande i den Danske gennemshitbefolkning. *Paa grundlag af en katamnestisk underøgelsse af 5500 personer født I, 1883–87.* Munksgaard, Copenhagen.

Geddes, J.R. & Juszczak, E. (1995) Period trends in rate of suicide in first 28 days after discharge from psychiatric hospital in Scotland, 1968–92. *British Medical Journal* **311**, 357–360.

Geddes, J.R. & Lawrie, S.M. (1995) Obstetric complications and schizophrenia: a meta-analysis. *British Journal of Psychiatry* **167**, 786–793.

Gold, J.M. & Weinberger, D.R. (1995) Cognitive deficits and the neurobiology of schizophrenia. *Current Opinion in Neurobiology* **5**, 225–230.

Goldberg, E.M. & Morrison, S.L. (1963) Schizophrenia and social class. *British Journal of Psychiatry* **109**, 785–802.

Goldberg, T.E., Hyde, T.M., Kleinman, J.E. & Weinberger, D.R. (1993) Course of schizophrenia: neuropsychological evidence for a static encephalopathy. *Schizophrenia Bulletin* **19**, 797–804.

Goldstein, M. (1987) The UCLA high-risk project. *Schizophrenia Bulletin* **13**, 505–514.

Gottesman, I.I., McGuffin, P. & Farmer, A.E. (1987) Clinical genetics as clues to the 'real' genetics of schizophrenia. *Schizophrenia Bulletin* **13**, 23–47.

Grech, A., Takei, N. & Murray, R.M. (1997) Maternal exposure to influenza and paranoid schizophrenia. *Schizophrenia Research* **26**, 121–125.

Gupta, S., Andreasen, N.C., Arndt, S. *et al.* (1997a) The Iowa Longitudinal Study of Recent Onset Psychosis: one-year follow-up of first episode patients. *Schizophrenia Research* **23**, 1–13.

Gupta, S., Masand, P.S., Kaplan, D., Bhandary, A. & Hendricks, S. (1997b) The relationship between schizophrenia and irritable bowel syndrome (IBS). *Schizophrenia Research* **23**, 265–268.

Häfner, H. & Reimann, H. (1970) Spatial distribution of mental disorders in Mannheim, 1965. In: *Psychiatric Epidemiology* (eds. E.H. Hare & J.K. Wing), pp. 341–354. Oxford University Press, London.

Häfner, H., Maurer, K., Löffler, W. & Riecher-Rössler, A. (1993) The influence of age and sex on the onset and early course of schizophrenia. *British Journal of Psychiatry* **162**, 80–86.

Häfner, H., Hambrecht, M., Löffler, P., Munk-Jørgensen, P. & Riecher-Rössler, A. (1998) Is schizophrenia a disorder of all ages? A comparison of first episodes and early course across the life-cycle. *Psychological Medicine* **28**, 351–365.

Häfner, H., Löffler, W., Maurer, K., Hambrecht, M. & van der Heiden, W. (1999) Depression, negative symptoms, social stagnation and social decline in the early course of schizophrenia. *Acta Psychiatrica Scandinavica* **100**, 105–118.

Häfner, H., Löffler, W., Riecher-Rössler, A. & Häfner-Ranabauer, W. (2001) Schizophrenie und Wahn im höheren und hohen Lebensalter. *Nervenarzt* **72**, 347–357.

Hagnell, O. (1966) *A Prospective Study of the Incidence of Mental Disorder*. Svenska Bokforlaget, Lund.

Hambrecht, M. & Häfner, H. (2000) Cannabis, vulnerability, and the onset of schizophrenia: an epidemiological perspective. *Australian and New Zealand Journal of Psychiatry* **34**, 468–475.

Hare, E. (1983) Was insanity on the increase? *British Journal of Psychiatry* **142**, 439–445.

Hare, E.H. & Price, J.S. (1968) Mental disorder and season of birth: comparison of psychoses with neuroses. *British Journal of Psychiatry* **115**, 533–540.

Harrison, G., Cooper, J.E. & Gancarczyk, R. (1991) Changes in the administrative incidence of schizophrenia. *British Journal of Psychiatry* **159**, 811–816.

Harrison, G., Glazebrook, C., Brewin, J. *et al.* (1997) Increased incidence of psychotic disorders in migrants from the Caribbean to the United Kingdom. *Psychological Medicine* **27**, 799–806.

Harrison, G., Amin, S., Singh, S., Croudace, T. & Jones, P. (1999) Outcome of psychosis in people of African-Caribbean family origin. *British Journal of Psychiatry* **175**, 43–49.

Haslam, J. (1809) *Observations on Madness and Melancholy*, 2nd edn. Callow, London.

Hassiotis, A., Ukoumunne, O., Tyrer, P. *et al.* (1999) Prevalence and characteristics of inpatients with severe mental illness and borderline intellectual functioning. *British Journal of Psychiatry* **175**, 135–140.

Hatta, K., Takahashi, T., Nakamura, H. *et al.* (1999) Laboratory findings in acute schizophrenia. *General Hospital Psychiatry* **21**, 220–227.

Helgason, T. (1964) Epidemiology of mental disorders in Iceland. *Acta Psychiatrica Scandinavica Supplement* **173**.

Helgason, T. & Magnusson, H. (1989) The first 80 years of life: a psychiatric epidemiological study. *Acta Psychiatrica Scandinavica* **79** (Suppl. 348), 85–94.

Hemsi, L.K. (1967) Psychiatric morbidity of West Indian immigrants. *Social Psychiatry* **2**, 95–100.

Hickling, F.W. & Rodgers-Johnson, P. (1995) The incidence of first contact schizophrenia in Jamaica. *British Journal of Psychiatry* **167**, 193–196.

Hickling, F.W., McKenzie, K., Mullen, R. & Murray, R. (1999) A Jamaican psychiatrist evaluates diagnoses at a London psychiatric hospital. *British Journal of Psychiatry* **175**, 283–285.

Hilger, T., Propping, P. & Haverkamp, F. (1983) Is there an increase of reproductive rates in schizophrenics? *Archiv für Psychiatrie und Nervenkrankheiten* **233**, 177–186.

Hoek, H.W., Susser, E., Buck, K.A. *et al.* (1996) Schizoid personality disorder after prenatal exposure to famine. *American Journal of Psychiatry* **153**, 1637–1639.

Honer, W.G., Kopala, L.C., Locke, J.J. & Lapointe, J.S. (1996) Left cerebral hemiatrophy and schizophrenia-like psychosis in an adolescent. *Schizophrenia Research* **20**, 231–234.

Hovatta, I., Varilo, T., Suvisaari, J. *et al.* (1999) A genomewide screen for schizophrenia genes in an isolated Finnish subpopulation, suggesting multiple susceptibility loci. *American Journal of Human Genetics* **65**, 1114–1124.

Hultman, C.M., Öhman, A., Cnattingius, S., Wieselgren, I.M. & Lindström, L.H. (1997) Prenatal and neonatal risk factors for schizophrenia. *British Journal of Psychiatry* **170**, 128–133.

Hultman, C.M., Sparén, P., Takei, N., Murray, R.M. & Cnattingius, S. (1999) Prenatal and perinatal risk factors for schizophrenia, affective psychosis, and reactive psychosis of early onset: case–control study. *British Medical Journal* **318**, 421–426.

Hutchinson, G., Takei, N., Fany, T.A. *et al.* (1996) Morbid risk of schizophrenia in first-degree relatives of White and African-Caribbean patients with psychosis. *British Journal of Psychiatry* **169**, 776–780.

Hutchinson, G., Takei, N., Bhugra, D. *et al.* (1997) Increased rate of psychosis among African-Caribbeans in Britain is not due to an excess of pregnancy and birth complications. *British Journal of Psychiatry* **171**, 145–147.

Hutchinson, G., Takei, N., Sham, P., Harvey, I. & Murray, R.M. (1999) Factor analysis of symptoms in schizophrenia: differences between White and Caribbean patients in Camberwell. *Psychological Medicine* **29**, 607–612.

Hyde, T.M., Ziegler, J.C. & Weinberger, D.R. (1992) Psychiatric disturbances in metachromatic leukodystrophy. *Archives of Neurology* **49**, 401–406.

Hyman, S. (1999) Introduction to the complex genetics of mental disorders. *Biological Psychiatry* **45**, 518–521.

Ichiki, M., Kunugi, H., Takei, N. *et al.* (2000) Intra-uterine physical growth in schizophrenia: evidence confirming excess of premature birth. *Psychological Medicine* **30**, 597–604.

Indian Council of Medical Research (ICMR) (1988) *Multi-Centered Collaborative Study of Factors Associated with Course and Outcome of Schizophrenia*. ICMR, New Delhi.

Imamura, Y., Nakane, Y., Ohta, Y. & Kondo, H. (1999) Lifetime prevalence of schizophrenia among individuals prenatally exposed to atomic bomb radiation in Nagasaki City. *Acta Psychiatrica Scandinavica* **100**, 344–349.

Ismail, B., Cantor-Graae, E. & McNeil, T.F. (1998) Minor physical abnormalities in schizophrenic patients and their siblings. *American Journal of Psychiatry* **155**, 1695–1702.

Isohanni, I., Jarvelin, M.R., Nieminen, P. *et al.* (1998) School performance as a predictor of pychiatric hospitalizaiton in adult life. A 28-year follow-up in the Northern Finland 1966 Birth Cohort. *Psychological Medicine* 28, 967–974.

Jablensky, A. (1986) Epidemiology of schizophrenia: a European perspective. *Schizophrenia Bulletin* **12**, 52–73.

Jablensky, A. & Cole, S.W. (1997) Is the earlier age at onset of schizophrenia in males a confounded finding? Results from a cross-cultural investigation. *British Journal of Psychiatry* **170**, 234–240.

Jablensky, A., Sartorius, N., Ernberg, G. *et al.* (1992) Schizophrenia: manifestations, incidence and course in different cultures: a World Health Organization 10-Country Study. *Psychological Medicine*. Monograph (Suppl. 20). Cambridge University Press, Cambridge.

Jablensky, A., Hugler, H., von Cranach, M. & Kalinov, K. (1993) Kraepelin revisited: a reassessment and statistical analysis of dementia praecox and manic-depressive insanity in 1908. *Psychological Medicine* **23**, 843–858.

Jablensky, A., McGrath, J., Herrman, H. *et al.* (1999) *People Living with Psychotic Illness: an Australian Study 1997–98*. National Survey of Mental Health and Wellbeing Report 4. Commonwealth of Australia, Canberra.

Jablensky, A., McGrath, J., Herrman, H. *et al.* (2000) Psychotic disorders in urban areas: an overview of the Study of Low Prevalence Disorders. *Australian and New Zealand Journal of Psychiatry* **34**, 221–236.

Jarman, B., Hirsch, S., White, P. & Driscoll, R. (1992) Predicting psychiatric admission rates. *British Medical Journal* **304**, 1146–1151.

Jaspers, K. (1963) *General Psychopathology*. Manchester University Press, Manchester.

Javitt, D.C., Strous, R.D., Cowan, N., Grochowski, S. & Ritter, W. (1997) Impaired precision, but normal retention, of auditory sensory ('echoic') memory information in schizophrenia. *Journal of Abnormal Psychology* **106**, 315–324.

Jeffreys, S.E., Harvey, C.A., McNaught, A.S. *et al.* (1997) The Hampstead Schizophrenia Survey 1991. I. Prevalence and service use comparisons in an inner London health authority, 1986–91. *British Journal of Psychiatry* **170**, 301–306.

Jeste, D.V., Gladsjo, J.A., Lindamer, L.A. & Lacro, J.P. (1996) Medical comorbidity in schizophrenia. *Schizophrenia Bulletin* **22**, 413–430.

Jones, P., Rodgers, B., Murray, R. & Marmot, M. (1994) Child developmental risk factors for adult schizophrenia in the British 1946 birth cohort. *Lancet* **344**, 1398–1402.

Jones, P.B., Rantakallio, P., Hartikainen, A.L., Isohanni, M. & Sipila, P. (1998) Schizophrenia as a long-term outcome of pregnancy, delivery, and perinatal complications: a 28-year follow-up of the 1966 North Finland general population birth cohort. *American Journal of Psychiatry* **155**, 355–364.

Kebede, D. & Alem, A. (1999) Major mental disorders in Adis Ababa, Ethiopia. I. Schizophrenia, schizoaffective and cognitive disorders. *Acta Psychiatrica Scandinavica* **100**, 11–17.

Kendell, R.E. & Adams, W. (1991) Unexplained fluctuations in the risk for schizophrenia by month and year of birth. *British Journal of Psychiatry* **158**, 758–763.

Kendell, R.E., McInneny, K., Juszczak, E. & Bain. M. (2000) Obstetric complications and schizophrenia. *British Journal of Psychiatry* **176**, 516–522.

Kendler, K.S. & Eaves, L.J. (1986) Models for the joint effect of genotype and environment on liability to psychiatric illness. *American Journal of Psychiatry* **143**, 279–289.

Kendler, K.S. & Walsh, D. (1995) Gender and schizophrenia: results of an epidemiologically based family study. *British Journal of Psychiatry* **167**, 184–192.

Kendler, K.S., Masterson, C.C., Ungaro, R. & Davis, K.L. (1984) A family history study of schizophrenia-related personality disorders. *American Journal of Psychiatry* **141**, 424–427.

Kendler, K.S., Gallagher, T.J., Abelson, J.M. & Kessler, R.C. (1996a) Lifetime prevalence, demographic risk factors, and diagnostic validity of non-affective psychosis as assessed in a US community sample: the National Comorbidity Survey. *Archives of General Psychiatry* **53**, 1022–1031.

Kendler, K.S., Karkowski-Shuman, L. & Walsh, D. (1996b) Age at onset in schizophrenia and risk of illness in relatives. *British Journal of Psychiatry* **169**, 213–218.

Kessler, R.C., McGonagle, K.A., Zhao, S. *et al.* (1994) Lifetime and 12-month prevalence of DSM-IIIR psychiatric disorders in the United States. *Archives of General Psychiatry* **51**, 8–19.

Khoury, M.J., Beaty, T.H. & Cohen, B.H. (1993) *Fundamentals of Genetic Epidemiology*, pp. 59–61. Oxford University Press, New York.

Kläning, U. (1999) Greater occurrence of schizophrenia in dizygotic but not monozygotic twins. *British Journal of Psychiatry* **175**, 407–409.

Klemperer, J. (1933) Zur Belastungsstatistik der Durchschnittsbevölkerung: Psychosehäufigkeit unter 1000 stichprobemässig ausgelesenen Probanden. *Zeitschrift für die gesamte Neurologie und Psychiatrie* **146**, 277–316.

Kraepelin, E. (1919) *Dementia Praecox and Paraphrenia*. Livingstone, Edinburgh.

Krebs, M.O., Leroy, S., Duaux, E. *et al.* (2002) Vulnerability to cannabis, schizophrenia and the (ATT) N polymorphism of the cannabinoid receptor type 1 gene [Abstract]. *Schizophrenia Research* **53** (Suppl.), 72.

Kretschmer, E. (1936) *Physique and Character*, 2nd edn. Trubner, New York.

Kringlen, E. (1978) Adult offspring of two psychotic parents, with special reference to schizophrenia. In: *The Nature of Schizophrenia* (eds L.C. Wynne, R.L. Cromwell & S. Matthysse), pp. 9–24. Wiley, New York.

Kunugi, H., Nanko, S., Takei, N. *et al.* (1995) Schizophrenia following *in utero* exposure to the 1957 influenza epidemics in Japan. *American Journal of Psychiatry* **152**, 450–452.

Lander, E.S. & Schork, N.J. (1994) Genetic dissection of complex traits. *Science* **265**, 2037–2048.

Lane, A., Byrne, M., Mulvany, F. *et al.* (1995) Reproductive behaviour in schizophrenia relative to other mental disorders: evidence for increased fertility in men despite decreased marital rate. *Acta Psychiatrica Scandinavica* **91**, 222–228.

Lane, E. & Albee, G.W. (1964) Early childhood intellectual differences between schizophrenic adults and their siblings. *Journal of Abnormal and Social Psychology* **68**, 193–195.

Larson, C.A. & Nyman, G.E. (1973) Differential fertility in schizophrenia. *Acta Psychiatrica Scandinavica* **9**, 272–280.

Lauerma, H., Lehtinen, V., Joukamaa, M. *et al.* (1998) Schizophrenia among patients treated for rheumatoid arthritis and appendicitis. *Schizophrenia Research* **29**, 255–261.

Lawrence, D., Holman, C.D.J., Jablensky, A., Threfall, T.J. & Fuller, S.A. (2000a) Excess cancer mortality in Western Australian psychiatric patients due to higher case fatality rates. *Acta Psychiatrica Scandinavica* **101**, 382–388.

Lawrence, D., Jablensky, A.V., Holman, C.D.J. & Pinder, T.J. (2000b) Mortality in Western Australian psychiatric patients. *Social Psychiatry and Psychiatric Epidemiology* **35**, 341–347.

Lee, C.K., Kwak, Y.S., Yamamoto, J. *et al.* (1990) Psychiatric epidemiology in Korea. *Journal of Nervous and Mental Disorders* **178**, 242–252.

Lemkau, P., Tietze, C. & Cooper, M. (1943) A survey of statistical studies on the prevalence and incidence of mental disorder in sample populations. *Public Health Reports* **58**, 1909–1927.

Leweke, F.M., Giuffrida, A., Wurster, U., Emrich, H.M. & Piomelli, D. (1999) Elevated endogenous cannabinoids in schizophrenia. *Neuroreport* **10**, 1665–1669.

Lewis, M.S. & Griffin, T. (1981) An explanation for the season of birth effect in schizophrenia and certain other diseases. *Psychological Bulletin* **89**, 589–596.

Lewis, S.W. & Mezey, G.C. (1985) Clinical correlates of septum pellucidum cavities: an unusual association with psychosis. *Psychological Medicine* **15**, 43–54.

Lewis, S.W., Reveley, A.M., David, A.S. & Ron, M.A. (1988) Agenesis of the corpus callosum and schizophrenia. *Psychological Medicine* **18**, 341–347.

Lieberman, Y.I. (1974) The problem of incidence of schizophrenia: material from a clinical and epidemiological study [in Russian]. *Zhurnal Nevropatologii I Psikhiatrii* **74**, 1224–1232.

Lieberman, J.A. (1999) Is schizophrenia a neurodegenerative disorder? A clinical and neurobiological perspective. *Biological Psychiatry* **46**, 729–739.

Lin, T.Y., Chu, H.M., Rin, H. *et al.* (1989) Effects of social change on mental disorders in Taiwan: observations based on a 15-year follow-up survey of general populations in three communities. *Acta Psychiatrica Scandinavica* **79** (Suppl. 348), 11–34.

Link, B. & Dohrenwend, B.P. (1980) Formulation of hypotheses about the ratio of untreated to treated cases in the true prevalence studies of functional psychiatric disorders in adults in the United States. In: *Mental Illness in the United States: Epidemiologic Estimates* (eds B.P. Dohrenwend, B.S. Dohrenwend, M.S. Gould *et al.*), pp. 133–148. Praeger, New York.

Linszen, D.H., Dingemans, P.M. & Lenior, M.E. (1994) Cannabis abuse and the course of recent-onset schizophrenic disorders. *Archives of General Psychiatry* **51**, 273–279.

Loebel, A.D., Lieberman, J.A., Alvir, J.M.J. *et al.* (1992) Duration of psychosis and outcome in first-episode schizophrenia. *American Journal of Psychiatry* **149**, 1183–1188.

McGorry, P.D., Edwards, J., Mihalopoulos, C., Harrigan, S.M. & Jackson, H.J. (1996) EPPIC: an evolving system of early detection and optimal management. *Schizophrenia Bulletin* **22**, 305–326.

McGrath, J.J. & Welham, J.L. (1999) Season of birth and schizophrenia: a systematic review and meta-analysis of data from the Southern Hemisphere. *Schizophrenia Research* **35**, 237–242.

McGrath, J.J., Hearle, J., Jenner, L. *et al.* (1999) The fertility and fecundity of patients with psychoses. *Acta Psychiatrica Scandinavica* **99**, 441–446.

McGuire, P.K., Jones, P., Harvey, I. *et al.* (1995) Morbid risk of schizophrenia for relatives of patients with cannabis-associated psychosis. *Schizophrenia Research* **15**, 277–281.

McNaught, A., Jeffreys, S.E., Harvey, C.A. *et al.* (1997) The Hampstead Schizophrenia Survey 1991. II. Incidence and migration in inner London. *British Journal of Psychiatry* **170**, 307–311.

McNeil, T.F. & Kaij, L. (1987) Swedish high-risk study: sample characteristics at age 6. *Schizophrenia Bulletin* **13**, 373–381.

McNeil, T.F., Cantor-Graae, E. & Ismail, B. (2000) Obstetric complications and congenital malformations in schizophrenia. *Schizophrenia Research* **31**, 166–178.

Mahy, E., Mallett, R., Leff, J. & Bhugra, D. (1999) First contact rate incidence of schizophrenia on Barbados. *British Journal of Psychiatry* **175**, 28–33.

Mäkikirö, T., Isohanni, M., Moring, J. *et al.* (1997) Is a child's risk of early onset schizophrenia increased in the highest social class? *Schizophrenia Research* **23**, 245–252.

Mäkikirö, T., Karvonen, J.T., Hakko, H. *et al.* (1998) Comorbidity of hospital-treated psychiatric and physical disorders with special reference to schizophrenia: a 28 year follow-up of the 1966 Northern Finland general population birth cohort. *Public Health* **112**, 221–228.

Mallard, E.C., Rehn, A., Rees, S., Tolcos, M. & Copolov, D. (1999) Ventriculomegaly and reduced hippocampal volume following intrauterine growth-restriction: implications for the aetiology of schizophrenia. *Schizophrenia Research* **40**, 11–21.

Malmberg, A., Lewsi, G., David, A. & Allebeck, P. (1998) Premorbid adjustment and personality in people with schizophrenia. *British Journal of Psychiatry* **172**, 308–313.

Marcelis, M., Takei, N. & van Os, J. (1999) Urbanization and risk for schizophrenia: does the effect operate before or around the illness onset? *Psychological Medicine* **29**, 1197–1203.

Mason, P.R. & Winton, F.E. (1995) Ear disease and schizophrenia: a case–control study. *Acta Psychiatrica Scandinavica* **91**, 217–221.

Mednick, S.A. (1970) Breakdown in individuals at high risk for schizophrenia: possible predispositional perinatal factors. *Mental Hygiene* **54**, 50–63.

Mednick, S.A., Machon, R.A., Huttunen, M.O. & Bonett, D. (1988) Adult schizophrenia following prenatal exposure to an influenza epidemic. *Archives of General Psychiatry* **45**, 189–192.

Meehl, P.E. (1962) Schizotaxia, schizotypy, schizophrenia. *American Psychologist* **17**, 827–838.

Michie, P.T., Budd, T.W., Todd, J. *et al.* (2000) Duration and frequency mismatch negativity in schizophrenia. *Clinical Neurophysiology* **111**, 1054–1065.

Mino, Y., Oshima, I., Tsuda, T. & Okagami, K. (2000) No relationship between schizophrenic birth and influenza epidemics in Japan. *Journal of Psychiatric Research* **34**, 133–138.

Mirsky, A.F., Ingraham, L.J. & Kugelmass, S. (1995) Neuropsychological assessment of attention and its pathology in the Israeli cohort. *Schizophrenia Bulletin* **21**, 193–204.

Mischler, E.G. & Scotch, N.A. (1983) Sociocultural factors in the epidemiology of schizophrenia: a review. *Psychiatry* **26**, 315–351.

Morgan, V., Castle, D., Page, A. *et al.* (1997) Influenza epidemics and incidence of schizophrenia, affective disorders and mental retardation in Western Australia: no evidence of a major effect. *Schizophrenia Research* **26**, 25–39.

Mortensen, P.B. (1987) Neuroleptic treatment and other factors modifying cancer risk in schizophrenic patients. *Acta Psychiatrica Scandinavica* **75**, 585–590.

Mortensen, P.B. (1994) The occurrence of cancer in first admitted schizophrenic patients. *Schizophrenia Research* **12**, 185–194.

Mortensen, P.B. & Juel, K. (1993) Mortality and causes of death in first admitted schizophrenic patients. *British Journal of Psychiatry* **163**, 183–189.

Mortensen, P.B., Pedersen, C.B., Westergaard, T. *et al.* (1999) Effects of family history and place and season of birth on the risk of schizophrenia. *New England Journal of Medicine* **340**, 603–608.

Munk-Jørgensen, P. (1986) Decreasing first-admission rates of schizophrenia among males in Denmark from 1970 to 1984. *Acta Psychiatrica Scandinavica* **73**, 645–650.

Munk-Jørgensen, P. & Mortensen, P.B. (1992) Incidence and other aspects of the epidemiology of schizophrenia in Denmark, 1971–87. *British Journal of Psychiatry* **161**, 489–495.

Murphy, K.C. & Owen, M.J. (1996) Minor physical anomalies and their relationship to the aetiology of schizophrenia. *British Journal of Psychiatry* **168**, 139–142.

Murthy, G.V.S., Janakiramaiah, N., Gangadhar, B.N. & Subbarrishna, D.K. (1998) Sex difference in age at onset of schizophrenia: discrepant findings from India. *Acta Psychiatrica Scandinavica* **97**, 321–325.

Nicole, L., Lesage, A. & Lalonde, P. (1992) Lower incidence and increased male : female ratio in schizophrenia. *British Journal of Psychiatry* **161**, 556–557.

Nicolson, R. & Rapoport, J.L. (1999) Childhood-onset schizophrenia: rare but worth studying. *Biological Psychiatry* **46**, 1418–1428.

Nimgaonkar, V.L., Ward, S.E., Agarde, H., Weston, N. & Ganguli, R. (1997) Fertility in schizophrenia: results from a contemporary US cohort. *Acta Psychiatrica Scandinavica* **95**, 364–369.

Nimgaonkar, V.L., Fujiwara, T.M., Dutta, M. *et al.* (2000) Low prevalence of psychoses among the Hutterites, an isolated religious community. *American Journal of Psychiatry* **157**, 1065–1070.

Noupoulos, P., Flaum, M., O'Leary, D. & Andreasen, N.C. (2000) Sexual dimorphism in the human brain: evaluation of tissue volume, tissue composition and surface anatomy using magnetic resonance imaging. *Psychiatry Research* **98**, 1–13.

O'Flaithbheartaigh, S., Williams, P.A. & Jones, G.H. (1994) Schizophrenic psychosis and associated aqueduct stenosis. *British Journal of Psychiatry* **164**, 684–686.

Ødegaard, Ø. (1946a) A statistical investigation of the incidence of mental disorder in Norway. *Psychiatric Quarterly* **20**, 381–401.

Ødegaard, Ø. (1946b) Marriage and mental disease: a study in social psychopathology. *Journal of Mental Science* **92**, 35–59.

Ødegaard, Ø. (1952) The incidence of mental diseases as measured by census investigations versus admission statistics. *Psychiatric Quarterly* **26**, 212–218.

Ødegaard, Ø. (1980) Fertility of psychiatric first admissions in Norway, 1936–75. *Acta Pychiatrica Scandinavica* **62**, 212–220.

van Os, J. & Selten, J.P. (1998) Prenatal exposure to maternal stress and subsequent schizophrenia. The May 1940 invasion of the Netherlands. *British Journal of Psychiatry* **172**, 324–326.

van Os, J., Driessen, G., Gunther, N. & Delespaul, P. (2000) Neighbourhood variation in incidence of schizophrenia: evidence for person–environment interaction. *British Journal of Psychiatry* **176**, 243–248.

Ösby, U., Correia, N., Brandt, L., Ekbom, A. & Sparén, P. (2000) Mortality and causes of death in schizophrenia in Stockholm County, Sweden. *Schizophrenia Research* **45**, 21–28.

Österberg, E. (1978) Schizophrenia and rheumatic disease. *Acta Psychiatrica Scandinavica* **58**, 339–359.

Padmavathi, R., Rajkumar, S., Kumar, N., Manoharan, A. & Kamath, S. (1987) Prevalence of schizophrenia in an urban community in Madras. *Indian Journal of Psychiatry* **31**, 233–239.

Pallast, E.G.M., Jongbloet, P.H., Straatman, P.H. & Zielhuis, G.A. (1994) Excess seasonality of births among patients with schizophrenia and seasonal ovopathy. *Schizophrenia Bulletin* **20**, 269–275.

Palmer, B.W., McClure, F.S. & Jeste, D.V. (2001) Schizophrenia in late life: findings challenge traditional concepts. *Harvard Review of Psychiatry* **9**, 51–58.

Pinel, P. (1803) *Nosographie philosophique: ou la methode de l'analyse apliquée a la médecine*, 2nd edn, Vol. 3. Brosson, Paris.

Propping, P. (1983) Genetic disorders presenting as 'schizophrenia': Karl Bonhoeffer's early view of the psychosis in the light of medical genetics. *Human Genetics* **65**, 1–10.

Puri, B.K., Hall, A.D. & Lewis, S.W. (1994) Cerebral hemiatrophy and schizophrenia. *British Journal of Psychiatry* **165**, 403–405.

Rajkumar, S., Padmavathi, R., Thara, R. & Sarada Menon, M. (1993) Incidence of schizophrenia in an urban community in Madras. *Indian Journal of Psychiatry* **35**, 18–21.

Raman, A.C. & Murphy, H.M.M. (1972) Failure of traditional prognostic indicators in Afro-Asian psychotics: results from a long-term follow-up study. *Journal of Nervous and Mental Disease* **154**, 238–247.

Rantakallio, P., Jones, P., Moring, J. & von Wendt, L. (1997) Association between central nervous system infections during childhood and adult onset schizophrenia and other psychoses: a 28-year follow-up. *International Journal of Epidemiology* **26**, 837–843.

Regier, D.A., Kaelber, C.T., Rae, D.S. *et al.* (1998) Limitations of diagnostic criteria and assessment instruments for mental disorders: implications for research and policy. *Archives of General Psychiatry* **55**, 109–115.

Reid, D.D. (1960) *Epidemiological Methods in the Study of Mental Disorders*. Public Health Papers No. 2. World Health Organization, Geneva.

Reveley, A.M. & Reveley, M.A. (1983) Aqueduct stenosis and schizophrenia. *Journal of Neurology, Neurosurgery and Psychiatry* **46**, 18–22.

Riecher Rössler, A., Fatkenheuer, B., Löffler, W., Maurer, K. & Häfner, H. (1992) Is age of onset in schizophrenia influenced by marital status? *Social Psychiatry and Psychiatric Epidemiology* **27**, 122–128.

Rin, H. & Lin, T.Y. (1962) Mental illness among Formosan aborigines as compared with the Chinese in Taiwan. *Journal of Mental Science* **198**, 134–146.

Risch, N. (1997) Evolving methods in genetic epidemiology. II. Genetic linkage from an epidemiological perspective. *Epidemiologic Reviews* **19**, 24–32.

Roberts, J.K.A., Trimble, M.R. & Robertson, M. (1983) Schizophrenic psychosis associated with aqueduct stenosis in adults. *Journal of Neurology, Neurosurgery and Psychiatry* **46**, 892–898.

Robins, L.N. (1989) Diagnostic grammar and assessment: translating criteria into questions. *Psychological Medicine* **19**, 57–68.

Robins, L.N., Helzer, J.E., Croughan, J. *et al.*(1981) National Institute of Mental Health Diagnostic Interview Schedule. Its History, characteristics, and validity. *Archives of General Psychiatry* **38**, 381–389.

Robins, L.N. & Regier, D.A., eds. (1991) *Psychiatric Disorders in America: the Epidemiologic Catchment Area Study*, pp. 1–10. Free Press, New York.

Robins, L.N., Wing, J.K., Wittchen, H.U. *et al.* (1988) The Composite International Diagnostic Interview: an epidemiologic instrument suitable for use in conjunction with different diagnostic systems and in different cultures. *Archives of General Psychiatry* **45**, 1069–1077.

Rosenthal, R.N. (1998) Is schizophrenia addiction prone? *Current Opinion in Psychiatry* **11**, 45–48.

Rotstein, V.G. (1977) Material from a psychiatric survey of sample groups from the adult population in several areas of the USSR [in Russian]. *Zhurnal Nevropatologii i Psikhiatrii* 77, 569–574.

Sacker, A., Done, J., Crow, T.J. & Golding, J. (1995) Antecedents of schizophrenia and affective illness: obstetric complications. *British Journal of Psychiatry* **166**, 734–741.

Salan, R. (1992) Epidemiology of schizophrenia in Indonesia (the Tambora I study). *ASEAN Journal of Psychiatry* **2**, 52–57.

Sanderson, T.L., Doody, G.A., Best, J., Owens, D.G.C. & Johnstone, E.C. (2001) Correlations between clinical and historical variables, and cerebral structural variables in people with mild intellectual disability and schizophrenia. *Journal of Intellectual Disability Research* **45**, 89–98.

Sartorius, N., Jablensky, A., Korten, A. *et al.* (1986) Early manifestations and first-contact incidence of schizophrenia in different cultures: a preliminary report on the initial evaluation phase of the WHO Collaborative Study on Determinants of Outcome of Severe Mental Disorders. *Psychological Medicine* **16**, 909–928.

Saugstad, L.F. & Ødegaard, Ø. (1979) Mortality in psychiatric hospitals in Norway, 1950–74. *Acta Psychiatrica Scandinavica* **59**, 431–447.

Schulsinger, F., Parnas, J., Petersen, E.T. *et al.* (1984) Cerebral ventricular size in the offspring of schizophrenic mothers. *Archives of General Psychiatry* **41**, 602–606.

Selten, J.P., Slaets, J. & Kahn, R.S. (1997) Schizophrenia in Surinamese and Dutch Antillean immigrants to the Netherlands: evidence of an increased incidence. *Psychological Medicine* **27**, 807–811.

Selten, J.P., Slaets, J. & Kahn, R. (1998) Prenatal exposure to influenza and schizophrenia in Surinamese and Dutch Antillean immigrants to the Netherlands. *Schizophrenia Research* **30**, 101–103.

Selten, J.P., Brown, A.S., Moons, K.G.M. *et al.* (1999a) Prenatal exposure to the 1957 influenza pandemic and non-affective psychosis in the Netherlands. *Schizophrenia Research* **38**, 85–91.

Selten, J.P., van der Graaf, Y., van Duursen, R., Gispen-de Wied, C. & Kahn, R.S. (1999b) Psychotic illness after prenatal exposure to the 1953 Dutch flood disaster. *Schizophrenia Research* **35**, 243–245.

Sewell, D.D. (1996) Schizophrenia and HIV. *Schizophrenia Bulletin* **22**, 465–473.

Sham, P.C., O'Callaghan, E., Takei, N. *et al.* (1992) Schizophrenia following prenatal exposure to influenza epidemics between 1939 and 1960. *British Journal of Psychiatry* **160**, 461–466.

Shields, J. (1977) High risk for schizophrenia: genetic considerations. *Psychological Medicine* **7**, 7–10.

Sierra-Honigmann, A.M., Carbone, K.M. & Yolken, R.H. (1995) Polymerase chain reaction (PCR) search for viral nucleic acid sequences in schizophrenia. *British Journal of Psychiatry* **166**, 55–60.

Silver, H. & Abboud, E. (1994) Drug abuse in schizophrenia: comparison of patients who began drug abuse before their first admission with those who began abusing drugs after their first admission. *Schizophrenia Research* **13**, 57–63.

Sirota, P., Frydman, M. & Sirota, L. (1990) Schizophrenia and Marfan syndrome. *British Journal of Psychiatry* **157**, 433–436.

Sjögren, T. (1948) Genetic-statistical and psychiatric investigations of a West Swedish population. *Acta Psychiatrica et Neurologica Scandinavica Supplement* **52**.

Srinivasan, T.N. & Padmavati, R. (1997) Fertility and schizophrenia: evidence for increased fertility in the relatives of schizophrenic patients. *Acta Psychiatrica Scandinavica* **96**, 260–264.

Stabenau, J.R. & Pollin, W. (1967) Early characteristics of monozygotic twins discordant for schizophrenia. *Archives of General Psychiatry* **17**, 723–734.

Stephens, J.H., Astrup, C., Carpenter, W.T., Shaffer, J.W. & Goldberg, J. (1982) A comparison of nine systems to diagnose schizophrenia. *Psychiatry Research* **6**, 127–143.

Strakowski, S.M., Tohen, M., Stoll, A.L. *et al.* (1993) Comorbidity in psychosis at first hospitalization. *American Journal of Psychiatry* **150**, 752–757.

Strömgren, E. (1935) Zum Ersatz des Weinbergschen 'abgekurzten Verfahren': Zugleich ein Beitrag zur Frage der Erblichkeit des Erkrankungsalters bei der Schizophrenie. *Zeitschrift für die gesamte Neurologie und Psychiatrie* **153**, 784–797.

Strömgren, E. (1938) Beiträge zur psychiatrischen Erblehre, auf Grund von Untersuchungen an einer Inselbevölkerung. *Acta Psychiatrica et Neurologica Scandinavica Supplement* **19**.

Susser, E.S. & Lin, S.P. (1992) Schizophrenia after prenatal exposure to the Dutch hunger winter of 1944–45. *Archives of General Psychiatry* **49**, 983–988.

Susser, E.S., Schaefer, C.A., Brown, A.S., Begg, M.D. & Wyatt, R.J. (2000) The design of the prenatal determinants of schizophrenia study. *Schizophrenia Bulletin* **26**, 257–273.

Suvisaari, J.M., Haukka, J.K. & Lönnqvist, J.K. (2001) Season of birth among patients with schizophrenia and their siblings: evidence for the procreational habits hypothesis. *American Journal of Psychiatry* **158**, 754–757.

Szymanski, S.R., Cannon, T.D., Gallacher, F., Erwin, R.J. & Gur, R.E. (1996) Course of treatment response in first-episode and chronic schizophrenia. *American Journal of Psychiatry* **153**, 519–525.

Taieb, O., Baleyte, J.M., Mazet, P. & Fillet, A.M. (2001) Borna disease virus and psychiatry. *European Psychiatry* **16**, 3–10.

Takei, N., Sham, P., O'Callaghan, E. *et al.* (1994) Prenatal exposure to influenza and the development of schizophrenia: is the effect confined to females? *American Journal of Psychiatry* **151**, 117–119.

Taller, A., Asher, D.M., Pomeroy, K.L. *et al.* (1996) Search for viral nucleic acid sequences in brain tissues of patients with schizophrenia using nested polymerase chain reaction. *Archives of General Psychiatry* **53**, 32–40.

Tien, A.Y. & Eaton, W.W. (1992) Psychopathologic precursors and sociodemographic risk factors for the schizophrenia syndrome. *Archives of General Psychiatry* **49**, 37–46.

Tienari, P. (1991) Interaction between genetic vulnerability and family environment: the Finnish adoptive family study of schizophrenia. *Acta Psychiatrica Scandinavica* **84**, 460–465.

Torrey, E.F. (1980) *Schizophrenia and Civilization.* Jason Aronson, New York.

Torrey, E.F. (1987) Prevalence studies of schizophrenia. *British Journal of Psychiatry* **150**, 598–608.

Torrey, E.F. (1995) Prevalence of psychosis among the Hutterites: a reanalysis of the 1950–53 study. *Schizophrenia Research* **16**, 167–170.

Torrey, E.F., Taylor, E.H., Bracha, H.S. *et al.* (1994) Prenatal origin of schizophrenia in a subgroup of discordant monozygotic twins. *Schizophrenia Bulletin* **20**, 423–432.

Torrey, E.F., Bowler, A.E. & Clark, K. (1997a) Urban birth and residence as risk factors for psychoses: an analysis of 1880 data. *Schizophrenia Research* **25**, 169–176.

Torrey, E.F., Miller, J., Rawlings, R. & Yolken, R.H. (1997b) Seasonality of births in schizophrenia and bipolar disorder: a review of the literature. *Schizophrenia Research* **28**, 1–38.

Tracy, J.I., Josiassen, R.C. & Bellack, A.S. (1995) Neuropsychology of dual diagnosis: understanding the combined effects of schizophrenia and substance use disorders. *Clinical Psychology Review* **15**, 67–97.

Tramer, M. (1929) Über die biologische Bedeutung des Geburtsmonats, insbesondere für die Psychosenerkrankung. *Schweizer Archiv für Neurologie, Neurochirurgie und Psychiatrie* **24**, 17–24.

Verdoux, H., Geddes, J.R., Takei, N. *et al.* (1997) Obstetric complications and age at onset in schizophrenia: an international collaborative meta-analysis of individual patient data. *American Journal of Psychiatry* **154**, 1220–1227.

Verheij, R.A., van de Mheen, H.D., de Bakker, D.H., Groenewegen, P.P. & Mackenbach, J.P. (1998) Urban–rural variations in health in the Netherlands: does selective migration play a part? *Journal of Epidemiology and Community Health* **52**, 487–493.

Waddington, J.L. & Youssef, H.A. (1996) Familial-genetic and reproductive epidemiology of schizophrenia in rural Ireland: age at onset, familial morbid risk and parental fertility. *Acta Psychiatrica Scandinavica* **93**, 62–68.

Waddington, J.L., Youssef, H.A. & Kinsella, A. (1998) Mortality in schizophrenia. *British Journal of Psychiatry* **173**, 325–329.

Wahlbeck, K., Forsén, T., Osmond, C., Barker, D.J. & Eriksson, J.G. (2001) Association of schizophrenia with low maternal body mass index, small size at birth, and thinness during childhood. *Archives of General Psychiatry* **58**, 48–52.

Wahlberg, K.E., Wynne, L.C., Oja, H. *et al.* (1997) Gene–environment interaction in vulnerability to schizophrenia: findings from the Finnish Adoptive Family Study of Schizophrenia. *American Journal of Psychiatry* **154**, 355–362.

Waldo, M.C. (1999) Schizophrenia in Kosrae, Micronesia: prevalence, gender ratios, and clinical symptomatology. *Schizophrenia Research* **35**, 175–181.

Weeke, A. & Strömgren, E. (1978) Fifteen years later: a comparison of patients in Danish psychiatric institutions in 1957, 1962, 1967 and 1972. *Acta Psychiatrica Scandinavica* **57**, 129–144.

Weinberg, W. (1925) Methoden und Technik der Statistik mit besonderer Berücksichtigung der Sozialbiologie. *Handbuch der Sozialen Hygiene und Gesundheitsfürsorge*. Band I. Springer, Berlin.

World Health Organization (1973) *Report of the International Pilot Study of Schizophrenia*, Vol. I. World Health Organization, Geneva.

World Health Organization (1979) *Schizophrenia. An International Follow-Up Study*. Wiley, Chichester.

Wilson, R.I. & Nicoll, R.A. (2001) Endogenous cannabinoids mediate retrograde signalling at hippocampal synapses. *Nature* **410**, 588–592.

Wing, J.K., Cooper, J.E. & Sartorius, N. (1974) *The Measurement and Classification of Psychiatric Symptoms*. Cambridge University Press, Cambridge.

Wing, J.K., Babor, T., Brugha, T. *et al.* (1990) SCAN: Schedules for Clinical Assessment in Neuropsychiatry. *Archives of General Psychiatry* **47**, 589–593.

Wing, J.K., Sartorius, N. & Üstün, T.B. (1998) *Diagnosis and Clinical Measurement in Psychiatry: A Reference Manual for SCAN*. Cambridge University Press, Cambridge.

Zornberg, G.L., Buka, S.L. & Tsuang, M.T. (2000) Hypoxic-ischemia fetal/neonatal complications and risk of schizophrenia and other nonaffective psychoses: a 19-year longitudinal study. *American Journal of Psychiatry* **157**, 196–202.

13 Risk factors for schizophrenia: from conception to birth

J.J. McGrath and R. M. Murray

The neurodevelopmental hypothesis of schizophrenia can be traced back to the end of the nineteenth century (Lewis 1989), but re-emerged in the mid-1980s (Weinberger 1987; Murray *et al.* 1988; Lyon *et al.* 1989). In short, the rediscovered hypothesis regards schizophrenia as a distal consequence of disturbed brain development during the pre- or perinatal period, but does not specify the nature of the early brain disruption, nor define the pathogenesis of the disorder. The neurodevelopmental hypothesis has heuristic appeal in that it directs attention to early life exposures, decades before the onset of the clinical syndrome. However, it has become clear that the model proposed in the 1980s was oversimplistic, and therefore contemporary revisions of the hypothesis regard neurodevelopmental deviance as one component of a more complex aetiology. Thus, the 'developmental risk factor' model talks in terms of an interaction between early and late risk factors, and of a cascade of increasing deviance finally culminating in psychosis (McDonald *et al.* 1999; Murray & Fearon 1999).

The sturdiest of the known risk factors for schizophrenia is the presence of an affected relative. The evidence for a genetic contribution to schizophrenia is addressed in Chapter 14, but it is worth noting here that this may operate in part through one or more of the genes involved in the control of early brain development (Jones & Murray 1991). In this chapter we concentrate on non-genetic risk factors that operate prior to or around birth. The first section examines minor physical anomalies and quantitative measures of dysmorphogenesis as risk indicators (i.e. proxy markers) of developmental disturbance. Subsequently, we examine the broad clues provided by epidemiology that allow us to generate candidate exposures, and detail the evidence for several of these candidates (e.g. pregnancy and birth complications, prenatal infection, prenatal nutrition).

What is a risk factor?

In recent times there has been an effort to clarify terminology surrounding risk factors (Susser 1991; Kraemer *et al.* 1997). Variables that correlate with an outcome, but do not precede the outcome, are sequelae and should not be labelled risk factors. Variables that precede an outcome, but are not causally related to that outcome, are defined as risk indicators or proxy markers. The term 'risk modifying factor' should be reserved for factors that appear to operate within the causal chain (contribute to the outcome). In neurodevelopmental models of schizophrenia, we are looking for distal or 'upstream' risk modifying variables. These factors may operate directly or indirectly. Risk modifying factors can be fixed (e.g. gender) or variable (alcohol intake), endogenous (e.g. genetic factors) or exogenous (e.g. obstetric complications), protective or adverse.

Proxy markers of disturbed early development

Minor physical abnormalities

In the late nineteenth century, Thomas Clouston noted that palatal abnormalities (steep narrow-roofed palates) were more common in those patients he regarded as having 'adolescent insanity' – a type of psychosis that he considered had a strong familial tendency (Clouston 1891). Since then, a sizeable body of research has examined minor physical anomalies (MPAs) in schizophrenia and other psychiatric disorders. MPAs are subtle variations in soft-tissue, cartilaginous and bony structures that are the result of an uncertain mix of genetic and environmental factors that operate prenatally. They include variations in the shape and proportions of the head, face, mouth, fingers, hands and toes. Variations of dermatoglyphics (e.g. finger and palm prints) can also be included under this broad heading.

Minor physical anomalies are of interest because they may serve as persistent markers or 'fossilized' evidence of deviant development in fetal life and, in particular, as markers of early events that could have impacted on brain development. They may arise from teratogenic or genetic factors. The latter may result from a general vulnerability to developmental disruption, or to more specific genes underlying infrequent phenotypic variants. The nature of the MPAs may provide clues to the timing of the disruption (e.g. the major features of the palate are essentially complete by 16–17 weeks).

Table 13.1 lists the key findings of studies that have compared the prevalence of MPAs in schizophrenic patients vs. well controls. Overall, the majority of studies indicate an excess of MPAs in schizophrenia (Gualtieri *et al.* 1982; Lohr & Flynn 1993; Cantor-Graae *et al.* 1994; Green *et al.* 1994; Lane *et al.* 1997; Lohr *et al.* 1997; Griffiths *et al.* 1998; Ismail *et al.* 2000; McGrath *et al.* 2002) but two studies failed to find an association (McNeil *et al.* 1992; Alexander *et al.* 1994). However, high rates of MPAs are by no means specific to schizophrenia or psychosis, being found in a range of other neurodevelopmental disorders such as mental retardation (Alexander *et al.* 1994), cerebral palsy (Illingworth 1979; Coorssen *et al.* 1992) and schizotypal personality disorder (Weinstein *et al.* 1999).

The Waldrop scale (Waldrop *et al.* 1968), while widely used to assess MPAs from a broad qualitative perspective, is acknowledged to be unsatisfactory by most authors in the field. As a result of problems with the reliance on qualitative measures, two groups have used quantitative craniofacial measures in order to examine dysmorphogenesis. Lane *et al.* (1997) included quantitative anthropomorphic measures in their study of 174 patients with schizophrenia and 80 control subjects. They reported an overall elongation of the mid- and lower face, widening of the skull base and a concentration of qualitative MPAs in the eyes, ears and mouth in the patient group. McGrath *et al.* (2002) replicated these findings in a group of 303 subjects with psychotic disorders and 313 well controls. The odds of having a psychotic disorder were increased in those with wider skull bases, smaller lower facial heights, protruding ears, and shorter and wider palates. The ratio of skull width : length was significantly larger in those with psychotic disorders compared to the well controls.

Waddington *et al.* (1999) have drawn attention to the close links between brain growth and development of the face. The relationship between wider skulls and shorter middle/lower faces noted in the two studies examining craniofacial measures in schizophrenia has also been noted by research on variation in, and evolution of, the human skull (Weidenreich 1941; Enlow & Bhatt 1984; Enlow 1990; Cheverud *et al.* 1992; Lieberman *et al.* 2000). Exposures that can impact on these structures include prenatal viral exposures, obstetric complications, general nutritional deficiencies and low vitamin D (Engstrom *et al.* 1982; Sperber 1989).

Uncommon genetic disorders that may be associated with MPAs have also received increasing attention in recent times. Velocardiofacial syndrome (VCFS) is caused by a microdeletion in the long arm of chromosome 22 and is associated with an increased frequency of schizophrenia and bipolar mood disorder (Gothelf *et al.* 1999). Waddington *et al.* (1999) have suggested that genes involved in craniofacial development warrant close inspect in schizophrenia research. Also, informative craniofacial quantitative measures (e.g. skull base width, facial heights) may serve as useful correlated phenotypes in genetic studies of psychosis (Pulver 2000).

Some investigators have tried to characterize those patients with schizophrenia with high total MPA scores. Studies have shown that patients with high MPA scores tend to have more orofacial tardive dyskinesia (Waddington *et al.* 1995), have impaired performance on neurognitive tasks (O'Callaghan *et al.* 1991a; McGrath *et al.* 1995) and are more likely to be male (O'Callaghan *et al.* 1991a; Griffiths *et al.* 1998). This clinical profile has features in common with early descriptions of dementia praecox (Murray 1994).

The relationship between MPAs and the family history of schizophrenia and/or other psychiatric conditions is still not clear, with one group reporting higher MPAs in those with a positive family history (O'Callaghan *et al.* 1991a), while others have reported either no association (McGrath *et al.* 1995) or an excess of MPAs in those without a family history (Griffiths *et al.* 1998). Two studies have compared MPAs in patients with schizophrenia vs. their unaffected siblings. Both studies found that patients had higher total MPA scores compared to the sibling group (Green *et al.* 1994; Ismail *et al.* 1998). The study by Ismail *et al.* also found that siblings had higher total MPA scores compared to well controls, and that while MPA scores were positively correlated within families, there was little correlation in the specific nature of MPAs between patients and their unaffected siblings. These findings suggest (but do not prove) that those with higher total MPA scores have a general developmental instability related to genetic factors but, in the absence of other non-genetic factors, this vulnerability is not sufficient to lead to schizophrenia.

The results concerning age of onset have also been inconsistent, with some groups reporting an association between higher total MPA scores and earlier age of onset (Green *et al.* 1989; McGrath *et al.* 2002), while others find no such association (O'Callaghan *et al.* 1991a; Lohr & Flynn 1993; McGrath *et al.* 1995; Akabaliev & Sivkov 1998).

Dermatoglyphic features

Many dermatoglyphic features also provide clues to early developmental disturbances because most of these features have stabilized by the second trimester. Quantitative features include measures related to ridge counts (e.g. total ridge count, differences between right- and left-hand total ridge counts, ridge counts between tri-radii at the base of the first and second fingers) and angles related to the shape of the palm and the hand. Qualitative features include the assessment of finger pad patterns (e.g. loops, whorls), palmar creases and ridge dissociations.

Several investigators have found significant group differences when comparing schizophrenia patients vs. well controls on various measures derived from finger and hand prints (Markow &

Table 13.1 Minor physical anomalies and schizophrenia.

Reference	Samples	Method	Comment
Gualtieri *et al.* (1982)	*n* = 64 Sz *n* = 127 other psychiatric disorders *n* = 171 controls	Subset of Waldrop scale	Highest scores found in the Sz group. Significantly higher scores in Sz compared to controls. High scores also in hyperkinetic and autistic children
Guy *et al.* (1983)	*n* = 40 Sz	Waldrop scale	The patient group had higher rates of MPAs than unpublished norms
Green *et al.* (1989)	*n* = 67 Sz *n* = 88 controls	Waldrop scale	Sz had significantly more abnormalities. Patients had high incidence of mouth abnormalities. Younger age of onset for the high MPA group
O'Callaghan *et al.* (1991)	*n* = 41 Sz	Waldrop scale	Higher levels of MPAs were associated with positive family history, male sex, poor score on test of mental flexibility, and presence of PBCs. No association with age of onset
McNeil *et al.* (1992)	*n* = 84 offspring of women with non-organic psychosis *n* = 100 offspring of controls	Congenital malformations Ekelund system	No significant difference between the groups. Suggests that the higher rates of MPAs in Sz are due more to PBCs than genes
Alexander *et al.* (1994)	*n* = 41 Sz *n* = 8 BAD *n* = 19 mentally retarded *n* = 14 controls	Waldrop scale	An increased prevalence of minor physical anomalies was found in the mentally retarded adults relative to the other groups. There was a non-significant trend for the total mean Waldrop score of the schizophrenic group to be higher than the mean score of the normal group
Lohr and Flynn (1993)	*n* = 118 Sz *n* = 33 mood disorders *n* = 31 controls	Waldrop scale	Sz (but not mood disorders) had more anomalies than controls. Patients with tardive dyskinesia had more MPAs than those without tardive dyskinesia. In Sz, MPAs were unrelated to severity of psychopathology, age of onset, positive/negative symptoms or socio-economic status
Cantor-Graae *et al.* (1994)	*n* = 22 discordant MZ pairs *n* = 10 concordant MZ pairs *n* = 6 control MZ pairs	Waldrop scale plus additional items	Trend for higher total MPA scores in affected vs. non-affected discordant Sz MZ twin. In the overall group, those with pregnancy and birth complications had more MPAs
Green *et al.* (1994)	*n* = 63 Sz *n* = 33 sibs *n* = 26 BAD *n* = 9 sibs *n* = 40 controls	Modified Waldrop scale	Sz had higher MPAs than controls and BAD. Those with Sz pts had higher MPA scores than their sibs; sibs did not differ from controls
McGrath *et al.* (1995)	*n* = 79 Sz *n* = 31 SA *n* = 24 mania *n* = 13 major dep *n* = 8 organic psychosis n-2 other organic psychosis *n* = 63 controls	Modified Waldrop scale	MPAs not associated with any particular psychotic disorder. For white subjects, the Sz group had more MPAs than controls. For males there was a weak association between MPAs and family history of major psychiatric disorder. Those with more MPAs had more admissions and longer admissions. MPAs were not associated with gender, age at onset, negative symptoms, premorbid functioning/intelligence, PBCs and selected CT scan variables

Table 13.1 (cont.)

Reference	Samples	Method	Comment
Lane *et al.* (1997)	$n = 174$ Sz $n = 80$ controls	Modified Waldrop and craniofacial and bodily quantitative measures	Patients had significantly higher MPA scores and displayed multiple anomalies of the craniofacial region with an overall narrowing and elongation of the mid-face and lower face. Twelve craniofacial anomalies independently distinguished patients from controls and these variables correctly classified 95% of patients and 80% of control subjects
Lohr *et al.* (1997)	$n = 15$ Sz onset after 45 + year $n = 8$ Sz onset before 45 years $n = 11$ Alzheimer's $n = 11$ depression $n = 15$ controls		Early and late-onset Sz and unipolar depression had more MPAs than normal comparisons Alzheimer's were no different from well controls
Akabaliev and Sivkov (1998)	$n = 42$ Sz $n = 36$ controls	Waldrop scale	Sz had more anomalies of head (mouth, ears and eyes) than controls. Higher MPA scores were associated with later birth order. No association with age at onset or season of birth
Ismail *et al.* (1998)	$n = 60$ Sz $n = 21$ non-psychotic sibs $n = 75$ controls	Waldrop scale and other MPA items	Higher MPA scores found in Sz and their sibs when compared to controls in all body areas, with Sz having higher scores than sibs. Higher MPA scores shared by patients and their sibs but little similarity in specific anomalies within families. MPAs frequently found in, but not limited to, head region
Griffiths *et al.* (1998)	$n = 32$ Sz (familial) $n = 63$ 1st degree rel (familial) $n = 28$ Sz (sporadic) $n = 44$ 1st degree rel (sporadic) $n = 47$ controls	Weighted Waldrop scale	Compared prevalence of MPAs in familial and sporadic Sz and their 1st degree relatives The Sz group had increased MPAs. More MPAs in sporadic group patients (those without a positive family history of Sz). The group difference was significant for males; trend for females Patients with Sz and a positive family history and the sibling group did not differ from well controls
McGrath *et al.* (2002)	$n = 310$ psychosis $n = 313$ controls	Modified Waldrop scale and craniofacial quantitative measures	Psychosis group had higher MPA total score. The odds of having a psychotic disorder were increased in those with wider skull bases, smaller lower facial heights, protruding ears, and shorter and wider palates. The ratio of skull width/skull length was significantly larger in those with psychotic disorders compared to the well controls. Earlier age of onset was associated with more MPAs and with smaller skull width/length ratios

Sz = schizophrenia, MPA = minor physical anomaly, PBCs = pregnancy and birth complications, BAD = bipolar affective disorder, MZ = monozygotic, sibs = sibling, SA = schizoaffective psychosis, CT = computerized tomography.

Gottesman 1989; Fananas *et al.* 1990; Bracha *et al.* 1991; Mellor 1992; Cannon *et al.* 1994). Fananas *et al.* have been the main contributors to the recent literature on this subject (Fananas *et al.* 1990, 1996a,b; Van Os *et al.* 1997, 2000; Gutierrez *et al.* 1998; Rosa *et al.* 2000a). In their twin studies, qualitative dermatoglyphic features (ridge dissociation and palmar creases) were significantly more likely to be found in the affected cotwin in monozygotic twins discordant for psychosis (Rosa *et al.* 2000b).

In summary, the excess of MPAs and dermatoglyphic abnormalities in schizophrenia provides tantalizing but tangential evidence about the earliest phases of the pathogenesis of schizophrenia. The role of genes and/or teratogens in the production of the MPAs and dermatoglyphic abnormalities may shed light on their parallel role in the orderly development of the brain. However, despite the theoretical association between MPAs and brain development, attempts to link MPAs to adult brain structure and function have been disappointing, with no associations found between MPAs and selected measures derived from computerized tomography (McGrath *et al.* 1995), magnetic resonance spectroscopy (Buckley *et al.* 1994) or hippocampal or ventricle size (McNeil *et al.* 2000). However, Fananas and colleagues (Van Os *et al.* 2000; Rosa *et al.* 2001) have reported a relationship between abnormalities in dermatoglyphics (a-b-ridge count) and ventricular volume as measured on magnetic resonance imaging (MRI) scans.

The search for candidate exposures

Season of birth

One of the most consistently replicated epidemiological features of schizophrenia is the slight excess of births in the late winter and spring in the northern hemisphere; many studies also show a small decrement in births in the late summer–autumn (Bradbury & Miller 1985; Torrey *et al.* 1997). In one of the most impressive studies, which was based on a comprehensive Danish record-linkage study, Mortensen *et al.* (1999) found that the small seasonal excess of schizophrenia births (relative risk = 1.11) was associated with a sizeable (10.5%) population attributable fraction (PAF) for the disorder. The reason for this high PAF is, of course, that birth in late winter–spring is such a common exposure.

While data on the season of birth effect in the northern hemisphere population are quite robust, the same cannot be said for the southern hemisphere. A meta-analysis performed on data from southern hemisphere studies (in Australia, South Africa and the Reunion Islands) did not support a season of birth effect (McGrath & Welham 1999). There have also been some suggestions of a decrease in the magnitude of the season of birth effect over time in the northern hemisphere (Eagles *et al.* 1995; Suvisaari *et al.* 2000).

Explanations proposed for the seasonal effect range from unusual parental procreational habits to a variety of more specific candidate risk-modifying variables. Candidate exposures that have been proposed as underlying the season of birth effect include perinatal viral exposures (Torrey *et al.* 1997) and various nutritional deficiencies.

Place of birth

Several groups have suggested that being born and/or raised in urban regions is associated with an increased risk of developing schizophrenia compared to rural regions (Lewis *et al.* 1992; O'Callaghan *et al.* 1992a; Takei *et al.* 1992). The quality of evidence for place of birth as a risk factor is now more robust following the publication of two major population-based studies: one from Holland (Marcelis *et al.* 1998a) and one from Denmark (Mortensen *et al.* 1999). The relative risk of developing schizophrenia when born in the city vs. being born in the country is about 2.4. However, as urban-birth is relatively frequent, the two studies reported the PAF for this variable to be substantial (about 30%). Place of birth could be a proxy marker for a risk-modifying variable operating at or before birth. However, because most people who are born in a city are also brought up there, it is difficult to disentangle pre- and perinatal effects from those operating later in childhood. Indeed, there is some recent evidence that the more years spent in an urban area during childhood, the greater the risk of developing schizophrenia (Pedersen & Mortensen 2001).

Pregnancy and birth complications

There is considerable evidence that pregnancy and birth complications (PBCs) are detrimental to the health of the developing fetus and, in particular, its neurodevelopment (Low *et al.* 1985; Taylor *et al.* 1985; Paneth & Pinto-Martin 1991). It seems obvious therefore to examine the possible role of PBCs in increasing the risk of later schizophrenia.

A substantial body of research is now available that examines the association between PBCs and schizophrenia. Key details from some of these studies are summarized in Table 13.2. The studies have employed a range of designs (e.g. case–control studies, cohort studies), measures of the exposure (based on maternal recall, records, midwife notes, different scoring systems) and measures of the outcome (diagnosis confirmed on interview, register-based diagnosis). Meta-analyses of these data are now available (Geddes & Lawrie 1995; Verdoux *et al.* 1997; Geddes *et al.* 1999). Overall, there is robust evidence that PBCs have a significant but modest effect in increasing the risk of later schizophrenia (odds ratio of about 2).

Determining exposure status

Many studies have relied upon maternal recall to evaluate PBCs (Pollack *et al.* 1966), and the Lewis–Murray scale (Owen *et al.* 1988) has been widely used for this purpose (McCreadie *et al.* 1992; Marcelis *et al.* 1998b). However, studies that have compared maternal recall and birth records have found discrepancies between the two methods (O'Callaghan *et al.* 1990; Cantor-Graae *et al.* 1998; Buka *et al.* 2000) and there is general agreement that birth records provide a more reliable source of data. The majority of the studies in Table 13.2 have been able to access birth records (which themselves can vary in detail and reliability).

Methods to score PBCs have also been refined in recent years with the development of more detailed operationalized systems (McNeil & Sjostrom 1995) and of scoring systems related to pathological processes such as hypoxia/ischaemia (Zornberg *et al.* 2000). The hope has been that an 'ideal' scoring system may allow the identification of particular types of PBCs related to the risk of schizophrenia. However, it is likely that our ability to fractionate PBCs into pathophysiological domains (e.g. infection, inflammation, hypoxia/ischaemia, undernutrition) does not adequately reflect the complex interconnected nature of events that disturb maternal–fetal homeostasis. Also, traditional items included as PBCs are clearly only a small subset of all teratogens. It seems likely that many exposures that impact on

Table 13.2 The association between pregnancy and birth complications and schizophrenia.

Reference	Samples	Source of PBC information Research design	Conclusions
Pollack *et al.* (1966)	*n* = 33 Sz *n* = 33 well sibs	Maternal recall Case–control study	Non-significant trend for more PBCs in the Sz group
Lane and Albee (1966)	*n* = 52 Sz *n* = 115 well sibs	Birth records Case–control study	The Sz group had significantly lower birth weight and had higher rates of prematurity
Woerner *et al.* (1971)	*n* = 34 Sz *n* = 42 well sibs	Birth records Case–control study	Non-significant trend for lower birth weight in the Sz group
Woerner *et al.* (1973)	*n* = 46 Sz *n* = 37 well sibs *n* = 17 affected sibs	Maternal recall and birth records Case–control study	The Sz group had more PBCs than well sibs
McNeil and Kaij (1978)	*n* = 54 process Sz *n* = 46 Sz-like psychoses *n* = 100 controls	Birth records Case–control study	Process Sz group had more PBCs
Jacobsen and Kinney (1980)	*n* = 63 Sz *n* = 63 controls	Birth records Case–control study	The Sz group had significantly more PBCs
Parnas *et al.* (1982)	*n* = 12 Sz *n* = 25 schizotypal *n* = 55 controls	Birth records Case–control study	The Sz group had more PBCs, the schizotypal group had least PBCs. All subjects had mothers with Sz
Lewis and Murray (1987)	*n* = 955 psychiatric patients	Maternal recall Case–control study	The patients with Sz had more PBCs than other psychiatric patients
Schwarzkopf *et al.* (1989)	*n* = 15 Sz *n* = 6 schizoaffective *n* = 10 BAD	Maternal recall Case–control study	The Sz and schizoaffective groups had significanly more perinatal complications than the bipolar group
Eagles *et al.* (1990)	*n* = 27 Sz *n* = 27 well sibs	Birth records Case–control study	The Sz group had significantly more PBCs than the well sibls
Done *et al.* (1991)	*n* = 57 Sz *n* = 32 affective disorder *n* = 16980 full cohort	Birth records Birth cohort	The Sz group did not have an excess of PBCs, however, the affective psychoses group had decreased length of gestation and increased rates of Vitamin K administration at birth
Foerster *et al.* (1991)	*n* = 45 Sz *n* = 28 affective disorders	Maternal recall Case–control study	The Sz group had significantly more PBCs than the affective group
O'Callaghan *et al.* (1992)	*n* = 65 Sz *n* = 65 controls	Birth records Case–control study	The Sz group, especially males, had an excess of PBCs. Those with PBCs had an earlier age of onset
McCreadie *et al.* (1992)	*n* = 54 Sz *n* = 114 sibs (4 with Sz)	Maternal recall Case–control study	No difference found in levels of PBCs between the groups
Heun and Maier (1993)	*n* = 47 Sz and schizoaffective *n* = 70 sibs	Maternal recall Case–control study	Patients had more often suffered perinatal complications (42%) than their sibs (29%)
Stober *et al.* (1993)	*n* = 80 Sz *n* = 80	Maternal recall Case–control study	Patients had more PBCs compared to well controls as assessed by two different PBC scales
Verdoux and Bourgeois (1993)	*n* = 23 Sz *n* = 23 BAD *n* = 23 controls	Maternal recall Case–control study	The Sz group had significantly more PBCs than the BAD and the well sibs

Table 13.2 (cont.)

Reference	Samples	Source of PBC information Research design	Conclusions
Gunther-Genta *et al.* (1994)	*n* = 23 Sz *n* = 40 well sibs	Birth records Case–control study	The patients with Sz had more frequent umbilical cord complications and atypical presentations, as well as higher scores on a scale measuring PBCs linked to possible neonatal asphyxia
Rifkin *et al.* (1994)	*n* = 110 Sz *n* = 100 controls	Maternal recall Case–control study	The patients with Sz were more likely to have been of lower birth weight. In schizophrenic men, lower birth weight was correlated with poorer premorbid social and cognitive ability, and with impairment in adult cognitive function
Kunugi *et al.* (1996)	*n* = 59 Sz *n* = 31 healthy sibs *n* = 108 well controls	Birth records Case–control study	Female patients with Sz had experienced significantly more perinatal complications than their sibs and controls
Hollister *et al.* (1996)	*n* = 1867 Sz males only	Birth records Case–control study nested within hospital-based cohort	Incidence of Sz significantly higher in the Rh-incompatible group compared with Rh-compatible group
Hultman *et al.* (1997)	*n* = 107 psychotic disorders (82 with Sz) *n* = 214 controls	Birth records Case–control study	Higher total PBC score was associated with Sz A disproportionate birth weight for body length and small head circumference were the strongest independent risk factors for Sz
Jones *et al.* (1998)	*n* = 76 Sz *n* = 11017 total cohort	Birth records Birth cohort	Combination of low birth weight (<2.5 kg) and short gestation (<37 weeks) was more common among the Sz
Marcelis *et al.* (1998)	*n* = 151 psychosis *n* = 100 controls	Maternal recall Case–control study	Familial morbid risk of Sz and related psychosis was not associated with PBCs, where there was a positive association with PBCs and familial morbid risk of affective psychosis
Alvir *et al.* (1999)	*n* = 59 Sz	Birth records Case–control study	A history of PBCs predicted poor response to treatment in the first episode of Sz
Hultman *et al.* (1999)	*n* = 167 Sz *n* = 198 affective psychosis *n* = 292 reactive psychosis *n* = 3285 controls	Birth records Population-based Case–control study	Sz was associated with multiparity and maternal bleeding during the pregnancy. For males, small for gestational age was associated with Sz. Affective psychosis was associated with uterine atony. Reactive psychosis was associated with later birth order
Nicolson *et al.* (1999)	*n* = 36 Sz *n* = 35 sib controls	Interview and birth records Case–control study	No significant differences between case and controls in rates of OCs. Patients with OCs did not have early age of onset of Sz
Gunduz *et al.* (1999)	*n* = 61 Sz *n* = 26 schizoaffective *n* = 28 affective psychosis *n* = 21 controls	Birth records and interview Case–control study	No significant group differences identified

Table 13.2 (cont.)

Reference	Samples	Source of PBC information Research design	Conclusions
Preti *et al.* (2000)	*n* = 44 Sz *n* = 44 controls	Birth records Case–control study	Sz spectrum patients were more likely than controls to have experienced PBCs
Ichiki *et al.* (2000)	*n* = 312 Sz *n* = 517 controls	Birth records Case–control study	Sz have more preterm birth (< 36 weeks), low birth weight, and smaller head circumference than controls
Byrne *et al.* (2000)	*n* = 413 Sz *n* = 413 controls	Birth records Case–control study	No group difference found. Males with early onset Sz had more PBCs compared to their well, matched controls
Eaton *et al.* (2000)	*n* = 132 Sz *n* = 1266 controls	Birth records Case–control study nested within birth cohort	PBCs were associated with Sz, but the relationship of urban birth to Sz was unaffected by adjustment for obstetric complications
Kendell *et al.* (2000)	*n* = 296 Sz probands *n* = 296 controls	Birth records Case–control study nested within birth cohort	No significant association was observed between OCs and Sz probands in 1971–74 birth cohort
Kendell *et al.* (2000)	*n* = 156 Sz probands *n* = 156 controls	Birth records Case–control study nested within birth cohort	Emergency Caesarean section and labour lasting over 12 h were significantly more common in the Sz probands in 1975–78 birth cohort
Schaefer *et al.* (2000)	*n* = 63 Sz *n* = 6570 controls	Birth records Birth cohort	High maternal prepregnant BMI (>30.0), compared to average BMI, was significantly associated with Sz
Brown *et al.* (2000)	*n* = 71 Sz *n* = 7725 controls	Birth records Birth cohort	Second trimester exposure to respiratory infection associated with a significant risk of Sz spectrum disorder
Zornberg *et al.* (2000)	*n* = 693 Sz and non-affective psychoses	Maternal recall and birth records Cohort	There was an elevated, graded and independent risk of Sz and non-affective psychoses association with antecedent hypoxic-ischaemia-related fetal/neonatal complications
Wahlbeck *et al.* (2001)	*n* = 114 Sz or schizoaffective disorder *n* = 7086 total cohort	Birth records Cohort study	Mothers of cases had lower BMI. Cases had lower birth weight, were shorter and had lower placental weight
Rosso *et al.* (2000)	*n* = 80 Sz *n* = 56 sib controls *n* = 26 273 total cohort	Maternal recall and birth records Birth records Case–control study nested within birth cohort	Hypoxia-associated PBCs significantly increased the odds of early onset but not later-onset Sz, after prenatal infection and fetal growth retardation were controlled

Sz = schizophrenia, sibs = siblings, PBCs = pregnancy and birth complications, BAD = bipolar affective disorder, BMI = body mass index.

the very early development of the brain are 'silent' and, as such, are not open to measurement with available technology (Niswander & Kiely 1991).

Specific pregnancy and birth complications

Mindful of these caveats, the majority of studies, using various sources of data and various scoring methods, have supported an association between the presence of PBCs and an increased risk of schizophrenia. The specific PBCs implicated have included low birth weight (Lane & Albee 1966; Woerner *et al.* 1971; Rifkin *et al.* 1994), prematurity and 'small for dates' status (McNeil & Kaij 1978; Jones *et al.* 1998; Ichiki *et al.* 2000), pre-eclampsia (McNeil & Kaij 1978; Dalman *et al.* 1999), prolonged labour (McNeil & Kaij 1978; Kendell *et al.* 2000), asphyxia and hypoxia-related PBCs (McNeil & Kaij 1978;

Rosso *et al.* 2000; Zornberg *et al.* 2000), antepartum haemorrhage (Hultman *et al.* 1997, 1999), rhesus incompatibility (Hollister *et al.* 1996), both high (Jones *et al.* 1998; Schaefer *et al.* 2000) and low (Wahlbeck *et al.* 2001) body mass index (BMI), multiparity (Hultman *et al.* 1999) and fetal distress (O'Callaghan *et al.* 1991a). In an individual-patient meta-analysis including 700 schizophrenia subjects and 835 controls, Geddes *et al.* (1999) reported that there were significant associations between schizophrenia and premature rupture of the membranes, gestational age less than 37 weeks and the use of resuscitation or incubator. There was a trend level association between low birth weight (less than 2500 g) and schizophrenia.

However, not all studies have been positive (Done *et al.* 1991; McCreadie *et al.* 1992; Gunduz *et al.* 1999; Byrne *et al.* 2000; Kendell *et al.* 2000). What are we to make of these apparent contradictions? First, there is wide consensus about the lack of specificity and predictive power of PBCs. Most fetuses exposed to the broad range of PBCs do not develop schizophrenia and most patients with schizophrenia have not had overt PBCs. Goodman (1988) concluded that PBCs (as currently detected) increase the risk of schizophrenia from about 0.6 to only about 1.5% and the individual-patient meta-analysis found very low attributable fractions for the handful of individual PBCs that were significantly associated with schizophrenia (Geddes *et al.* 1999).

Demographic and clinical correlates of pregnancy and birth complications in schizophrenia

It seems that only some PBCs have a risk-increasing effect, and even these are only indirect indicators of likely hazards to the developing brain. In addition, any increased risk may be for a subtype of schizophrenia rather than the whole spectrum of conditions. Thus, a number of studies suggest that PBCs are particularly associated with schizophrenia of severe rather than mild type (McNeil & Kaij 1978), male sex (O'Callaghan *et al.* 1991a) and early onset (Verdoux *et al.* 1997). Rifkin *et al.* (1994) found that low birth weight in male (but not female) schizophrenics was associated with cognitive and social impairment in childhood, and cognitive defects and negative symptoms in adult life. These findings are reminiscent of the evidence that PBCs predict increasing risk of cognitive impairment in the general population (Stewart *et al.* 1999; Seidman *et al.* 2000).

There is no doubt that in the general population of infants and children, exposure to obstetric hazards is associated with an increased risk of brain injury and of resultant neurological and neuropsychological deficits. Furthermore, the anatomical sequelae of the brain injury persist into adolescence. Thus, Stewart *et al.* (1999) noted that over half of the MRI scans of a cohort of adolescents (mean age 15 years) who had been born before 32 weeks were rated as abnormal by neuroradiologists, compared with only 5% of controls. Increased ventricular volume, corpus callosal abnormalities and white matter lesions were particularly common in the preterm adolescents. Subsequent volumetric analysis on the same subjects revealed decrements in whole brain volume, grey matter and hippocampi as well as strikingly increased ventricular volume, findings reminiscent of, but more severe than, those found in schizophrenia (Nosarti *et al.* 2001).

Many studies have therefore attempted to relate obstetric complications to brain structure in patients with schizophrenia. Several groups have reported an association between the presence of PBCs and either enlarged ventricles or wider sulci and fissures (Roberts 1980; Reveley *et al.* 1984; Schulsinger *et al.* 1984; Silverton *et al.* 1985; DeLisi *et al.* 1986; Turner *et al.* 1986; Lewis & Murray 1987; Owen *et al.* 1988; Cannon *et al.* 1989; Pearlson *et al.* 1989; Smith *et al.* 1998; Stefanis *et al.* 1999). These studies included different designs and a range of brain measures, and included high-risk offspring of schizophrenics and twins. On the other hand, many studies have found no association between PBCs and increased ventricular volume in schizophrenia (DeLisi *et al.* 1988; Nimgaonkar *et al.* 1988; Johnstone *et al.* 1989; Kaiya *et al.* 1989; Reddy *et al.* 1990; Nasrallah *et al.* 1991; Harvey *et al.* 1993).

Some studies found that PBCs were more common among individuals with schizophrenia without a family history of the illness (McNeil & Kaij 1978; Lewis & Murray 1987). Against this are reports that PBCs are only of aetiological importance in those individuals who already carry some genetic predisposition to schizophrenia (Schulsinger *et al.* 1987; Cannon 1997). One study reported that the individuals with schizophrenia who had an obvious genetic predisposition were more prone to develop increased ventricular and decreased hippocampal volume in response to obstetric complications (Cannon *et al.* 1989).

Stefanis *et al.* (1999) selected patients with schizophrenia without any family history of the disorder but who had been exposed to PBCs. Those with a history of PBCs had decreased hippocampal volume, especially on the left. McNeil *et al.* (2000) have shown that in monozygotic twins discordant for schizophrenia, the differences in brain structure are largely explained by exposure to delivery complications in the affected twins.

Putative mechanism of action

The direction of causality between PBCs and risk of schizophrenia remains open to question. A century ago, Freud noted that the links between cerebral palsy and birth complications may be the result of pre-existing abnormalities of brain development causing the birth complications (Freud 1897). A pre-existing neural defect can be the cause of PBCs (Nelson & Ellenberg 1986) and, in theory, it is possible that the postulated neurodevelopmental abnormality underlying schizophrenia is directly or indirectly the cause of the increase rates of PBCs. Nevertheless, McNeil and Cantor-Graae (1999) provide arguments against this being the case in schizophrenia.

A common denominator of many PBCs is their ability to produce fetal hypoxia. As with all lesions of the developing brain, the long-term sequelae of hypoxia depend not only on the extent of the damage (the 'dose') but also on the timing of the event. For example, prior to the last few weeks of gestation, the cerebral vasculature is fragile and more sensitive to perturbations of oxygenation. Haemorrhages and secondary ischaemic damage at this stage may result in periventricular leucomalacia, a potential antecedent of ventricular enlargement (Leichty *et al.* 1983). Hypoxia later in gestation can result in more damage to the cortex, especially the hippocampus and subiculum, as well as the more familiar patterns of 'watershed' infarcts seen in adults (Lewis & Owen 1989). In brief, PBCs may impact on the complex temporal and spatial cascade of brain development via a multitude of mechanisms including cell proliferation, cell migration, cell differentiation, synaptic connectivity and apoptosis (see Chapter 17).

There is good evidence that PBCs are associated with an increased risk of schizophrenia, and robust evidence that they are associated with a broad range of adverse neurocognitive outcomes. The links between PBCs and schizophrenia raise the question of whether there may be candidate genes that mediate the brain's vulnerability to hypoxic–ischaemic damage (Cannon 1997). They also indicate the potential value of seeking practical ways to reduce the incidence of PBCs for women with schizophrenia and consequently high-risk fetuses (Barkla & McGrath 2000; McGrath 2000).

Prenatal infection

One possible cause of the late winter–spring excess of schizophrenic births is maternal exposure to winter-borne viruses. Many groups have now examined prenatal exposure to influenza as a candidate risk factor for schizophrenia. A number of studies have suggested that fetuses exposed to the 1957 A2 influenza pandemic during the second trimester have an increased risk of schizophrenia (Mednick *et al.* 1988, 1990a, 1993; O'Callaghan *et al.* 1991b; Fahy *et al.* 1992; Kunugi *et al.* 1992, 1995; McGrath *et al.* 1994; Izumoto *et al.* 1999). Furthermore, the link with influenza exposure has also been found when the relationship between influenza epidemics and schizophrenic births was assessed over several decades (Watson *et al.* 1984). Several of the studies have found an effect for female but not for male schizophrenics (Table 13.3).

While the body of evidence linking influenza epidemics and increased risk of schizophrenia seems impressive, there are also many studies that have not identified an association (Crow *et al.* 1991; Torrey *et al.* 1992; Erlenmeyer-Kimling *et al.* 1994; Selten & Slaets 1994; Susser *et al.* 1994; Takei *et al.* 1995; Cannon *et al.* 1996; Grech *et al.* 1997; Morgan *et al.* 1997; Battle *et al.* 1999; Westergaard *et al.* 1999; Mino *et al.* 2000). How can we reconcile this literature? While animal experiments have improved the biological plausibility of prenatal influenza as a factor impacting on brain development (Fatemi *et al.* 1999, 2000), the lack of consistency across the studies has seriously weakened the case that prenatal exposure to the influenza virus, *per se*, is causally related to schizophrenia (McGrath & Castle 1995). When assessing this literature it is important to recall that most of the studies are ecological (i.e. it is known that the population were exposed to influenza during a certain period, but not specifically that the mothers of people who later developed schizophrenia contracted it). It should also be noted that some of the studies lack adequate power to detect true but small effects.

Schizophrenia births have been found to be increased in association with epidemics of other prenatal infectious agents: diphtheria, measles, varicella and polio (Watson *et al.* 1984; Torrey *et al.* 1988). Prenatal exposure to poliovirus has been associated with increased schizophrenia births in a population-based Finnish study (Suvisaari *et al.* 1999). In a rare study with individual data on maternal antibody levels, an association between rubella and schizophrenia has been found (Brown *et al.* 2000).

In summary, in spite of the inconsistencies in the data, infective agents remain attractive candidate exposures from a public health perspective, because of the potential to avert cases by vaccination.

Prenatal nutrition

There has been considerable interest in recent years in the impact of prenatal nutrition and various adult-onset disorders such as diabetes, cardiovascular disease and hypertension – the so-called 'Barker hypothesis' (Barker 1992). Even in the absence of overt nutritional deficits, supplementing nutrition before and after birth warrants consideration. For example, supplementing folate to women periconceptually is associated with a reduction in the incidence of neural tube defects in their offspring (Scott *et al.* 1994). Recent evidence from a randomized controlled trial of nutritional supplements for preterm infants found not only that cognitive outcomes (measured at age 7 years) were superior in the group allocated the enriched infant formulae, but this group also had less cerebral palsy (Lucas *et al.* 1998). This study suggested that suboptimal nutrition during a critical period of brain growth could impair functional compensation in those sustaining an earlier brain insult.

Because the role of diet in crucial phases of development can have important neurological consequences for the offspring (Stein & Susser 1985), by inference prenatal nutritional deprivation is a biologically plausible risk factor for schizophrenia (Brown *et al.* 1996). While studies of the incidence of schizophrenia in developing nations (where more fetuses are exposed to poor nutrition) do not appear to show higher rates, there remains the possibility that deficits in specific micronutrients may have a role.

Susser *et al.* (1996) identified an increased risk of schizophrenia in the offspring of women who were pregnant during a famine in Holland during World War II. A range of adverse health outcomes have been associated with exposure to this prenatal famine (e.g. neural tube defect and intellectual handicap).

Cannon, T.D., Mednick, S.A. & Parnas, J. (1989) Genetic and perinatal determinants of structural brain deficits in schizophrenia. *Archives of General Psychiatry* **46**, 883–889.

Cannon, M., Byrne, M., Cotter, D. *et al.*. (1994) Further evidence for anomalies in the hand-prints of patients with schizophrenia: a study of secondary creases. *Schizophrenia Research* **13**, 179–184.

Cannon, M., Cotter, D., Coffey, V.P. *et al.* (1996) Prenatal exposure to the 1957 influenza epidemic and adult schizophrenia: a follow-up study. *British Journal of Psychiatry* **168**, 368–371.

Cantor-Graae, E., McNeil, T.F., Torrey, E.F. *et al.* (1994) Link between pregnancy complications and minor physical anomalies in monozygotic twins discordant for schizophrenia. *American Journal of Psychiatry* **151**, 1188–1193.

Cantor-Graae, E., Cardenal, S., Ismail, B. & McNeil, T.F. (1998) Recall of obstetric events by mothers of schizophrenic patients. *Psychological Medicine* **28**, 1239–1243.

Cheverud, J.M., Kohn, L.A., Konigsberg, L.W. & Leigh, S.R. (1992) Effects of fronto-occipital artificial cranial vault modification on the cranial base and face. *American Journal of Physical Anthropology* **88**, 323–345.

Clouston, T.S. (1891) *The Neuroses of Development: the Morison Lectures for 1890*. Oliver & Boyd, Edinburgh.

Coorssen, E.A., Msall, M.E. & Duffy, L.C. (1992) Multiple minor malformations as a marker for prenatal etiology of cerebral palsy. *Developmental Medicine and Child Neurology* **33**, 730–736.

Crow, T.J., Done, D.J. & Johnstone, E.C. (1991) Schizophrenia and influenza. *Lancet* **338**, 116–117.

Dalman, C., Allebeck, P., Cullberg, J., Grunewald, C. & Koster, M. (1999) Obstetric complications and the risk of schizophrenia: a longitudinal study of a national birth cohort. *Archives of General Psychiatry* **56**, 234–240.

DeLisi, L.E., Goldin, L.R., Hamovit, J.R. *et al.* (1986) A family study of the association of increased ventricular size with schizophrenia. *Archives of General Psychiatry* **43**, 148–153.

DeLisi, L.E., Dauphinais, I. & Gershon, E.S. (1988) Perinatal complications and reduced size of brain limbic structures in familial schizophrenia. *Schizophrenia Bulletin* **14**, 185–191.

Done, D.J., Johnstone, E.C., Frith, C.D. *et al.* (1991) Complications of pregnancy and delivery in relation to psychosis in adult life: data from the British perinatal mortality survey sample. *British Medical Journal* **302**, 1576–1580.

Eagles, J.M., Gibson, I., Bremner, M.H. *et al.* (1990) Obstetric complications in DSM-III schizophrenics and their siblings. *Lancet* **335**, 1139–1141.

Eagles, J.M., Hunter, D. & Geddes, J.R. (1995) Gender-specific changes since 1900 in the season-of-birth effect in schizophrenia [see comments]. *British Journal of Psychiatry* **167**, 469–472.

Eaton, W.W., Mortensen, P.B. & Frydenberg, M. (2000) Obstetric factors, urbanization and psychosis. *Schizophr Research* **43**, 117–123.

Engstrom, C., Magnusson, B.C. & Linde, A. (1982) Changes in craniofacial suture metabolism in rats fed a low calcium and vitamin D-deficient diet. *Journal of Anatomy* **134**, 443–458.

Enlow, D.H. (1990) *Facial Growth*, 3rd edn. W.B. Saunders, Philadelphia.

Enlow, D.H. & Bhatt, M.K. (1984) Facial morphology variations associated with headform variations. *Journal of Charles Tweed Foundation* **12**, 21–23.

Erlenmeyer-Kimling, L., Folnegovic, Z., Hrabak-Zerjavic, V. *et al.* (1994) Schizophrenia and prenatal exposure to the 1957, A2 influenza epidemic in Croatia. *American Journal of Psychiatry* **151**, 1496–1498.

Fahy, T.A., Jones, P.B., Sham, P.C. & Murray, R.M. (1992) Schizophrenia in afro-Carribeans in the UK following prenatal exposure to the 1957, A2 influenza epdiemic. *Schizophrenia Research* **6**, 98–99.

Fananas, L., Moral, P. & Bertranpetit, J. (1990) Quantitative dermatogyphics in schizophrenia: study of family history subgroups. *Human Biology* **62**, 421–427.

Fananas, L., Gutierrez, B., Bosch, S., Carandell, F. & Obiols, J.E. (1996a) Presence of dermatoglyphic ridge dissociation in a schizotypy-affected subject in a pair of discordant MZ twins. *Schizophrenia Research* **21**, 125–127.

Fananas, L., Van Os, J., Hoyos, C. *et al.* (1996b) Dermatoglyphic a-b ridge count as a possible marker for developmental disturbance in schizophrenia: replication in two samples. *Schizophrenia Research* **20**, 307–314.

Fatemi, S.H., Emamian, E.S., Kist, D. *et al.* (1999) Defective corticogenesis and reduction in Reelin immunoreactivity in cortex and hippocampus of prenatally infected neonatal mice. *Molecular Psychiatry* **4**, 145–154.

Fatemi, S.H., Cuadra, A.E., El Fakahany, E.E., Sidwell, R.W. & Thuras, P. (2000) Prenatal viral infection causes alterations in nNOS expression in developing mouse brains. *Neuroreport* **11**, 1493–1496.

Foerster, A., Lewis, S., Owen, M. & Murray, R. (1991) Low birth weight and a family history of schizophrenia predict poor premorbid functioning in psychosis. *Schizophrenia Research* **5**, 13–20.

Freud, S. (1897) *Infantile Cerebral Paralysis*. Translated by L.A. Russin, [*Die infantile cerebrallähmung*]. University of Miami Press, Coral Cables.

Geddes, J.R. & Lawrie, S.M. (1995) Obstetric complications and schizophrenia: a meta-analysis. *British Journal of Psychiatry* **167**, 786–793.

Geddes, J.R., Verdoux, H., Takei, N. *et al.* (1999) Schizophrenia and complications of pregnancy and labour: an individual patient data meta-analysis. *Schizophrenia Bulletin* 1999, **25**, 413–423.

Goodman, R. (1988) Are complications of pregnancy and birth causes of schizophrenia? *Developmental Medicine and Child Neurology* **30**, 391–395.

Gothelf, D., Frisch, A., Munitz, H. *et al.* (1999) Clinical characteristics of schizophrenia associated with velocardiofacial syndrome. *Schizophrenia Research* **35**, 105–112.

Grech, A., Takei, N. & Murray, R.M. (1997) Maternal exposure to influenza and paranoid schizophrenia. *Schizophrenia Research* **26**, 121–125.

Green, M.F., Satz, P., Gaier, D.J., Ganzell, S. & Kharabi, F. (1989) Minor physical anomalies in schizophrenia. *Schizophrenia Bulletin* **15**, 91–99.

Green, M.F., Satz, P. & Christenson, C. (1994) Minor physical anomalies in schizophrenia patients, bipolar patients, and their siblings. *Schizophrenia Bulletin* **20**, 433–440.

Griffiths, T.D., Sigmundsson, T., Takei, N. *et al.* (1998) Minor physical anomalies in familial and sporadic schizophrenia: the Maudsley family study. *Journal of Neurology, Neurosurgery and Psychiatry* **64**, 56–60.

Gualtieri, C.T., Adams, A., Shen, C.D. & Loiselle, D. (1982) Minor physical anomalies in alcoholic and schizophrenic adults and hyperactive and autistic children. *American Journal of Psychiatry* **139**, 640–643.

Gunduz, H., Woerner, M.G., Alvir, J.M., Degreef, G. & Lieberman, J.A. (1999) Obstetric complications in schizophrenia, schizoaffective disorder and normal comparison subjects. *Schizophrenia Research* **40**, 237–243.

Gunther-Genta, F., Bovet, P. & Hohlfeld, P. (1994) Obstetric complications and schizophrenia: a case–control study. *British Journal of Psychiatry* **164**, 165–170.

Gutierrez, B., van Os, J., Valles, V. *et al.* (1998) Congenital dermatoglyphic malformations in severe bipolar disorder. *Psychiatry Research* **78**, 133–140.

Guy, J.D., Majorski, L.V., Wallace, C.J. & Guy, M.P. (1983) The incidence of minor physical anomalies in adult male schizophrenics. *Schizophrenia Bulletin* **9**, 571–582.

Hansen, D., Lou, H.C. & Olsen, J. (2000) Serious life events and congenital malformations: a national study with complete follow-up. *Lancet* **356**, 875–880.

Harvey, I., de Boulay, G., Wicks, D. *et al.* (1993) Reduction of cortical volume in schizophrenia on magnetic resonance imaging. *Psychological Medicine* **23**, 591–604.

Heun, R. & Maier, W. (1993) The role of obstetric complications in schizophrenia. *Journal of Nervous and Mental Disease* **181**, 220–226.

Hollister, J.M., Laing, P. & Mednick, S.A. (1996) Rhesus incompatibility as a risk factor for schizophrenia in male adults. *Archives of General Psychiatry* **53**, 19–24.

Hornig, M., Weissenbock, H., Horscroft, N. & Lipkin, W.I. (1999) An infection-based model of neurodevelopmental damage. *Proceedings of the National Academy of Sciences of the USA* **96**, 12102–12107.

Hultman, C.M., Ohman, A., Cnattingius, S., Wieselgren, I.M. & Lindstrom, L.H. (1997) Prenatal and neonatal risk factors for schizophrenia. *British Journal of Psychiatry* **170**, 128–133.

Hultman, C., Sparen, P., Takei, N., Murray, R.M. & Cnattingius, S. (1999) Prenatal and perinatal risk factors for schizophrenia, affective psychosis, and reactive psychosis for early onset: case–control study. *British Medical Journal* **318**, 421–426.

Huttunen, M.O. & Niskanen, P. (1978) Prenatal loss of father and psychiatry disorders. *Archives of General Psychiatry* **35**, 429–431.

Ichiki, M., Kunugi, H., Takei, N. *et al.* (2000) Intra-uterine physical growth in schizophrenia: evidence confirming excess of premature birth. *Psychological Medicine* **30**, 597–604.

Illingworth, R.S. (1979) Why blame the obsetrician? *British Medical Journal* **1**, 797–801.

Ismail, B., Cantor-Graac, E. & McNeil, T.F. (1998) Minor physical anomalies in schizophrenic patients and their siblings. *American Journal of Psychiatry* **155**, 1695–1702.

Ismail, B., Cantor-Graae, E. & McNeil, T.F. (2000) Minor physical anomalies in schizophrenia: cognitive, neurological and other clinical correlates. *Journal of Psychiatrics Research* **34**, 45–56.

Izumoto, Y., Inoue, S. & Yasuda, N. (1999) Schizophrenia and the influenza epidemics of 1957 in Japan. *Biological Psychiatry* **46**, 119–124.

Jacobsen, B. & Kinney, D.K. (1980) Perinatal complications in adopted and non-adopted schizophrenics and their controls: preliminary results. *Acta Psychiatrica Scandinavica* **285** (Suppl.), 337–351.

Johnstone, E.C., Owens, D.G.C., Bydder, G.M. *et al.* (1989) The spectrum of structural brain changes in schizophrenia: age of onset as a predictor of cognitvie and clinical impairments and their correlates. *Psychological Medicine* **19**, 91–103.

Jones, P. & Murray, R.M. (1991) The genetics of schizophrenia is the genetics of neurodevelopment. *British Journal of Psychiatry* **158**, 615–623.

Jones, P.B., Rantakallio, P., Hartikainen, A.L., Isohanni, M. & Sipila, P. (1998) Schizophrenia as a long-term outcome of pregnancy, delivery, and perinatal complications: a 28-year follow-up of the 1966 north Finland general population birth cohort. *American Journal of Psychiatry* **155**, 355–364.

Kaiya, H., Uematsu, M., Ofuji, M. *et al.* (1989) Computerised tomography in schizophrenia: familial versus non-familial forms of illness. *British Journal of Psychiatry* **155**, 444–450.

Kendell, R.E. & Kemp, I.W. (1989) Maternal influenza in the etiology of schizophrenia. *Archives of General Psychiatry* **46**, 878–882.

Kendell, R.E., McInneny, K., Juszczak, E. & Bain, M. (2000) Obstetric complications and schizophrenia: two case–control studies based on structured obstetric records. *British Journal of Psychiatry* **176**, 516–522.

Kraemer, H.C., Kazdin, A.E., Offord, D.R. *et al.* (1997) Coming to terms with the terms of risk. *Archives of General Psychiatry* **54**, 337–343.

Kuller, L.H. (1999) Circular epidemiology [see comments]. *American Journal of Epidemiology* **150**, 897–903.

Kunugi, H., Nanko, S. & Takei, N. (1992) Influenza and schizophrenia in Japan. *British Journal of Psychiatry* **161**, 274–275.

Kunugi, H., Nanko, S., Takei, N. *et al.* (1995) Schizophrenia following *in utero* exposure to the 1957 influenza epidemics in Japan. *American Journal of Psychiatry* **152**, 450–452.

Kunugi, H., Nanko, S., Takei, N. *et al.* (1996) Perinatal complications and schizophrenia: data from the *Maternal and Child Health Handbook* in Japan. *Journal of Nervous and Mental Disease* **184**, 542–546.

Lane, A., Kinsella, A., Murphy, P. *et al.* (1997) The anthropometric assessment of dysmorphic features in schizophrenia as an index of its developmental origins. *Psychological Medicine* **27**, 1155–1164.

Lane, E.A. & Albee, G.W. (1966) Comparative birth weight of schizophrenics and their siblings. *Journal of Psychology* **64**, 227–231.

Leichty, E.A., Gilmore, R.L., Bryson, C.Q. & Bull, J. (1983) Outcome of high risk neonates with ventriculomegaly. *Developmental Medicine and Child Neurology* **25**, 162–168.

Lewis, G., David, A. & Andreasson, S.A.P. (1992) Schizophrenia and city life. *Lancet* **340**, 137–140.

Lewis, S.W. (1989) Congenital risk factors for schizophrenia. *Psychological Medicine* **19**, 5–13.

Lewis, S.W. & Murray, R.M. (1987) Obstetric complications, neurodevelopmental deviance, and risk of schizophrenia. *Journal of Psychiatric Research* **21**, 413–421.

Lewis, S.W., Owen, M.J. & Murray, R.M. (1989) Obstetric complications and schizophrenia: methodology and mechanisms. In: *Schizophrenia: Scientific Progress* (eds S.C. Schulz & C.A. Tamminga), pp. 56–68. Oxford University Press, Oxford.

Lieberman, D.E., Pearson, O.M. & Mowbray, K.M. (2000) Basicranial influence on overall cranial shape. *Journal of Human Evolution* **38**, 291–315.

Lipska, B.K., Jaskiw, G.E. & Weinberger, D.R. (1993) Postpubertal emergence of hyperresponsiveness to stress and to amphetamine after neonatal excitotoxic hippocampal damage: a potential animal model of schizophrenia. *Neuropsychopharmacology* **9**, 67–75.

Lohr, J.B. & Flynn, K. (1993) Minor physical anomalies in schizophrenia and mood disorders. *Schizophrenia Bulletin* **19**, 551–556.

Lohr, J.B., Alder, M., Flynn, K., Harris, M.J. & McAdams, L.A. (1997) Minor physical anomalies in older patients with late-onset schizophrenia, early-onset schizophrenia, depression, and Alzheimer's disease. *American Journal of Geriatrics Psychiatry* **5**, 318–323.

Low, J.A., Galbraith, R.S., Muir, D.W. *et al.* (1985) The contribution of fetal–newborn complications to motor and cognitive deficits. *Developmental Medicine and Child Neurology* **27**, 578–587.

Lucas, A., Morley, R. & Cole, T.J. (1998) Randomised trail of early diet in preterm babies and later intelligence quotient. *British Medical Journal* **317**, 1481–1487.

Lyon, M., Barr, C.E., Cannon, T.D., Mednick, S.A. & Shore, D. (1989) Fetal neurodevelopment and schizophrenia. *Schizophrenia Bulletin* **15**, 149–161.

McCreadie, R.G., Hall, D.J., Berry, I.J. *et al.* (1992) The Nithdale schizophrenia surveys. X. Obstetric complications, family history and abnormal movements. *British Journal of Psychiatry* **161**, 799–805.

McDonald, C., Fearon, P. & Murray, R.M. (1999) Neurodevelopmental hypothesis of schizophrenia 12 years on: data and doubts. In: *Childhood Onset of Adult Psychopathology* (ed. J. Rapopart), pp. 193–220. American Psychiatric Press, Washington.

McGrath, J. (1999) Hypothesis: is low prenatal vitamin D a risk-modifying factor for schizophrenia? *Schizophrenia Research* **40**, 173–177.

McGrath, J. (2000) Universal interventions for the primary prevention of schizophrenia. *Australian and New Zealand Journal of Psychiatry* **34**, 58–64.

McGrath, J. & Castle, D. (1995) Does influenza cause schizophrenia? A five year review. *Australian and New Zealand Journal of Psychiatry* **29**, 23–31.

McGrath, J.J. & Welham, J.L. (1999) Season of birth and schizophrenia: a systematic review and meta-analysis of data from the southern hemisphere. *Schizophrenia Research* **35**, 237–242.

McGrath, J., El-Saadi, O., Grim, V. *et al.* (2002) Minor physical anomalies and quantitative measures of the head and face in psychosis. *Archives of General Psychiatry* **59**, 458–464.

McGrath, J.J., Pemberton, M.R., Welham, J.L. & Murray, R.M. (1994) Schizophrenia and the influenza epidemics of 1954, 1957 and 1959: a southern hemisphere study. *Schizophrenia Research* **14**, 1–8.

McGrath, J.J., Van Os, J., Hoyos, C. *et al.* (1995) Minor physical anomalies in psychoses: associations with clinical and putative aetiological variables. *Schizophrenia Research* **18**, 9–20.

McNeil, T.F. & Cantor-Graae, E. (1999) Does pre-existing abnormality cause labor–delivery complications in fetuses who will develop schizophrenia? *Schizophrenia Bulletin* **25**, 425–435.

McNeil, T.F. & Kaij, L. (1978) Obstetric factors in the development of schizophrenia: complications in the births of preschizophrenics and in reproductions by schizophrenic parents. In: *The Nature of Schizophrenia: New Approaches to Research and Treatment*, 1st edn. (eds L.C. Wynne, R.L. Cromwell & S. Matthysse), pp. 401–429. John Wiley, New York.

McNeil, T.F. & Sjostrom, K. (1995) *The McNeil–Sjostrom Scale for Obstetric Complications*. Department of Psychiatry, Lund University, Malmo.

McNeil, T.F., Blennow, G. & Lundberg, L. (1992) Congenital malformations and structural developmental anomalies in groups at high risk for psychosis. *American Journal of Psychiatry* **149**, 57–61.

McNeil, T.F., Cantor-Graae, E. & Weinberger, D.R. (2000) Relationship of obstetric complications and differences in size of brain structures in monozygotic twin pairs discordant for schizophrenia. *American Journal of Psychiatry* **157**, 203–212.

Mallard, E.C., Rehn, A., Rees, S., Tolcos, M. & Copolov, D. (1999) Ventriculomegaly and reduced hippocampal volume following intrauterine growth-restriction: implications for the aetiology of schizophrenia. *Schizophrenia Research* **40**, 11–21.

Marcelis, M., Navarro-Mateu, F., Murray, R., Selten, J.-P. & Van Os, J. (1998a) Urbanization and psychosis: a study of 1942–78 birth cohorts in the Netherlands. *Psychological Medicine* **28**, 871–879.

Marcelis, M., Van Os, J., Sham, P. *et al.* (1998b) Obstetric complications and familial morbid risk of psychiatric disorders. *American Journal of Medical Genetics* **81**, 29–36.

Markow, T.A. & Gottesman, I.I. (1989) Fluctuating dermatoglyphic asymmetry in psychotic twins. *Psychiatry Research* **29**, 37–43.

Mednick, S.A., Machón, R.A., Huttunen, M.O. & Bonett, D. (1988) Adult schizophrenia following prenatal exposure to an influenza epidemic. *Archives of General Psychiatry* **45**, 189–192.

Mednick, S.A., Machon, R.A., Huttunen, M.O. & Barr, C.E. (1990a) Influenza and schizophrenia: Helsinki vs. Edinburgh. *Archives of General Psychiatry* **47**, 875–878.

Mednick, S.A., Machon, R.A. & Huttunen, M.O. (1990b) An update on the Helsinki Influenza Project. *Archives of General Psychiatry* **47**, 292.

Mednick, S.A., Huttunen, M.O. & Machón, R.A. (1994) Prenatal influenza infections and adult schizophrenia. *Schizophrenia Bulletin* **20**, 263–267.

Mellor, C.S. (1992) Dermatoglyphic evidence of fluctuating asymmetry in schizophrenia [see comments]. *British Journal of Psychiatry* **160**, 467–472.

Mino, Y., Oshima, I., Tsuda, T. & Okagami, K. (2000) No relationship between schizophrenic birth and influenza epidemics in Japan. *Journal of Psychiatric Research* **34**, 133–138.

Morgan, V., Castle, D., Page, A. *et al.* (1997) Influenza epidemics and incidence of schizophrenia, affective disorders and mental retardation in Western Australia: no evidence of a major effect. *Schizophrenia Research* **26**, 25–39.

Morris, M., Cotter, D., Takei, N. *et al.* (1993) An association between schizophrenic births and influenza deaths in Ireland in the years 1921–71. *Schizophrenia Research* **9**, 137.

Mortensen, P.B., Pedersen, C.B., Westergaard, T. *et al.* (1999) Effects of family history and place and season of birth on the risk of schizophrenia. *New England Journal of Medicine* **340**, 603–608.

Murray, R.M. (1994) Neurodevelopmental schizophrenia: the rediscovery of dementia praecox. *British Journal of Psychiatry Supplement* **6–12**.

Murray, R.M. & Fearon, P. (1999) The developmental 'risk factor' model of schizophrenia. *Journal of Psychiatric Research* **33**, 497–499.

Murray, R.M., Lewis, S.W., Owen, M.J. & Foerster, A. (1988) The neurodevelopmental origins of dementia praecox. In: *Schizophrenia: The Major Issues* (eds P. Bebbington & P. McGuffin), pp. 90–106. Heinemann, London.

Nasrallah, H.A., Schwarzkopf, S.B., Olson, S.C. & Coffman, J.A. (1991) Perinatal brain injury and cerebellar vermal lobules I–X in schizophrenia. *Biological Psychiatry* **29**, 567–574.

Nelson, K.B. & Ellenberg, J.H. (1986) Antecendents of cerebral palsy: multivariate analysis of risk. *New England Journal of Medicine* **315**, 81–86.

Nicolson, R., Malaspina, D., Giedd, J.N. *et al.* (1999) Obstetrical complications and childhood-onset schizophrenia. *American Journal of Psychiatry* **156**, 1650–1652.

Nimgaonkar, V.L., Wessely, S. & Murray, R.M. (1988) Prevalence of familiality, obstetric complications, and structural brain damage in schizophrenic patients. *British Journal of Psychiatry* **153**, 191–197.

Niswander, K. & Kiely, R.M. (1991) Intrapartum asphyxia and cerebral palsy. In: *Reproductive and Perinatal Epidemiology*, 1st edn. (ed. M. Kiely), pp. 357–368. CRC Press, Boca Ranton.

Nosarti, C.A.I., Asady, M.H., Rifkin, L., Stewart, A. & Murray, R.M. (2001) Brain abnormalities as measured by magnetic resonance imaging (MRI) in very preterm adolescents: a model for schizophrenia? *Schizophrenia Research* **49**, 162.

O'Callaghan, E., Larkin, C. & Waddington, J.L. (1990) Obstetric complications in schizophrenia and the validity of maternal recall. *Psychological Medicine* **20**, 89–94.

O'Callaghan, E., Larkin, C., Kinsella, A. & Waddington, J.L. (1991a) Familial, obstetric, and other clinical correlates of minor physical anomalies in schizophrenia. *American Journal of Psychiatry* **148**, 479–483.

O'Callaghan, E., Sham, P., Takei, N., Glover, G. & Murray, R.M. (1991b) Schizophrenia after prenatal exposure to 1957, A2 influenza epidemic. *Lancet* **337**, 1248–1250.

O'Callaghan, E., Colgan, K., Cotter, D. *et al.* (1992a) Evidence for confinement of winter birth excess in schizophrenia to those born in cities. *Schizophrenia Research* **6**, 102.

O'Callaghan, E., Gibson, T., Colohan, H.A. *et al.* (1992b) Risk of schizophrenia in adults born after obstetric complications and their associatin with early onset of illness: a controlled study. *British Medical Journal* **305**, 1256–1259.

Owen, M.J., Lewis, S.W. & Murray, R.M. (1988) Obstetric complications and schizophrenia: a computed tomographic study. *Psychological Medicine* **18**, 331–339.

Paneth, N. & Pinto-Martin, J. (1991) The epidemiology of germinal matrix/intraventricular hemorrhage. In: *Reproductive and Perinatal Epidemiology* (ed. M. Kiely), pp. 371–399. CRC Press, Boca Ranton.

Parnas, J., Schulsinger, F., Teasdale, T.W. *et al.* (1982) Perinatal complications and clinical outcome within the schizophrenia spectrum. *British Journal of Psychiatry* **140**, 416–420.

Pearlson, G.D., Kim, W.S., Kubos, K.L. *et al.* (1989) Ventricle–brain ratio; computed tomographic density, and brain area in 50 schizophrenics. *Archives of General Psychiatry* **46**, 690–697.

Pedersen, C.B. & Mortensen, P.B. (2001) Evidence of a dose–response relationship between urbanicity during upbringing and schizophrenia risk. *Archives of General Psychiatry* **58**, 1039–1046.

Pollack, M., Woerner, M.G., Goodman, W. & Greenberg, I.M. (1966) Childhood developmental patterns of hospitalized adult schizophrenic and non-schizophrenic patients and their siblings. *American Journal of Orthopsychiatry* **36**, 510.

Preti, A., Cardascia, L., Zen, T. *et al.* (2000) Risk for obstetric complications and schizophrenia. *Psychiatry Research* **96**, 127–139.

Pulver, A.E. (2000) Search for schizophrenia susceptibility genes. *Biological Psychiatry* **47**, 221–230.

Reddy, R., Mukherjee, S., Schnur, D.B., Chin, J. & Degreef, G. (1990) History of obstetric complications, family history, and CT scan findings in schizophrenic patients. *Schizophrenia Research* **3**, 311–314.

Reveley, A.M., Reveley, M.A. & Murray, R.M. (1984) Cerebral ventricular enlargement in non-genetic schizophrenia: a controlled twin study. *British Journal of Psychiatry* **144**, 89–93.

Rifkin, L., Lewis, S.W., Jones, P.B., Toone, B.K. & Murray, R.M. (1994) Low birth weight and schizophrenia. *Schizophrenia Research* **11**, 94.

Roberts, J. (1980) *The use of the CT scanner in psychiatry*. MPhil thesis, University of London.

Rosa, A., Fananas, L., Marcelis, M. & Van Os, J. (2000a) a-b Ridge count and schizophrenia. *Schizophrenia Research* **46**, 285–286.

Rosa, A., Fananas, L., Bracha, H.S., Torrey, E.F. & Van Os, J. (2000b) Congenital dermatoglyphic malformations and psychosis: a twin study. *American Journal of Psychiatry* **157**, 1511–1513.

Rosa, A., Marcelis, M., Suckling, J. *et al.* (2001) Replication of an association between cerebral and dermatoglyphic abnormalities pointing to a possible early prenatal origin of psychosis. *Schizophrenia Research* **49**, 164.

Rose, G. (1992) *The Strategy of Preventive Medicine*. Oxford University Press, Oxford.

Rosso, I.M., Cannon, T.D., Huttunen, T. *et al.* (2000) Obstetric risk factors for early-onset schizophrenia in a Finnish birth cohort. *American Journal of Psychiatry* **157**, 801–807.

Schaefer, C.A., Brown, A.S., Wyatt, R.J. *et al.* (2000) Maternal prepregnant body mass and risk of schizophrenia in adult offspring. *Schizophrenia Bulletin* **26**, 275–286.

Schulsinger, F., Parnas, J., Petersen, E.T. *et al.* (1984) Cerebral ventricular size in the offspring of schizophrenic mothers: a preliminary study. *Archives of General Psychiatry* **41**, 602–606.

Schulsinger, F., Parnas, J., Mednick, S., Teasdale, T.W. & Schulsinger, H. (1987) Heredity–environment interaction and schizophrenia. *Journal of Psychiatric Research* **21**, 431–436.

Schwarzkopf, S.B., Nasrallah, H.A., Olson, S.C., Coffman, J.A. & McLaughlin, J.A. (1989) Perinatal complications and genetic loading in schizophrenia: preliminary findings. *Psychiatry Research* **27**, 233–239.

Scott, J.M., Weir, D.G., Molloy, A. *et al.* (1994) *Folic Acid Metabolism and Mechanisms of Neural Tube Defects*. John Wiley, West Sussex.

Seidman, L.J., Buka, S.L., Goldstein, J.M. *et al.* (2000) The relationship of prenatal and perinatal complications to cognitive functioning at age 7 in the New England cohorts of the National Collaborative Perinatal Project. *Schizophrenia Bulletin* **26**, 309–321.

Selten, J.P. & Slaets, J.P. (1994) Evidence against maternal influenza as a risk factor for schizophrenia. *British Journal of Psychiatry* **164**, 674–676.

Sham, P.C., O'Callaghan, E., Takei, N. *et al.* (1992) Schizophrenia following prenatal exposure to influenza epidemics between 1939 and 1960 [see comments]. *British Journal of Psychiatry* **160**, 461–466.

Silverton, L., Finello, K.M., Mednick, S.A. & Schulsinger, F. (1985) Low birth weight and ventricular enlargement in a high-risk sample. *Journal of Abnormal Psychology* **94**, 405–409.

Smith, G.N., Kopala, L.C., Lapointe, J.S. *et al.* (1998) Obstetric complications, treatment response and brain morphology in adult-onset and early-onset males with schizophrenia. *Psychological Medicine* **28**, 645–653.

Sperber, G.H. (1989) *Craniofacial Embryology*, 4th edn. Wright, London.

Stefanis, N., Frangou, S., Yakeley, J. *et al.* (1999) Hippocampal volume reduction in schizophrenia: effects of genetic risk and pregnancy and birth complications. *Biological Psychiatry* **46**, 697–702.

Stein, Z. & Susser, M. (1985) Effects of early nutrition on neurological and mental competence in human beings. *Psychological Medicine* **15**, 717–726.

Stewart, A.L., Rifkin, L., Amess, P.N. *et al.* (1999) Brain structure and neurocognitive and behavioural function in adolescents who were born very preterm. *Lancet* **353**, 1653–1657.

Stober, G., Franzek, E. & Beckmann, H. (1993) Pregnancy and labor complications – their significance in the development of schizophrenic psychoses. *Fortschritte der Neurologie-Psychiatrie* **61**, 329–337.

Susser, E., Lin, S.P., Brown, A.S., Lumey, L.H. & Erlenmeyer-Kimling, L. (1994) No relation between risk of schizophrenia and prenatal exposure to influenza in Holland. *American Journal of Psychiatry* **151**, 922–924.

Susser, E., Neugebauer, R., Hoek, H. *et al.* (1996) Schizophrenia after prenatal famine: further evidence. *Archives of General Psychiatry* **53**, 25–31.

Susser, M. (1991) What is a cause and how do we know one? A grammar for pragmatic epidemiology. *American Journal of Epidemiology* **133**, 635–648.

Suvisaari, J., Haukka, J., Tanskanen, A., Hovi, T. & Lonnqvist, J. (1999) Association between prenatal exposure to poliovirus infection and adult schizophrenia. *American Journal of Psychiatry* **156**, 1100–1102.

Suvisaari, J.M., Haukka, J.K., Tanskanen, A.J. & Lonnqvist, J.K. (2000) Decreasing seasonal variation of births in schizophrenia. *Psychological Medicine* **30**, 315–324.

Takei, N., O'Callaghan, E., Sham, P., Glover, G. & Murray, R.M. (1992)

Winter birth excess in schizophrenia: its relationship to place of birth. *Schizophrenia Research* **6**, 102.

Takei, N., Sham, P., O'Callaghan, E., Glover, G. & Murray, R.M. (1994) Prenatal influenza and schizophrenia: is the effect confined to females? *American Journal of Psychiatry* **151**, 117–119.

Takei, N., Van Os, J. & Murray, R.M. (1995) Maternal exposure to influenza and risk of schizophrenia: a 22 year study from the Netherlands. *Journal of Psychiatric Research* **29**, 435–445.

Takei, N., Mortensen, P.B., Klaening, U. *et al.* (1996) Relationship between *in utero* exposure to influenza epidemics and risk of schizophrenia in Denmark. *Biological Psychiatry* **40**, 817–824.

Taylor, D.J., Howie, P.W., Davidson, J., Davidson, D. & Drillien, C.M. (1985) Do pregnancy complications contribute to neurodevelopmental disability? *Lancet* **i**, 713–716.

Torrey, E.F., Rawlings, R. & Waldman, I.N. (1988) Schizophrenic births and viral diseases in two states. *Schizophrenia Research* **1**, 73–77.

Torrey, E.F., Bowler, A.E. & Rawlings, R. (1992) Schizophrenia and the 1957 influenza epidemic. *Schizophrenia Research* **6**, 100.

Torrey, E.F., Miller, J., Rawlings, R. & Yolken, R.H. (1997) Seasonality of births in schizophrenia and bipolar disorder: a review of the literature. *Schizophrenia Research* **28**, 1–38.

Turner, S.W., Toone, B.K. & Brett-Jones, J.R. (1986) Computerised tomographic scan changes in early schizophrenia: preliminary findings. *Psychological Medicine* **16**, 219–225.

Van Os, J., Fananas, L., Cannon, M., Macdonald, A. & Murray, R. (1997) Dermatoglyphic abnormalities in psychosis: a twin study. *Biological Psychiatry* **41**, 624–626.

Van Os, J., Woodruff, P.W., Fananas, L. *et al.* (2000) Association between cerebral structural abnormalities and dermatoglyphic ridge counts in schizophrenia. *Comprehensive Psychiatry* **41**, 380–384.

Verdoux, H. & Bourgeois, M. (1993) A comparative study of obstetric history in schizophrenics, bipolar patients and normal subjects. *Schizophrenia Research* **9**, 67–69.

Verdoux, H., Geddes, J.R., Takei, N. *et al.* (1997) Obstetric complications and age at onset in schizophrenia: an international collaborative meta-analysis of individual patient data [see comments]. *American Journal of Psychiatry* **154**, 1220–1227.

Waddington, J.L., O'Callaghan, E., Buckley, P. *et al.* (1995) Tardive dyskinesia in schizophrenia: relationship to minor physical anomalies, frontal lobe dysfunction and cerebral structure on magnetic resonance imaging. *British Journal of Psychiatry* **167**, 41–44.

Waddington, J.L., Lane, A., Scully, P. *et al.* (1999) Early cerebro-craniofacial dysmorphogenesis in schizophrenia: a lifetime trajectory model from neurodevelopmental basis to 'neuroprogressive' process. *Journal of Psychiatric Research* **33**, 477–489.

Wahlbeck, K., Forsen, T., Osmond, C., Barker, D.J. & Eriksson, J.G. (2001) Association of schizophrenia with low maternal body mass index, small size at birth, and thinness during childhood. *Archives of General Psychiatry* **58**, 48–52.

Waldrop, M.F., Pedersen, F.A. & Bell, R.Q. (1968) Minor physical anomalies and behavior in preschool children. *Child Development* **39**, 391–400.

Watson, C.G., Kucala, T., Tilleskjor, C. & Jacobs, L. (1984a) Schizophrenic birth seasonality in relation to the incidence of infectious diseases and temperature extremes. *Archives of General Psychiatry* **41**, 85–90.

Watson, C.G., Kucala, T., Tilleskjor, C. & Jacobs, L. (1984b) Schizophrenic birth seasonality in relation to the incidence of infectious diseases and temperature extremes. *Archives of General Psychiatry* **41**, 85–90.

Weidenreich, F. (1941) The brain and its role in the phylogenetic transformation of the human skull. *Transactions of the American Philosophical Society,* **31**(5), 321–442.

Weinberger, D.R. (1987) Implications of normal brain development for the pathogenesis of schizophrenia. *Archives of General Psychiatry* **44**, 660–669.

Weinstein, D.D., Diforio, D., Schiffman, J., Walker, E. & Bonsall, R. (1999) Minor physical anomalies, dermatoglyphic asymmetries, and cortisol levels in adolescents with schizotypal personality disorder. *American Journal of Psychiatry* **156**, 617–623.

Westergaard, T., Mortensen, P.B., Pedersen, C.B., Wohlfahrt, J. & Melbye, M. (1999) Exposure to prenatal and childhood infections and the risk of schizophrenia: suggestions from a study of sibship characteristics and influenza prevalence. *Archives of General Psychiatry* **56**, 993–998.

Woerner, M.G., Pollack, M. & Klein, D.F. (1971) Birth weight and length in schizophrenics, personality disorders, and their siblings. *British Journal of Psychiatry* **118**, 461–464.

Woerner, M.G., Pollack, M. & Klein, D.F. (1973) Pregnancy and birth complications in psychiatric patients: a comparison of schizophrenic and personality disorder patients with their siblings. *Acta Psychiatrica Scandinavica* **49**, 712–721.

Zornberg, G.L., Buka, S.L. & Tsuang, M.T. (2000) Hypoxic–ischemia-related fetal/neonatal complications and risk of schizophrenia and other non-affective psychoses: a 19-year longitudinal study. *American Journal of Psychiatry* **157**, 196–202.

14 Genetics and schizophrenia

B. Riley, P.J. Asherson and P. McGuffin

It has long been recognized that schizophrenia runs in families, and there is compelling evidence from family twin and adoption studies that inherited genetic factors are important (McGue & Gottesman 1991). Such evidence and the enormous rate of progress in molecular methods have together led to a great deal of activity over the last 10–15 years, with probably more researchers engaged in genetic studies than at any time in the history of the disorder. However, before discussing molecular genetics – a comparative recent arrival on the scene – it is necessary to review the 'classical' genetic methods of study.

Early family studies

The first systematic family study was published by Rudin in 1916, who found that dementia praecox was more common among the siblings of probands than in the general population. Following this, a large study of over a thousand schizophrenic probands was published by Kallman in 1938, which showed that both siblings and offspring had increased rates of the disorder.

These early workers recognized the need for systematically ascertaining index cases or probands for family studies in order to ensure that the cases were representative of schizophrenia as a whole. In most studies this was done by taking consecutive admissions referred to a clinic. They also recognized that in order to make accurate estimates of the lifetime expectancy or morbid risk to various classes of relatives, they had to take account of the age of those being studied and make appropriate corrections. This is important when considering the status of unaffected relatives, some of whom will be too young to have entered the age of risk, while others who are within the age of risk may develop the disorder in the future. Only those who are beyond the age of risk can be unequivocally classified as unaffected. Lifetime expectancy for a particular class of relatives can therefore be calculated by dividing the number of affecteds by an age-corrected total. The method most often used is Weinberg's shorter method, the denominator being known as the *Bezugsziffer* (BZ), but more complicated approaches include so-called life table methods (Slater & Cowie 1971).

The results of all Western European studies from before the current era of operational diagnostic criteria, looking at the frequency of the disorder among various classes of relatives, has been summarized by Gottesman and Shields (Table 14.1). In order to interpret these data, comparisons must be made with the morbid risk in the general population, which is generally thought to be in the region of 1%. Shields calculated a lifetime risk of 0.86% using the Camberwell Register of all known hospital contacts within a borough of London, while Essen-Moller, who personally studied a small rural population in southern Sweden, found a lifetime risk of 1.39% (Gottesman & Shields 1982).

These studies clearly show that the risk of developing schizophrenia is increased among the relatives of schizophrenic probands, but there are some apparent anomalies. The first is that while the risk to siblings and offspring of a schizophrenic is in the order of 10%, the risk to the parent of a schizophrenic is only about 6%. This finding is likely to be explained by reduced fecundity which follows the development of schizophrenia, because illness among parents of index cases occurs mainly in those who developed the disease after they had children. It has been calculated that if this were taken into account, the risk among parents would be about 11% (Essen-Moller 1955). This decrease in reproduction may also account for the finding in

Table 14.3 Proband-wise concordance for operationally defined schizophrenia.

Reference	Criteria	Monozygotic (MZ)		Dizygotic (DZ)	
		No.	Concordance (%)	No.	Concordance (%)
Farmer *et al.* (1987)	DSM-III	21	48	21	10
Onstad *et al.* (1991)	DSM-IIIR	31	48	28	4

Table 14.4 Twin studies 1996–99 (modified from Cardno & Gottesman 2000).

Authors	Country	Ascertainment	Diagnostic criteria	MZ concordance (%)	DZ concordance (%)	Heritability (%)
Kläning (1996)	Denmark	Population register	ICD-10	7/16 (44)	2/19 (11)	83
Cannon *et al.* (1998)	Finland	Population register	ICD-8/ DSM-IIIR	40/87 (46)	18/195 (9)	
Franzek & Beckmann (1998)	Germany	Hospital admissions	DSM-IIIR	20/31 (65)	7/25 (28)	
Cardno *et al.* (1999a)	UK	Hospital register	DSM-IIIR ICD-10	20/47 (43) 21/50 (42)	0/50 (0) 1/58 (2)	84 83
Tsujita *et al.* (1992)	Japan	Hospital admissions	DSM-IIIR	11/22 (50)	1/7 (14)	
Combined			DSM-IIIR ICD-10	57/114 (50) 28/66 (42.4)	4/97 (4.1) 3/77 (3.9)	88 83

liability, to schizophrenia was about 84% for the DSM-IIIR and 83% for the ICD-10 definition of schizophrenia. Interestingly, the model fitting analyses also suggested the presence of non-additive genetic effects, something that we return to later in the chapter when we consider modes of transmission.

Subsequently, Cardno and Gottesman (2000) combined their own data with those from the four other studies giving a pooled MZ proband-wise concordance of 50% and a DZ concordance of 4.1% for DSM-IIIR schizophrenia. Using ICD-10 criteria, the pooled concordances were 42.4% for MZ and 3.9% for DZ twins. Again model fitting gave very high heritability estimates of 88% for DSM-IIIR criteria and 83% for ICD-10. For both sets of criteria, the remainder of the variance was explained by non-shared environment. That is, shared environmental effects appeared to play no part in causing twin similarity with respect to liability to schizophrenia.

Criticisms of twin studies

Twin studies have been criticized for making the assumption that the environments are equal between members of MZ and DZ twins: MZ twins are more likely to dress alike, have similar interests and be treated in the same way than DZ twins. The argument is that the 'microenvironment' of MZ and DZ twins differs, and this could account for the increased concordance rates among MZ pairs. There is no direct evidence for this hypothesis, while on the other hand there is some evidence against it from data on MZ twins reared apart (MZA). Gottesman and Shields (1982) reviewed all systematic twin studies of schizophrenia and found 12 MZA pairs. Seven (58%) were concordant for the disorder, a rate similar to MZ twins reared together, suggesting that a shared environment contributed little to the development of the disorder.

An alternative hypothesis is that there are other non-genetic factors which occur more commonly between MZ twins. It has been suggested that birth trauma, where the risk is higher in MZ than DZ twins, may predispose to schizophrenia. However, this is unlikely to account for greater MZ than DZ concordance because there is little evidence that twins in general have a higher risk for schizophrenia than other members of the population (Gottesman & Shields 1982). Only one study gave evidence for an increased rate of schizophrenia in twins, and this was found only in DZ pairs, counter to the prediction of the hypothesis above (Kläning 1996).

However, there has been a continued interest in the relationship between the development of schizophrenia, subtle neurological signs and birth trauma. Twins discordant for schizophrenia have been examined for brain abnormalities using computerized tomography (CT) (Reveley *et al.* 1982) and magnetic resonance imaging (MRI) (Suddath *et al.* 1990). These studies show that individuals with schizophrenia have larger cerebral ventricles than their unaffected cotwins. Other studies have examined series of unrelated schizophrenics and show that ventricular enlargement is found in at least a proportion of acute-onset first episode cases (Turner *et al.* 1986). These observations have led some to propose that where there is evidence of such brain changes, schizophrenia is likely to be the result of intrauterine infection, birth complications or other trauma affecting neurodevelopment. Because it is no longer feasible to reject the view that inherited genetic factors are of major importance in the aetiology of schizophrenia, it has been proposed that there are in effect two separate mechanisms: one predominantly genetic and the other predominantly non-genetic (Murray *et al.* 1985). If this were the case, we would expect that at least a proportion of those MZ twins discordant for schizophrenia would have the 'non-genetic' form of schizophrenia. However, the evidence from the study of twins does not support this view. Early evidence was provided by Luxenberger (1928), who showed that the relatives of discordant MZ pairs had an equally high risk for schizophrenia as the relatives of concordant twin pairs. Further evidence was provided by Fischer (1971), and this work has been subsequently expanded and updated by Gottesman and Bertelsen (1989). The results are shown in Table 14.4 and show that in discordant MZ pairs there is an equally high risk among the offspring of the affected as among the offspring of the unaffected cotwin. By contrast, discordant DZ twins show a marked difference in the risks of schizophrenia among the offspring.

Although a smaller but similar study by Kringlen and Cramer (1989) produced less clear-cut results, the data of Gottesman and Bertelsen strongly argue for two important principles. First, non-genetic forms of the disorder (phenocopies), if they exist, are relatively uncommon. Secondly, genotypes which give susceptibility to schizophrenia may not be expressed. As we shall see later, this is important for linkage analysis where genetic parameters must be estimated.

Adoption studies

Adoption studies are also important in distinguishing inherited from non-inherited factors. These studies use various strategies, giving compelling evidence that schizophrenia has an important genetic component.

The first major adoption study was carried out by Heston (1966). He was able to study the adopted-away offspring of 47 schizophrenic mothers and compare them to an age- and sex-matched group of adopted-away offspring of psychiatrically well mothers. The schizophrenic mothers all gave birth within Oregon State mental hospitals at a time when it was the state law that their offspring must be fostered or adopted within 72 h of birth. At the time of the study, the offspring had all entered the age of risk for schizophrenia and Heston, along with two other psychiatrists, made diagnoses blind to the parental diagnosis. Among the offspring of the 47 schizophrenic mothers, five (10.6%; 16% after age correction) were themselves schizophrenic compared with none of the offspring of the psychiatrically well mothers.

Rosenthal *et al.* (1971), using a similar approach, were able to obtain subjects from Danish adoption registrars. This had the advantage over Heston's study that most of the affected parents gave up their children for adoption before their first admissions and about one-third of the affected parents were fathers. This provided safeguards against illness in adoptees being either a result of early contact with an overtly schizophrenic parent, or intrauterine maternal environment. These researchers thought that a variety of conditions, especially 'borderline schizophrenia' and schizoid or paranoid traits, might be biologically similar to more narrowly defined schizophrenia and they used the term 'schizophrenia spectrum disorder' (SSD) to describe this group of disorders. Their initial report found that three of the offspring of schizophrenic parents developed schizophrenia, compared with none of 47 matched controls. When they later extended the study and considered SSD, they found that 13 (18.8%) of 69 adoptees of schizophrenic parents had SSD compared with eight (10.1%) of 79 matched controls.

These researchers were also able to employ a 'cross-fostering' study design (Wender *et al.* 1974). Here, they considered the rate of SSD among the adopted offspring of affected parents, and were able to obtain a sample of 28 individuals whose biological parents were normal but who were adopted by parents one of whom later developed schizophrenia. In this comparison group 10.7% of the offspring were diagnosed as having SSD, a figure very close to that found among the 79 matched controls.

An alternative approach is the 'adoptees family study' design (Kety *et al.* 1976), where the probands are individuals who were adopted in early life and subsequently developed schizophrenia. A comparison is then made between the rate of schizophrenia among the biological and adoptive relatives. It was found that 20.3% of 118 biological parents of adopted-away schizophrenics had SSD, compared with only 5.8% of 224 adoptive parents of schizophrenics and parents of control adoptees.

More recently, the results of Kety's study have been re-examined using more explicit and stricter criteria (Kendler & Gruenberg 1984). This reanalysis served to emphasize the genetic relationship by increasing the separation between the different groups studied. Kendler took DSM-III schizophrenia and DSM-III schizotypal personality disorder as the definition of an affected case and found that 13.3% of 105 biological relatives of adopted-away schizophrenics were affected, compared with only 1.3% of the 224 adoptive parents.

The most recent adoption study was carried out in Finland by Tienari (1991). The author has promised further analyses, combining attempts to incorporate more detailed family environmental measures with genetic analyses, but the results reported so far are in line with previous adoptee studies in showing a lifetime prevalence of 9.4% in the adopted-away offspring of schizophrenic parents and a lifetime prevalence in control adoptees of 1.2%. In addition, this study attempts to measure environmental influences in detail. Interestingly, the preliminary results regarding family environment show a significant association between the genetic predisposition to schizophrenia and psychological abnormalities in adopting parents, a result that, it could be argued, indicates the importance of psychological environmental factors in the aetiology of schizophrenia. This will need to be reconciled, if it is confirmed in more definitive analyses, with the twin model fitting results suggesting no effect of shared environment on twin concordance.

What is the mode of transmission?

It is clear from the preceding discussion that family, twin and adoption studies demonstrate the existence of inherited genetic factors in the aetiology of schizophrenia. However, analyses of families segregating schizophrenia and studies of the risks to various classes of relatives are unable to demonstrate a simple Mendelian mode of transmission. In other words, the pattern of inheritance is complex or irregular and it is not clear whether familial clustering in schizophrenia is brought about by one gene, a few genes or many genes. Attempts to define the mode of transmission are important for two main reasons. First, the knowledge of how many genes are involved and the size of their effect determines the approach taken to their eventual isolation. Secondly, in order to perform linkage analysis, the genetic parameters of penetrance and gene frequency must be defined.

Single gene models

In the simplest models, single genes are considered to be the sole source of genetic influence resulting in resemblance among relatives. These are termed single major locus (SML) models. If this were the situation in schizophrenia, how could we account for the irregular pattern of transmission observed? One possible explanation is variable expressivity. An example of this is tuberous sclerosis in which an affected individual may show occult skin lesions only visible with a Woods lamp, whereas in others a severe condition with multiple skin tumours and systemic involvement can occur. Likewise, it has been suggested that schizophrenia might be a single gene dominant disorder with highly variable expression, ranging from a 'core' syndrome through milder schizoid traits to a range of minor psychological characteristics among relatives (Heston 1970). Another possible explanation for irregular transmission of a single gene disorder is reduced *penetrance*. Penetrance is the degree to which phenotype is determined by genotype. In classical Mendelian disorders, penetrance is close to or equal to 100%. Reduced penetrance implies that less than 100% of people carrying a disease-causing genotype will develop the disease. Indeed, evidence from the study of discordant MZ twin pairs strongly suggests that this is the case, because the risk in offspring of the unaffected cotwin is as high as that in the offspring of the affected twin (see Table 14.4; Gottesman & Bertelsen 1989).

Slater (1958) proposed a gene with intermediate penetrance for schizophrenia with 100% penetrance in homozygotes and 16% penetrance in heterozygotes. This 'intermediate' model, although a poor fit statistically (McGuffin & Owen 1991), in fact turns out to be close to that suggested by the use of more sophisticated computer model fitting (Elston & Campbell 1970).

However, it has been pointed out by James (1971) that attempts to fit a single gene model to data in pairs of relatives may give misleading results because of mathematical underidentification (i.e. there is not enough information to specify all of the parameters that specify the model). This problem can be partly overcome by constraining parameter values to within biologically meaningful limits (i.e. between 0 and 1 for penetrances and gene frequencies). However, on doing this and testing a general SML model on published Western European data, O'Rourke *et al.* (1982) showed that single gene inheritance provided a mathematically unsatisfactory explanation and McGue *et al.* (1985) showed that an SML model could be rejected statistically.

Multifactorial threshold model

Under a polygenic or multifactorial liability/threshold (MFT) model, genetic factors are assumed to be brought about by the additive effect of many genes at different loci. In other words, several or many genes, each of small effect, combine additively with the effects of non-inherited factors to influence liability to schizophrenia. Liability to develop the disorder is considered to be a continuously distributed variable in the population and individuals who develop the disorder are considered to have liability above a threshold value along that continuum (Falconer 1965; Gottesman & Shields 1967).

The MFT model of inheritance can account for the observed risks to different classes of relatives, which appears to decline exponentially as you pass from monozygous twins, to first-, to second- and then to third-degree relatives. This is explained by a reduction in the genetic risk because of a shift of the liability curve with successive generations, as the number of shared genes reduces from 1 to 1/2 to 1/4 to 1/8 and so on. There are several other observations which best fit an MFT model. For example, the risk for schizophrenia in an individual increases with the number of affected relatives and schizophrenia persists in the population despite selective disadvantage (e.g. reduced fecundity) conferred by the condition. Finally, if severity of the condition is related to the degree of liability for the disorder, this would explain the observation that concordance in twins or first-degree relatives increases with severity of the disorder in the proband.

However, it is important to note that although McGue *et al.* (1985) were unable to reject the MFT model statistically, the observed data do not fit this model well. Such comparisons of model and observed data are made with the goodness-of-fit test, which asks how similar observed and predicted patterns of risk are, and assesses the probability that the model is generating the observed data. A P-value of 0.05 in such a test indicates that the observed data would only be generated by the model 5% of the time, and is taken as significant evidence that the model is incorrect. McGue *et al.* found that the observed risks in relatives would only occur 6–7% of the time if the MFT model was the true generating model, very close to the limit of what is conventionally regarded as acceptable. This, together with the more recent twin analysis by Cardno *et al.* (1999a), suggests that the mode of transmission of schizophrenia is more complicated than a purely additive combination of gene effects as dictated by the classic MFT model.

Mixed models

What is now referred to as a 'mixed model' (Morton & MacLean 1974) was first proposed as an explanation for the transmission of schizophrenia by Meehl (1973). He suggested that the expression of a single major gene is modified by interaction or coaction with a number of other genes, each having only a small effect on their own. There have been several studies of the mixed model in schizophrenia (Carter & Chung 1980; Risch & Baron 1984; Vogler *et al.* 1990) where iterative procedures have been used to define the model of 'best fit'. These tests provide some evidence in favour of MFT over SML models, but they have been inconclusive and, while they do not support SML models, they lack power to differentiate mixed vs. MFT models. Perhaps the best evidence against a mixed model comes from recent linkage studies involving large numbers of families (see below), which have failed to find any genes of large effect across the disorder as a whole. It is possible that mixed models (and the major genes they hypothesize) may account for a small minority of families.

Models involving gene or allele interaction effects

The classic polygenic (or multifactorial) model of complex diseases (Falconer 1965) assumes that many genes of small effect simply add together to contribute a liability to disorder. An alternative explanation is that some of the genetic effects are non-additive. The two types of non-additive effects that can occur are allele–allele interaction within a single gene (*dominance*) and interactions between different genes (*epistasis*). In a dominant system, one allele of a gene exerts a stronger effect on the resulting phenotype than the other allele does, and the phenotype of the heterozygote is shifted away from the mean of the two homozygotes. In an epistatic system, different genes, each with their own contribution to liability, have a multiplicative interaction and the total liability from n genes is greater than the sum of the n individual liabilities. Earlier we noted that the twin analyses of Cardno *et al.* (1999a) found non-additive effects in schizophrenia. In fact Cardno *et al.* found evidence suggestive of dominance effects. However, in practice in twin analyses it is difficult to distinguish between epistasis and dominance.

One of the implications of postulating epistasis is that just a few genes, an oligogenic model, could explain all of the differences between the risk of disorder in relatives of schizophrenics and that in the population at large. Risch (1990) defined the quantity λ_R, the ratio of risks in relatives of type R to the population risk. ($\lambda_R - 1$) decreases by a factor of 2 with each degree of kinship for monogenic or additive polygenic traits, and by a factor of more than 2 for polygenic traits with epistasis. The fall-off in concordance rates for a trait in first-, second- and third-degree relatives allows estimation of the number of different genetic loci involved and their interaction type. Data from US schizophrenics and their relatives are most consistent with several epistatically interacting loci (Risch 1990). Basic modelling with minimal assumptions shows that as the number of loci increases, the risk-bearing alleles at those loci become very common in the population, of the order of 14–20% (Riley *et al.* 1997).

Such loci show smaller effects when examined singly than additively interacting ones, because the proportion of total risk associated with a single locus in an epistatic system is less than that for a single locus in an additive system with the same n genes. Such loci must also be biologically related – functionally, temporally or spatially. Epistatic interaction is only possible if the *genotype* (the two *alleles*, or variable forms, of a gene) or *phenotype* (the observable effect of the genotype) from one gene exerts an effect on the genotype or phenotype from another. Modelling such synergistic interaction for hypothesis testing or data analysis is much more complex than modelling additive interaction, because the risk for particular genotypes (the penetrance) at different loci must be defined, and this requires specifying the loci and genotypes, and their contribution a priori. At our current stage in studies of most complex genetic traits, where the individual genes contributing to risk are unknown, this is clearly not possible.

Aetiological heterogeneity

So far it has proven impossible to demonstrate clearly which genetic model is most applicable to schizophrenia (McGue & Gottesman 1991). Furthermore, most studies aimed at defining the mode of inheritance consider schizophrenia as a unitary disorder, whereas in reality there may well be genetic heterogeneity as has now been demonstrated in a number of other common genetic disorders. One of the best examples of this is Alzheimer's disease, in which genes on chromosome 21 (amyloid precursor protein) (Goate *et al.* 1991) and chromosome 14 (Van Broeckhoven *et al.* 1992) have been detected that may be the main determinants of genetically different forms of the disease in individuals from multiply affected families. Interestingly, the illness differs in these 'familial Alzheimer's disease' (FAD) cases from that more commonly found by having an earlier age of onset and more rapidly progressive course. Other common disorders, such as non-insulin-dependent diabetes (NIDDM), coronary artery disease and breast cancer, also display this type of heterogeneity with a small proportion of multiply affected families characterized by early age of onset resulting from a highly penetrant single gene defect.

In schizophrenia there are a number of pedigrees that are highly loaded with affected individuals and have a 'dominant-like' appearance (McGuffin & Owen 1991). It is entirely possible that in these rare families single genes are the sole or main source of resemblance between relatives. The observation that affected individuals from multiply affected families on average show an earlier age of onset than seen in those with schizophrenia among the general population lends some support for the existence of major genes in such families. However, this finding is equally compatible with polygenic inheritance (Walsh *et al.* 1993) or with genetic mechanisms such as *anticipation*.

Much has been written about anticipation and dynamic mutations in schizophrenia. The term anticipation, meaning earlier onset and more severe course in successive generations, now known to be brought about by unstable expanding trinucleotide repeat sequences, was first put forward in the context of 'inherited insanity' (Mott 1910). Some studies have shown evidence for earlier onset and more severe course measured by age of first, and total frequency of, hospitalization in the schizophrenic offspring of schizophrenics (Asherson *et al.* 1994; Bassett & Honer 1994; Chotai *et al.* 1995; Yaw *et al.* 1996; Gorwood *et al.* 1997; Imamura *et al.* 1998; Heiden *et al.* 1999) but these results need to be treated cautiously because of a variety of potential biases originally pointed out by Penrose (Asherson *et al.* 1994).

There may be more than one mutation at a single genetic locus (*allelic heterogeneity*) and different pedigrees may segregate completely different disease genes (*locus heterogeneity*). Furthermore, as single genes are unlikely to account for all cases of schizophrenia, aetiological heterogeneity might exist with different forms resulting from mixed genetic and environmental effects. As we shall see below, the combined results of both modelling and molecular genetic studies seem to be most consistent with aetiological heterogeneity resulting from different subsets (in a patient or family) of a larger pool of predisposing genes (in a population) combined with varying environmental effects.

Linkage and association studies

The two main strategies employed to locate disease genes with DNA markers are positional cloning (linkage analysis) and association studies. In order to understand these methods it is essential to understand the concepts of *crossover* and *recombination* (Fig. 14.1). During meiosis (cell division resulting in the production of eggs or sperm) there is physical exchange of material, or crossover, between the chromosome pairs. Recombination, the occurrence of new chromosomes with alleles at some loci from one of the parental chromosomes and alleles at some loci from the other parental chromosome, is observed genetically and is the result of this crossover. If two genetic loci are on different chromosomes the probability that they are inherited together will be 0.5. This phenomenon of *independent assortment*, as Mendel described it, is also true for two loci far apart on the same chromosome when there is an even chance that they will be separated by crossovers at meiosis. On the other hand, linkage is observed between two loci when they are in such close proximity on the same chromosome that

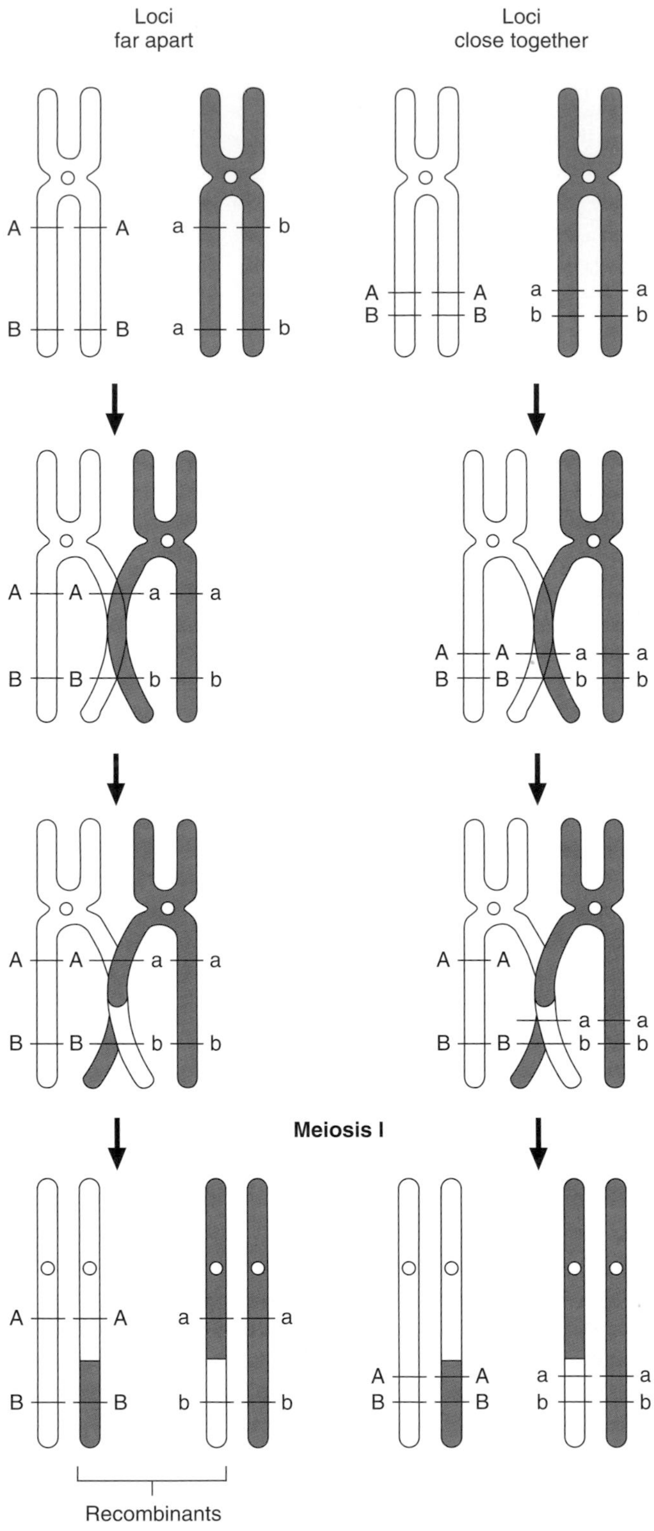

Fig 14.1 Recombination between homologous chromosomes in meiosis. The left diagram illustrates two loci which are far apart on the same chromosome. These loci have an even chance that they will be separated by crossovers at meiosis. On the right, the two loci are close together so they are less likely to recombine.

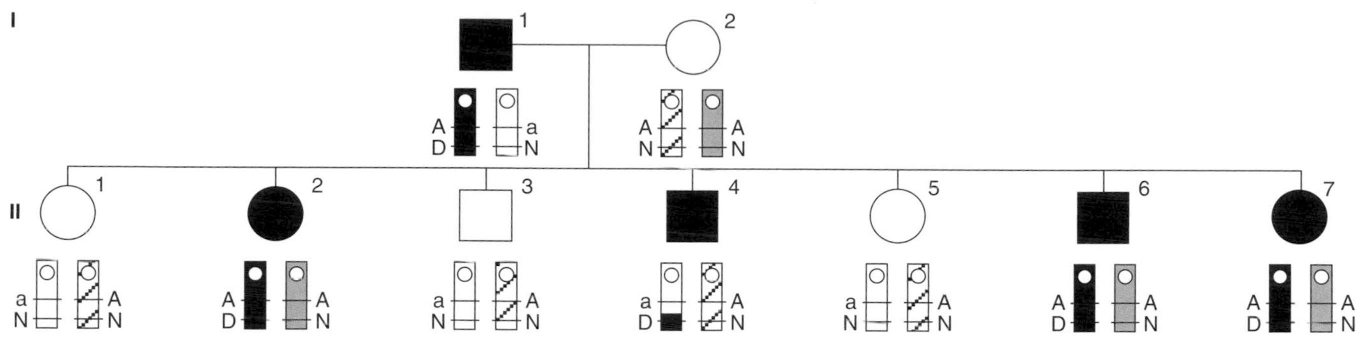

Fig 14.2 Linkage between a disease gene and marker locus close together on the same chromosome. Allele D is a dominantly inherited disease gene, whereas N is the normal allele at the disease locus. A and a are alternative alleles at a marker locus. Individuals indicated by a solid symbol are affected by disease. Among three of the four affected offspring, the disease gene (D) is inherited with the marker allele A. The three unaffected offspring inherit the normal allele (N) along with the marker allele a. These individuals demonstrate linkage between the two loci. However, individual II-4 is a recombinant because D has been inherited along with a; crossover has occurred between the disease locus and marker locus in the paternal meiosis.

their alleles are separated by crossing over less than half the time. In other words there is a departure from the law of independent assortment (see Fig. 14.2).

In linkage analysis, the approximate distance between two linked loci can be estimated by observing the number of individuals within a sibship where recombination has occurred and calculating the recombination fraction θ; i.e. the number of recombinants divided by the total number within the sibship. Thus, $\theta = 1/2$ indicates that there is independent assortment, but where $\theta < 1/2$ the loci are linked. Genetic distance is usually expressed in centimorgans (cM), where 1 cM is equivalent to a 1% chance of recombination between two loci. The most common method of estimating the degree of support for linkage is to calculate log of the odds (LOD) scores, abbreviated as Z, as below.

In practice, the LOD score is plotted for a range of possible values of θ between zero and 0.5. Where the maximum LOD score is obtained provides the maximum likelihood (or best fit) estimate of θ. By convention, for simple Mendelian traits, a LOD score of 3 or more, corresponding to odds favouring linkage of 1000:1 or greater, is taken as acceptable evidence that linkage is present. Linkage analysis also allows for *heterogeneity*, more than one gene producing the same phenotype, provided that within families the gene causing disease is the same one. Here, the likelihood ratio is maximized over two parameters, the recombination fraction, θ, and the proportion of families linked, α, and results from these analyses are referred to as HLODs.

Non-parametric methods, based on testing for deviations from expected allele-sharing distributions, avoid many of the problems (discussed below) of linkage analysis. One alternative approach for detecting linkage is the study of affected sibling pairs (Penrose 1935; Green & Woodrow 1977). This approach is much simpler and is based upon the assumption that two siblings both affected with the same disorder will share one or more susceptibility loci. This method compares the distribution of marker alleles inherited by the affected siblings with that expected under random segregation. Statistical tests then assess whether alleles are shared *identical by state* (IBS) beyond chance expectation. Unlike the LOD score approach, it is not model-dependent and therefore does not require the specification of genetic parameters. A drawback is that large samples are required, especially in the face of genetic heterogeneity, and the method cannot estimate the distance between the disease gene and the marker.

However, because marker alleles are *not* the gene of interest, it is more compelling to see that affected relatives share alleles inherited from the same source *identical by descent* (IBD). Not only siblings, but all classes of relatives have predefined probabilities of sharing zero, one or two marker alleles at a random locus. The most common non-parametric method currently used is the non-parametric linkage (NPL) score, a multipoint IBD approach (Kruglyak *et al.* 1996) that considers all loci simultaneously to examine for excess sharing in affected relative pairs IBD. When the data are fully informative, and often they are not, the method specifies exactly which of the distinct founder alleles each individual has inherited at every point in the linear map of marker loci.

Numerous authors have suggested that linkage tests for complex traits be interpreted relative to the probability of observing results by chance in a complete screen of the genome (Morton 1955; Lander & Kruglyak 1995). Lander and Kruglyak suggest that nominal *P*-values of 0.000049 (for parametric analysis) or 0.000022 (for non-parametric analysis) will be observed by chance in 5% of genome screens, giving an approximate cut-off for 'significance' in linkage studies. This is equivalent to a LOD of 3.3 or an NPL of 3.6, very similar to Morton's original proposal for Mendelian traits. Nominal *P*-values of 0.0017 and 0.00074 will be observed by chance once per genome scan, and they suggest these as cut-offs for 'suggestive' linkage, equivalent to a LOD of 1.9 or an NPL of 2.2. Few linkage studies of schizophrenia have ever produced 'significant' results under these criteria (for an exception see Chromosome 1, below). Even the original report on chromosome 6p from the Irish sample (see Chromosome 6, below), which did achieve this level of significance, would require correction for the numerous models tested.

In contrast, association studies compare the frequencies of marker alleles in a group of affected individuals and a sample of controls without the disease or drawn from the general population. A statistically significant difference suggests either very tight linkage resulting in *linkage disequilibrium* between a marker allele and the disease mutation, or that a marker allele itself confers susceptibility to disease. Linkage disequilibrium refers to the phenomena of two loci being so close together on a chromosome (1 cM apart or less) that they are not separated by recombination over many generations. Alleles at the two loci will therefore appear to be associated, even in individuals from different families. A recent example of this is the population association between a marker near to the insulin gene and IDDM. This finding has led to identification of mutations within the insulin gene, which have a definite role in the aetiology of diabetes.

Linkage studies are more difficult to carry out because they involve the study of multiply affected pedigrees, which are more difficult to collect than the unrelated individuals required for association studies. However, linkage is a powerful technique for locating genes of major effect and a single DNA marker may give information over a large genetic distance. In contrast, association studies are able to identify genes of small effect (Edwards 1965; Nothen *et al.* 1993) if the mutation rates of both the DNA marker and the disease gene are sufficiently low.

DNA markers

Investigators working before DNA markers became readily accessible were restricted to the use of 'classical' genetic markers, such as red blood cell antigens (ABO, MNS and Rhesus) and the human leucocyte antigens (HLA) (McGuffin *et al.* 1992). However, these are limited in number and informativity and unlikely to lead to the eventual location of disease genes. The revolution in molecular genetics, which has resulted in the localization of a host of disease genes, has followed the discovery of techniques for measuring variation within genomic DNA. Variation is common in genomes and methods have been developed to exploit these differences. At loci where variation occurs there will be two or more different sequences or *alleles*, which are inherited in a simple Mendelian fashion and behave as codominant markers. Loci at which two or more of the alleles have frequencies of at least 1% are described as polymorphisms. It is important that marker loci show a high degree of polymorphism because this increases the chance of there being a different allele on each of the parental chromosomes (i.e. the parents are heterozygous at the marker locus). Where the parent is homozygous at a marker locus, the cosegregation of that locus and a putative disease locus cannot be examined, so the meioses are not informative for linkage.

The detection of one class of DNA markers depends on the use of restriction endonucleases (REs), which are enzymes isolated from bacteria that cut DNA according to a specific base sequence; for example, one of these enzymes recognizes and cuts only at the sequence:

GAATTC

CTTAAG.

The specific sequences where REs cut are known as restriction sites. Where variation in base sequence creates or deletes one of these restriction sites, DNA fragments of different lengths are produced known as *restriction fragment length polymorphisms* (RFLPs). The standard method used to detect RFLPs is known as Southern blotting, named after its author E.M. Southern. In this technique, genomic DNA is incubated with the RE. The resulting fragments are then separated according to size on an agarose gel. The DNA is then transferred from the gel to a nylon membrane to produce a long-lasting copy of the DNA fragment pattern. A piece of DNA complementary to the region of the polymorphism is then labelled with the isotope ^{32}P and used as a probe. The probe binds or hybridizes to the fragments on the nylon membrane, to produce a pattern of bands on an autoradiograph.

More recently, it has been found that between restriction sites and within non-coding regions of genomic DNA there are multiple repeats of nucleotide sequences. The number of repeats of the core sequence can be highly variable and are inherited in a Mendelian fashion. Some of these sequences are located only at one locus on a pair of homologous chromosomes – the so-called *variable number of tandem repeats* (VNTR). Most of these VNTR markers are located in the subtelomeric region of the chromosome, so limiting their usefulness in mapping studies.

A subset of VNTR markers consisting of 1–4 base pair (bp) repeat units is one of the most useful tools to genetic mappers, as they are widely distributed throughout the human genome. These units are known as *microsatellites* or *simple sequence repeat* (SSR) polymorphisms. These tandem repeats of di-, tri- or tetranucleotides often show length polymorphism. Generally, the longer the run of perfect repeat units the more polymorphic the marker, and sequences with 12 or fewer repeats are usually not polymorphic. On average, one microsatellite greater than 19 bp in length is found every 6000 base pairs (6 kb).

The most common of these repeat units is the AC repeat, one of which occurs approximately every 30 kb (Weber & May 1989). All SSRs can be analysed relatively simply by amplifying a small segment of DNA that contains the repeat unit and a little sequence on either side. This is only possible using the polymerase chain reaction (PCR), an innovation which has revolutionized molecular biology (Mullis & Faloona 1987). In this technique, the starting material is total genomic DNA which can be extracted easily from whole blood. Two primers are made, which are small stretches of about 20 DNA bases, complementary to sequences flanking the region to be amplified. The total DNA is heated and then cooled, which first separates the usually doubly stranded DNA into single strands and then allows the primers to bind onto their complementary flanking sites. By adding a mixture of precursors for the four DNA bases (2′-deoxyribonucleoside 5′-triphosphates) and a heat-resistant polymerase (usually Taq polymerase), a new strand of DNA is synthesized between the two primers. The process is then repeated many times over, each step doubling the number of double-stranded target molecules, so that a rapid amplification of the target region is achieved. The amplified fragments can then be separated on a gel by electrophoresis so that different length fragments can be identified. The benefits of this method are that very small amounts of DNA are needed initially and it results in the amplification of specified regions. In addition, the method is relatively easy, rapid and can be automated.

It has been calculated that the number of polymorphic AC repeat sequences in the human genome will be around 12 000. Assuming a total genetic length of 3300 cM, these markers would yield genetic maps with average resolution of approximately 0.3–0.5 cM (White & Lalouel 1988).

More recently, the importance of another kind of DNA variation, the single nucleotide polymorphism (SNP), has been recognized. The publication of draft versions of the human genome (Lander *et al.* 2001; Venter *et al.* 2001) has provided an enormous amount of data about the base-by-base variability of the human genome. Some now think that the key step will not be the sequencing of the first human genome, but rather the sequencing of numerous genomes and the identification of the several million base pairs that differ between us (McGuffin *et al.* 2001). As of early 2001, there were 1.65 million non-redundant SNPs deposited in dbSNP, the public SNP database, of which approximately 80% are true polymorphisms (as opposed to errors in the draft genome sequence) and about 50% have frequencies of the rarer allele large enough (20% or greater) to make them useful for fine mapping of genetic loci (Marth *et al.* 2001). Again assuming a map of total length 3300 cM, these numbers would yield a map with average resolution of 0.004 cM (or about 4 kb pairs based on the average figure of ~ 1 megabase per cM).

Problems in linkage analysis

The current emphasis on linkage analysis in schizophrenia research assumes that genes of major effect exist in at least some families. However, we cannot be certain of this and even if major genes contribute to liability in schizophrenia in some multiply affected families, it seems likely that the most common mode of transmission is either polygenic or oligogenic. In addition, to carry out linkage analysis, penetrance values and frequency of the disease gene must be specified. Failure to specify them accurately reduces the power to detect linkage leading to false-negative findings (Clerget-Darpoux *et al.* 1986; Ott 1991). There are also the uncertainties concerning aetiological heterogeneity. Interpretation of positive LOD scores under these circumstances is very difficult (Ott 1991) and, as we shall see, even seemingly very high LOD scores found in a schizophrenia linkage study have turned out to be false-positive results. On the other hand, it is equally difficult to interpret negative results, which can only exclude regions of the genome assuming specific genetic models. Additionally, it has been shown recently that even with large numbers of families, chance variation in the location estimate (essentially the chromosomal position) of a LOD score is significant, making both positioning of results from individual studies and interpretation of replication studies difficult and unreliable (Roberts *et al.* 1999).

There are substantial problems with the linkage analysis of complex traits, whether undertaken by parametric or non-parametric means. Classical genetic illnesses are assumed to have a single faulty gene, located at a single place on a chromosome. Because these illnesses are rare, the rare risk allele must segregate from parents with a family history into affected offspring, or arise as an even rarer *de novo* mutation. By following the segregation of marker alleles from the affected lineage into offspring, chromosome regions in which affected offspring inherit one marker allele and unaffected offspring the other can be identified. Likelihood-based tests can be maximized over one or more parameters, so the focus is often the relative likelihood of one parameter value compared with another, expressed as a likelihood ratio. In LOD score analyses, the likelihood ratio is maximized over θ, the rate of recombination, which increases with the physical distance between loci. More than one gene can produce the same phenotype, and LOD score analyses which allow for aetiological heterogeneity are maximized over both θ and the proportion of families linked to a given locus, α.

Recombination in the search for disease genes is an *apparent* event between real genetic marker alleles and the conceptual alleles 'affected' and 'unaffected'. In real terms, what is being examined is whether affected members of a family share one of the two possible alleles they can inherit and unaffected members the other. Differences between affected individuals or similarities between an affected and an unaffected individual appear in the calculation as recombinations, increasing θ artificially. This can be partly overcome by treating all unaffected relatives as unknown, the *affected only* analysis, but this leaves several problems just in considering the affected members of a family.

First, in a disease with multiple common inputs, no two individuals (even in the same family) need to share input from any individual gene (because there are many genes) or from one particular lineage (because the risk alleles at all these genes are relatively common). Secondly, this will increase apparent recombination, even in affected-only analyses, inflating the apparent distance between marker and disease and making accurate positioning of a putative gene impossible. Thirdly, it will unavoidably decrease the magnitude of the statistic: because the LOD score is the log of a ratio, as the value of θ increases toward 0.5, the value of the ratio decreases towards 1, and that of the statistic decreases towards 0.

The inescapable conclusion is that while parametric linkage analysis is extremely powerful for monogenic traits, much of its power is lost in complex traits. Multipoint parametric linkage analysis, a powerful tool for defining regions of the genome which *do not* contain the single gene responsible for a monogenic trait, has been shown to be statistically invalid for polygenic traits (Risch & Giuffra 1992).

The non-parametric IBD method is also not ideal, however, because the high population frequency of risk alleles and the apparently large number of predisposing genes means that risk alleles may be inherited from different parents or in different genes. Additionally, two different groups have shown that when data are not fully informative, the NPL test is overly conservative (Davis & Weeks 1997; Kong & Cox 1997).

These problems may at first sight seem to preclude the successful application of linkage analysis to schizophrenia. However, we have also seen that this disorder can occur in large pedigrees with multiple affected members, and these may be segregating single disease genes with more regular modes of transmission. These loaded families are atypical, and the resulting Mendelian appearance can be misleading (Sturt & McGuffin 1985), but no bias with respect to detection of linkage should be introduced (Ott 1991).

Broadly, there are two approaches to searching for major genes conferring liability to schizophrenia. The first is to try to focus on a specific region or locus which appears promising. Several clues, such as cytogenetic abnormalities or other genetic disorders co-occurring with schizophrenia, as well as targeting genes which are a priori good candidates (i.e. search for proteins which might plausibly be involved in aetiology), have been followed up by investigators and these will be described later. However, the issue of whether or not major genes for schizophrenia exist within these families may only be resolved following a second approach, which is to perform a systematic screening of the entire genome in a large sample of multiply affected families. Because the genome spans a genetic distance of approximately 3000 cM and each DNA marker should be informative for 10 cM either side of itself, most genome screens use a total of 300 markers evenly spaced throughout the genome. Although an enormous undertaking, this is a common study design. Studies using 3000 markers, for a resolution of 1 cM, have also been undertaken. The development of maps of highly informative SSR markers throughout the genome and the use of automated PCR technology now makes this entirely possible (Dib *et al.* 1996).

The possibility of genome-wide searches for linkage disequilibrium has been proposed in the past (McGuffin *et al.* 1992) but this has usually been dismissed as unfeasible. Recent advances encourage greater optimism; testing every gene in the genome for association may ultimately be more practical than a linkage approach (Risch & Merikangas 1996). For example, a locus with genotype relative risk (GRR) of 1.5 would require 950–2200 trios (parents and one affected child) or 500–900 sib pairs for detection, compared with a sample size of 18 000–68 000 families required to detect linkage. However, not every gene in the genome is yet known or characterized, so this approach is not yet practicable. High-density high-throughput mapping may be available soon using methods that detect single nucleotide polymorphisms on microarrays. Other methods using DNA pooling are already being employed in attempts to screen whole chromosomes for linkage disequilibrium with complex traits (Fisher *et al.* 1999; Hill *et al.* 1999). The most important realization is that, even for allelic association studies, the necessary sample sizes are far larger than has previously been thought.

Linkage studies in schizophrenia

Early linkage studies, before DNA markers became available, used classical markers. Studies with HLA showed promise when a maximum LOD score of 2.57 was obtained at a recombination fraction of 0.15 between a broadly defined phenotype 'schizotaxia' (similar to Kety's schizophrenia spectrum disease) and HLA (Turner 1979). The analysis assumed an autosomal dominant mode of transmission. However, these findings were not replicated by a further four linkage studies and a 'model free' sib-pair analysis which showed substantial evidence against linkage. Studies with other classical markers have not provided evidence of linkage. Such early attempts must now, with hindsight, be viewed as optimistic. Indeed, taken together the linkage results using classical markers could at best scan about 6% of the genome (McGuffin & Sturt 1986; Owen & McGuffin 1991).

The major change that occurred in the 1980s and 1990s was the discovery of a new generations of DNA markers and the construction of more detailed and complete linkage maps. There have subsequently been many studies using DNA markers. Indeed, linkage analysis has, over the past decade and a half, been one of the most intensive areas of research in schizophrenia. Despite the high volume of activity, discerning a signal or signals among the noise has proven very difficult (Riley & McGuffin 2000). Here we review the findings in the main regions of interest which have been implicated in more than one study.

Chromosome 5

The segregation of a chromosomal abnormality such as a translocation or deletion with the disorder may provide clues to the localization of disease genes. This is because the altered segment of chromosome may contain a disrupted gene (the disruption of which is pathogenic) or because the disease gene is nearby and in linkage with the chromosomal lesion. In 1988, Bassett *et al.* reported a Canadian family of oriental origin in which a young man who was schizophrenic and his schizophrenic uncle both had a partial trisomy of the long (q) arm of chromosome 5 resulting from an unbalanced translocation. In one of the first linkage studies of schizophrenia ever undertaken, data from seven families of UK and Icelandic origin gave a LOD of 6.49 using a very broad definition at marker p105–599Ha on chromosome 5q11–q13 (Sherrington *et al.* 1988). Numerous replication studies failed to support this finding and a combined reanalysis of published data effectively ruled out straightforward linkage heterogeneity (Aschauer *et al.* 1990; Crowe *et al.* 1991; Campion *et al.* 1992a). Follow-up and reanalysis of the original 'linked' pedigrees, using more informative markers, have confirmed that the original results were falsely positive (Kalsi *et al.* 1999).

Errors can be easily introduced by mistyping individuals, transferring incorrect genotype data onto computer files and lack of strict blindness between investigators carrying out marker analysis and those making clinical diagnosis. There are many other problems which beset the study of complex disorders such as unknown mode of inheritance, late age of onset and variable expressivity and uncertainties in diagnosis. To overcome these problems, multiple tests using a range of parameters are often employed. In the study of Sherrington *et al.* this process may have acted to falsely inflate the LOD score, although it has been suggested that this alone could not have generated LOD scores of the size observed (McGuffin *et al.* 1990; J. Ott, personal communication).

Two groups have subsequently found suggestive evidence of linkage on chromosome 5q22–q31 in a region that appears distinct from either of those in the earlier study. Data from the western Irish sample gave an HLOD of 3.04 in this region (Straub *et al.* 1997b). Results were positive (although of variable magnitude) across the entire set of 14 markers spanning 45 cM of this region. Markers in the same region gave positive results first in a sample of 14 families from Germany, with a LOD of 1.8, and then in a sample of 44 families from Germany and Israel (including four from the first sample), with a marker 2 cM away, also with a LOD of 1.8. This value dropped to 1.27 when the four families common to both samples were removed. Sib pair analyses of the 44 family sample gave evidence for excess allele sharing across a region of 8 cM from D5S666 to D5S658 which includes the markers IL9 and D5S393. Excess allele sharing peaked at 61.5% ($P < 0.005$) for marker D5S399 (Schwab *et al.* 1997). The second multicentre collaborative study did not find additional support for this region (Levinson *et al.* 2000).

Chromosome 22q

Several reports from independent samples initially suggested that loci at chromosome 22q12–q13.1 might be linked to susceptibility to schizophrenia, with the result that this small chromosome has been one of the most intensively studied for putative schizophrenia susceptibility genes. Early results in a genome screen of families from the USA gave a LOD of 1.54 for 22q13, which increased to 2.82 after maximizing the LOD score over several parameters (Pulver *et al.* 1994b). The strongest results came from allele sharing analysis and gave a *P*-value of 0.009 (Lasseter *et al.* 1995). In an independent sample of US families, first round genome screen data produced a LOD of 1.45 and further analyses of these families with a dense map of markers across the region yielded a LOD of 2.09 (Coon *et al.* 1994).

A collaboration involving four centres, and containing 256 pedigrees from Europe and the USA, examined three loci on 22q12–q13 and found negative LODs across this set, both in the total and the individual samples (Pulver *et al.* 1994a). A large collaborative study using non-parametric analysis on the combined samples of 11 different groups found 252 alleles shared vs. 188 not shared ($\chi^2 = 9.31$, $P = 0.001$) at one locus in the 292 complete sib pairs available (Gill *et al.* 1996). However, using the relationship between excess proportion of alleles shared IBD and the parameters of a single locus model (Suarez *et al.* 1978), the authors conclude that it is likely to be responsible for no more than 2% of the total variance in liability for schizophrenia. Further reports, split evenly between positive and negative results for the region, have continued to appear, both direct replication attempts and data from other genome screens (Kalsi *et al.* 1995a; Vallada *et al.* 1995; Riley *et al.* 1996a; Straub *et al.* 1997a; Hallmayer *et al.* 1998; Levinson *et al.* 1998; Shaw *et al.* 1998).

Velocardiofacial syndrome (VCFS, including DiGeorge's syndrome) is associated with haploinsufficiency of genes at chromosome 22q11 because of submicroscopic deletions (Kelly *et al.* 1993), and it was noted that early linkage results for schizophrenia were near this region (Pulver *et al.* 1994b). Ten per cent of VCFS patients present with a psychotic phenotype (Shprintzen *et al.* 1992). This region also contains the gene for catechol-O-methyl transferase (*COMT*) located at 22q11, which has been suggested (Dunham *et al.* 1992) to be involved in the psychiatric symptoms observed in VCFS, and which is known to be functionally as well as genetically polymorphic (Weinshilboum & Raymond 1977). In studies of VCFS patients, rates of schizophrenia or schizoaffective disorder from 25% to 29% have been found (Pulver *et al.* 1994c; Murphy & Owen 1997). Numerous studies of polymorphisms in this gene have been performed with mixed results. Although most studies of the *COMT* gene have tested for association with the low activity allele, a recent report suggests that the high activity allele, through its increased capacity for the catabolism of dopamine and specifically via this increased catabolism in the prefrontal cortex, may slightly increase the risk of schizophrenia (Egan *et al.* 2001).

Chromosome 8p

Data from one of the two studies which first suggested linkage to chromosome 22q also showed very significant excess allele sharing and small positive LOD scores on chromosome 8p22–p21 (Pulver *et al.* 1995). Across a region of 10 cM containing six markers, affected sib-pair analysis gave *P*-values of between 0.00004 and 0.0097. Parametric analysis yielded LOD scores between 2.2 and 2.35, depending on the model in affected pedigree members only. The Schizophrenia Linkage Collaborative Group study found an HLOD of 2.22 in the independent samples only, and 3.06 when the original families were included (Levinson *et al.* 1996). Allele sharing was higher in the original families alone at 70.4% shared (multipoint maximum likelihood score (MLS) = 2.90, $P = 0.0002$) than in the replication samples (54.1%, MLS = 1.58, $P = 0.005$) or the combined data (55.3%, MLS = 2.73, $P = 0.0003$). This analysis method is similar to the NPL test, but is an earlier version (Kruglyak & Lander 1995). Preliminary data from a denser map of markers in the original sample showed an HLOD of 5.12 with 58% of families linked and an NPL of 3.73, $P = 0.00014$, close to the end of the original region of interest in this sample (Dombroski *et al.* 1997). Data from an independent sample gave a LOD of 3.49, but this decreased to 2.13 in a multipoint analysis (Brzustowicz *et al.* 1999).

Chromosome 6p

Analyses of a 265 family cohort from western Ireland found a maximum HLOD score of 3.51 with 15% of families linked (Straub *et al.* 1995). To date, six independent reports of analyses of this region of 6p have been published. Three of these (Gurling *et al.* 1995; Mowry *et al.* 1995; Riley *et al.* 1996b) found strongly negative LOD scores in the region which become very weakly positive only at large values of Θ, and three (Antonarakis *et al.* 1995; Moises *et al.* 1995; Schwab *et al.* 1995) supported the original finding. The Schizophrenia Linkage Collaborative Group study, which contained data from most of the samples above, examined the region 6p24–p22 and found some support for a susceptibility locus in this region. Across the set of markers tested, allele sharing (again using the multipoint maximum likelihood method) of 55.9% and an MLS of 2.19, $P = 0.001$, was found at in the replication sample only, and MLS = 2.68, $P = 0.0004$ in the replication sample plus the Irish families (Levinson *et al.* 1996). It is also of interest to note that eye tracking dysfunction, a widely used secondary phenotype for schizophrenia, has been mapped to chromosome 6p although at a fairly large distance (approximately 30 cM) from the peak in the Irish data (Arolt *et al.* 1996).

McGuffin and Sturt (1986) reviewed linkage and association results from the 'premolecular' era of classical genetic markers. The most consistent result was an association with the histocompatibilty allele *HLA-A9*, found in seven out of nine studies, but this finding was complicated in a number of ways. Positive results were found only for paranoid subtypes of schizophrenia and there was no overall support from linkage studies (McGuffin *et al.* 1983). Recent studies, while not ruling out a role for HLA, have tended to focus on other components of the HLA complex and on potential mediating mechanisms such as susceptibility to viral infections *in utero* (Wright *et al.* 1998). The findings are nevertheless of some interest in view of the results on chromosome 6p.

Chromosome 10p

Another independent genome screen of 43 US families of European descent gave suggestive evidence on chromosome 10p15–q21 (Faraone *et al.* 1998). Across a set of nine markers, NPL scores were consistently above 2.0 (P-values < 0.03), with a peak of 3.36 ($P = 0.0004$). Data from the western Irish (Straub *et al.* 1998) and German and Israeli (Schwab *et al.* 1998) samples supported linkage of schizophrenia to this same region. These results were unusual and particularly exciting because of the close agreement in location shown by different samples using different diagnostic and analytical approaches. A second multicentre collaborative study found rather modest support for linkage to this region with significant evidence for heterogeneity between samples (Levinson *et al.* 2000).

Chromosome 6q

A sample of 53 US families of mixed ethnicity containing a total of 81 affected sib pairs provided evidence for a susceptibility locus on chromosome 6q21–q22.3 (Cao *et al.* 1997). This study is unique in that a second independent sample of families held by the same researchers was used to replicate the finding internally. In the first sample, excess allele sharing among affected siblings at one locus was 69% IBD sharing ($P = 0.00024$). In the replication data set, 69 families containing 109 affected sib pairs gave maximum IBD allele sharing between 62% ($P = 0.0009$) and 64% ($P = 0.0004$) across a set of three markers. A total of seven markers spanning approximately 3.5 cM gave sharing between 55% and 65%, and P-values < 0.04. A follow-up study by the same group found positive but less significant maxima using a third independent sample, with 62% IBD sharing ($P = 0.022$) (Martinez *et al.* 1999). Combining the data from both replication samples, the interval between two of the markers used previously gave a LOD of 3.82 and IBD sharing of 63.8% ($P = 0.000014$). Data from the African American pedigrees in the National Institute of Mental Health/Millenium schizophrenia genome screen also provided support for these findings (Kaufmann *et al.* 1998). The second multicentre collaborative study found support for linkage to this region with empirical P-values of < 0.002 with the original sample included and 0.004 without it, again with significant evidence for heterogeneity between samples (Levinson *et al.* 2000). A recent study found further evidence for linkage in this region in a very large Swedish pedigree (Lindholm *et al.* 2001).

Chromosome 13q

Data from a mixed sample of 11 UK and two Japanese families initially suggested the possibility of a schizophrenia susceptibility locus on chromosome 13q14.1–q32 (Lin *et al.* 1995), already an area of interest because of the presence of the 5-HT_{2A} receptor gene (Williams *et al.* 1997). Preliminary data from two other groups gave some initial support (Antonarakis *et al.* 1996; Kalsi *et al.* 1996). A further study by the original group using an independent sample of 34 Taiwanese and 10 UK families yielded negative LOD sores over most of the region, except for a single marker which gave a LOD of 1.06 (Lin *et al.* 1997). However, when data from both samples were combined and families of European and Asian origin were analysed separately, the European pedigrees gave an HLOD of 1.41 at one locus with 100% of families suggesting involvement and 1.54 at a second 30% of families linked. A multipoint model free (MFLOD) analysis (Curtis & Sham 1995) of the European sample yielded a LOD of 2.58 around two markers located at 13q32. Positive scores were found around these two markers, but they were separated by a region where the values of both statistics dropped almost to zero. Other studies have been mixed, with two supporting this region (Blouin *et al.* 1998; Shaw *et al.* 1998), two giving weak positive results (Straub *et al.* 1997a; Riley *et al.* 1998) and two giving negative data (Jensen *et al.* 1998; Barden *et al.* 1999). Recently, three point analyses using pairs of adjacent markers in a sample of 21 narrowly defined Canadian pedigrees gave an HLOD of 4.42 with 65% of families linked at marker D13S793 (Brzustowicz *et al.* 1999). The second multicentre collaborative study did not find additional support for this region (Levinson *et al.* 2000).

Chromosome 15q13–q14

The first evidence for a possible chromosome 15 schizophrenia susceptibility locus was the report of linkage of the p50 sensory gating deficit (an evoked potential abnormality which is common in schizophrenics and relatively rare in controls, and which segregates as a single gene trait in families) to chromosome 15q13–q14 (Freedman *et al.* 1997). In nine US families, a marker within the $\alpha7$ nicotinic cholinergic receptor subunit gene (*CHRNA7*) gave a LOD of 5.3 when tested against the sensory gating phenotype, and 1.33 when tested against schizophrenia. This gene is an attractive candidate because of the high incidence of smoking in schizophrenics (De Leon *et al.* 1995), because both nicotine (Adler *et al.* 1993) and clozapine (Nagamoto *et al.* 1996) ameliorate the sensory gating deficit, and because the secondary phenotype common in schizophrenics is strongly linked to this region.

Data from South African Bantu families in a dense map of markers at 1 cM intervals around this gene showed some evidence in support of this finding, with positive NPL results across the entire map (Riley *et al.* 2000). Analyses by the original group in an independent sample showed 58% IBD allele sharing ($P < 0.0024$) at D15S1360 (Leonard *et al.* 1998). Two studies have failed to find any evidence for involvement of this locus in five families from eastern Canada (Neves-Pereira *et al.* 1998) and 54 families from the Maryland sample (Curtis *et al.* 1999).

Chromosome 18

Initial interest in chromosome 18 began with several reports of the co-occurrence of psychiatric disorders and chromosomal anomalies (Bassett 1992; Calzolari *et al.* 1996; Mors *et al.* 1997), and was strengthened by the initial report of linkage between this chromosome and bipolar disorder (BP) (Berrettini *et al.* 1997). Data from chromosome 18 in schizophrenic families comes partly from the inclusion of data from all chromosomes in whole genome screens, and partly from replication attempts, because of the possible overlap between BP and schizophrenia. Two initial replication attempts following the putative BP linkage gave no evidence of linkage between schizophrenia and chromosome 18 (DeLisi *et al.* 1995; Fang *et al.* 1995). In contrast, data from the families in the German/Israeli sample gave a LOD of 3.1 when both schizophrenics and affective disorder cases were included in the analysis, and using the schizophrenics alone (Wildenauer *et al.* 1997). Transmission disequilibrium studies of the 124 base pair (bp) allele in a polymorphism in the α subunit gene of the olfactory G-protein (GOLF) showed 41 transmitted and 13 non-transmitted ($P = 0.0007$) considering schizophrenia and schizoaffective disorder, and 45 transmitted and 13 non-transmitted ($P = 0.00012$) when the affective disorder cases were included.

Chromosome 1q

Interest in chromosome 1 in schizophrenia began with reports of a balanced 1:11 translocation segregating with serious mental illness in a large pedigree from Scotland (St Clair *et al.* 1990), although this region was not studied in the same intensive manner as the region around the chromosome 11 breakpoint, which contains the dopamine D_2 receptor gene (*DRD2*). Numerous studies of the chromosome 11 region were undertaken and gave no evidence for linkage in other family samples (Gill *et al.* 1993; Su *et al.* 1993; Zhe Wu *et al.* 1993; Kalsi *et al.* 1995c; Mulcrone *et al.* 1995). The chromosome 1 breakpoint lies at 1q42.1, and two groups had reported preliminary suggestive linkage findings in this region. A three-stage genome screen of a population isolate from Finland gave a LOD of 3.82 in this region in the dense-mapping third stage of the genome screen (Hovatta *et al.* 1999). Another sample also gave some preliminary evidence for this region, with an NPLZ of 1.39, $P = 0.084$, at D1S304 (1q44) (Blouin *et al.* 1998). Recently, two genes directly disrupted by the translocation were cloned (Millar *et al.* 2000a,b) although their function remains to be described in detail. It seems likely that the effect of the translocation, and the disruption of surrounding genes, is specific to this large pedigree and not a common susceptibility factor in schizophrenia, but the characterization of the disrupted genes may identify sequences or gene families relevant to more common psychoses, and the linkage evidence may suggest other variants in these genes which predispose to schizophrenia. In one of the most significant reported findings ever seen in linkage studies of schizophrenia, a third group found a LOD score of 5.79 in a different region at chromosome 1q22 (Brzustowicz *et al.* 2000).

X chromosome

The X chromosome was initially hypothesized as a potential source of genetic liability because of the well documented differences between the sexes for various aspects of schizophrenia, including higher concordance in same sex twin pairs, age of onset (which is generally lower in males) and the greater risk if a female, rather than a male, relative is affected (reviewed by Crow 1988). A pseudoautosomal locus for a schizophrenia susceptibility gene that would account for these differences was suggested (Crow *et al.* 1989). An early study using sib-pair analysis reported evidence of excess sharing at DXYS14 (Collinge *et al.* 1991), which was supported in one non-parametric replication (D'Amato *et al.* 1992), but was not supported by a number of other studies using both parametric and non-parametric analyses (Asherson *et al.* 1992; Wang *et al.* 1993; Barr *et al.* 1994; Crow *et al.* 1994; Kalsi *et al.* 1995b; Maier *et al.* 1995).

A large collaborative study examining markers within band

Xp11 near the *MAO* loci found a LOD of 1.97 under a dominant model for DXS7 in a set of 92 sib pairs selected for maternal inheritance. In a second analysis, 34 families not selected for inheritance pattern gave a LOD of 2.16 at *MAOB* under a dominant model (Dann *et al.* 1997). Results from a number of recent genome screens have suggested a possible X chromosome locus, but these results are of weaker magnitude than the most positive loci in these studies (Paterson *et al.* 1999).

Other chromosomal regions

Other reports have implicated numerous other chromosomes: chromosome 2, based on a balanced 2:18 translocation (Maziade *et al.* 1993) and supported by some linkage evidence (Aschauer *et al.* 1993; Coon *et al.* 1998; Levinson *et al.* 1998; Shaw *et al.* 1998), although this was spread over an enormous region of approximately 100 cM of chromosome 2, from 2p22–q21; chromosome 4 (Kaufmann *et al.* 1998; Hovatta *et al.* 1999); chromosome 5p (Silverman *et al.* 1996; Garver *et al.* 1998); chromosome 7 (Blouin *et al.* 1998); chromosome 9, in two different locations, one centromeric (Moises *et al.* 1995; Levinson *et al.* 1998; Hovatta *et al.* 1999), and one at the telomere of the p-arm (Riley *et al.* 1997; Kaufmann *et al.* 1998).

Overall, the collected data from linkage studies of schizophrenia are not in good agreement about the involvement of any region. This is likely to be a result of the small GRR associated with any individual gene contributing to susceptibility to schizophrenia. The numbers of families required to detect linkage vs. association depend strongly on both the GRR and the population frequency of the risk allele, which is likely to be relatively high for schizophrenia susceptibility loci (Risch & Merikangas 1996). If GRR for a particular genotype is 4 and the allele frequency in the population is between 10% and 50%, then the number of families required is roughly 200–300, a large but just about practical sample size. However, if the GRR is 2 (and the frequency is in the same range) then the number of families increases to 2500–5400. If the GRR drops to 1.5, the number of families increases to 18 000–68 000, which is clearly not practical. GRR can be converted into the relative risk measure most widely used currently: λ_s (Scott *et al.* 1997). If GRR is < 2, λ_s is < 1.3. The data for schizophrenia are most compatible with several genes all having λ_s less than 2 (Risch 1990), and the sample sizes currently held appear to be inadequate to generate unequivocal results.

Results are also often of lesser magnitude when new data are added to the sample, as in the collaborative replication study of chromosomes 3, 6 and 8 (Levinson *et al.* 1996). The simplest interpretation of these differences is random variation in the inputs to the disease found in any given sample. Simulation studies suggest that in a polygenic disease, initial positive findings may be difficult to replicate, and require much larger samples than the original, because detection of linkage with any one of several susceptibility loci is always more probable than replication of just one specific locus (Suarez *et al.* 1995).

It has become clear over the last 10 years that mutations in the coding sequence of genes are not the only way to produce illness. Much of what we currently know about complex trait genetics comes from the study of insulin-dependent diabetes mellitus (IDDM). In genome-wide studies, affected sib pairs share alleles IBD significantly more often than expected by chance at numerous loci. After the HLA region on chromosome 6 (responsible for the autoimmune destruction of the pancreatic β cells), the locus with the greatest degree of excess sharing was the insulin gene on chromosome 11 (Davies *et al.* 1994). This locus had long shown association with IDDM (Bell *et al.* 1984) but had been excluded from linkage using parametric analysis (Hitman *et al.* 1985; Ferns *et al.* 1986; Elbein *et al.* 1988; Donald *et al.* 1989). Further, the effect at the insulin gene is now known to be a quantitative one. A VNTR polymorphism lies between the promoter and the start of the first exon (Bell *et al.* 1982), and IDDM susceptibility at this locus is determined by this VNTR (Bennett *et al.* 1995). Transcription of the insulin gene (and thus insulin expression) is regulated by alleles of this VNTR (Kennedy *et al.* 1995), and *all* alleles of this variable DNA region are within the range of normal variation.

Association studies

While linkage analysis enables the detection of genes of major effect, it will not detect genes of small effect contributing in an additive or interactive way with other genes or with genes plus environment. However, genes of minor effect have been successfully isolated in a number of other complex genetic disorders, such as the transforming growth factor α (TGF-α) gene in cleft lip and palate (Holder *et al.* 1992), the glucokinase and glycogen synthase genes in NIDDM (Chiu *et al.* 1993) and IDDM (Bell *et al.* 1984) and the myelin basic protein gene in multiple sclerosis (Tienari *et al.* 1992), using association methods.

Association studies in schizophrenia using DNA markers have unfortunately thrown up a number of contradictory results. This has been in part because of the problems of diagnosis and the question of comparability of patient populations from different centres. However, the major confounding factor in these studies is the selection of controls which can result in so-called stratification effects. The problem is that there may be a section of the population in which a particular marker and a certain disorder are common without there being any causal relationship. For example, HLA BW16 is more common in Ashkenazi Jews, so that an excess of Jewish patients in an affected sample could lead to the false conclusion that an association exists between the disorder and that antigen. A recent solution to this problem is to compare the frequencies of the parental alleles not inherited by an affected individual with the alleles that are inherited, thus providing a perfectly matched internal control in the *transmission disequilibrium test* (TDT) (Falk & Rubinstein 1987). The samples for this approach are, however, less easy to collect than those for traditional association studies.

Another problem is the statistical handling of results. Because the prior probability of obtaining a true association is extremely remote, the conventional level of statistical significance ($P < 0.05$) is probably not sufficiently stringent. In addition, account must be made of the use of multiple markers in these studies. A conservative correction is to multiply the obtained P-value by the number of markers tested.

The task of carrying out a systematic search for association throughout the entire genome would involve the use of a very large series of markers, each showing linkage disequilibrium with its neighbours. While this is at present an impossibly large amount of work, it is likely to become increasingly feasible as automated technology is developed. For the moment, the best strategy is probably to focus upon markers that are close to or within candidate genes.

An alternative to the use of DNA markers resulting from variations in non-coding sequences in the vicinity of candidate genes is the study of sequence *variations that affect protein structure or expression* (VAPSEs) (Sobell *et al.* 1992) and to look for these gene mutations directly among schizophrenic probands. This has the advantage that a VAPSE disease association is not affected by recombination and directly identifies the pathogenic mutation. On the other hand, if the VAPSE is not the pathogenic mutation itself, it may well be very close to a mutation within the same gene that is pathogenic or in linkage disequilibrium with a mutation in a nearby gene. The problem here is that we understand little about the pathophysiology of schizophrenia and plausible candidate genes are few and far between.

Association studies in schizophrenia

Early association studies in schizophrenia used classical markers such as the ABO and other blood groups and the HLA system. The results of these studies are inconsistent but when considered overall no clear evidence for association has been found (McGuffin & Sturt 1986). The main reasons for this, multiple testing and stratification, are discussed above.

An interesting finding was of association between a subtype of schizophrenia (paranoid schizophrenia) and HLA A9 in seven out of nine studies. Combining the data and applying a correction for multiple testing gave a P-value of 0.0003 (McGuffin & Sturt 1986). However, several conflicting findings have been found. Two groups found A9 to be decreased in paranoid schizophrenia compared with controls (Miyanaga *et al.* 1984; Rudduck 1984), while others using samples from the same countries found A9 to be increased (Eberhard *et al.* 1975; Asaka *et al.* 1981). A9 consists of two subspecificities: AW23 and AW24. Two studies suggested an association with AW23 (Crowe *et al.* 1979; Asaka *et al.* 1981), while others found a stronger relationship with AW24 (Ivanyi *et al.* 1983). More recently, a study found no association between paranoid schizophrenia and either AW23 or AW24 (Alexander *et al.* 1990). Another recent study of 33 pedigrees collected in France failed to find evidence of linkage between HLA and the schizophrenic phenotype (Campion *et al.* 1992b). In addition, they performed an association study using pooled data from six independent studies and were unable to show a significant excess of HLA A9 in the affected group, but they did not subdivide their sample into paranoid vs. hebephrenic subforms.

Disturbances in dopamine neurotransmission and dopamine receptors have long been postulated to underlie schizophrenia and genes coding for dopamine receptors have been targeted as candidates. Until recently, two types of dopamine receptor had been identified, known as D_1 and D_2, which differ from each other functionally, with D_1 suppressing adenylate cyclase and D_2 stimulating adenylate cyclase. However, recent work in this field has identified a further three dopamine receptor genes known as D_3, D_4 and D_5 (Sunahara *et al.* 1990; Van Tol *et al.* 1991; Sokoloff *et al.* 1992). D_3 and D_4 have a similar structure to D_2 and bind D_2-selective ligands, while D_5 is similar in structure to D_1. It was thought that the therapeutic effects of antipsychotic drugs are related to their high affinity for D_2 receptors, and this view has been revised to include D_3 and D_4.

The D_3 receptor may be of particular interest because its expression is restricted to limbic regions implicated in schizophrenia. Furthermore, expression of D_3 in brain is, unlike D_1 and D_2, increased by both typical and atypical neuroleptics (Buckland *et al.* 1993; see below). The gene for this receptor has been localized to the long arm of chromosome 3 (Le Coniat *et al.* 1991) and contains a polymorphic site in its coding region which gives rise to a glycine to serine substitution and results in a restriction site for the enzyme BalI (Lannfelt *et al.* 1992). Study of this polymorphism is an example of the VAPSE approach in a candidate gene.

Initially, two independent groups from Wales and France carried out studies of this polymorphism in the dopamine D_3-receptor gene in samples of patients with DSM-IIIR schizophrenia and normal controls (Crocq *et al.* 1992). In both studies, more patients than controls were homozygotes of either type ($P = 0.005$, $P = 0.008$). Pooling of the data gave a highly significant result ($P = 0.0001$) with a relative risk of schizophrenia in homozygotes of 2.61 (95% confidence intervals 1.60–4.26). There have subsequently been many attempts to replicate this finding with variable and, to an extent, controversial results. There is little doubt that some of the 'negative' studies (in common with many allegedly negative association results) have simply not had enough power to detect the originally reported effect. Williams *et al.* (1998) have performed a meta-analysis of over 30 case–control studies and observed an odds ratio of 1.21 for the association between schizophrenia and homozygosity at the BalI D_3 polymorphism, which, although a smaller effect than that originally reported, was highly significant. There was no evidence of publishing bias (preferential publishing of positive results). The same authors also undertook a family-based association analysis using TDT, which guards against spurious positive results arising from recently mixed populations, a phenomenon called population stratification (McGuffin *et al.* 1994b). The TDT also showed a significant excess of homozygotes among schizophrenics.

Another potentially interesting candidate gene is the serotonin receptor 5-HT_{2A} gene. The 5-HT_{2A} receptor is one of the sites of action of 'atypical' neuroleptics and a multicentre

European study (Williams *et al.* 1996) found a significant excess of the 2 allele of a polymorphism 5-HT_{2A} T102C in the first exon or coding region of the gene among schizophrenics compared with controls. Again, other groups reported both replications and failure to replicate. Williams *et al.* (1997) performed a meta-analysis combining the findings on nearly 200 patients and a similar number of controls. The odds ratio once more turned out to be small but the result was of a highly significant association and no suggestion of distortion by publication bias.

Numerous other candidate genes, based either on biochemistry or location near linkage signals, have been investigated for allele or genotype association with schizophrenia. Many of these have had an initial report of association with no positive replications. For example, porphobilinogen deaminase (*PBGD*) was of interest briefly because of its location on chromosome 11. Several polymorphisms were identified within this gene, and an initial report (Sanders *et al.* 1993) suggested strong association between schizophrenia and one of these markers. In seeking to replicate this finding, Owen *et al.* (1992) found no evidence for allelic association between the PBGD gene and schizophrenia.

Phospholipase A2 (*PLA2*) is a key enzyme in the metabolism of phospholipids. PLA2 is enriched in neuronal membranes and has an essential role in the functioning of membrane structures in the brain. A disordered phospholipid metabolism has been postulated in schizophrenia (Gattaz *et al.* 1990), and there is evidence for increased PLA2 activity in schizophrenic cases (Noponen *et al.* 1993; Gattaz *et al.* 1995). Two reports show association between marker alleles in this gene and schizophrenia (Hudson *et al.* 1996; Peet *et al.* 1998), while three do not (Price *et al.* 1997; Strauss *et al.* 1999; Frieboes *et al.* 2001).

Markers in the *NOTCH4* gene, located on chromosome 6p in the major histocompatibility (MHC) region, gave a *P*-value of 0.000036 for a single marker and 0.0000078 for a two-marker haplotype in a recent report (Wei & Hemmings 2000). This level of significance suggests an odds ratio of 2.7 conferred by the associated alleles, which would correspond to a large population-attributable risk, and a major locus for schizophrenia susceptibility (Sklar *et al.* 2001). Replication studies of this locus in three independent family samples and a case–control sample of diverse ethnic origin (Sklar *et al.* 2001), a Scottish population-based case–control sample (McGinnis *et al.* 2001) and a Japanese case–control sample (Ujike *et al.* 2001) failed to show any evidence for the association.

Earlier we discussed the controversy surrounding the idea that anticipation occurs in schizophrenia and mentioned that in several other diseases involving the nervous system that are more simply transmitted via single genes the phenomenon of anticipation is now known to have a molecular basis. This is the result of unstable or dynamic mutations involving trinucleotide repeat sequences that can increase in length over generations. Examples include Huntington's disease, mytonic dystrophy and fragile X mental retardation. Could such mechanisms also occur in more complex polygenic or oligogenic systems such as those involved in schizophrenia? *Repeat expansion detection* (RED) analysis allows a search for trinucleotide expansion occurring anywhere in the genome and, applied to schizophrenia, has provided evidence of larger repeats *somewhere* in the genomes of schizophrenics than controls (Schalling *et al.* 1993). Where that *somewhere* might be is still unknown but one candidate is a gene that codes for a calcium gated ion channel called *hKCa3* (Bowen *et al.* 1998). There is some evidence that long trinucleotide repeats in *hKCa3* are particularly associated with negative symptoms of schizophrenia (Cardno *et al.* 1999b).

Molecular neurobiology

Molecular techniques have also resulted in major advances to our understanding of neurobiology, much of which may be of relevance in schizophrenia. For example, the cloning of five separate dopamine receptor genes along with genes coding for enzymes and other proteins involved in dopaminergic transmission has opened up new approaches to examining hypotheses involving the dopamine system.

The expression of these genes can be studied in animals exposed to antipsychotic drugs in order to examine the mechanisms involved in their therapeutic action. Buckland *et al.* (1993) have studied the effect in rat brain of chronic treatment (32 days) with the 'atypical' antipsychotics sulpiride and clozapine. They demonstrated that dopamine D_3 receptor messenger ribonucleic acid (mRNA) levels increased by fourfold, whereas no effect was observed on the mRNA levels encoding D_1 or D_2 receptors, or tyrosine hydroxylase. They postulate that D_3 receptor mRNA may be associated with the therapeutic action of antipsychotic drugs. These results contrast with other studies which have shown increases in both D_2 and D_3 mRNA with 'typical' neuroleptics such as chlorpromazine and haloperidol.

A different approach is to look for variations within these genes that may be associated with drug responsiveness. Of recent interest has been the drug clozapine, which is widely reported to reduce symptoms of schizophrenia that are unresponsive to other antipsychotic medication (McKenna & Bailey 1993). However, some patients remain unresponsive to clozapine and it has been suggested that response to this drug may be related to variation of the D_4 receptor. This view arises from the observations that clozapine has a particularly high affinity for D_4 receptors and that the D_4 receptor shows a high degree of variation (Van Tol *et al.* 1992). Clozapine and other 'atypical' antipsychotics also tend to show a high affinity for 5-HT_{2A} receptors and it is of interest that treatment response may be predicted by genetic profiling, i.e. genotyping patients over a number of polymorphisms in genes encoding serotonergic and dopaminergic receptors (Arranz *et al.* 2000).

Genetic counselling

At present, it is not possible to determine the specific risk that a particular individual will develop schizophrenia. Because of the complex mode of inheritance and variable expressivity of the disorder, the only reasonable information to provide to relatives regarding recurrence risks of the disorder in other family members is based upon the empirical data from family studies. Probably the most useful figures are those provided by Gottesman (1991) based upon a compilation of results from many Western European studies (see Table 14.1). Despite this there is a definite role for counselling based upon an informed and responsible approach (McGuffin *et al.* 1994a).

There is now considerable experience in genetic counselling and the principal approaches are the same regardless of the disorder in question. Most counsellors take a non-directive educational approach (Harper *et al.* 1988). The aim is to impart accurate information and help the counsellee to fully understand the risks and potential burdens so that they can make an informed decision. It is important to emphasize that it is the counsellee who must make the ultimate decisions.

Most of those who seek counselling are concerned about the potential risks to their children or, if they are an unaffected relative, about their own chances of developing the disorder. At present the only information that is useful to impart comes from empirical sources (i.e. family, twin and adoption studies). For example, a couple planning a family, one of whom has a parent with schizophrenia, would be informed that the average risk to each of their children is about 3% or three times that in the general population. In some rare cases the counsellee may come from a family which has multiple affected members and gives the appearance of Mendelian transmission. However, in our current state of knowledge it would be wrong to assume that this is the case because these loaded families would also be expected to exist as a result of multifactorial/polygenic inheritance. In these families the risks to relatives appear to increase in relation to the number of affected family members and decrease in relation to the number of well family members (Gottesman 1991).

Empirical data also tell us that schizophrenia is in most, if not all, cases, a complex disease with both inherited and non-inherited causative factors. In schizophrenia the nature of these non-inherited factors remains controversial (McGuffin *et al.* 1995) and some, such as exposure of the fetus to viral infections, are not easily avoided. On the other hand, it would be useful to advise relatives of patients with schizophrenia to avoid the 'experimental' use of drugs such as LSD, PCP, cocaine and amphetamine, because they may be especially vulnerable to drug-precipitated psychoses as a result of high genetic loading.

In the future, advances in our understanding of the molecular basis of schizophrenia may allow the use of prenatal and presymptomatic testing. The complexity of this disorder suggests that in most cases it will not be possible to attain high levels of predictive certainty, but there may be rare families that show true single gene inheritance and here accurate testing is a realistic possibility. The issues are best exemplified by work with relatives and patients from families with Huntington's disease. Until recently, risk calculations in this disorder relied upon DNA marker testing involving the genotyping of individuals in several generations, although the identification of the disease causing mutation (Huntington's Disease Collaborative Research Group 1993) makes a specific test in individuals possible. Predictive testing is usually carried out in specialist centres with expert counselling. Counsellees are given advice prior to testing to allow them to make an informed decision about the usefulness of such testing. In one series (Tyler *et al.* 1992), out of 238 initial requests for testing, only 40 results were eventually given out as a result of such pretest counselling. We would suggest that if presymptomatic or prenatal testing were possible in schizophrenia, similar principles should be adopted. This would involve skilled counselling, with adequate consideration given to the severity of the disorder, the age of onset, variable expressivity and other aspects of the phenotype. This would allow counsellees to be fully informed before making any final decisions.

Conclusions

Family, twin and adoption studies provide compelling evidence that schizophrenia has an important genetic component and quantitative analyses suggest that most of the variance in liability to the disorder (perhaps 80% or more) is accounted for by genetic factors. However, the pattern of transmission in families is complex and, although some multigeneration pedigrees with a Mendelian-like appearance exist, they are very much the exception rather than the rule. It seems likely that schizophrenia at a molecular level will turn out to be heterogeneous, even though so far attempts to relate clinical heterogeneity to aetiological heterogeneity have failed. This may partly account for the disappointingly inconclusive results of attempts to resolve the mode (or modes) of transmission statistically. However, it now seems that genes of major effect are rare in schizophrenia and that most cases are polygenic (or oligogenic) in origin. Such susceptibility loci are more difficult to detect and localize using molecular genetic approaches and this almost certainly accounts for the current complexity of linkage and association study results. Nevertheless, the detection and identification of susceptibility loci is now becoming increasingly feasible and it seems probable that schizophrenia, like many other common familial disorders, will have a molecular basis that will begin to be understood within the forseeable future.

References

Adler, L.E., Hoffer, L.D., Wiser, A. & Freedman, R. (1993) Normalization of auditory physiology by cigarette smoking in schizophrenic patients. *American Journal of Psychiatry* **150**, 1856–1861.

Alexander, R.C., Coggiano, M., Daniel, D.G. & Wyatt, R.J. (1990) HLA antigens in schizophrenia. *Psychiatry Research* **31**, 221–233.

Antonarakis, S.E., Blouin, J.-L., Pulver, A.E. *et al.* (1995) Schizophrenia susceptibility and chromosome 6p24–22. *Nature Genetics* **11**, 235–236.

Antonarakis, S.E., Blouin, J.L., Curran, M. *et al.* (1996) Linkage and sib-pair analysis reveal a potential schizophrenia susceptibility gene on chromosome 13q32. *American Journal of Human Genetics* **59**, A210.

Arolt, V., Lencer, R., Nolte, A. *et al.* (1996) Eye tracking dysfunction is a putative phenotypic susceptibility marker of schizophrenia and maps to a locus on chromosome 6p in families with multiple occurrence of the disease. *American Journal of Medical Genetics and Neuropsychiatric Genetics* **67**, 564–579.

Arranz, M.J., Munro, J., Birkett, J. *et al.* (2000) Pharmacogenetic prediction of clozapine response. *Lancet* **355**, 1615–1616.

Asaka, A., Okazaki, Y., Namura, I. *et al.* (1981) Study of HLA antigens among Japanese schizophrenics. *British Journal of Psychiatry* **138**, 498–500.

Aschauer, H.N., Aschauer-Treiber, G., Isenberg, K.E. *et al.* (1990) No evidence for linkage between choromosome 5 markers and schizophrenia. *Human Heredity* **40**, 109–115.

Aschauer, H.N., Fischer, G., Isenberg, K.E. *et al.* (1993) No proof of linkage between schizophrenia-related disorders including schizophrenia and chromosome 2q21 region. *European Archives of Psychiatry and Clinical Neuroscience* **243**, 193–198.

Asherson, P., Parfitt, E., Sargeant, M. *et al.* (1992) No evidence for a pseudoautosomal locus for schizophrenia linkage analysis of multiply affected families. *British Journal of Psychiatry* **161**, 63–68.

Asherson, P., Walsh, C., Williams, J. *et al.* (1994) Imprinting and anticipation: are they relevant to genetic studies of schizophrenia? *British Journal of Psychiatry* **164**, 619–624.

Barden, N., Morissette, J., Blaveri, K. *et al.* (1999) Chromosome 13 workshop report. *American Journal of Medical Genetics and Neuropsychiatric Genetics* **88**, 260–262.

Barr, C.L., Kennedy, J.L., Pakstis, A.J. *et al.* (1994) Linkage study of a susceptibility locus for schizophrenia in the pseudoautosomal region. *Schizophrenia Bulletin* **20**, 277–286.

Bassett, A.S. (1992) Chromosomal aberrations and schizophrenia: autosomes. *British Journal of Psychiatry* **161**, 323–334.

Bassett, A.S. & Honer, W.G. (1994) Evidence for anticipation in schizophrenia. *American Journal of Human Genetics* **54**, 864–870.

Bell, G.I., Selby, M. & Rutter, W.J. (1982) The highly polymorphic region near the human insulin gene is composed of simple tandemly repeating sequences. *Nature* **395**, 31–35.

Bell, G.I., Horita, S. & Karam, J.H. (1984) A polymorphic locus near the human insulin gene is associated with insulin-dependent diabetes mellitus. *Diabetes* **33**, 176–183.

Bennett, S.T., Lucassen, A.M., Gough, S.C.L. *et al.* (1995) Susceptibility to human type I diabetes at IDDM2 is determined by tandem repeat variation at the insulin gene minisatellite locus. *Nature Genetics* **9**, 284–292.

Berrettini, W.H., Ferraro, T.N., Goldin, L.R. *et al.* (1997) A linkage study of bipolar illness. *Archives of General Psychiatry* **54**, 27–35.

Blouin, J.L., Dombroski, B.A., Nath, S.K. *et al.* (1998) Schizophrenia susceptibility loci on chromosomes 13q32 and 8p21. *Nature Genetics* **20**, 70–73.

Bowen, T., Guy, C.A., Craddock, N. *et al.* (1998) Further support for an association between a polymorphic CAG repeat in the *hKCa3* gene and schizophrenia. *Molecular Psychiatry* **3**, 266–269.

Brzustowicz, L.M., Honer, W.G., Chow, E.W.C. *et al.* (1999) Linkage of familial schizophrenia to chromosome 13q32. *American Journal of Human Genetics* **65**, 1096–1103.

Brzustowicz, L.M., Hodgkinson, K.A., Chow, E.W.C., Honer, W.G. & Bassett, A.S. (2000) Location of a major susceptibility locus for familial schizophrenia on chromosome 1q21–q22. *Science* **288**, 678–682.

Buckland, P.R., O'Donovan, M.C. & McGuffin, P. (1993) Clozapine and sulpiride up-regulate dopamine D_3 receptor mRNA levels. *Neuropharmacology* **32**, 901–907.

Calzolari, E., Aiello, V., Palazzi, P. *et al.* (1996) Psychiatric disorder in a familial 15; 18 translocation and sublocalization of myelin basic protein to 18q22.3. *American Journal of Medical Genetics and Neuropsychiatric Genetics* **67**, 154–161.

Campion, D., D'Amato, T., Laklou, H. *et al.* (1992a) Failure to replicate linkage between chromosome 5q11–q13 markers and schizophrenia in 28 families. *Psychiatry Research* **44**, 171–179.

Campion, D., Leboyer, M., Hillaire, D. *et al.* (1992b) Relationship of HLA to schizophrenia not supported in multiplex families. *Psychiatry Research* **41**, 99–105.

Cannon, T.D., Kaprio, J., Lonnqvist, J., Huttunen, M. & Koskenvuo, M. (1998) The genetic epidemiology of schizophrenia in a Finnish twin cohort: a population-based modeling study. *Archives of General Psychiatry* **55**, 67–74.

Cao, Q., Martinez, M., Zhang, J. *et al.* (1997) Suggestive evidence for a schizophrenia susceptibility locus on chromosome 6q and a confirmation in an independent series of pedigrees. *Genomics* **43**, 1–8.

Cardno, A.G. & Gottesman, I.I. (2000) Twin studies of schizophrenia: from bow-and-arrow concordances to Star Wars Mx and functional genomics. *American Journal of Medical Genetics* **97**, 12–17.

Cardno, A.G., Marshall, E.J., Cold, B. *et al.* (1999a) Heritability estimates for psychotic disorders: the Maudsley Twin psychosis series. *Archives of General Psychiatry* **56**, 162–168.

Cardno, A.G., Bowen, T., Guy, C.A. *et al.* (1999b) CAG repeat length in the *hKCa3* gene and symptom dimensions in schizophrenia. *Biological Psychiatry* **45**, 1592–1596.

Carter, C.L. & Chung, C.S. (1980) Segregation analysis of schizophrenia under a mixed genetic model. *Human Heredity* **30**, 350–356.

Chiu, K.C., Tanizawa, Y. & Permutt, M.A. (1993) Glucokinase gene variants in the common form of NIDDM. *Diabetes* **42**, 579–582.

Chotai, J., Engstrom, C., Ekholm, B. *et al.* (1995) Anticipation in Swedish families with schizophrenia. *Psychiatric Genetics* **5**, 181–186.

Clerget-Darpoux, F., Goldin, L.R. & Gershon, E.S. (1986) Clinical methods in psychiatric genetics. III. Environmental stratification may simulate a genetic effect in adoption studies. *Acta Psychiatrica Scandinavica* **74**, 305–311.

Collinge, J., DeLisi, L.E., Boccio, A. *et al.* (1991) Evidence for a pseudoautosomal locus for schizophrenia using the method of affected sibling pairs. *British Journal of Psychiatry* **158**, 624–629.

Coon, H., Holik, J., Hoff, M. *et al.* (1994) Analysis of chromosome 22 markers in nine schizophrenia pedigrees. *American Journal of Medical Genetics* **54**, 72–79.

Coon, H., Myles-Worsley, M., Tiobech, J. *et al.* (1998) Evidence for a chromosome 2p13–14 schizophrenia susceptibility locus in families from Palau, Micronesia. *Molecular Psychiatry* **3**, 521–527.

Crocq, M.-A., Mant, R., Asherson, P. *et al.* (1992) Association between schizophrenia and homozygosity at the dopamine D_3 receptor gene. *Journal of Medical Genetics* **29**, 858–860.

Crow, T.J. (1988) Sex chromosomes and psychosis: the case for a pseudoautosomal locus. *British Journal of Psychiatry* **153**, 675–683.

Crow, T.J., DeLisi, L.E. & Johnstone, E.C. (1989) Concordance by sex in sibling pairs with schizophrenia is paternally inherited: evidence for a pseudoautosomal locus. *British Journal of Psychiatry* **155**, 92–97.

Crow, T.J., DeLisi, L.E., Lofthouse, R. *et al.* (1994) An examination of linkage of schizophrenia and schizoaffective disorder to the pseudoautosomal region (Xp22.3). *British Journal of Psychiatry* **164**, 159–164.

Crowe, R.R., Black, D.W., Wesner, R. *et al.* (1991) Lack of linkage to chromosome 5q11–q13 markers in six schizophrenia pedigrees. *Archives of General Psychiatry* **48**, 357–361.

Crowe, R.R., Thompson, J.S., Flink, R. & Weinberger, B. (1979) HLA antigens and schizophrenia. *Archives of General Psychiatry* **36**, 231–233.

Curtis, D. & Sham, P.C. (1995) Model-free linkage analysis using likelihoods. *American Journal of Human Genetics* **57**, 703–716.

Curtis, L., Blouin, J.L., Radhakrishna, U. *et al.* (1999) No evidence for linkage between schizophrenia and markers at chromosome 15q13–14. *American Journal of Medical Genetics and Neuropsychiatric Genetics* **88**, 109–112.

D'Amato, T., Campion, D., Gorwood, P. *et al.* (1992) Evidence for a pseudoautosomal locus for schizophrenia. II. Replication of a non-random segregation of alleles at the *DXYS14* locus. *British Journal of Psychiatry* **161**, 59–62.

Dann, J., DeLisi, L.E., Devoto, M. *et al.* (1997) A linkage study of schizophrenia to markers within Xp11 near the *MAOB* gene. *Psychiatry Research* **70**, 131–143.

Davies, J.L., Kawaguchi, Y., Bennett, S.T. *et al.* (1994) A genome-wide search for human type 1 diabetes susceptibility genes. *Nature* **371**, 130–136.

Davis, S. & Weeks, D.E. (1997) Comparison of nonparametric statistics for detection of linkage in nuclear families: single marker evaluation. *American Journal of Human Genetics* **61**, 1431–1444.

De Leon, J., Dadvand, M., Canuso, C. *et al.* (1995) Schizophrenia and smoking: an epidemiological survey in a state hospital. *American Journal of Psychiatry* **152**, 453–455.

DeLisi, L.E., Lofthouse, R., Lehner, T. *et al.* (1995) Failure to find a chromosome 18 pericentric linkage in families with schizophrenia. *American Journal of Medical Genetics and Neuropsychiatric Genetics* **60**, 532–534.

Dib, C., Faure, S., Fizames, C. *et al.* (1996) A comprehensive genetic map of the human genome based on 5264 microsatellites. *Nature* **380**, 152–154.

Dombroski, B.A., Ton, C.C., Nath, S.K. *et al.* (1997) A susceptibility locus for schizophrenia on chromosome 8p. *American Journal of Medical Genetics and Neuropsychiatric Genetics* **74**, 668.

Donald, J.A., Barendse, W. & Cooper, D.W. (1989) Linkage studies of HLA and insulin gene restriction fragment length polymorphisms in families with IDDM. *Genetic Epidemiology* **6**, 77–81.

Dunham, I., Collins, J., Wadey, R. & Scambler, P. (1992) Possible role for COMT in psychosis associated with velocardiofacial syndrome. *Lancet* **340**, 1361–1362.

Eberhard, G., Franzen, G. & Low, B. (1975) Schizophrenia susceptibility and HL-A antigen. *Neuropsychobiology* **1**, 211–217.

Edwards, T.H. (1965) The meaning of the associations between blood groups and disease. *Annals of Human Genetics* **29**, 77–83.

Egan, M.F., Goldberg, T.E., Kolachana, B.S. *et al.* (2001) Effect of *COMT* Val108/158 Met genotype on frontal lobe function and risk for schizophrenia. *Proceedings of the National Academy of Sciences of the USA* **98**, 6917–6922.

Elbein, S.C., Corsetti, L., Goldgar, D., Skolnick, M. & Permutt, M.A. (1988) Insulin gene in familial NIDDM: lack of linkage in Utah mormon pedigrees. *Diabetes* **37**, 569–576.

Elston, R.C. & Campbell, M.A. (1970) Schizophrenia: evidence for the major gene hypothesis. *Behavior Genetics* **1**, 3–10.

Essen-Moller, E. (1955) The calculation of morbid risk in parents of index cases, as applied to a family sample of schizophrenics. *Acta Genetica et Statistica Medica* **5**, 334–342.

Falconer, D.S. (1965) The inheritance of liability to certain diseases, estimated from the incidence among relatives. *Annals of Human Genetics* **29**, 51–76.

Falk, C.T. & Rubinstein, P. (1987) Haplotype relative risks: an easy reliable way to construct a proper control sample for risk calculations. *Annals of Human Genetics* **51**, 227–233.

Fang, N., Coon, H., Hoff, M. *et al.* (1995) Search for a schizophrenia susceptibility gene on chromosome 18. *Psychiatric Genetics* **5**, 31–35.

Faraone, S.V., Matise, T., Svrakic, D. *et al.* (1998) Genome scan of European-American schizophrenia pedigrees: results of the NIMH Genetics Initiative and Millennium Consortium. *American Journal of Medical Genetics and Neuropsychiatric Genetics* **81**, 290–295.

Farmer, A.E., McGuffin, P. & Gottesman, I.I. (1987) Twin concordance for DSM-III schizophrenia: scrutinizing the validity of the definition. *Archives of General Psychiatry* **44**, 634–640.

Feighner, J.P., Robins, E., Guze, S.B. *et al.* (1972) Diagnostic criteria for use in psychiatric research. *Archives of General Psychiatry* **26**, 57–63.

Ferns, G.A.A., Hitman, G.A. & Trembath, R. (1986) DNA polymorphic haplotypes on the short arm of chromosome 11 and the inheritance of type I diabetes mellitus. *Journal of Medical Genetics* **23**, 210–216.

Fischer, M. (1971) Psychoses in the offspring of schizophrenic monozygotic twins and their normal co-twins. *British Journal of Psychiatry* **118**, 43–52.

Fisher, P.J., Turic, D., Williams, N.M. *et al.* (1999) DNA pooling identifies QTLs on chromosome 4 for general cognitive ability in children. *Human Molecular Genetics* **8**, 915–922.

Franzek, E. & Beckmann, H. (1998) Different genetic background of schizophrenia spectrum psychoses: a twin study. *American Journal of Psychiatry* **155**, 76–83.

Freedman, R., Coon, H., Myles-Worsley, M. *et al.* (1997) Linkage of a neurophysiological deficit in schizophrenia to a chromosome 15 locus. *Proceedings of the National Academy of Sciences of the USA* **94**, 587–592.

Frieboes, R.M., Moises, H.W., Gattaz, W.F. *et al.* (2001) Lack of association between schizophrenia and the phospholipase-A (2) genes *cPLA2* and *sPLA2*. *American Journal of Medical Genetics* **105**, 246–249.

Garver, D.L., Barnes, R., Holcombe, J. *et al.* (1998) Genome-wide scan and schizophrenia in African Americans. *American Journal of Medical Genetics and Neuropsychiatric Genetics* **81**, 454–455.

Gattaz, W.F., Nevalainen, T.J. & Kinnunen, P.K.J. (1990) Possible involvement of phospholipase A2 in the pathogenesis of schizophrenia. *Fortschritte der Neurologie und Psychiatrie* **58**, 148–153.

Gattaz, W.F., Schmitt, A. & Maras, A. (1995) Increased platelet phospholipase A2 activity in schizophrenia. *Schizophrenia Research* **16**, 1–6.

Gershon, E.S., DeLisi, L.E., Hamovit, J. *et al.* (1988) A controlled family study of chronic psychoses: schizophrenia and schizoaffective disorder. *Archives of General Psychiatry* **45**, 328–336.

Gill, M., McGuffin, P., Parfitt, E. *et al.* (1993) A linkage study of schizophrenia with DNA markers from the long arm of chromosome 11. *Psychological Medicine* **23**, 27–44.

Gill, M., Vallada, H., Collier, D. *et al.* (1996) A combined analysis of *D22S278* marker alleles in affected sib-pairs: support for a susceptibility locus for schizophrenia at chromosome 22q12. *American Journal of Medical Genetics and Neuropsychiatric Genetics* **67**, 40–45.

Goate, A., Chartier-Harlin, M.C., Mullan, M. *et al.* (1991) Segregation of a missense mutation in the amyloid precursor protein gene with familial Alzheimer's disease [see comments]. *Nature* **349**, 704–706.

Gorwood, P., Leboyer, M., Falissard, B. *et al.* (1997) Further epidemiological evidence for anticipation in schizophrenia. *Biomedicine and Pharmacotherapy* **51**, 376–380.

Gottesman, I.I. (1991) *Schizophrenia Genesis*. W.H. Freeman, New York.

Gottesman, I.I. & Bertelsen, A. (1989) Confirming unexpressed genotypes for schizophrenia: risks in the offspring of Fischer's Danish identical and fraternal discordant twins. *Archives of General Psychiatry* **46**, 867–872.

Gottesman, I.I. & Shields, J. (1967) A polygenic theory of schizophrenia. *Proceedings of the National Academy of Sciences of the USA* **58**, 199–205.

Gottesman, I.I. & Shields, J. (1972) *Schizophrenia and Genetics: a Twin Study Vantage Point*. Academic Press, London.

Gottesman, I.I. & Shields, J. (1982) *Schizophrenia: the Epigenetic Puzzle*. Cambridge University Press, Cambridge.

Green, J.R. & Woodrow, J.C. (1977) Sibling method for detecting HLA-linked genes in the disease. *Tissue Antigens* **31**, 31–35.

Gurling, H., Kalsi, G., Chen, A.H.S. *et al.* (1995) Schizophrenia susceptibility and chromosome 6p24–22. *Nature Genetics* **11**, 234–235.

Hallmayer, J., Schwab, S., Albus, M. *et al.* (1998) A potential schizophrenia susceptibility locus for schizophrenia on 22q12–q13: re-evaluation in 72 families. *American Journal of Medical Genetics and Neuropsychiatric Genetics* **81**, 529.

Harper, P.S., Quarrell, O.W. & Youngman, S. (1988) Huntington's disease: prediction and prevention. *Philosophical Transactions of the Royal Society of London B: Biological Science* **319**, 285–298.

Heiden, A., Willinger, U., Scharfetter, J. *et al.* (1999) Anticipation in schizophrenia. *Schizophrenia Research* **35**, 25–32.

Heston, L.L. (1966) Psychiatric disorders in foster home reared children of schizophrenic mothers. *British Journal of Psychiatry* **112**, 819–825.

Heston, L.L. (1970) The genetics of schizophrenic and schizoid disease. *Science* **167**, 249–256.

Hill, L., Craig, I.W., Asherson, P. *et al.* (1999) DNA pooling and dense marker maps: a systematic search for genes for cognitive ability. *Neuroreport* **10**, 843–848.

Hitman, G.A., Tarn, A.C. & Winter, R.M. (1985) Type 1 (insulin-dependent) diabetes and a highly variable locus close to the insulin gene on chromosome 11. *Diabetologia* **28**, 218–222.

Holder, S.E., Vintiner, G.M., Farren, B., Malcolm, S. & Winter, R.M. (1992) Confirmation of an association between RFLPs at the transforming growth factor-alpha locus and non-syndromic cleft lip and palate. *Journal of Medical Genetics* **29**, 390–392.

Hovatta, I., Varilo, T., Suvisaari, J. *et al.* (1999) A genome-wide screen for schizophrenia genes in an isolated Finnish subpopulation suggesting multiple susceptibility loci. *American Journal of Human Genetics* **65**, 1114–1124.

Hudson, C.J., Kennedy, J.L., Gotowiec, A. *et al.* (1996) Genetic variant near cytosolic phospholipase A2 associated with schizophrenia. *Schizophrenia Research* **21**, 111–116.

Huntington's Disease Collaborative Research Group (1993) A novel gene containing a trinucleotide repeat that is expanded and unstable on Huntington's disease chromosomes. *Cell* **72**, 971–983.

Imamura, A., Honda, S., Nakane, Y. & Okazaki, Y. (1998) Anticipation in Japanese families with schizophrenia. *Journal of Human Genetics* **43**, 217–223.

Ivanyi, P., Droes, J., Schreuder, G.M., D'Amaro, J. & van Rood, J.J. (1983) A search for association of HLA antigens with paranoid schizophrenia: A9 appears as a possible marker. *Tissue Antigens* **22**, 186–193.

James, J.W. (1971) Frequency in relatives for an all-or-none trait. *Annals of Human Genetics* **35**, 47–49.

Jensen, J., Coon, H., Hoff, M. *et al.* (1998) Search for a schizophrenia susceptibility gene on chromosome 13. *Psychiatric Genetics* **8**, 239–243.

Kalsi, G., Brynjolfsson, J., Butler, R. *et al.* (1995a) Linkage analysis of chromosome 22q12–13 in a United Kingdom/Icelandic sample of 23 multiplex schizophrenia families. *American Journal of Medical Genetics and Neuropsychiatric Genetics* **60**, 298–301.

Kalsi, G., Curtis, D., Brynjolfsson, J. *et al.* (1995b) Investigation by linkage analysis of the XY pseudoautosomal region in the genetic susceptibility to schizophrenia. *British Journal of Psychiatry* **167**, 390–393.

Kalsi, G., Mankoo, B.S., Curtis, D. *et al.* (1995c) Exclusion of linkage of schizophrenia to the gene for the dopamine D_2 receptor (*DRD2*) and chromosome 11q translocation sites. *Psychological Medicine* **25**, 531–537.

Kalsi, G., Chen, C.H., Smyth, C. *et al.* (1996) Genetic linkage analysis in an Icelandic/British sample fails to exclude the putative chromosome 13q14.1–q32 schizophrenia susceptibility locus. *American Journal of Human Genetics* **59**, A388.

Kalsi, G., Mankoo, B., Curtis, D. *et al.* (1999) New DNA markers with increased informativeness show diminished support for a chromosome 5q11–13 schizophrenia susceptibility locus and exclude linkage in two new cohorts of British and Icelandic families. *Annals of Human Genetics* **63**, 235–247.

Kaufmann, C.A., Suarez, B., Malaspina, D. *et al.* (1998) NIMH genetics initiative millennium schizophrenia consortium: linkage analysis of African-American pedigrees. *American Journal of Medical Genetics and Neuropsychiatric Genetics* **81**, 282–289.

Kelly, D., Goldberg, R., Wilson, D. *et al.* (1993) Confirmation that the velocardiofacial syndrome is associated with haplo-insufficiency of genes at chromosome 22q11. *American Journal of Medical Genetics* **45**, 308–312.

Kendler, K.S. & Gruenberg, A.M. (1984) An independent analysis of the Danish Adoption Study of schizophrenia. VI. The relationship between psychiatric disorders as defined by DSM-III in the relatives and adoptees. *Archives of General Psychiatry* **41**, 555–564.

Kendler, K.S., Masterson, C.C. & Davis, K.L. (1985) Psychiatric illness in first-degree relatives of patients with paranoid psychosis, schizophrenia and medical illness. *British Journal of Psychiatry* **147**, 524–531.

Kennedy, G.C., German, M.S. & Rutter, W.J. (1995) The minisatellite in the diabetes susceptibility locus IDDM2 regulates insulin transcription. *Nature Genetics* **9**, 293–298.

Kety, S.S., Rosenthal, D., Wender, P.H., Schulsinger, F. & Jacobsen, B. (1976) Mental illness in the biological and adoptive families of adopted individuals who have become schizophrenic. *Behavior Genetics* **6**, 219–225.

Kläning, U. (1996) *Schizophrenia in twins: incidence and risk factors*. PhD thesis, University of Aarhus, Denmark.

Kong, A. & Cox, N.J. (1997) Allele-sharing models: LOD score and accurate linkage tests. *American Journal of Human Genetics* **61**, 1179–1188.

Kringlen, E. (1976) Twins: still our best method. *Schizophrenia Bulletin* **2**, 429–433.

Kringlen, E. & Cramer, G. (1989) Offspring of monozygotic twins discordant for schizophrenia. *Archives of General Psychiatry* **46**, 873–877.

Kruglyak, L. & Lander, E.S. (1995) Complete multipoint sib-pair analysis of qualitative and quantitative traits. *American Journal of Human Genetics* **57**, 439–454.

Kruglyak, L., Daly, M.J., Reeve-Daly, M.P. & Lander, E.S. (1996) Parametric and non-parametric linkage analysis: a unified multipoint approach. *American Journal of Human Genetics* **58**, 1347–1363.

Lander, E. & Kruglyak, L. (1995) Genetic dissection of complex traits: guidelines for interpreting and reporting linkage results. *Nature Genetics* **11**, 241–247.

Lander, E.S., Linton, L.M., Birren, B. *et al.* and the International Human Genome Sequencing Consortium (2001) Initial sequencing and analysis of the human genome. *Nature* **409**, 860–921.

Lannfelt, L., Sokoloff, P. & Martres, M.P. (1992) Amino-acid substitution in the dopamine D_3 receptor as a ueful polymorphism for investigating psychiatric disorders. *Psychiatric Genetics* **2**, 249–256.

Lasseter, V.K., Pulver, A.E., Wolyniec, P. *et al.* (1995) Follow-up report of potential linkage for schizophrenia on chromosome 22q. Part III. *American Journal of Medical Genetics* **60**, 172–173.

Leboyer, M. & McGuffin, P. (1991) Collaborative strategies in the molecular genetics of the major psychoses. *British Journal of Psychiatry* **158**, 605–610.

Le Coniat, M., Sokoloff, P., Hillion, J. *et al.* (1991) Chromosomal localization of the human D_3 dopamine receptor gene. *Human Genetics* **87**, 618–620.

Leonard, S., Gault, J., Moore, T. *et al.* (1998) Further investigation of a chromosome 15 locus in schizophrenia: analysis of affected sibpairs from the NIMH genetics initiative. *American Journal of Medical Genetics and Neuropsychiatric Genetics* **81**, 308–312.

Levinson, D.F., Wildenauer, D.B., Schwab, S.G. *et al.* (1996) Additional support for schizophrenia linkage on chromosomes 6 and 8: a multicenter study. *American Journal of Medical Genetics and Neuropsychiatric Genetics* **67**, 580–594.

Levinson, D.F., Mahtani, M.M., Nancarrow, D.J. *et al.* (1998) Genome scan of schizophrenia. *American Journal of Psychiatry* **155**, 741–750.

Levinson, D.F., Holmans, P., Straub, R.E. *et al.* (2000) Multicenter linkage study of schizophrenia candidate regions on chromosomes 5q, 6q, 10p, and 13q: schizophrenia linkage collaborative group III. *American Journal of Human Genetics* **67**, 652–663.

Lin, M.W., Curtis, D., Williams, N. *et al.* (1995) Suggestive evidence for linkage of schizophrenia to markers on chromosome 13q14.1–q32. *Psychiatric Genetics* **5**, 117–126.

Lin, M.W., Sham, P., Hwu, H.G. *et al.* (1997) Suggestive evidence for linkage of schizophrenia to markers on chromosome 13 in Caucasian but not Oriental populations. *Human Genetics* **99**, 417–420.

Lindholm, E., Ekholm, B., Shaw, S. *et al.* (2001) A schizophrenia-susceptibility locus at 6q25, in one of the world's largest reported pedigrees. *American Journal of Human Genetics* **69**, 96–105.

Luxenberger, H. (1928) Vorlaufizer Bericht uber psychiatrische Serien Untersuchungen an Zwillinger. *Zeitschift Fur Gesante Neurologie und Psychiatrie* **116**, 297–326.

McGinnis, R.E., Fox, H., Yates, P. *et al.* (2001) Failure to confirm NOTCH4 association with schizophrenia in a large population-based sample from Scotland. *Nature Genetics* **28**, 128–129.

McGue, M. & Gottesman, I. (1991) The genetic epidemiology of schizophrenia and the design of linkage studies. *European Archives of Psychiatry and Clinical Neuroscience* **240**, 174–181.

McGue, M., Gottesman, I. & Rao, D.C. (1985) Resolving genetic models for the transmission of schizophrenia. *Genetic Epidemiology* **2**, 99–110.

McGuffin, P. & Owen, M. (1991) The molecular genetics of schizophrenia: an overview and forward view. *European Archives of Psychiatry and Clinical Neuroscience* **240**, 169–173.

McGuffin, P. & Sturt, E. (1986) Genetic markers in schizophrenia. *Human Heredity* **36**, 461–465.

McGuffin, P., Festenstein, H. & Murray, R. (1983) A family study of HLA antigens and other genetic markers in schizophrenia. *Psychological Medicine* **13**, 31–43.

McGuffin, P., Farmer, A.E. & Gottesman, I.I. (1984) Twin concordance for operationally defined schizophrenia: confirmation of familiality and heritability. *Archives of General Psychiatry* **41**, 541–545.

McGuffin, P., Sargeant, M., Hetti, G. *et al.* (1990) Exclusion of a schizophrenia susceptibility gene from the chromosome 5q11–q13 region: new data and a reanalysis of previous reports. *American Journal of Human Genetics* **47**, 524–535.

McGuffin, P., Owen, M. & Gill, M. (1992) Molecular genetics of schizophrenia. In: *Genetic Research in Psychiatry* (eds I. Mendlewiecz & H. Hippius), pp. 25–48. Springer-Verlag, Berlin.

McGuffin, P., Asherson, P., Owen, M. & Farmer, A. (1994a) The strength of the genetic effect: is there room for an environmental influence in the aetiology of schizophrenia? *British Journal of Psychiatry* **164**, 593–599.

McGuffin, P., Owen, M.J., O'Donovan, M.C., Thapar, A. & Gottesman, I.I. (1994b) *Seminars in Psychiatric Genetics*. Gaskell, London.

McGuffin, P., Owen, M.J. & Farmer, A.E. (1995) Genetic basis of schizophrenia. *Lancet* **346**, 678–682.

McGuffin, P., Riley, B. & Plomin, R. (2001) Genomics and behavior; toward behavioral genomics. *Science* **291**, 1232–1249.

McKenna, P.J. & Bailey, P.E. (1993) The strange story of clozapine. *British Journal of Psychiatry* **162**, 32–37.

Maier, W., Schmidt, F., Schwab, S.G. *et al.* (1995) Lack of linkage between schizophrenia and markers at the telomeric end of the pseudoautosomal region of the sex chromosomes. *Biological Psychiatry* **37**, 344–347.

Marth, G., Yeh, R., Minton, M. *et al.* (2001) Single-nucleotide polymorphisms in the public domain: how useful are they? *Nature Genetics* **27**, 371–372.

Martinez, M., Goldin, L.R., Cao, Q. *et al.* (1999) Follow-up study on a susceptibility locus for schizophrenia on chromosome 6q. *American Journal of Medical Genetics and Neuropsychiatric Genetics* **88**, 337–343.

Maziade, M., Debraekeleer, M., Genest, P. *et al.* (1993) A balanced 2:18 translocation and familial schizophrenia: falling short of an association. *Archives of General Psychiatry* **50**, 73–75.

Meehl, P.E. (1973) *Psychodiagnosis: Selected Papers*. University of Minnesota Press, Minneapolis.

Millar, J.K., Christie, S., Semple, C.A.M. & Porteous, D.J. (2000a) Chromosomal location and genomic structure of the human translin-associated factor X gene (*TRAX*; *TSNAX*) revealed by intergenic splicing to *DISC1*, a gene disrupted by a translocation segregating with schizophrenia. *Genomics* **67**, 69–77.

Millar, J.K., Wilson-Annan, J.C., Anderson, S. *et al.* (2000b) Disruption of two novel genes by a translocation co-segregating with schizophrenia. *Human Molecular Genetics* **9**, 1415–1423.

Miyanaga, K., Machiyama, Y. & Juji, T. (1984) Schizophrenic disorders and HLA-DR antigens. *Biological Psychiatry* **19**, 121–129.

Moises, H.W., Yang, L., Kristbjarnarson, H. *et al.* (1995) An international two-stage genome-wide search for schizophrenia susceptibility genes. *Nature Genetics* **11**, 321–324.

Mors, O., Ewald, H., Blackwood, D. & Muir, W. (1997) Cytogenetic abnormalities on chromosome 18 associated with bipolar affective disorder or schizophrenia. *British Journal of Psychiatry* **170**, 278–280.

Morton, N.E. (1955) Sequential tests for the detection of linkage. *American Journal of Human Genetics* **7**, 277–318.

Morton, N.E. & MacLean, C.J. (1974) Analysis of family resemblance. III. Complex segregation of quantitative traits. *American Journal of Human Genetics* **26**, 489–503.

Mott, F.W. (1910) Hereditary aspects of nervous and mental diseases. *British Medical Journal* **2**, 1013.

Mowry, B.J., Nancarrow, D.J., Lennon, D.P. *et al.* (1995) Schizophrenia susceptibility and chromosome 6p24–22. *Nature Genetics* **11**, 233–234.

Mulcrone, J., Whatley, S.A., Marchbanks, R. *et al.* (1995) Genetic linkage analysis of schizophrenia using chromosome 11q13–24 markers in Israeli pedigrees. *American Journal of Medical Genetics and Neuropsychiatric Genetics* **60**, 103–108.

Mullis, K.B. & Faloona, F.A. (1987) Specific synthesis of DNA *in vitro* via a polymerase-catalyzed chain reaction. *Methods in Enzymology* **155**, 335–350.

Murphy, K.C. & Owen, M.J. (1997) The behavioral phenotype in velocardiofacial syndrome. *American Journal of Medical Genetics and Neuropsychiatric Genetics* **74**, 660.

Murray, R.M., Lewis, S.W. & Reveley, A.M. (1985) Towards an aetiological classification of schizophrenia. *Lancet* **1**, 1023–1026.

Nagamoto, H.T., Adler, L.E., Hea, R.A. *et al.* (1996) Gating of auditory

P50 in schizophrenics: unique effects of clozapine. *Biological Psychiatry* **40**, 181–188.

Neves-Pereira, M., Bassett, A.S., Honer, W.G. *et al.* (1998) No evidence for linkage of the *CHRNA7* gene region in Canadian schizophrenia families. *American Journal of Medical Genetics and Neuropsychiatric Genetics* **81**, 361–363.

Noponen, M., Sanfilipo, M., Samanich, K. *et al.* (1993) Elevated PLA2 activity in schizophrenics and other psychiatric patients. *Biological Psychiatry* **34**, 641–649.

Nothen, M.M., Propping, P. & Fimmers, R. (1993) Association versus linkage studies in psychosis genetics. *Journal of Medical Genetics* **30**, 634–637.

Onstad, S., Skre, I., Torgersen, S. & Kringlen, E. (1991) Twin concordance for DSM-IIIR schizophrenia. *Acta Psychiatrica Scandinavica* **83**, 395–401.

O'Rourke, D.H., Gottesman, I.I., Suarez, B.K., Rice, J. & Reich, T. (1982) Refutation of the general single-locus model for the etiology of schizophrenia. *American Journal of Human Genetics* **34**, 630–649.

Ott, J. (1991) *Analysis of Human Genetic Linkage.* Johns Hopkins University Press, Baltimore.

Owen, M.J. & McGuffin, P. (1991) DNA and classical genetic markers in schizophrenia. *European Archives of Psychiatry and Clinical Neuroscience* **240**, 197–203.

Owen, M.J., Mant, R., Parfitt, E. *et al.* (1992) No association between RFLPs at the porphobilinogen deaminase gene and schizophrenia. *Human Genetics* **90**, 131–132.

Paterson, A.D., DeLisi, L., Faraone, S.V. *et al.* (1999) Sixth World Congress of Psychiatric Genetics X chromosome workshop. *American Journal of Medical Genetics and Neuropsychiatric Genetics* **88**, 279–286.

Peet, M., Ramchand, C.N., Lee, J. *et al.* (1998) Association of the Ban I dimorphic site at the human cytosolic phospholipase A2 gene with schizophrenia. *Psychiatric Genetics* **8**, 191–192.

Penrose, L.S. (1935) The detection of autosomal linkage in data which conists of pairs of brothers and sisters of unspecified parentage. *Annals of Eugenics* **6**, 133–138.

Pollin, W., Allen, M.G., Hoffer, A., Stabenau, J.R. & Hrubec, Z. (1969) Psychopathology in 15 909 pairs of veteran twins: evidence for a genetic factor in the pathogenesis of schizophrenia and its relative absence in psychoneurosis. *American Journal of Psychiatry* **126**, 597–610.

Price, S.A., Fox, H., St Clair, D. & Shaw, D.J. (1997) Lack of association between schizophrenia and a polymorphism close to the cytosolic phospholipase A2 gene. *Psychiatric Genetics* **7**, 111–114.

Pulver, A.E., Karayiorgou, M., Lasseter, V.K. *et al.* (1994a) Follow-up of a report of a potential linkage for schizophrenia on chromosome 22q12–q13.1: Part II. *American Journal of Medical Genetics* **54**, 44–50.

Pulver, A.E., Karayiorgou, M., Wolyniec, P.S. *et al.* (1994b) Sequential strategy to identify a susceptibility gene for schizophrenia: report of potential linkage on chromosome 22q12–q13.1: Part 1. *American Journal of Medical Genetics* **54**, 36–43.

Pulver, A.E., Nestadt, G., Goldberg, R. *et al.* (1994c) Psychotic illness in patients diagnosed with velocardiofacial syndrome and their relatives. *Journal of Nervous and Mental Disease* **182**, 476–478.

Pulver, A.E., Lasseter, V.K., Kasch, L. *et al.* (1995) Schizophrenia: a genome scan targets chromosomes 3p and 8p as potential sites of susceptibility genes. *American Journal of Medical Genetics and Neuropsychiatric Genetics* **60**, 252–260.

Reveley, A.M., Reveley, M.A., Clifford, C.A. & Murray, R.M. (1982) Cerebral ventricular size in twins discordant for schizophrenia. *Lancet* **1**, 540–541.

Riley, B.P. & McGuffin, P. (2000) Linkage and associated studies of schizophrenia. *American Journal of Medical Genetics Seminars in Medical Genetics* **97**, 23–44.

Riley, B., Mogudi-Carter, M., Jenkins, T. & Williamson, R. (1996a) No evidence for linkage of chromosome 22 markers to schizophrenia in southern African Bantu-speaking families. *American Journal of Medical Genetics and Neuropsychiatric Genetics* **67**, 515–522.

Riley, B.P., Rajagopalan, S., Mogudi-Carter, M., Jenkins, T. & Williamson, R. (1996b) No evidence for linkage of chromosome 6p markers to schizophrenia in Southern African Bantu-speaking families. *Psychiatric Genetics* **6**, 41–49.

Riley, B.P., Tahir, E., Rajagopalan, S. *et al.* (1997) A linkage study of the *N*-methyl-D-aspartate receptor subunit gene loci and schizophrenia in southern African Bantu-speaking families. *Psychiatric Genetics* **7**, 57–74.

Riley, B.P., Lin, M.W., Mogudi-Carter, M. *et al.* (1998) Failure to exclude a possible schizophrenia susceptibility locus on chromosome 13q14.1–q32 in Southern African Bantu-speaking families. *Psychiatric Genetics* **8**, 155–162.

Riley, B.P., Makoff, A., Mogudi-Carter, M. *et al.* (2000) Haplotype transmission disequilibrium and evidence for linkage of the *CHRNA7* gene region to schizophrenia in southern African Bantu families. *American Journal of Medical Genetics and Neuropsychiatric Genetics* **96**, 196–201.

Risch, N. (1990) Linkage strategies for genetically complex traits. I. Multilocus models. *American Journal of Human Genetics* **46**, 222–228.

Risch, N. & Baron, M. (1984) Segregation analysis of schizophrenia and related disorders. *American Journal of Human Genetics* **36**, 1039–1059.

Risch, N. & Giuffra, L. (1992) Model misspecification and multipoint linkage analysis. *Human Heredity* **42**, 77–92.

Risch, N. & Merikangas, K. (1996) The future of genetic studies of complex human diseases. *Science* **273**, 1516–1517.

Roberts, S.B., MacLean, C.J., Neale, M.C., Eaves, L.J. & Kendler, K.S. (1999) Replication of linkage studies of complex traits: an examination of variation in location estimates. *American Journal of Human Genetics* **65**, 876–884.

Rosenthal, D., Wender, P.H., Kety, S.S., Welner, J. & Schulsinger, F. (1971) The adopted-away offspring of schizophrenics. *American Journal of Psychiatry* **128**, 307–311.

Rudduck, C. (1984) *Genetic markers and schizophrenia.* Thesis, University of Lund.

Sanders, A.R., Rincon-Limas, D.E., Chakraborty, R. *et al.* (1993) Association between genetic variation at the porphobilinogen deaminase gene and schizophrenia. *Schizophrenia Research* **8**, 211–221.

Schalling, M., Hudson, T.J., Buetow, K.H. & Housman, D.E. (1993) Direct detection of novel expanded trinucleotide repeats in the human genome. *Nature Genetics* **4**, 135–139.

Schwab, S.G., Albus, M., Hallmayer, J. *et al.* (1995) Evaluation of a susceptibility gene for schizophrenia on chromosome 6p by multipoint affected sib-pair linkage analysis. *Nature Genetics* **11**, 325–327.

Schwab, S.G., Eckstein, G.N., Hallmayer, J. *et al.* (1997) Evidence suggestive of a locus on chromosome 5q31 contributing to susceptibility for schizophrenia in German and Israeli families by multipoint affected sib-pair linkage analysis. *Molecular Psychiatry* **2**, 156–160.

Schwab, S.G., Hallmayer, J., Albus, M. *et al.* (1998) Further evidence for a susceptibility locus on chromosome 10p14–p11 in 72 families with schizophrenia by non-parametric linkage analysis. *American Journal of Medical Genetics and Neuropsychiatric Genetics* **81**, 302–307.

Scott, W.K., Pericak-Vance, M.A., Haines, J.L. *et al.* (1997) Genetic analysis of complex diseases. *Science* **275**, 1327–1330.

Shaw, S.H., Kelly, M., Smith, A.B. *et al.* (1998) A genome-wide search for schizophrenia susceptibility genes. *American Journal of Medical Genetics and Neuropsychiatric Genetics* **81**, 364–376.

Sherrington, R., Brynjolfsson, J., Petursson, H. *et al.* (1988) Localization of a susceptibility locus for schizophrenia on chromosome 5. *Nature* **336**, 164–167.

Shprintzen, R.J., Goldberg, R., Golding-Kushner, K.J. & Marion, R.W. (1992) Late-onset psychosis in the velocardiofacial syndrome. *American Journal of Medical Genetics* **42**, 141–142.

Silverman, J.M., Greenberg, D.A., Altstiel, L.D. *et al.* (1996) Evidence of a locus for schizophrenia and related disorders on the short arm of chromosome 5 in a large pedigree. *American Journal of Medical Genetics and Neuropsychiatric Genetics* **67**, 162–171.

Sklar, P., Schwab, S.G., Williams, N.M. *et al.* (2001) Association analysis of *NOTCH4* loci in schizophrenia using family and population-based controls. *Nature Genetics* **28**, 126–128.

Slater, E. (1958) The monogenic theory of schizophrenia. *Acta Genetica* **8**, 50–56.

Slater, E. & Cowie, V. (1971) *The Genetics of Mental Disorder*. Oxford University Press, Oxford.

Sobell, J.L., Heston, L.L. & Sommer, S.S. (1992) Delineation of genetic predisposition to multifactorial disease: a general approach on the threshold of feasibility. *Genomics* **12**, 1–6.

Sokoloff, P., Giros, B., Martres, M.P. *et al.* (1992) Localization and function of the D_3 dopamine receptor. *Arzneimittel Forschung* **42**, 224–230.

Spitzer, R.L., Endicott, J. & Robins, E. (1978) Research diagnostic criteria: rationale and reliability. *Archives of General Psychiatry* **35**, 773–782.

St Clair, D., Blackwood, D., Muir, W. *et al.* (1990) Association within a family of a balanced autosomal translocation with major mental illness. *Lancet* **336**, 13–16.

Straub, R.E., MacLean, C.J., O'Neill, F.A. *et al.* (1995) A potential vulnerability locus for schizophrenia on chromosome 6p24–22: evidence for genetic heterogeneity. *Nature Genetics* **11**, 287–293.

Straub, R.E., MacLean, C.J., O'Neill, F.A., Walsh, D. & Kendler, K.S. (1997a) Genome scan for schizophrenia genes: a detailed progress report in an Irish cohort. *American Journal of Medical Genetics and Neuropsychiatric Genetics* **74**, 558.

Straub, R.E., MacLean, C.J., O'Neill, F.A., Walsh, D. & Kendler, K.S. (1997b) Support for a possible schizophrenia vulnerability locus in region 5q22–31 in Irish families. *Molecular Psychiatry* **2**, 148–155.

Straub, R.E., MacLean, C.J., Martin, R.B. *et al.* (1998) A schizophrenia locus may be located in region 10p15–p11. *American Journal of Medical Genetics and Neuropsychiatric Genetics* **81**, 296–301.

Strauss, J., Zhang, X.R., Barron, Y., Ganguli, R. & Nimgaonkar, V.L. (1999) Lack of association between schizophrenia and a pancreatic phospholipase A-2 gene (*PLA2G1B*) polymorphism. *Psychiatric Genetics* **9**, 153–155.

Sturt, E. & McGuffin, P. (1985) Can linkage and marker association resolve the genetic aetiology of psychiatric disorders? Review and argument. *Psychological Medicine* **15**, 455–462.

Su, Y., Burke, J., O'Neill, F.A. *et al.* (1993) Exclusion of linkage between schizophrenia and the D_2 dopamine receptor gene region of chromosome 11q in 112 Irish multiplex families. *Archives of General Psychiatry* **50**, 205–211.

Suarez, B.K., Rice, J. & Reich, T. (1978) The generalized sib-pair IBD distribution: its use in the detection of linkage. *Annals of Human Genetics* **42**, 87–94.

Suarez, B., Hampe, C.L. & van Eerdewegh, P. (1995) Problems of replicating linkage claims in psychiatry. In: *New Genetic Approaches to Mental Disorders* (eds E.S. Gershon & C.R. Cloninger), pp. 23–46. American Psychiatric Press, Washington, DC.

Suddath, R.L., Christison, G.W., Torrey, E.F., Casanova, M.F. & Weinberger, D.R. (1990) Anatomical abnormalities in the brains of monozygotic twins discordant for schizophrenia. *New England Journal of Medicine* **322**, 789–794.

Sunahara, R.K., Niznik, H.B., Weiners, D.M. *et al.* (1990) Human dopamine D_1 receptor encoded by an intronless gene on chromosome 5. *Nature* **347**, 80–83.

Tienari, P. (1971) Schizophrenia and monozygotic twins. *Psychiatria Fennica* **2**, 97–104.

Tienari, P. (1991) Interaction between genetic vulnerability and family environment: the Finnish adoptive family study of schizophrenia. *Acta Psychiatrica Scandinavica* **84**, 460–465.

Tienari, P.J., Wikstrom, J., Sajantila, A., Palo, J. & Peltonen, L. (1992) Genetic susceptibility to multiple sclerosis linked to myelin basic protein gene. *Lancet* **340**, 987–991.

Tsujita, T., Okazaki, Y., Fujimaru, K. *et al.* (1992) Twin concordance rates of DSM-IIIR schizophrenia in a new Japanese sample. *Abstracts of the Seventh International Congress on Twin Studies, Tokyo. Japan* **152**.

Turner, S.W., Toone, B.K. & Brett-Jones, J.R. (1986) Computerized tomographic scan changes in early schizophrenia: preliminary findings. *Psychological Medicine* **16**, 219–225.

Turner, W.J. (1979) Genetic markers for schizotaxia. *Biological Psychiatry* **14**, 177–206.

Tyler, A., Morris, M., Lazarou, L. *et al.* (1992) Presymptomatic testing for Huntington's disease in Wales 1987–90. *British Journal of Psychiatry* **161**, 481–488.

Ujike, H., Takehisa, Y., Takaki, M. *et al.* (2001) *NOTCH4* gene polymorphism and susceptibility to schizophrenia and schizoaffective disorder. *Neuroscience Letters* **301**, 41–44.

Vallada, H.P., Gill, M., Sham, P. *et al.* (1995) Linkage studies on chromosome 22 in familial schizophrenia. *American Journal of Medical Genetics and Neuropsychiatric Genetics* **60**, 139–146.

Van Broeckhoven, C., Backhovens, H., Cruts, M. *et al.* (1992) Mapping of a gene predisposing to early-onset Alzheimer's disease to chromosome 14q24.3. *Nature Genetics* **2**, 335–339.

Van Tol, H.H., Bunzow, J.R., Guan, H.C. *et al.* (1991) Cloning of the gene for a human dopamine D_4 receptor with high affinity for the antipsychotic clozapine. *Nature* **350**, 610–614.

Van Tol, H.H., Wu, C.M., Guan, H.C. *et al.* (1992) Multiple dopamine D_4 receptor variants in the human population. *Nature* **358**, 149–152.

Venter, J.C., Adams, M.D., Myers, E.W. *et al.* (2001) The sequence of the human genome. *Science* **291**, 1304–1351.

Vogler, G.P., Gottesman, I.I., McGue, M.K. & Rao, D.C. (1990) Mixed-model segregation analysis of schizophrenia in the Lindelius Swedish pedigrees. *Behavior Genetics* **20**, 461–472.

Walsh, C., Asherson, P. & Sham, P. (1993) Familial schizophrenia shows no gender difference in age of onset. *Schizophrenia Research* **9**, 127.

Wang, Z.W., Black, D., Andreasen, N. & Crowe, R.R. (1993) Pseudoautosomal locus for schizophrenia excluded in 12 pedigrees. *Archives of General Psychiatry* **50**, 199–204.

Weber, J.L. & May, P.E. (1989) Abundant class of human DNA polymorphisms which can be typed using the polymerase chain reaction. *American Journal of Human Genetics* **44**, 388–396.

Wei, J. & Hemmings, G.P. (2000) The *NOTCH4* locus is associated with susceptibility to schizophrenia. *Nature Genetics* **25**, 376–377.

Weinshilboum, R.M. & Raymond, F.A. (1977) Inheritance of low erythrocyte catechol-O-methyltransferase in man. *American Journal of Medical Genetics* **29**, 125–135.

Wender, P.H., Rosenthal, D., Kety, S.S., Schulsinger, F. & Welner, J.

(1974) Crossfostering: a research strategy for clarifying the role of genetic and experiential factors in the etiology of schizophrenia. *Archives of General Psychiatry* **30**, 121–128.

White, R. & Lalouel, J.M. (1988) Chromosome mapping with DNA markers. *Scientific American* **258**, 40–48.

Wildenauer, D., Hallmayer, J., Schwab, S. *et al.* (1997) 18p-Support for a locus conferring susceptibility to functional psychoses as evidenced by linkage and linkage disequilibrium studies in families with schizophrenia. *American Journal of Medical Genetics and Neuropsychiatric Genetics* **74**, 676–677.

Williams, J., Spurlock, G., McGuffin, P. *et al.* (1996) Association between schizophrenia and T102C polymorphism of the 5-hydroxytryptamine type 2a-receptor gene. European Multicentre Association Study of Schizophrenia (EMASS) Group. *Lancet* **347**, 1294–1296.

Williams, J., McGuffin, P., Nothen, M. & Owen, M.J. (1997) Meta-analysis of association between the 5-HT (2a) receptor T102C polymorphism and schizophrenia. *Lancet* **349**, 1221.

Williams, J., Spurlock, G., Holmans, P. *et al.* (1998) A meta-analysis and transmission disequilibrium study of association between the dopamine D_3 receptor gene and schizophrenia. *Molecular Psychiatry* **3**, 141–149.

Wright, P., Dawson, E., Donaldson, P.T. *et al.* (1998) A transmission/disequilibrium study of the DRB1*04 gene locus on chromosome 6p21.3 with schizophrenia. *Schizophrenia Research* **32**, 75–80.

Yaw, J., Myles-Worsley, M., Hoff, M. *et al.* (1996) Anticipation in multiplex schizophrenia pedigrees. *Psychiatric Genetics* **6**, 7–11.

Zhe Wu, W., Black, D., Andreasen, N.C. & Crowe, R.R. (1993) A linkage study of chromosome 11q in schizophrenia. *Archives of General Psychiatry* **50**, 212–216.

15 Intermediate phenotypes in genetic studies of schizophrenia

M.F. Egan, M. Leboyer and D.R. Weinberger

Recent advances in molecular genetics have produced breakthroughs in the genetics of complex traits such as diabetes, coronary heart disease and Alzheimer's disease. By contrast, molecular genetic studies of schizophrenia have not yet had similar successes. This may in part be a result of obstacles that complicate efforts to identify genes for any complex disorder such as unknown mode of inheritance, genetic heterogeneity, phenocopies, incomplete penetrance and variable expressivity (Pauls 1993; Lander & Schork 1994). These issues are described in more detail elsewhere in this volume (see Chapter 14). A second obstacle is the uncertainty of the heritable phenotype. Tsuang *et al.* (1993) have pointed out that ambiguities in identifying the phenotype may be the 'rate-limiting step' in psychiatric genetic studies. Indeed, although reliable diagnostic criteria and structured psychiatric interviews have been used in psychiatric genetics, little is known about how to choose the diagnostic system that best describes the most heritable form of the illness or most heritable aspects of psychopathology. Within apparently affected subjects various types of phenotypic misclassification reduce the power of linkage studies because of phenocopies or genetic heterogeneity. For example, family studies of schizophrenic probands have revealed that familial/genetic aspects of schizophrenia were more apparent when broadening the affected status to include subsyndromal variants such as schizophrenia-like personality disorders (schizotypal, paranoid and schizoid personality disorders). However, broadening the definition of affected status might increase the risk of false-positive misclassification, which can dramatically confound linkage studies. Furthermore, using multiple diagnostic classifications in a linkage study inflates the number of comparisons (e.g. Straub *et al.* 1995), raising the possibility of type I errors.

To minimize imprecision introduced by categorical diagnoses, new strategies have been described aiming at identifying more elemental neurobiological traits related to genetic risk for schizophrenia, so-called endophenotypes or, more aptly, intermediate phenotypes (Egan & Weinberger 1997; Leboyer *et al.* 1998). Intermediate phenotypes may be any neurobiological measure related to the underlying molecular genetics of the illness, including biochemical, endocrinological, neurophysiological, neuroanatomical or neuropsychological markers. A true intermediate phenotype, by virtue of being closer to the direct effects of susceptibility alleles, should have a simpler genetic architecture, with individual loci contributing a greater percentage of total phenotypic variance than one could hope to find with the more complex clinical phenotypes. This simpler genetic architecture thus increases the power of both linkage and association studies. For example, endophenotypes might be underlined by a Mendelian inheritance pattern which would considerably diminish the sample size required to detect the responsible genetic mutation (Freedman *et al.* 1999). Furthermore, because biological measures are more tractable for molecular research, a set of compelling candidate genes can be more readily generated, relative to clinical phenotypes, for association studies. Thus, using intermediate phenotypes is a promising strategy to enhance the power of both linkage and association studies of schizophrenia.

There are several examples from somatic diseases where biological measures helped in defining the genetic basis of the illness in molecular terms. For instance, understanding the mode of inheritance of idiopathic haemochromatosis was unclear until serum iron concentration was selected as a biological indicator of intrinsic liability to the disease. Including serum iron in the analysis uncovered a linkage with the HLA-A locus (Lalouel *et al.* 1985). To identify a genetic susceptibility factor in juvenile myoclonic epilepsy, investigators chose a subclinical trait (i.e. a characteristic EEG abnormality) as an endophenotype in affected and non-affected family members and found linkage to chromosome 6 (Greenberg *et al.* 1988). Focusing on families with the highest serum glucose levels as a specific phenotype led to the discovery of a genetic deficit underlying type 2 diabetes (Mahtani *et al.* 1996).

One way to conceptualize this approach is to view schizophrenia as emerging from the interaction of a variety of elementary neurobiological abnormalities, each underlined by specific defects in a unique set of candidate genes, and interacting with non-genetic factors (Fig. 15.1). If this is the case, then it becomes clear how measuring intermediate phenotypes can improve the power to find genes. Studies of family members of patients with schizophrenia have often found that even relatives with no psychiatric disease may have one of a number of subtle neurobiological alterations typically seen in patients. This suggests, but does not prove, that intermediate phenotypes may exist. To date, such studies have provided a variety of potential intermediate phenotypes, but only two have been related to specific genes. Freedman *et al.* (1997) found linkage between a deficit in the inhibition of the P50 waveform of the auditory evoked response to repeated auditory stimuli and markers near the α7 nicotinic acid receptor gene. More recently, Egan *et al.* (2001b) found evidence for an association between the high activity valine at codon 108 (158 for the membrane-bound protein) allele of the gene for *COMT* and several measures of prefrontal function. The *COMT* valine allele, in contrast to the methionine allele, was also weakly associated with schizophrenia. These initial successes demonstrate the plausibility of this approach.

In this chapter, we review the existing literature on intermediate phenotypes associated with schizophrenia. First, we review methodological issues in genetic studies using intermediate phenotypes. Next we describe studies of family members that have employed a variety of methodologies including clinical, cognitive, electrophysiology, biochemical, structural or functional brain imaging.

Methodological issues

Assumptions

Using biological measures in genetic studies assumes that genes increase susceptibility to schizophrenia by virtue of their effects on these measures (Fig. 15.1). Just as increased serum cholesterol is a risk factor for coronary artery disease, one assumes that the putative intermediate phenotype fits in the causal chain between gene, protein, physiology and manifest illness. This assumption could be wrong, in that many schizophrenia genes may not exert any impact except in conjunction with one another to produce a single final common pathophysiology (Fig. 15.2). This approach also assumes that the genetic architecture of a given measure is simpler or more approachable than schizophrenia itself, which could also be wrong. For example, IQ is lower in patients with schizophrenia but it is very possible that the genetic architecture of IQ is more complex than that of schizophrenia.

Characteristics of intermediate phenotypes

Quantitative measures vary in their suitability for use in genetic studies. Two useful characteristics of intermediate phenotypes are high test–retest reliability and stability over time. Variance as a result of measurement error and other state-dependent processes are forms of environmental variance that reduce the genetic component of total phenotypic variance. This in turn reduces one's power to detect genes. In other words, poor reliability or stability adds 'noise'. Related to this, measures should be relatively unaffected by neuroleptics and other medications, as

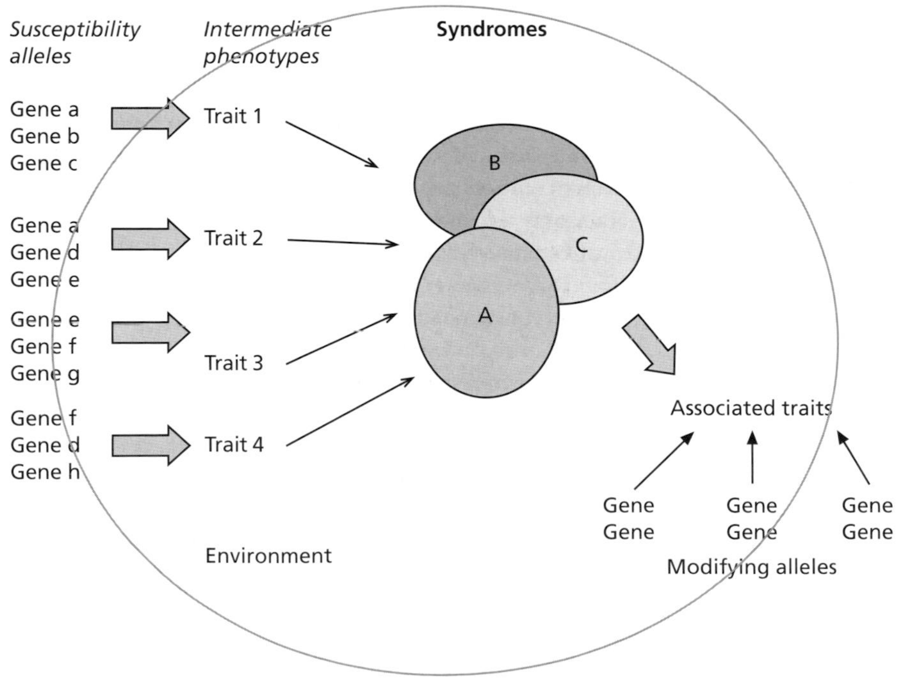

Fig 15.1 Intermediate phenotypes are biological measures more closely related to the effects of genes that increase risk for illness in complex genetic disorders such as schizophrenia. These measures can increase the power for finding disease genes because of their simpler genetic architecture and because often their underlying molecular biology is more certain, providing a stronger basis for selecting candidate genes.

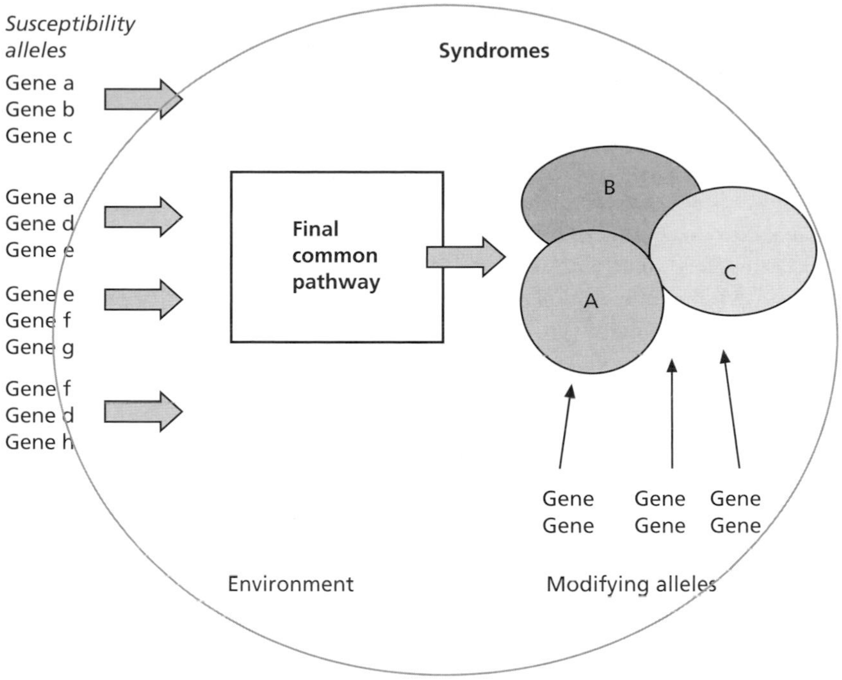

Fig 15.2 An alternative model of a complex genetic disorder. In this model, susceptibility genes act in concert to produce a final common pathway and a clinical phenotype. By themselves, genes or groups of genes do not produce specific detectable effects on biological measures. In this case, the intermediate phenotype approach is not useful.

this increases environmental and reduces genetic components of variance. Unfortunately, these data are lacking for many candidate phenotypes discussed below. Given the high rates of tobacco, caffeine and alcohol use in patients, if these substances markedly impact on a phenotypic measure, the increased environmental variance may dilute genetic effects. While patients using these substances could be excluded, this will increase ascertainment difficulties.

Biological traits that have an approachable neurobiology, e.g. through animal models, neuroimaging, etc., have an added advantage because they offer more obvious molecular targets for association studies. For example, sensory gating has been examined in an animal model and a prime candidate gene has been shown to be related to this phenotype (Freedman *et al.* 1997). In contrast, phenotypes such as paranoia or hallucinations are not amendable to molecular studies using animal models. Phenotypes that appear to be related to a critical aspect of the neurobiology and morbidity may have certain advantages over those whose role in the illness is vague. For example, cognitive deficits, such as impaired working memory, appear to predict outcome (Goldberg *et al.* 1995; Green 1996) and may have a key role in pathophysiology (Weinberger 1987). In contrast, it is unclear if correcting eye tracking deficits would have any detectable impact on illness or outcome. Alternatively, eye tracking deficits may be a surrogate measure for a broader deficit in prefrontal function. Finally, to be useful, intermediate phenotypes *per se* must offer some additional genetic information beyond psychiatric diagnosis. A biological test with 100% sensitivity and specificity for schizophrenia may not offer any additional genetic information beyond what one could already obtain with diagnosis.

Determining genetic variance for intermediate phenotypes

Many biological aspects of schizophrenia may be related to environmental factors, such as chronic illness or neuroleptic treatment, rather than to schizophrenia genes. Thus, a critical issue in selecting an intermediate phenotype for genetic studies is to demonstrate a significant genetic component related to risk for schizophrenia. The traditional genetic epidemiological approach is to study a variety of relatives (i.e. first, second and third degree), spouses and adoptees to infer the genetic and environmental components of total phenotypic variance (Plomin *et al.* 1990; Falconer & Mackay 1996). These studies have essentially not been performed to any significant degree for most putative intermediate phenotypes. The overwhelming majority of studies have looked exclusively at siblings and/or parents. Correlations between first-degree relatives set an upper limit on heritability (Falconer & Mackay 1996). Such studies of first-degree relatives are unable to exclude shared environment as a cause for family correlations. However, there are reasons, at least for some phenotypes, to think that shared environment has only a small role and that much of the variance in familial correlations is brought about by genetic factors that increase risk for schizophrenia.

Data from family studies suggest that familial aggregation of schizophrenia is largely accounted for by genetic and not environmental factors (Rao *et al.* 1981; McGue & Gottesman 1989). In other words, there are no environmental factors shared between siblings that increase risk for schizophrenia (Plomin *et al.* 1990; Cannon *et al.* 1998a). This implies that all environmental variance related to increased risk for schizophrenia may be uniquely experienced by the proband. If true, healthy siblings differ from controls in two ways: increased genetic risk for schizophrenia and environmental factors associated with having a sibling with serious mental illness. Differences between sibs and controls for intermediate phenotypic measures, such as cognitive deficits (see below), should be a result of one of these factors. It seems unlikely that environmental factors would account for all of this variance, so the real issue is the magnitude of the genetic portion of variance. Efforts to test such hypotheses more directly have been undertaken; for example, for cognitive deficits. These deficits, which are common in patients and their siblings, appear to be unrelated to at least one putative environmental risk factor, *in utero* insults (Cannon *et al.* 2000a). Furthermore, children of schizophrenic parents raised by foster parents show impaired cognitive performance on some tests (Asarnow *et al.* 1978). Both findings support the notion that environmental factors shared between affected and unaffected sibs may not account for their cognitive deficits. However, in contrast to such family studies, studies of environmental risk factors do point to some that may be shared, such as birth in an urban area (see Chapters 12 and 31). Thus, determining genetic variance based solely on correlations between first-degree relatives, which is the most commonly used method, involves assumptions that may be somewhat inaccurate.

Most studies of intermediate phenotypes begin by looking for a difference between first-degree relatives and controls. Some family cohorts have included relatives who do not have schizophrenia spectrum disorders. One advantage to studying these subjects is that affected sib pairs may share a variety of illness-related environmental factors impacting on neurobiological measures. Thus, studies of only affected sib pairs could be misleading and underestimate environmental components of phenotypic variance. A second advantage to studying 'healthy' relatives is that they are far easier to ascertain than affected sib pairs. The strength of genetic effect can be estimated using the intraclass correlation coefficient (ICC) or relative risk measures. The former is the classic method used with quantitative traits. Relative risk (percentage sibs 'affected'/percentage controls 'affected'), on the other hand, reduces quantitative to qualitative measures, thus 'throwing away' information; however, using relative risk to look specifically for degree of *impairment* (e.g. 1 SD below the control mean) may provide additional evidence that *impairment* itself is heritable (Egan *et al.* 2000, 2001a). For most biological traits, such as cognitive performance, prior studies have already clearly demonstrated a genetic component. Deriving an ICC value from families with schizophrenia does not directly address the question of the heritability of impaired function.

A recurring theme in the sections below relates to the difficulties with replication. Several factors may be involved. First, initial reports of putative intermediate phenotypes typically include small numbers of subjects that are not systematically ascertained. Secondly, control groups are sometimes poorly described. More recent studies have screened out controls with significant psychopathology or recruit controls with higher IQs than relatives, often from the hospital staff (referred to herein as 'supernormal' controls). In contrast, family cohorts are frequently mixtures of parents and siblings with a variety of psychiatric disorders, including depression and schizophrenia spectrum disorders. While it is critical to describe the normal control group carefully, failure to match control subjects to family members on variables such as age, gender, education, IQ or psychiatric morbidity may introduce bias by reducing neurobiological deficits in the control group, increasing differences between controls and sibs and artificially elevating relative risk scores. Thus, in comparing studies below, specific methodological aspects are highlighted when appropriate in an effort to shed light on inconsistent findings.

Design of genetic studies using intermediate phenotypes

The two general approaches to finding genes for complex disorders are linkage and association (see Chapter 14). Linkage, which uses two or more members from the same family, may be underpowered relative to association studies for complex traits (Risch & Merikangas 1996), although for phenotypes with a simple mode of inheritance this may not be the case. For example, abnormal sensory gating, assessed using the P50 wave, appears to have a simple Mendelian inheritance pattern in families studied thus far. Most of the intermediate phenotypes described below, however, do not have a clear genetic architecture and seem likely to be at least oligogenic or polygenic. Therefore, using linkage with densely affected family members may not be optimal for some phenotypes. A second concern with linkage is that using either elderly or very young subjects in multigenerational families can introduce additional variance from ageing and developmental processes. Using age as a covariate may not adequately adjust measures because they may have a non-linear relationship to age. Thus, it may be difficult, for example, to attribute enlarged ventricles in elderly subjects to the effects of schizophrenia genes, in contrast to ageing, medical illness, etc. A second linkage design, using affected sib pairs, can also be difficult given the high rates of drug and alcohol abuse that confound most phenotypic measures described below. Excluding such subjects makes recruiting adequate numbers extremely difficult. An alternate strategy is to use quantitative genetic methods with unaffected and affected sibs. One example of this type of study uses extreme discordant sib pairs, which may provide much of the power in genetic analyses of unselected sib pairs (Risch & Zhang 1995).

Some of the limitations of linkage can be avoided using association methods, which include case–control and family-based designs and both qualitative (e.g. diagnoses) or quantitative traits. Briefly, with case–control designs, gene frequencies are compared between probands and controls, but poor matching for ethnicity (or population stratification) can produce spurious results. Using additional genetic markers to test for such stratification (Pritchard & Rosenberg 1999; Pritchard *et al.* 2000) may circumvent this problem. Family-based designs use genotypes of family members as controls, including parents (for qualitative phenotypes; Spielman *et al.* 1993) or siblings (for qualitative or quantitative measures; Allison *et al.* 1999). Given that age is likely to affect many intermediate phenotypes, using sibs may provide an advantage over multigenerational designs. Such sib pairs could also be used for sib linkage analyses, such as the extreme discordant method. However, recruitment is more difficult with family-based designs, but allows one to assess familiality of putative intermediate phenotypes if not previously known. Finally, future studies are likely to involve a combination of linkage and association, whereby case–control samples are compared for all genetic variation. This approach takes advantage of linkage disequilibrium to look for haplotypes shared by affected subjects more often than controls.

Eye tracking dysfunction

Abnormalities in eye tracking are one of the first and most extensively studied candidate intermediate phenotypes in schizophrenia. Observed early in the twentieth century, eye tracking dysfunction (ETD) was rediscovered by Holzman (Holzman *et al.* 1973) who also noted impairment in unaffected relatives (Holzman *et al.* 1974). The initial excitement that ETD may identify a simple Mendelian trait related to risk for schizophrenia (Holzman *et al.* 1988) gradually gave way as additional studies produced conflicting findings. A review of this extensive literature highlights many of the issues that confront and confound studies of intermediate phenotypes. For example, which measures should be used? Is ETD affected by neuroleptics? To what degree is ETD genetic and how is it related to risk for schizophrenia? Unfortunately, despite many years of intensive effort, it remains uncertain how useful ETD may be for finding susceptibility genes for schizophrenia.

Studies of eye tracking dysfunction in patients with schizophrenia

Over 100 studies have been published on ETD in patients with schizophrenia, addressing issues ranging from frequency, specificity, effects of medications, familiality and underlying neurobiology. An important consideration in evaluating and comparing these studies is the methods used to record eye movements, the task employed, outcome measures and the nature of the control and patient groups. Electro-oculography and, more recently, high-resolution infrared oculography have been the primary methods used to assess and quantify ETD. Qualitative ratings of how closely the eye tracks the target have been advanced as a dependable method of assessing overall performance, but such measures do little to clarify the precise mechanism underlying global impairment. Consequently, most recent studies include a variety of quantitative parameters. The two most frequently studied aspects of eye tracking are the smooth pursuit and saccade systems (Table 15.1; for review see Levy *et al.* 1993). Gain, or speed of the eye, is a measure of the smooth pursuit system and is slowed in patients. Saccades are very rapid movements used to move the eye quickly toward a target, such as when one hears a voice and rapidly turns the eye to the estimated position of the speaker. Patients with schizophrenia, during smooth pursuit, follow the target slowly and often show compensatory saccades to catch-up to the target ('catch-up saccades') (Levy *et al.* 1994). Subjects may also move ahead of the target ('anticipatory saccades'). Thus, the most commonly reported pattern in patients is reduced gain, with a compensatory increase in catch-up saccades to correct the increasing error in eye position (Levy *et al.* 1994). Some studies have reported normal gain and a primary deficit in intrusive saccades (Levin *et al.* 1982). Another frequently used outcome measure is root mean square (RMS) error, which captures how closely the eye remains foveated on the target and is thus reduced by slow gain and saccades that move the fovea off target. RMS error is typically reduced in patients but does not distinguish which system is responsible for the impairment. Estimates of the frequency of ETD (typically using qualitative ratings, gain and/or RMS error) in patients with schizophrenia range from 20% to 80%. Reasons for this large range are unclear but may be related to differences in methodology, the measures used and/or ascertainment issues (see below).

Table 15.1 Eye tracking measures.

Gain: speed of eye relative to speed of target

Root mean square (RMS) error: measure of how closely the eye is foveated on the target throughout the task
Example: Gain (eye speed) may closely match target speed but consistently lag behind target. In this case gain would be normal while RMS error would be reduced

Saccades: rapid movement of eye toward a target
Example: during eye tracking, the eye may jump ahead of target (anticipatory saccade) or, if gain is reduced and the eye falls behind the target, a 'catch-up' saccade can bring the eye back to the target
Saccades may have varying amplitudes. 'Small' saccades are generally those that travel less than 4° of the visual field

Antisaccade task: subjects have to move eyes rapidly to a specified location on the *opposite* side of the visual field from a remembered target. This task is very difficult, particularly for patients. One must inhibit the initial temptation to look towards the remembered target

Other abnormalities in eye movement during visual tasks have also been found. For example, simple fixation, or the ability to stay focused on a fixed target, may be impaired in patients (Amador *et al.* 1995). Patients also simply spend less time engaged in pursuit tasks (Friedman *et al.* 1995). Increased small-amplitude saccades, increased phase lag and increased intrusive saccades have been reported as well (Levy *et al.* 1994). In an 'antisaccade' task, subjects must produce a 'volitional' saccade in the direction opposite to the target (McDowell & Clementz 1996). Patients and relatives have difficulty in this (Clementz 1998). Yet another type of eye tracking abnormality, again for

Neurochemical phenotypes

(see also Chapter 16)

Investigation of neurochemical abnormalities among unaffected relatives of schizophrenic patients is a convenient method to explore biochemical predisposition to schizophrenia in natural conditions, without any pharmacological challenge and in the absence of confounding factors such as chronicity of illness or effects of medication. Dopamine (DA) abnormalities have been explored in non-psychotic relatives as negative and positive symptoms are hypothesized to be caused by decreased and increased brain DA functions.

Amin *et al.* (1999) showed that healthy first-degree relatives of schizophrenic patients ($n = 55$) had decreased plasma homovanillic acid (HVA), the major DA metabolite, compared with 20 normal subjects. This finding is supported by similar results in a subgroup of relatives (Waldo *et al.* 1992). Such decreased plasma HVA in relation to negative symptoms is hypothesized to be a result of mesocortical DA activity, but it is unclear whether and to what degree plasma HVA is a measure of central DA function. In schizophrenic patients, proteins involved in DA uptake and metabolism have been extensively studied; i.e. platelet monamine oxidase-B (MAO-B), D_2 lymphocyte binding sites, positron emission tomography (PET) studies of DA receptors and measures of prolactin (PRL) or growth hormone (GH) have been used for assessment of static and dynamic DA function, but so far there have been very few studies of these parameters in unaffected relatives of schizophrenic patients. Increased densities of postsynaptic DA function [^{3}H]spiperone binding sites on lymphocytes have been reported in one-third of the well relatives of schizophrenic probands (Bondy & Ackenheil 1987). Sautter *et al.* (1987) have investigated the familiality of the GH response to apomorphine in patients with schizophrenia. They found that the GH response differentiated the relative risk of schizophrenia in families; probands with high GH response had the lowest familial risk. Regarding serotonergic parameters, two studies have reported higher cerebrospinal fluid 5-hydroxyindoleacetic acid (5-HIAA) concentrations in schizophrenic patients with a strong positive family history of schizophrenia (Sedvall & Wode-Helgodt 1980). To our knowledge, studies of neuroendocrine measures of 5-hydroxytryptamine (5-HT) function and platelet markers of 5-HT function have not yet been undertaken in individuals at risk for schizophrenia.

Electrophysiological markers

Cognitive event-related potentials (ERPs) have been widely used as potential indicators of risk for schizophrenia (for review see Friedman & Squires-Wheeler 1994). ERPs are usually measured in terms of amplitude, latency and topography of a component. ERPs elicited by infrequent auditory targets, for example during an oddball paradigm, are characterized successively by an early component, N100, which reflects the sensory analysis of the physical parameters of the stimulus (Näätänen & Picton 1987), then N200, which reflects selective attention processes conducting to stimulus categorization, which is followed by P300 classically related to the postperceptual updating of short-term working memory traces of expected environmental stimuli (Donchin & Isreal 1980). The ERP technique is a safe non-invasive approach to the study of psychophysiological correlates of human mental processes. However, several methodological issues have to be taken into account to infer an underlying physiological deficit, such as whether to use single or several electrode sites and the need to control for age, as amplitude and latency differ as a function of increasing age (Pfefferbaum *et al.* 1984).

The most robust ERP abnormality in patients with schizophrenia is that of reduced P300 amplitude and increased latency using an oddball paradigm (for review see Friedman & Squires-Wheeler 1994). This finding has been reported in both medicated and unmedicated schizophrenic patients using an auditory modality, whereas the visual modality varies and may serve as a state marker (Duncan *et al.* 1987; Pfefferbaum *et al.* 1989; St Claire *et al.* 1989). Altogether, the abnormal auditory P300 waveform in schizophrenics appears to be independent of medication effect, clinical state (Blackwood *et al.* 1987), duration of symptoms and clinical subtype of the illness (St Clair *et al.* 1989). However, reduced P300 is not specific to schizophrenia as it has been reported in a variety of different disorders such as dementia (Pfefferbaum *et al.* 1984), alcoholism (Porjesz *et al.* 1980) and bipolar disorder (Muir *et al.* 1991; Souza *et al.* 1995). Discrepant results have been obtained concerning the observation of a reduction in the P300 amplitude over the left, compared with the right, temporal scalp in schizophrenic subjects. This finding was originally reported by Morstyn *et al.* (1983), but has not always been replicated (Pfefferbaum *et al.* 1989).

High-risk studies provided evidence that P300 abnormalities can be considered as vulnerability indicators. Schreiber *et al.* (1991) have reported a prolonged P300 latency in the offspring of schizophrenic patients, but no difference for P300 amplitude. Kidogami *et al.* (1991) observed a reduction in P300 amplitude in the schizophrenic sample and their relatives compared with controls. Blackwood *et al.* (1991) found P300 amplitude reduction and latency prolongation in the schizophrenia sample and half of their non-schizophrenic relatives showed prolonged P300 latency. However, in those two studies, P300 latency values were not age-adjusted and a single electrode was used. Furthermore, no difference between offspring of schizophrenics and controls was reported by Friedman *et al.* (1986). Latency prolongation or amplitude reduction has not been observed in schizotypal individuals (Condray & Steinhauser 1992) who are supposed to share genetic variance with schizophrenia. Squires-Wheeler *et al.* (1993) did not find a link between reduced P300 amplitude in adolescents at risk for schizophrenia and those who become schizophrenic in young adulthood. Thus, on the basis of the existing literature, which is based on small sample size, there is mixed evidence regarding whether P300 abnormalities can be considered as marker traits.

Other abnormalities of the components of the ERPs have been observed in schizophrenia. The negative component peaking at about 100 ms following auditory stimuli (N100) is also reduced in schizophrenia in the auditory but not the visual component (Roth *et al.* 1980). Frontal N100 and parietal P300 component reductions have also been observed in high-risk children compared with controls (Schreiber *et al.* 1992). Schizophrenic patients and their relatives showed similar amplitude reduction and latency prolongation of the N100, N200 and P300 waves compared with controls (Frangou *et al.* 1997). However, N100 reduction is not specific to schizophrenia as it is also observed in patients with major depressive disorder. N100 reduction might be the result of an overlapping component, the processing negativity, which is elicited during selective attention paradigms and appears to be reduced in schizophrenia patients (Michie *et al.* 1990; Shelley *et al.* 1999). A reduction in processing negativity is consistent with deficits in selective attention, which have been proposed to account for some schizophrenic symptomatology.

One of the most promising ERP phenotypes comes from studies of the P50 waveform. This paradigm examines P50 amplitude to two consecutive simple auditory stimuli (usually a clicking noise) (Freedman *et al.* 1983; Siegel *et al.* 1984). The clicks are separated by several hundred milliseconds. The normal response is for subjects to have a reduced P50 response to the second click, suggesting that this repeated stimulus is actively suppressed, perhaps because it is less relevant, and is referred to as sensory gating. Patients with schizophrenia and roughly 50% of their first-degree relatives seem to have impaired sensory gating in this paradigm, as demonstrated by a failure to suppress the P50 wave amplitude to the second click relative to the first. There is some controversy regarding whether the schizophrenia-related deficit represents a 'gating' phenomenon. Some studies have reported that the amplitude from the second click is the same in patients and controls, while the amplitude and/or latency of the first click is altered in patients, perhaps accounting for the decreased ratio (Jin & Potkin 1996; Jin *et al.* 1997). Failure of sensory gating in this paradigm has also been reported in acutely manic patients. It appears to be state-dependent in affective disorders but a stable trait abnormality in families with a schizophrenic proband (Baker *et al.* 1987). The neurobiology of sensory gating has been examined in rodent models and is critically dependent on cholinergic input to the hippocampus (Luntz-Leybman *et al.* 1992). This input is mediated in part by the $\alpha 7$ nicotinic receptor. Remarkably, the P50 phenotype has been used in linkage studies and has shown linkage to a marker very close to the gene for the $\alpha 7$ nicotinic receptor with the 15q32 region (Freedman *et al.* 1997). This constitutes one of the most impressive and successful uses of intermediate phenotypes to dissect the genetics of schizophrenia. However, it remains uncertain exactly what aspect of this gene is responsible for impaired gating and how it contributes to the clinical syndrome of schizophrenia (for discussion see Adler *et al.* 1998).

Neuroimaging phenotypes

(see also Chapter 22)

Neuroimaging techniques have been relatively underutilized in the search for intermediate phenotypes associated with schizophrenia. Nevertheless, they hold significant promise, as such measures appear, at least prima facie, to be closer to the biological effects of genes. Neuroimaging parameters are likely to be less subject to confounds related to understanding directions, motivation and other vicissitudes of testing that might affect, for example, eye tracking and neuropsychological tests. A recent demonstration of the surprising power of neuroimaging measures comes from a study of the effects of *COMT* genotype on prefrontal function (Egan *et al.* 2001b). In this study, the effects of the val108/158met polymorphism, which has a profound effect on enzyme activity and prefrontal dopamine catabolism, could be detected using functional magnetic resonance imaging (fMRI) measures of prefrontal efficiency during a working memory task with as few as 15 subjects. In contrast, several hundred subjects were needed to detect this effect using scores from the working memory task. This suggests that the fMRI-derived measures of frontal lobe function are much closer to the direct effects of *COMT*, compared with test scores. Efforts to uncover other neuroimaging phenotypes have generated promising leads. However, many of these studies have suffered some of the same methodological confounds seen with other techniques, such as small sample sizes and the use of 'supernormal' control groups. By far the most intensive efforts have been directed towards structural measures derived from computerized tomography (CT) and magnetic resonance imaging (MRI) scans. fMRI and magnetic resonance spectroscopy (MRS) have also been used in a handful of studies, while methods involving radioactive ligands, such as PET and single photon emission computerized tomography (SPECT), have not.

Structural measures derived from CT and MR images seem prime candidates to serve as intermediate phenotypes, given their hypothesized role in the pathophysiology of schizophrenia (see Chapter 22). However, the results from different studies are not consistent and no clear phenotype has emerged. In the first CT study of family members, Weinberger *et al.* (1981) found increased lateral ventricular size in 12 siblings compared with a well-matched control group. Ill siblings had larger ventricles compared with well siblings, who in turn had larger ventricles than controls, suggesting a relationship to genetic risk for schizophrenia. On the other hand, there was no correlation between ill and well siblings, indicating a lack of genetic effect. A second study by DeLisi *et al.* (1986) found just the opposite. Ten non-psychotic siblings were compared with 20 controls. Both groups included subjects with a variety of non-psychotic psychiatric disorders. No differences were seen on several volumetric measures between sibs and controls. However, there was clearly an effect of family membership on ventricular size in schizophrenic families (DeLisi *et al.* 1986). In a third study, DeLisi *et al.* looked at 11 sib pairs concordant for schizophrenia and found significant correlations for some measures, e.g. left posterior hippocampal volume, but not others, e.g. total left hippocampal volume (DeLisi *et al.* 1988). The small sample size makes these results and their anatomical specificities seem somewhat unreliable.

In a fourth and more ambitious CT study, Cannon *et al.* (1989) looked at 34 offspring who had either one or two parents with schizophrenia. Most of these offspring also had a schizophrenia spectrum diagnosis themselves. The authors found that increasing lateral ventricular size and reduced cortical volume were associated with increasing genetic risk (i.e. having a father with spectrum disorder) for schizophrenia. While consistent with a genetic effect, this could also be because of shared environmental effects of having two ill parents or simply as a result of confounds of the illness itself, because the offspring had high rates of schizophrenia spectrum disorder (Cannon *et al.* 1989, 1993). Looking at the factor structure of these CT measurements, Cannon *et al.* (1989) found two factors: one for cortical volumetric deficits and a second for lateral and third ventricular enlargement. Prospectively ascertained labour and delivery complications were correlated with the ventricular factor but not the cortical factor, suggesting two independent processes. Cannon *et al.* (1993) expanded their sample in a remarkable second study of 97 offspring, and found similar results. Genetic risk for schizophrenia again predicted cortical and ventricular volumetric abnormalities, and the latter interacted with labour and delivery complications. This was seen in the total group as well as a group including only the new subjects, and even when patients with schizophrenia were excluded. These provocative findings were, nevertheless, somewhat clouded by possible methodological issues, such as the inclusion of subjects with organic brain syndromes and head injury, and the inherent imprecision of CT. Finally, a recent CT study by Silverman *et al.* (1998) reported essentially no differences between siblings ($n = 69$) and controls ($n = 22$), although a very strong correlation was found between family members, confirming that there is a family component for ventricular size *per se*. In this study, lateral ventricular enlargement was seen in probands compared with siblings but not controls, suggesting an atypical proband group. Overall, the CT literature provides support for the notion that structural abnormalities commonly seen in patients, such as ventricular enlargement, may also be present in family members; however, the findings are highly inconsistent, making it difficult to draw firm conclusions.

Despite improved resolution of MRI, studies using this technique have also been inconclusive. Initial series of reports were encouraging but were difficult to interpret because of small sample sizes. For example, Dauphinais *et al.* (1990) examined 12 sib pairs concordant for schizophrenia. While several volumetric abnormalities were found, only reduced volume of the cerebral hemisphere was familial. Waldo *et al.* (1994) used MRI to measure hippocampal and amygdala volume in 20 healthy sibs and 43 controls. A strong effect of family on hippocampal volume was observed in schizophrenic families, suggesting a genetic component for this trait, but no differences were observed between sibs and controls. Seidman *et al.* (1997) found reduced subcortical grey matter and lateral ventricular enlargement in a cohort of six healthy siblings, while Keshavan *et al.* (1997) found reduced left amygdala volume, enlarged third ventricular volume and smaller total brain volume in a group of 11 offspring (mean age 15.1 years) of schizophrenic mothers.

Several larger and better designed MRI studies followed. In an important partial replication of their original CT studies, Cannon *et al.* (1998b) reported reduced cortical grey volume in sibs compared with a well-matched control group. The sibling group included 60 non-psychotic subjects largely past the age of risk. Sibs did not differ from controls on ventricular volume, a measure that combined lateral and third ventricular volumes. In a second large MRI study (Sharma *et al.* 1998), 57 unaffected relatives (parents and siblings) from 16 families with at least two affected subjects were compared with a younger supernormal control group. Relatives had enlarged left but not right lateral ventricles. No difference in cortical grey or white matter volume was observed between patients, relatives and controls. In contrast, Lawrie *et al.* (1999) found reduced thalamic as well as amygdala–hippocampal volume in 100 subjects at 'high risk' (two relatives with schizophrenia) compared with a 'supernormal' control group. A weak trend ($P = 0.09$) was found for reduced left prefrontal volume but there was no difference in lateral ventricular volume. Many of these young at-risk subjects are likely to later develop schizophrenia, suggesting that these findings could be antecedents to the illness itself. In a follow-up study with an expanded sample size, similar findings were reported (Lawrie *et al.* 2001). Reduced amygdala–hippocampal volume was also recently reported in a small sample of healthy adult siblings ($n = 20$) compared with a well-matched control group (O'Driscoll *et al.* 2001) and in a cohort ($n = 28$) of healthy parents, sibs and adult children (Seidman *et al.* 1999). Finally, Staal *et al.* (1998, 2000) found only third ventricular enlargement and reduced thalamic volume in 16 healthy siblings compared with a carefully matched control group. Remarkably, no differences were seen between sibs and controls for volumes of a number of other structures, including the lateral ventricles, the hippocampi, and prefrontal grey or white matter (Staal *et al.* 2000). Thus, at least three fairly large studies of subjects with increased genetic risk for schizophrenia have reported three different abnormalities:

1 reduced cortical grey matter volume;
2 enlarged lateral ventricles; and
3 reduced amygdala–hippocampal and thalamic volume.

The third finding has also been seen in two smaller subsequent studies. Of the three large studies, two used 'supernormal' controls, which should accentuate differences between relatives and controls. While the reasons for the lack of replication are uncertain, these results indicate that structural measures are not robust discriminators of family members from controls.

Structural imaging studies of twins provide another avenue to explore genetic aspects of volumetric alterations but fail to clarify whether these measures are good intermediate phenotypes. Reveley *et al.* (1982) in a CT study of 11 MZ and eight DZ healthy twin pairs showed that lateral ventricular size is highly heritable. In a small sample of seven MZ pairs of twins discordant for schizophrenia, they also found high heritability (70% and above) which was less than the heritability estimated for normal twins (87–98%). Affected MZ twins generally had larger ventricles relative to their unaffected cotwin, who in turn tended to have increased ventricular size relative to normal twin pairs, suggesting that part of the ventricular enlargement in schizophrenia is genetic. Suddath *et al.* (1990), using MRI, looked at 15 discordant MZ twin pairs and found that affected twins had larger lateral and third ventricles and smaller rostral hippocampi. Similar findings emerged when the data set was expanded to 22 MZ discordant pairs (McNeil 2000). Unfortunately, the authors did not look at differences between the unaffected twin and controls or correlations between pairs, leaving it unclear whether these abnormalities were familial. Baare *et al.* (2001) replicated these findings to some degree in a study of 15 MZ and 14 DZ discordant twin pairs. They also reported reduced hippocampal, intracranial and frontal lobe volumes in the MZ twin pairs. The correlation coefficients suggested that the discordant MZ twins were much more similar for most structural measures compared with the discordant DZ twins, although confidence intervals were very large, making conclusions difficult. Nevertheless, this careful comparison provides additional support for the notion that prefrontal, intracranial and whole brain volume reductions could be useful intermediate phenotypes. Overall, both CT and MRI structural studies indicate that some volumetric abnormalities, such as ventricular enlargement or reduced cortical or mesial temporal volume, may be present in family members, but the inconsistencies suggest that the effect size may be small and that further study is needed.

Volumetric data from structural scans have been used to derive measures of asymmetry and to test these as potential intermediate phenotypes. For example, Frangou (1997) looked at volume and asymmetry of the planum temporale in 32 patients, 55 of their non-psychotic first-degree relatives and 39 controls. They found no difference between the control group and relatives or patients. DeLisi (1997) looked at sylvian fissure asymmetry in 14 pairs of schizophrenia siblings and found a meagre yet significant effect of family for one of three measures, consistent with a possible genetic component. Asymmetry based on volumetric measures does not seem to be a robust intermediate phenotype.

Only a handful of studies have looked at neuroimaging parameters other than volumetric measures. Klemm *et al.* (2001) used phosphorus-31 magnetic resonance spectroscopic imaging (MRSI) to study 14 first-degree relatives (sibs and offspring) compared with 14 age-matched controls. Relatives had increased phosphodiesters, interpreted by the authors as suggesting increased breakdown of phospholipids in the prefrontal cortex. Keshavan *et al.* (1997) found a trend for reduced cingulate *N*-acetylaspartate (NAA) measures in a small group ($n = 10$) of young offspring of schizophrenic mothers. Callicott *et al.* (1998a), in by far the largest cohort of siblings studied with MRSI to date, looked at 60 healthy siblings compared with 66 controls. Siblings had significant reduced hippocampal NAA measures, with relative risk estimates ranging from 3.8 to 9, depending on the criteria to define abnormal NAA (e.g. 1 or 2 SD below the control mean.). Block *et al.* (2000) found no differences in NAA levels in a cohort of 35 non-psychotic family members but only looked in the prefrontal cortex. Of note, Callicott *et al.* also found no reductions in sib prefrontal cortex. Two groups have reported abnormalities in prefrontal physiology in family members. First, Blackwood *et al.* (1999) noted reduced prefrontal blood flow in a cohort of 36 first-degree relatives using SPECT. Similarly, abnormalities in prefrontal blood flow ('inefficiency') were seen by Callicott *et al.* (1998b) using fMRI. As noted above, this phenotype was useful in demonstrating the effect of *COMT* val158met genotype on prefrontal function.

In summary, neuroimaging methods have been used to elucidate several potential intermediate phenotypes. Data from structural measures, particularly MRI studies, have provided some evidence of abnormalities including ventricular enlargement, reduced cortical volume and reduced mesial temporal volume, which vary from study to study. This troubling lack of consistency could either be a result of subtle methodological differences between studies, such as ascertainment issues, or may indicate that these are not robust phenotypes. Several other measurements, including neurochemical measurements from MRSI and physiological measures from fMRI, seem very promising but replications in large samples with well-matched control groups are needed.

Cognitive phenotypes

Neuropsychological deficits are a prominent dimension of schizophrenia and may account for a substantial portion of the functional impairments in daily living (see Chapter 10). An impressive number of studies of first-degree relatives also indicate that cognitive impairments may be familial and that the pattern of such deficits is similar to, albeit less severe than, that seen in patients themselves (Cannon *et al.* 1994; Kremen *et al.* 1994). Furthermore, the shared variance between tests of different cognitive domains is small, suggesting that there may be several cognitive phenotypes suitable for use as intermediate phenotypes (Egan *et al.* 2001a). Studies of neuropsychological deficits share some of the same problems described above for studies of other intermediate phenotypes, such as the use of 'supernormal' controls and inconsistent results. However, overall matching with controls is generally better than that seen in other studies: subjects with Axis I disorders are excluded but siblings with Axis II disorders are included, whereas controls with these disorders are not. Such studies of 'healthy' sibs and their matched 'supernormal' controls therefore are less likely to overestimate differences between sibs and controls. Furthermore, while inconsistencies exist, the majority of studies are positive, suggesting that the differences are real.

The earliest family studies focused on 'at risk' children of schizophrenic mothers. These children exhibited a variety of behavioural abnormalities including impaired attention (Fish

1977; Parnas *et al.* 1982). Studies using more rigorous neuropsychological testing, such as the continuous performance tests (CPT), soon followed (Nuechterlein & Dawson 1984; Cornblatt & Keilp 1994). 'At-risk' children do poorly on these tests, particularly on harder versions (Grunebaum *et al.* 1974; Asarnow *et al.* 1977; Rutschmann *et al.* 1977, 1986). The type of CPT used may be important, because more difficult CPT tasks are likely to involve cognitive demands beyond pure attention. Some versions (e.g. the identical pairs (IP) version) have significant working memory loads, which may therefore confound impaired attention with impaired working memory. Adult siblings largely past the age of risk for schizophrenia have also shown impairment on CPT performance, again primarily with more difficult versions (Nuechterlein & Dawson 1984; Mirsky *et al.* 1992; Franke *et al.* 1993; Cornblatt & Keilp 1994). Studies using simpler versions of the CPT have been mixed. One recent large study using well-matched controls found no overall differences between sibs ($n = 193$) and controls ($n = 47$) (Egan 2000), although sibs of probands with impaired attention were worse as a group compared with controls. Two studies have reported a trend for impaired attention in sibs (Keefe *et al.* 1997; Laurent *et al.* 2000), while five have reported marked impairments (Maier *et al.* 1992; Cannon *et al.* 1994; Finkelstein *et al.* 1997; Chen *et al.* 1998; Saoud *et al.* 2000). The reasons for discrepancies between studies are unclear. Some studies used 'supernormal' control groups (Finkelstein *et al.* 1997; Keefe *et al.* 1997) and have included sib groups with relatively high rates of schizophrenia spectrum disorders, such as personality disorders (Cannon *et al.* 1994; Finkelstein *et al.* 1997; Keefe *et al.* 1997). Some studies include both parents and siblings, leading to possible bias as a result of age effects (Chen *et al.* 1998).

Several studies have tried to quantify the magnitude of the familial effect on impaired attention. Grove *et al.* (1991) estimated heritability of CPT performance in 61 first-degree relatives using the ICC and found $h^2 = 0.79$, suggesting a substantial genetic component. A second study of a Taiwanese cohort (parents and siblings, $n = 148$) using the 1–9 version with degraded stimuli (Chen *et al.* 1998) found very high rates of impairment in relatives compared with controls. Relative risk of 'impaired attention' was 18–130, depending on the cut-off criteria, which is dramatically higher than the relative risk for schizophrenia itself. In contrast, a second large study of 193 siblings in a US cohort (Egan *et al.* 2000) found only slightly increased relative risk in a subgroup of siblings. The marked differences in these relative risk values could be a result of confounds such as ethnicity, recruitment biases, education and type of relatives (parent or sib) studied. Overall, it remains possible that subtle deficits in attention are present in siblings, or at least in a subgroup, that these deficits are not simply antecedents of illness and that CPT measures could serve as a useful intermediate phenotype, but the effect seems weak.

Soon after impaired attention was noted, a variety of additional cognitive deficits were reported in family members. In general, these include cognitive tasks referable to prefrontal and mesial temporal structures. Prefrontal deficits were seen using several tests, most notably the Wisconsin Card Sort Test (WCST) but also tests of verbal fluency and the 'N back' working memory task. Secondly, tests of declarative memory, such as the Wechsler Memory Scale, revised version (WMS-R) or the California Verbal List Test (CVLT), have also tended to be abnormal in first-degree family members. Thirdly, scores on the Trail Making tests, including A and B versions, are reduced, implicating oculomotor scanning/psychomotor speed. Poor Trails B performance, while a crude measure sensitive to many neurological insults, is also seen with prefrontal deficits. Other abnormalities have also been reported, although less consistently (Kremen *et al.* 1994).

Studies employing fairly comprehensive neuropsychological batteries, while somewhat inconsistent, suggest the effect size in the moderate range for several tests with abnormalities seen even in psychiatrically healthy relatives. First, Pogue-Geile *et al.* (1991), in 40 non-schizophrenic sibs, and then Franke *et al.* (1992, 1993), in 33 healthy sibs, both found impaired performance on the WCST, Trails B and verbal fluency compared with well-matched control groups. On the other hand, Scarone *et al.* (1993) found no differences in WCST in 35 well siblings compared with matched but supernormal controls. Yurgelun-Todd and Kinnney (1993) found lower scores on the WCST but not Trails B in a group of 15 healthy sibs. Shedlack *et al.* (1997) found essentially no differences between 14 well siblings from multiplex families and well-matched 'supernormal' controls on verbal memory. In contrast, Cannon *et al.* (1994) found impaired performance on a large battery of tests including attention, working memory/executive function and verbal memory in 16 non-schizophrenic siblings, but six of 16 had definite or likely schizotypal personality disorder compared with 'supernormal' controls. Larger studies have more consistently found differences. Keefe *et al.* (1994), in a cohort of 54 non-psychotic first-degree relatives, found impaired performance on Trails B and verbal fluency (both letter and category), but not on the WCST, compared with 'supernormal' controls. Faraone *et al.* (1995) found impairments in abstraction, verbal memory and attention in a group of 35 non-psychotic first-degree relatives similar to the results of Toomey *et al.* (1998), who found impaired working memory (WCST) and verbal memory in an overlapping sample of 54 first-degree healthy relatives. Both studies apparently used the same well-matched control group, screened using the Minnesota Multiphasic Personality Inventory (MMPI). Egan *et al.* (2001a), in a study of 193 siblings compared with a closely matched control group, found deficits on WCST, Trails B and CVLT, whether or not subjects with schizophrenia spectrum disorders were included in these groups. Thus, as studies have included larger groups of siblings, more consistent differences have emerged and implicate the same brain regions and cognitive functions that are typically seen in patients with schizophrenia, including prefrontal cortex/working memory and ventral temporal lobe/declarative memory.

Two major studies have examined cognitive deficits in twins. In the first study of discordant twins, Goldberg *et al.* (1993, 1994, 1995), using a wide neuropsychological battery, found that unaffected MZ twins have subtle cognitive deficits for the WMS-R, with trends for impairment on WCST perseverative errors (PE) and Trails A ($P < 0.05$) (Goldberg *et al.* 1995). A second study of 18 MZ and 34 DZ discordant twin pairs examined the relationship between cognitive deficits and genetic risk for schizophrenia using canonical discriminant analysis (Cannon *et al.* 2000b). Four tests contributed unique genetic variance to increased risk for schizophrenia. These tests were spatial working memory (visual span test of the WMS-R), divided attention (using a Brown–Peterson dual-task paradigm), intrusions during recall of a word list (CVLT) and choice reaction time (using a Posner paradigm related to the CPT). It is unclear whether the same group differences were seen with these MZ twins compared with the Goldberg sample. In Cannon's analysis, verbal memory was more impaired in affected MZ subjects, relative to cotwins, suggesting an effect of unique environmental variance related to illness. While these data leave open the question of which tests are most informative for genetic studies, the conclusions are similar to those of other relatives in one important respect. Several domains of cognition are impaired, including working memory/executive function and some aspects of verbal recall and attention, which are related to genetic risk for schizophrenia.

Finding deficits on several neuropsychological tests does not necessarily mean that these measure independent traits. An alternative possibility is that impairments are found on different tests because of one underlying abnormality. Attempts to address this question, using several statistical approaches, suggest that this is not the case. For example, correlations between measures are generally low in these groups (Yurgelun-Todd & Kinney 1993; Keefe *et al.* 1994). On the other hand, Toomey *et al.* (1998) found fairly high correlations between attention and verbal memory and between attention and abstraction in a cohort of 54 first-degree relatives, but no significant correlation between WCST and memory measures (on the WMS-R). Egan *et al.* (2001a), using multiple regression, found only modest shared variance (less than 15% in siblings) between measures of working memory, verbal memory and psychomotor speed. Using factor analysis, Mirsky *et al.* (1991) and Kremen *et al.* (1992) found that WCST and Trails B load on different factors, similar to Egan *et al.* (2001a). Finally, Cannon *et al.* (2000b), in a critical analysis of MZ and DZ twins, found evidence for four distinct independent cognitive deficits using canonical discriminant analysis. In non-patient populations, factor analysis has consistently shown that most of the variance on tests of different cognitive domains load significantly on the first factor, often referred to as 'g'. In contrast, analyses of patient and sib groups, which include subjects with a variety of impairments, tend to find somewhat less loading on the first factor and more evidence of additional orthogonal factors where both patients and siblings have lower scores than controls. Overall, these results suggest that several independent domains of cognitive dysfunction are related to genetic risk for schizophrenia and that correlation and factor analytic studies could show different results because of different patterns of impairments.

Is it plausible to use neuropsychological phenotypes to find schizophrenia genes? Support for this approach comes from a recent finding by Egan *et al.* (2001b) using working memory and the WCST as the phenotype. One attractive aspect of using working memory is that the neurobiology is increasingly well understood (Williams & Goldman-Rakic 1995; Goldman-Rakic *et al.* 1996). Specifically, D_1-mediated dopamine neurotransmission at glutamatergic neurones in the prefrontal cortex is critical. While there is essentially no known genetic variance affecting D_1-receptor function or other factors modulating dopamine prefrontal tone, an important exception is COMT. This enzyme is critical for inactivating released dopamine (Karoum *et al.* 1994) and knock-outs show increased prefrontal dopamine (Gogos *et al.* 1998), a regional specificity that is likely to be caused by the paucity of the dopamine transporter in prefrontal cortex (Sesack *et al.* 1998). Also, remarkably, several studies in animals and humans suggest that reduced COMT activity improves working memory (Kneavel *et al.* 2000). The val/met polymorphism produces a dramatic effect on COMT enzyme activity (Weinshilboum & Dunnette 1981). Thus, the *val* allele would be expected to be related to relatively reduced working memory. In a cohort of 175 patients, 200 siblings and 45 controls, Egan *et al.* (2001b) found that the *COMT* genotype was associated with working memory; subjects with the *val* allele had worse scores. Furthermore, the *val* allele was associated with schizophrenia using the transmission disequilibrium test (TDT). Thus, this intermediate phenotype pointed to gene and mechanism of action, making the weak association much more plausible.

Other phenotypes

A variety of other abnormalities found in patients with schizophrenia have also been examined in relatives. These include measures such as handedness, neurological signs (Egan *et al.* 2001c), minor physical anomalies (Ismail *et al.* 1998), finger ridge counts (Davis & Bracha 1996) and others. In general, these studies are relatively small, very few or inconclusive.

Conclusions

Do intermediate phenotypes exist and can they be used to find genes that increase risk for schizophrenia.? The substantial body of research reviewed above suggest that the answer to both is a qualified yes. Many phenotypic measures have been examined in relatives of patients with schizophrenia and many differences have been reported when compared with controls. Unfortunately, replication has often been difficult. Studies of eye tracking dysfunction, the archetypical intermediate phenotype, demonstrate many of the vicissitudes that can lead to inconsistent and misleading results. One reason for the inconsistencies seems to be ascertainment. Because both age and psychopathology may be related to intermediate phenotypic measures, relatives and controls should be matched closely on age and psychiatric status. Other variables may also be relevant, such as gender, IQ, smoking or others. Eye tracking dysfunction remains a viable candidate phenotype and has been used successfully in one linkage study, but it appears that the genetic architecture is more complex than initially imagined and the likely contribution of eye tracking dysfunction genes to risk for schizophrenia is far from clear.

Data on clinical phenotypes suggest that negative symptoms may be an important focus for future research, although the lack of neurobiological models for negative symptoms could reduce their utility and it is unclear if the genetics of negative symptoms are any more tractable than that of schizophrenia itself. The use of neurochemical and neuroimaging phenotypes is in its infancy, but both seem to be promising areas for future research. Studies using electrophysiological markers, such as those related to P300 waveform, have been plagued by inconsistencies. One bright spot has been the use of the P50 waveform and the sensory gating paradigm. Neuropsychological abnormalities, which are more reliably found in relatives, in contrast to many other phenotypic measures, also hold promise for the future. Sensory gating and working memory measures have been used to demonstrate the effects of two genes, the $\alpha7$ nicotinic receptor and *COMT*, on biology and risk for schizophrenia. While replication is needed, these findings provide some validation for the utility of this approach. Clearly, further work is needed to describe more elementary phenotypes that are related to mechanisms relevant for neural function and that have simpler genetic architecture. For example, deficits in memory could be caused by abnormal encoding, early or late phases of long-term potentiation (LTP), or to other factors related to dendrite formation and stabilization in response to learning (see e.g. Milner *et al.* 1998). Deficits in prefrontal function may be related to processes, such as neuronal migration, or presynaptic dopamine input. Unfortunately, at present, there are no methods to study such elemental phenotypes in human subjects.

Several problems confront future studies using intermediate phenotypes. First, it is unclear whether any of these phenotypes will provide substantially simpler genetic architecture. Most are themselves complex. Secondly, given the unknown genetic architecture, it is difficult to predict how many subjects are required to detect quantitative trait loci that account for only a few per cent of total phenotypic variance. Thirdly, intermediate phenotypes are also plagued with problems of phenocopies. Neurobiological abnormalities may occur because of medications, drug abuse or other problems associated with chronic mental illness. Finally, the relationship between various measures is also uncertain, and some are bound to overlap, wholly or in part.

Beyond the methodological problems, inconsistencies and weak findings in family studies of intermediate phenotypes may indicate something about the neurobiology of genetic risk for schizophrenia. The effects of susceptibility genes on psychiatrically healthy relatives, who must have some of these genes, seems slight. This could be because of a variety of factors, such as the need for specific environmental triggers or other genetic loci acting in a multiplicative or epistatic fashion. A second factor could be heterogeneity. If there are different neurobiological pathways to develop schizophrenia, only some families will demonstrate some abnormalities. This could dilute the findings in relatives if all types are lumped together. Overall, it remains uncertain how useful intermediate phenotypes will be to find genes. It is very possible that the bulk of schizophrenia susceptibility genes may be found using traditional methods without these measures. On the other hand, given the difficulties encountered using psychiatric nosology and the dramatic advances in molecular neuroscience, which offer increasingly attractive candidate genes for phenotypes such as verbal and working memory, intermediate phenotypes remain attractive targets for genetic studies of schizophrenia.

References

Addington, J. & Addington, D. (1991) Positive and negative symptoms of schizophrenia. Their course and relationship over time. *Schizophrenia Research* **5**, 51–59.

Adler, L.E., Olincy, A., Waldo, M. *et al.* (1998) Schizophrenia, sensory gating, and nicotinic receptors. *Schizophrenia Bulletin* **24**, 189–202.

Allison, D.B., Heo, M., Kaplan, N. & Martin, E.R. (1999) Sibling-based tests of linkage and association for quantitative traits. *American Journal of Human Genetics* **64**, 1754–1763.

Amador, X.F., Malaspina, D., Sackeim, H.A. *et al.* (1995) Visual fixation and smooth pursuit eye movement abnormalities in patients with schizophrenia and their relatives. *Journal of Neuropsychiatry and Clinical Neuroscience* **7**, 197–206.

American Psychiatric Association. (1994) *Diagnostic and Statistical Manual of Mental Disorders*, 4th edn (DSM-IV). American Psychiatric Association, Washington, DC.

Amin, F., Silverman, J.M., Siever, L.J. *et al.* (1999) Genetic antecedents of dopamine dysfunction in schizophrenia. *Biological Psychiatry* **45**, 1143–1150.

Andreasen, N.C. & Olsen, S. (1982) Negative v positive schizophrenia. Definition and validation. *Archives of General Psychiatry* **39**, 789–794.

Arolt, V., Lencer, R., Nolte, A. *et al.* (1996) Eye tracking dysfunction is a putative phenotypic susceptibility marker of schizophrenia and maps to a locus on chromosome 6p in families with multiple occurrence of the disease. *American Journal of Medical Genetics* **67**, 564–579.

Asarnow, R.F., Steffy, R.A., MacCrimmon, D.J. & Cleghorn, J.M. (1977) An attentional assessment of foster children at risk for schizophrenia. *Journal of Abnormal Psychology* **86**, 267–275.

Asarnow, R.F., Steffy, R.A., MacCrimmon, D.J. *et al.* (1978) The McMaster Waterloo project. In: *An Attentional and Clinical Assessment of Foster Children at Risk for Schizophrenia. The Nature of Schizophrenia: New Approaches to Research and Treatment.* (eds L.C. Wynne, R.L. Cromwell & S. Matthysse), pp. 339–358. Wiley, New York.

Baare, W.F., van Oel, C.J., Hulshoff Pol, H.E. *et al.* (2001) Volumes of brain structures in twins discordant for schizophrenia. *Archives of General Psychiatry* **58**, 33–40.

Baker, N., Adler, L.E., Franks, R.D. *et al.* (1987) Neurophysiological assessment of sensory gating in psychiatric inpatients: comparison between schizophrenia and other diagnoses. *Biological Psychiatry* **22**, 603–617.

Berenbaum, H. & McGrew, J. (1993) Familial resemblance of schizotypic traits. *Psychological Medicine* **23**, 327–333.

Blackwood, D.H., Whalley, L.J., Christie, J.E. *et al.* (1987) Changes in auditory P3 event-related potential in schizophrenia and depression. *British Journal of Psychiatry* **150**, 154–160.

Blackwood, D.H., St Clair, D.M., Muir, W.J. & Duffy, J.C. (1991) Auditory P300 and eye tracking dysfunction in schizophrenic pedigrees. *Archives of General Psychiatry* **48**, 899–909.

Blackwood, D.H., Glabus, M.F., Dunan, J. *et al.* (1999) Altered cerebral perfusion measured by SPECT in relatives of patients with schizophrenia: correlations with memory and P300. *British Journal of Psychiatry* **175**, 357–366.

Bleuler, E. (1911) Dementia praecox oder Die Gruppe der Schizophrenien. In: *Handbuch der Psychiatrie, hrsg.* Von G. Aschaffenburg, Deiticke.

Block, W., Bayer, T.A., Tepest, R. *et al.* (2000) Decreased frontal lobe ratio of *N*-acetyl aspartate to choline in familial schizophrenia: a proton magnetic resonance spectroscopy study. *Neuroscience Letters* **289**, 147–151.

Bondy, B. & Ackenheil, M. (1987) ^{3}H-Spiperone binding sites in lymphocytes as possible vulnerability marker in schizophrenia. *Journal of Psychiatric Research* **21**, 521–529.

Brzustowicz, L.M., Honer, W.G., Chow, E.W. *et al.* (1997) Use of a quantitative trait to map a locus associated with severity of positive symptoms in familial schizophrenia to chromosome 6p. *American Journal of Human Genetics* **61**, 1388–1396.

Callicott, J.H., Egan, M.F., Bertolino, A. *et al.* (1998a) Hippocampal *N*-acetyl aspartate in unaffected siblings of patients with schizophrenia: a possible intermediate neurobiological phenotype. *Biological Psychiatry* **44**, 941–950.

Callicott, J., Egan, M., Mattay V. *et al.* (1998b) Altered prefrontal cortical function in unaffected siblings of patients with schizophrenia. *Neuroimage* **7**, S895.

Campion, D., Thibaut, F., Denise, P. *et al.* (1992) SPEM impairment in drug-naive schizophrenic patients: evidence for a trait marker. *Biological Psychiatry* **32**, 891–902.

Cannon, T.D., Mednick, S.A. & Parnas, J. (1989) Genetic and perinatal determinants of structural brain deficits in schizophrenia. *Archives of General Psychiatry* **46**, 883–889.

Cannon, T.D., Mednick, S.A., Parnas, J. *et al.* (1993) Developmental brain abnormalities in the offspring of schizophrenic mothers. I. Contributions of genetic and perinatal factors. *Archives of General Psychiatry* **50**, 551–564.

Cannon, T.D., Zorrilla, L.E., Shtasel, D. *et al.* (1994) Neuropsychological functioning in siblings discordant for schizophrenia and healthy volunteers. *Archives of General Psychiatry* **51**, 651–661.

Cannon, T.D., Kaprio, J., Lonnqvist, J., Huttunen, M. & Koskenvuo, M. (1998a) The genetic epidemiology of schizophrenia in a Finnish twin cohort: a population-based modeling study. *Archives of General Psychiatry* **55**, 67–74.

Cannon, T.D., van Erp, T.G., Huttunen, M. *et al.* (1998b) Regional gray matter, white matter, and cerebrospinal fluid distributions in schizophrenic patients, their siblings, and controls. *Archives of General Psychiatry* **55**, 1084–1091.

Cannon, T.D., Bearden, C.E., Hollister, J.M. *et al.* (2000a) Childhood cognitive functioning in schizophrenia patients and their unaffected siblings: a prospective cohort study. *Schizophrenia Bulletin* **26**, 379–393.

Cannon, T.D., Huttunen, M.O., Lonnqvist, J. *et al.* (2000b) The inheritance of neuropsychological dysfunction in twins discordant for schizophrenia. *American Journal of Human Genetics* **67**, 369–382.

Chapman, L.J. & Chapman, J.P. (1984) Psychosis proneness. In: *Controversies in Schizophrenia: Changes and Constancies* (ed. M. Alpert), pp. 157–174. Guilford, New York.

Chapman, L.J., Chapman, J.P., Kwapil, T.R., Eckblad, M. & Zinser, M.C. (1994) Putatively psychosis-prone subjects 10 years later. *Journal of Abnormal Psychology* **103**, 171–183.

Chen, W.J., Liu, S.K., Chang, C.J. *et al.* (1998) Sustained attention deficit and schizotypal personality features in non-psychotic relatives of schizophrenic patients. *American Journal of Psychiatry* **155**, 1214–1220.

Chen, Y., Levy, D.L., Nakayama, K. *et al.* (1999a) Dependence of impaired eye tracking on deficient velocity discrimination in schizophrenia. *Archives of General Psychiatry* **56**, 155–161.

Chen, Y., Palafox, G.P., Nakayama, K. *et al.* (1999b) Motion perception in schizophrenia. *Archives of General Psychiatry* **56**, 149–154.

Clementz, B.A. (1998) Psychophysiological measures of (dis) inhibition as liability indicators for schizophrenia. *Psychophysiology* **35**, 648–668.

Clementz, B.A., Sweeney, J.A., Hirt, M. & Haas, G. (1990) Pursuit gain and saccadic intrusions in first-degree relatives of probands with schizophrenia. *Journal of Abnormal Psychology* **99**, 327–335.

Clementz, B.A., Grove, W.M., Katsanis, J. & Iacono, W.G. (1991) Psychometric detection of schizotypy: perceptual aberration and physical anhedonia in relatives of schizophrenics. *Journal of Abnormal Psychology* **100**, 607–612.

Condray, R. & Steinhauer, S.R. (1992) Schizotypal personality disorder in individuals with and without schizophrenic relatives: similarities and contrasts in neurocognitive and clinical functioning. *Schizophrenia Research* **7**, 33–41.

Cornblatt, B.A. & Keilp, J.G. (1994) Impaired attention, genetics, and the pathophysiology of schizophrenia. *Schizophrenia Bulletin* **20**, 31–46. [Published erratum appears in *Schizophrenia Bulletin* 1994; **20**, 248.]

Dauphinais, I.D., DeLisi, L.E., Crow, T.J. *et al.* (1990) Reduction in temporal lobe size in siblings with schizophrenia: a magnetic resonance imaging study. *Psychiatry Research* **35**, 137–147.

Davis, J.O. & Bracha, H.S. (1996) Prenatal growth markers in schizophrenia: a monozygotic co-twin control study. *American Journal of Psychiatry* **153**, 1166–1172.

DeLisi, L.E., Goldin, L.R., Hamovit, J.R. *et al.* (1986) A family study of the association of increased ventricular size with schizophrenia. *Archives of General Psychiatry* **43**, 148–153.

DeLisi, L.E., Dauphinais, I.D. & Gershon, E.S. (1988) Perinatal complications and reduced size of brain limbic structures in familial schizophrenia. *Schizophrenia Bulletin* **14**, 185–191.

DeLisi, L.E., Sakuma, M., Kushner, M. *et al.* (1997) Anomalous cerebral asymmetry and language processing in schizophrenia. *Schizophr Bull* **23**, 255–271.

Donchin, E. & Isreal, J.B. (1980) Event-related potentials and psychological theory. *Progress in Brain Research* **54**, 697–715.

Duncan, C.C., Perlstein, W.M. & Morihisa, J.M. (1987) The P300 metric in schizophrenia: effects of probability and modality. *Electroencephalogr and Clinical Neurophysiology* **40**, 670–674.

Dworkin, R.H. & Lenzenweger, M.F. (1984) Symptoms and the genetics of schizophrenia: implications for diagnosis. *American Journal of Psychiatry* **141**, 1541–1546.

Egan, M.F. & Weinberger, D.R. (1997) Neurobiology of schizophrenia. *Current Opinions in Neurobiology* **7**, 701–707.

Egan, M.F., Goldberg, T.E., Gscheidle, T. *et al.* (2000) Relative risk of attention deficits in siblings of patients with schizophrenia. *American Journal of Psychiatry* **157**, 1309–1316.

Egan, M.F., Goldberg, T.E., Gscheidle, T. *et al.* (2001a) Relative risk for cognitive impairments in siblings of patients with schizophrenia. *Biological Psychiatry* **50**, 98–107.

Egan, M.F., Goldberg, T.E., Kolachana, B.S. *et al.* (2001b) Effect of COMT Val108/158Met genotype on frontal lobe function and risk for schizophrenia. *Proceedings of the National Academy of Sciences of the USA* **98**, 6917–6922.

Egan, M.F., Hyde, T.M., Bonomo, J.B. *et al.* (2001c) Relative risk of neurological signs in siblings of patients with schizophrenia. *American Journal of Psychiatry* **158**, 1827–1834.

Falconer, D.S. & Mackay, T.F.C. eds. (1996) *Introduction to Quantitative Genetics*, Vol. 4, Longman, Essex.

Faraone, S.V., Seidman, L.J., Kremen, W.S. *et al.* (1995) Neuropsychological functioning among the nonpsychotic relatives of schizophrenic patients: a diagnostic efficiency analysis. *Journal of Abnormal Psychology* **104**, 286–304.

Finkelstein, J.R., Cannon, T.D., Gur, R.E., Gur, R.C. & Moberg, P. (1997) Attentional dysfunctions in neuroleptic-naive and neuroleptic-withdrawn schizophrenic patients and their siblings. *Journal of Abnormal Psychology* **106**, 203–212.

Fish, B. (1977) Neurobiologic antecedents of schizophrenia in children: evidence for an inherited, congenital neurointegrative defect. *Archives of General Psychiatry* **34**, 1297–1313.

Frangou, S., Sharma, T., Sigmudsson, T. *et al.* (1997) The Maudsley Family Study. 4. Normal planum temporale asymmetry in familial schizophrenia. A volumetric MRI study. *British Journal of Psychiatry* **170**, 328–333.

Franke, P., Maier, W., Hain, C. & Klingler, T. (1992) Wisconsin Card Sorting Test: an indicator of vulnerability to schizophrenia? *Schizophrenia Research* **6**, 243–249.

Franke, P., Maier, W., Hardt, J. & Hain, C. (1993) Cognitive functioning and anhedonia in subjects at risk for schizophrenia. *Schizophrenia Research* **10**, 77–84.

Freedman, R., Adler, L.E., Waldo, M.C., Pachtman, E. & Franks, R.D. (1983) Neurophysiological evidence for a defect in inhibitory pathways in schizophrenia: comparison of medicated and drug-free patients. *Biological Psychiatry* **18**, 537–551.

Freedman, R., Coon, H., Myles-Worsley, M. *et al.* (1997) Linkage of a neurophysiological deficit in schizophrenia to a chromosome 15 locus. *Proceedings of the National Academy of Sciences of the USA* **94**, 587–592.

Freedman, R., Adler, L.E. & Leonard, S. (1999) Alternative phenotypes for the complex genetics of schizophrenia. *Biological Psychiatry* **45**, 551–558.

Friedman, D. & Squires-Wheeler, E. (1994) Event-related potentials (ERPs) as indicators of risk for schizophrenia. *Schizophrenia Bulletin* **20**, 63–74.

Friedman, D., Cornblatt, B., Vaughan, H. Jr & Erlenmeyer-Kimling, L. (1986) Event-related potentials in children at risk for schizophrenia during two versions of the continuous performance test. *Psychiatry Research* **18**, 161–177.

Friedman, L., Jesberger, J.A., Siever, L.J. *et al.* (1995) Smooth pursuit performance in patients with affective disorders or schizophrenia and normal controls: analysis with specific oculomotor measures, RMS error and qualitative ratings. *Psychological Medicine* **25**, 387–403.

Gogos, J.A., Morgan, M., Luine, V. *et al.* (1998) Catechol-O-methyltransferase-deficient mice exhibit sexually dimorphic changes in catecholamine levels and behavior. *Proceedings of the National Academy of Sciences of the USA* **95**, 9991–9996.

Goldberg, T.E., Torrey, E.F., Gold, J.M. *et al.* (1993) Learning and memory in monozygotic twins discordant for schizophrenia. *Psychological Medicine* **23**, 71–85.

Goldberg, T.E., Torrey, E.F., Berman, K.F. & Weinberger, D.R. (1994) Relations between neuropsychological performance and brain morphological and physiological measures in monozygotic twins discordant for schizophrenia. *Psychiatry Research* **55**, 51–61.

Goldberg, T.E., Torrey, E.F., Gold, J.M. *et al.* (1995) Genetic risk of neuropsychological impairment in schizophrenia: a study of monozygotic twins discordant and concordant for the disorder. *Schizophrenia Research* **17**, 77–84.

Goldman-Rakic, P.S., Bergson, C., Mrzljak, L. & Williams G.V. (1996) Dopamine receptors and cognitive function in nonhuman primates. In Neve, K.A. & Neve, R.L. (eds), *The Dopamine Receptors*. New Jersey.: Human Press/Totowa, pp 499–522.

Gooding, D.C., Iacono, W.G., Katsanis, J., Beiser, M. & Grove, W.M. (1993) The association between lithium carbonate and smooth pursuit eye tracking among first-episode patients with psychotic affective disorders. *Psychophysiology* **30**, 3–9.

Gooding, D.C., Iacono, W.G. & Beiser, M. (1994) Temporal stability of smooth-pursuit eye tracking in first-episode psychosis. *Psychophysiology* **31**, 62–67.

Green, M.F. (1996) What are the functional consequences of neurocognitive deficits in schizophrenia? *American Journal of Psychiatry* **15**, 321–330.

Greenberg, D.A., Delgado-Escueta, A.V., Widelitz, H. *et al.* (1988) Juvenile myoclonic epilepsy (JME) may be linked to the BF and HLA loci on human chromosome 6. *American Journal of Medical Cenetics* **31**, 185–192.

Grove, W.M., Lebow, B.S., Clementz, B.A. *et al.* (1991) Familial prevalence and coaggregation of schizotypy indicators: a multitrait family study. *Journal of Abnormal Psychology* **100**, 115–121.

Grove, W.M., Clementz, B.A., Iacono, W.G. & Katsanis, J. (1992) Smooth pursuit ocular motor dysfunction in schizophrenia: evidence for a major gene. *American Journal of Psychiatry* **149**, 1362–1368.

Grunebaum, H., Weiss, J.L., Gallant, D. & Cohler, B.J. (1974) Attention in young children of psychotic mothers. *American Journal of Psychiatry* **131**, 887–891.

Holzman, P.S., Proctor, L.R. & Hughes, D.W. (1973) Eye-tracking patterns in schizophrenia. *Science* **181**, 179–181.

Holzman, P.S., Proctor, L.R., Levy, D.L. *et al.* (1974) Eye-tracking dysfunctions in schizophrenic patients and their relatives. *Archives of General Psychiatry* **31**, 143–151.

Holzman, P.S., Kringlen, E., Levy, D.L. *et al.* (1977) Abnormal-pursuit eye movements in schizophrenia: evidence for a genetic indicator. *Archives of General Psychiatry* **34**, 802–805.

Holzman, P.S., Kringlen, E., Levy, D.L. & Haberman, S.J. (1980) Deviant eye tracking in twins discordant for psychosis: a replication. *Archives of General Psychiatry* **37**, 627–631.

Holzman, P.S., Solomon, C.M., Levin, S. & Waternaux, C.S. (1984) Pursuit eye movement dysfunctions in schizophrenia: family evidence for specificity. *Archives of General Psychiatry* **41**, 136–139.

Holzman, P.S., Kringlen, E., Matthysse, S. *et al.* (1988) A single dominant gene can account for eye tracking dysfunctions and schizophrenia in offspring of discordant twins [see comments]. *Archives of General Psychiatry* **45**, 641–647.

Holzman, P.S., O'Brian, C. & Waternaux, C. (1991) Effects of lithium treatment on eye movements. *Biological Psychiatry* **29**, 1001–1015.

Hutton, S.B., Crawford, T.J., Gibbins, H. *et al.* (2001) Short- and long-term effects of antipsychotic medication on smooth pursuit eye tracking in schizophrenia. *Psychopharmacology* **157**, 284–291.

Iacono, W.G. & Lykken, D.T. (1979a) Electro-oculographic recording and scoring of smooth pursuit and saccadic eye tracking: a parametric study using monozygotic twins. *Psychophysiology* **16**, 94–107.

Iacono, W.G. & Lykken, D.T. (1979b) Eye tracking and psychopathology: new procedures applied to a sample of normal monozygotic twins. *Archives of General Psychiatry* **36**, 1361–1369.

Iacono, W.G., Moreau, M., Beiser, M., Fleming, J.A. & Lin, T.Y. (1992) Smooth-pursuit eye tracking in first-episode psychotic patients and their relatives. *Journal of Abnormal Psychology* **101**, 104–116.

Ismail, B., Cantor-Graae, E. & McNeil, T.F. (1998) Minor physical anomalies in schizophrenic patients and their siblings. *American Journal of Psychiatry* **155**, 1695–1702.

Jin, Y. & Potkin, S.G. (1996) P50 changes with visual interference in normal subjects: a sensory distraction model for schizophrenia. *Clinical Electroencephalography* **27**, 151–154.

Jin, Y., Potkin, S.G., Patterson, J.V. *et al.* (1997) Effects of P50 temporal variability on sensory gating in schizophrenia. *Psychiatry Research* **70**, 71–81.

Karoum, F., Chrapusta, S.J. & Egan, M.F. (1994) 3-Methoxytyramine is the major metabolite of released dopamine in the rat frontal cortex: reassessment of the effects of antipsychotics on the dynamics of dopamine release and metabolism in the frontal cortex, nucleus accumbens, and striatum by a simple two pool model. *Journal of Neurochemistry* **63**, 972–979.

Katsanis, J., Iacono, W.G. & Beiser, M. (1990) Anhedonia and perceptual aberration in first episode psychotic patients and their relatives. *Journal of Abnormal Psychology* **99**, 202–206.

Kay, S.R., Fiszbein, A., Lindenmayer, J.P. & Opler, I.A. (1986) Positive and negative syndromes in schizophrenia as a function of chronicity. *Acta Psychiatrica Scandinavica* **74**, 507–518.

Keefe, R.S., Silverman, J.M., Roitman, S.E. *et al.* (1994) Performance of non-psychotic relatives of schizophrenic patients on cognitive tests. *Psychiatry Research* **53**, 1–12.

Keefe, R.S., Silverman, J.M., Mohs, R.C. *et al.* (1997) Eye tracking, attention, and schizotypal symptoms in nonpsychotic relatives of patients with schizophrenia [see comments]. *Archives of General Psychiatry* **54**, 169–176.

Kendler, K.S., Ochs, A.L., Gorman, A.M. *et al.* (1991) The structure of schizotypy: a pilot multitrait twin study. *Psychiatry Research* **36**, 19–36.

Kendler, K.S., Thacker, L. & Walsh, D. (1996) Self-report measures of schizotypy as indices of familial vulnerability to schizophrenia. *Schizophrenia Bulletin* **22**, 511–520.

Keshavan, M.S., Montrose, D.M., Pierri, J.N. *et al.* (1997) Magnetic resonance imaging and spectroscopy in offspring at risk for schizophrenia: preliminary studies. *Progress in Neuropsychopharmacology and Biological Psychiatry* **21**, 1285–1295.

Kidogami, Y., Yoneda, H., Asaba, H. & Sakai, T. (1991) P300 in first degree relatives of schizophrenics. *Schizophrenia Research* **6**, 9–13.

Kinney, D.K., Levy, D.L., Yurgelun-Todd, D.A., Tramer, S.J. & Holzman, P.S. (1998) Inverse relationship of perinatal complications and eye tracking dysfunction in relatives of patients with schizophrenia: evidence for a two-factor model. *American Journal of Psychiatry* **155**, 976–978.

Klemm, S., Rzanny, R., Riehemann, S. *et al.* (2001) Cerebral phosphate metabolism in first-degree relatives of patients with schizophrenia. *American Journal of Psychiatry* **158**, 958–960.

Kneavel, M., Gogos, J., Karayiorgou, K. & Luine, V. (2000) *Interaction of COMT Gene Deletion and Environment on Cognition*, abstract 571.20. Society for Neuroscience, 30th Annual Meeting.

Kraepelin, E. (1919) *Dementia Praecox and Paraphrenia*. Livingstone, Edinburgh.

Kremen, W.S., Tsuang, M.T., Faraone, S.V. & Lyons, M.J. (1992) Using vulnerability indicators to compare conceptual models of genetic heterogeneity in schizophrenia. *Journal of Nervous and Mental Disease* **180**, 141–152.

Kremen, W.S., Seidman, L.J., Pepple, J.R. *et al.* (1994) Neuropsychological risk indicators for schizophrenia: a review of family studies. *Schizophrenia Bulletin* **20**, 103–119.

Kuechenmeister, C.A., Linton, P.H., Mueller, T.V. & White, H.B. (1977) Eye tracking in relation to age, sex, and illness. *Archives of General Psychiatry* **34**, 578–579.

Lalouel, J.M., Le Mignon, L. Simon, M. *et al.* (1985) Genetic analysis of idiopathic hemochromatosis using both qualitative (disease status) and quantitative (serum iron) information. *American Journal of Human Genetics* **37**, 700–718.

Lander, E.S. & Schork, N.J. (1994) Genetics dissection of complex traits. *Science* **265**, 2037–2048.

Laurent, A., Biloa-Tang, M., Bougerol, T. *et al.* (2000) Executive/attentional performance and measures of schizotypy in patients with schizophrenia and in their non-psychotic first-degree relatives. *Schizophrenia Research* **46**, 269–283.

Lawrie, S.M., Whalley, H., Kestelman, J.N. *et al.* (1999) Magnetic resonance imaging of brain in people at high risk of developing schizophrenia. *Lancet* **353**, 30–33.

Lawrie, S.M., Whalley, H.C., Abukmeil, S.S. *et al.* (2001) Brain structure, genetic liability, and psychotic symptoms in subjects at high risk of developing schizophrenia. *Biological Psychiatry* **49**, 811–823.

Leboyer, M., Bellivier, F., Nosten-Bertrand, M. *et al.* (1998) Psychiatric genetics: search for phenotypes. *Trends in Neuroscience* **21**, 102–105.

Lekwuwa, G.U. & Barnes, G.R. (1996) Cerebral control of eye movements. I. The relationship between cerebral lesion sites and smooth pursuit deficits. *Brain* **119**, 473–490.

Lenzenweger, M.E. Cornblatt, B.A. & Putnick, M. (1991) Schizotypy and sustained attention. *Journal of Abnormal Psychology* **100**, 84–89.

Levin, S., Jones, A., Stark, L., Merrin, E.L. & Holzman, P.S. (1982) Identification of abnormal patterns in eye movements of schizophrenic patients. *Archives of General Psychiatry* **39**, 1125–1130.

Levy, D.L., Dorus, E., Shaughnessy, R. *et al.* (1985) Pharmacologic evidence for specificity of pursuit dysfunction to schizophrenia: lithium carbonate associated with abnormal pursuit. *Archives of General Psychiatry* **42**, 335–341.

Levy, D.L., Holzman, P.S., Matthysse, S. & Mendell, N.R. (1993) Eye tracking dysfunction and schizophrenia: a critical perspective [see comments]. *Schizophrenia Bulletin* **19**, 461–536. [Published erratum appears in *Schizophrenia Bulletin* 1993; **19**, 685.]

Levy, D.L., Holzman, P.S., Matthysse, S. & Mendell, N.R. (1994) Eye tracking and schizophrenia: a selective review. *Schizophrenia Bulletin* **20**, 47–62.

Litman, R.E., Hommer, D.W., Clem, T. *et al.* (1989) Smooth pursuit eye movements in schizophrenia: effects of neuroleptic treatment and caffeine. *Psychopharmacological Bulletin* **25**, 473–478.

Litman, R.E., Hommer, D.W., Radant, A., Clem, T. & Pickar, D. (1994) Quantitative effects of typical and atypical neuroleptics on smooth pursuit eye tracking in schizophrenia. *Schizophrenia Research* **12**, 107–120.

Litman, R.E., Torrey, E.F., Hommer, D.W. *et al.* (1997) A quantitative analysis of smooth pursuit eye tracking in monozygotic twins discordant for schizophrenia. *Archives of General Psychiatry* **54**, 417–426.

Luntz-Leybman, V., Bickford, P.C. & Freedman, R. (1992) Cholinergic gating of response to auditory stimuli in rat hippocampus. *Brain Research* **587**, 130–136.

Lyons, M.J., Toomey, R., Faraone, S.V. *et al.* (1995) Correlates of psychosis proneness in relatives of schizophrenic patients. *Journal of Abnormal Psychology* **104**, 390–394.

MacAvoy, M.G. & Bruce, C.J. (1995) Comparison of the smooth eye tracking disorder of schizophrenics with that of non-human primates with specific brain lesions. *International Journal of Neuroscience* **80**, 117–151.

McDowell, J.E. & Clementz, B.A. (1996) Ocular-motor delayed response task performance among schizophrenia patients. *Neuropsychobiology* **34**, 67–71.

McGue, M. & Gottesman, I.I. (1989) Genetic linkage in schizophrenia: perspectives from genetic epidemiology. *Schizophrenia Bulletin* **15**, 453–464.

McNeil, T.E., Cantor-Graae, E. & Weinberger, D.R. (2000) Relationship of obstetric complications and differences in size of brain structures in monozygotic twin pairs discordant for schizophrenia. *American Journal of Psychiatry* **157**, 203–212.

Mahtani, M.M., Widen, E., Lehto, M. *et al.* (1996) Mapping of a gene for type 2 diabetes associated with an insulin secretion defect by a genome scan in Finnish Families. *Nature Genetics* **14**, 90–94.

Maier, W., Franke, P., Hain, C., Kopp, B. & Rist, F. (1992) Neuropsychological indicators of the vulnerability to schizophrenia. *Progress in Neuropsychopharmacology and Biological Psychiatry* **16**, 703–715.

Malaspina, D., Colemann, E.A., Quitkin, M. *et al.* (1994) Effects of pharmacologic catecholamine manipulation on smooth pursuit eye movements in normals. *Schizophrenia Research* **13**, 151–159.

Mather, J.A. (1985) Eye movements of teenage children of schizophrenics: a possible inherited marker of susceptibility to the disease. *Journal of Psychiatric Research* **19**, 523–532.

Meehl, P.E. (1962) Schizotaxia, schizotypy, schizophrenia. *American Psychologist* **17**, 827–839.

Michie, P.T., Fox, A.M., Ward, P.B., Catts, S.V. & McConaghy, N. (1990) Event-related potential indices of selective attention and cortical laterlization in schizophrenia. *Psychophysiology* **27**, 209–227.

Milner, B., Squire, L.R. & Kandel, E.R. (1998) Cognitive neuroscience and the study of memory. *Neuron* **20**, 445–468.

Mirsky, A.F., Anthony, B.J., Duncan, C.C., Ahearn, M.B. & Kellam, S.G. (1991) Analysis of the elements of attention: a neuropsychological approach. *Neuropsychology Review* **2**, 109–145.

Mirsky, A.F., Lochhead, S.J., Jones, B.P. *et al.* (1992) On familial factors in the attentional deficit in schizophrenia: a review and report of two new subject samples. *Journal of Psychiatric Research* **26**, 383–403.

Morstyn, R., Duffy, E.H. & McCarley, R.W. (1983) Altered topography of EEG spectral content in schizophrenia. *Electroencephalography and Clinical Neurophysiology* **56**, 263–271.

Muir, W.J., St Clair, D.M. & Blackwood, D.H. (1991) Long-latency auditory event-related potentials in schizophrenia and in bipolar and unipolar affective disorder. *Psychological Medicine* **21**, 867–879.

Naatanen, R. & Picton, T. (1987) The N1 wave of the human electric and magnetic response to sound: a review and an analysis of the component structure. *Psychophysiology* **24**, 375–425.

Nuechterlein, K.H. & Dawson, M.E. (1984) Information processing and attentional functioning in the developmental course of schizophrenic disorders. *Schizophrenia Bulletin* **10**, 160–203.

O'Driscoll, G.A., Benkelfat, C., Florencio, P.S. *et al.* (1999) Neural correlates of eye tracking deficits in first-degree relatives of schizophrenic patients: a positron emission tomography study. *Archives of General Psychiatry* **56**, 1127–1134.

O'Driscoll, G.A., Florencio, P.S., Gagnon, D. *et al.* (2001) Amygdala–hippocampal volume and verbal memory in first-degree relatives of schizophrenic patients. *Psychiatry Research* **107**, 75–85.

Park, S., Holzman, P.S. & Goldman-Rakic, P.S. (1995) Spatial working memory deficits in the relatives of schizophrenic patients. *Archives of General Psychiatry* **52**, 821–828.

Pauls, D. (1993) Behvioural disorders: lessons in linkage. *Nature Genetics* **3**, 4–5.

Parnas, J., Schulsinger, F., Schulsinger, H., Mednick, S.A. & Teasdale, T.W. (1982) Behavioral precursors of schizophrenia spectrum: a prospective study. *Archives of General Psychiatry* **39**, 658–664.

Pfefferbaum, A., Wenegrat, B.G., Ford, J.M., Roth, W.T. & Kopell, B.S. (1984) Clinical application of the P3 component of event-related potentials. II. Dementia. depression and schizophrenia. *Electroencephalography and Clinical Neurophysiology* **59**, 104–124.

Pfefferbaum, A., Ford, J.M., White, P.M. & Roth, W.T. (1989) P3 in schizophrenia is affected by stimulus modality, response requirements, medication status, and negative symptoms. *Archives of General Psychiatry* **46**, 1035–1144.

Plomin, R., DeFries, J.C. & McClearn, G.E. (1990) *Behavioral Genetics*, 2nd edn. W.H. Freeman, New York.

Pogue-Geile, M.F., Garrett, A.H., Brunke, J.J. & Hall, J.K. (1991) Neuropsychological impairments are increased in siblings of schizophrenic patients [Abstract]. *Schizophrenia Research* **4**, 390.

Porjesz, B., Begleiter, H. & Samuelly, I. (1980) Cognitive deficits in chronic alcoholics and elderly subjects assessed by evoked brain potentials. *Acta Psychiatrica Scandinavica* **286** (Suppl.), 15–29.

Pritchard, J.K. & Rosenberg, N.A. (1999) Use of unlinked genetic markers to detect population stratification in association studies. *American Journal of Human Genetics* **65**, 220–228.

Pritchard, J.K., Stephens, M. & Donnelly, P. (2000) Inference of population structure using multilocus genotype data. *Genetics* **155**, 945–959.

Rao, D.C., Morton, N.E., Gottesman, I.I. & Lew, R. (1981) Path analysis of qualitative data on pairs of relatives: application to schizophrenia. *Human Heredity* **31**, 325–333.

Reveley, A.M., Reveley, M.A., Clifford, C.A. & Murray, R.M. (1982) Cerebral ventricular size in twins discordant for schizophrenia. *Lancet* **1**, 540–541.

Risch, N. & Merikangas, K. (1996) The future of genetic studies of complex human diseases [see comments]. *Science* **273**, 1516–1517.

Risch, N. & Zhang, H. (1995) Extreme discordant sib pairs for mapping quantitative trait loci in humans. *Science* **268**, 1584–1589.

Ross, R.G., Olincy, A., Harris, J.G. *et al.* (1998) Anticipatory saccades during smooth pursuit eye movements and familial transmission of schizophrenia. *Biological Psychiatry* **44**, 690–697.

Roth, W.T., Pfefferbaum, A., Horvath, T.B., Berger, P.A. & Kopell, B.S. (1980) P3 reduction in auditory evoked potentials of schizophrenics. *Electroencephalography Clinical Neurophysiology* **49**, 497–505.

Rutschmann, J., Cornblatt, B. & Erlenmeyer-Kimling, L. (1977) Sustained attention in children at risk for schizophrenia: report on a continuous performance test. *Archives of General Psychiatry* **34**, 571–575.

Rutschmann, J., Cornblatt, B. & Erlenmeyer-Kimling, L. (1986) Sustained attention in children at risk for schizophrenia: findings with two visual continuous performance tests in a new sample. *Journal of Abnormal Child Psychology* **14**, 365–385.

Saoud, M., d'Amato, T., Gutknecht, C. *et al.* (2000) Neuropsychological deficit in siblings discordant for schizophrenia. *Schizophrenia Bulletin* **26**, 893–902.

Sautter, E., Garver, D.L., Zemlan, E.P. & Hirschowitz, J. (1987) Growth hormone response to apomorphine and family patterns of illness. *Biological Psychiatry* **22**, 717–724.

Sautter, E.J., McDermott, D.E. & Garver, D.L. (1987) Familial and social determinants of outcome. Presented as new research at the annual meeting of the American Psychiatric Association. May 12, 1987, Chicago, IL.

Scarone, S., Abbruzzese, M. & Gambini, O. (1993) The Wisconsin Card Sorting Test discriminates schizophrenic patients and their siblings. *Schizophrenia Research* **10**, 103–107.

Schreiber, H., Stolz-Born, G., Rothmeier, J. *et al.* (1991) Endogenous event-related brain potentials and psychometric performance in children at risk for schizophrenia. *Biological Psychiatry* **30**, 177–189.

Schreiber, H., Stolz-Born, G., Kornhuber, H.H. & Born, J. (1992) Event-related potential correlates of impaired selective attention in children at high risk for schizophrenia. *Biological Psychiatry* **32**, 634–651.

Sedvall, G.C. & Wode-Helgodt, B. (1980) Aberrant monoamine

metabolite levels in CSF and family history of schizophrenia. Their relationships in schizophrenic patients. *Archives of General Psychiatry* **37**, 1113–1116.

Seidman, L.J., Faraone, S.V., Goldstein, J.M. *et al.* (1997) Reduced subcortical brain volumes in nonpsychotic siblings of schizophrenic patients: a pilot magnetic resonance imaging study. *American Journal of Medical Genetics* **74**, 507–514.

Seidman, L.J., Faraone, S.V., Goldstein, J.M. *et al.* (1999) Thalamic and amygdala–hippocampal volume reductions in first-degree relatives of patients with schizophrenia: an MRI-based morphometric analysis. *Biological Psychiatry* **46**, 941–954.

Sesack, S.R., Hawrylak, V.A., Matus, C., Guido, M.A. & Levey, A.I. (1998) Dopamine axon varicosities in the prelimbic division of the rat prefrontal cortex exhibit sparse immunoreactivity for the dopamine transporter. *Journal of Neuroscience* **18**, 2697–2708.

Sharma, T., Lancaster, E., Lee, D. *et al.* (1998) Brain changes in schizophrenia: volumetric MRI study of families multiply affected with schizophrenia – the Maudsley Family Study 5. *British Journal of Psychiatry* **173**, 132–138.

Shedlack, K., Lee, G., Sakuma, M. *et al.* (1997) Language processing and memory in ill and well siblings from multiplex families affected with schizophrenia. *Schizophrenia Research* **25**, 43–52.

Shelley, A.M., Silipo, G. & Javitt, D.C. (1999) Diminished responsiveness of ERPs in schizophrenic subjects to changes in auditory stimulation parameters: implications for theories of cortical dysfunction. *Schizophrenia Research* **37**, 65–79.

Siegel, C., Waldo, M., Mizner, G., Adler, L.E. & Freedman, R. (1984) Deficits in sensory gating in schizophrenic patients and their relatives: evidence obtained with auditory evoked responses. *Archives of General Psychiatry* **41**, 607–612.

Silverman, J.M., Smith, C.J., Guo, S.L. *et al.* (1998) Lateral ventricular enlargement in schizophrenic probands and their siblings with schizophrenia-related disorders. *Biological Psychiatry* **43**, 97–106.

Souza, V.B., Muir, W.J., Walker, M.T. *et al.* (1995) Auditory P300 event-related potentials and neuropsychological performance in schizophrenia and bipolar affective disorder. *Biological Psychiatry* **37**, 300–310.

Spielman, R.S., McGinnis, R.E. & Ewens, W.J. (1993) Transmission test for linkage disequilibrium: the insulin gene region and insulin-dependent diabetes mellitus (IDDM). *American Journal of Human Genetics* **52**, 506–516.

Spohn, H.E., Coyne, L. & Spray, J. (1988) The effect of neuroleptics and tardive dyskinesia on smooth-pursuit eye movement in chronic schizophrenics. *Archives of General Psychiatry* **45**, 833–840.

Squires-Wheeler, E., Friedman, D., Skodol, A.E. & Erlenmeyer-Kimling, L. (1993) A longitudinal study relating P3 amplitude to schizophrenia spectrum disorders and to global personality functioning. *Biological Psychiatry* **33**, 774–785.

Staal, W.G., Hulshoff Pol, H.E., Schnack, H., van der Schot, A.C. & Kahn, R.S. (1998) Partial volume decrease of the thalamus in relatives of patients with schizophrenia. *American Journal of Psychiatry* **155**, 1784–1786.

Staal, W.G., Hulshoff Pol, H.E., Schnack, H.G. *et al.* (2000) Structural brain abnormalities in patients with schizophrenia and their healthy siblings. *American Journal of Psychiatry* **157**, 416–421.

St Clair, D., Blackwood, D. & Muir, W. (1989) P300 abnormality in schizophrenic subtypes. *Journal of Psychiatric Research* **23**, 49–55.

Straub, R.E., MacLean, C.J., O'Neill, F.A. *et al.* (1995) A potential vulnerability locus for schizophrenia on chromosome 6p24-22: evidence for genetic heterogeneity [see comments]. *Nature Genetics* **11**, 287–293.

Suddath, R.L., Christison, G.W., Torrey, E.F., Casanova, M.F. & Weinberger, D.R. (1990) Anatomical abnormalities in the brains of monozygotic twins discordant for schizophrenia. *New England Journal of Medicine* **322**, 789–794.

Sweeney, J.A., Clementz, B.A., Haas, G.L. *et al.* (1994a) Eye tracking dysfunction in schizophrenia: characterization of component eye movement abnormalities, diagnostic specificity, and the role of attention. *Journal of Abnormal Psychology* **103**, 222–230.

Sweeney, J.A., Haas, G.L., Li, S. & Weiden, P.J. (1994b) Selective effects of antipsychotic medications on eye-tracking performance in schizophrenia. *Psychiatry Research* **54**, 185–198.

Sweeney, J.A., Luna, B., Haas, G.L. *et al.* (1999) Pursuit tracking impairments in schizophrenia and mood disorders: step-ramp studies with unmedicated patients. *Biological Psychiatry* **46**, 671–680.

Sweeney, J.A., Luna, B., Srinivasagam, N.M. *et al.* (1998) Eye tracking abnormalities in schizophrenia: evidence for dysfunction in the frontal eye fields. *Biological Psychiatry* **44**, 698–708.

Taylor, M., Berenbaum, S., Jampala, V. & Cloninger, R. (1993) Are schizophrenia and affective disorder related? Preliminary data from a family study? *American Journal of Psychiatry* **150**, 278–285.

Thaker, G.K., Cassady, S., Adami, H., Moran, M. & Ross, D.E. (1996) Eye movements in spectrum personality disorders: comparison of community subjects and relatives of schizophrenic patients. *American Journal of Psychiatry* **153**, 362–368.

Toomey, R., Faraone, S.V., Seidman, L.J. *et al.* (1998) Association of neuropsychological vulnerability markers in relatives of schizophrenic patients. *Schizophrenia Research* **31**, 89–98.

Tsuang, M. (1993) Genotypes, phenotypes and the brain: a search for commections in schizophrenia. *British Journal of Psychiatry* **163**, 299–307.

Waldo, M., Gerhardt, G., Baker, N. *et al.* (1992) Auditory sensory gating and catecholamine metabolism in schizophrenic and normal subjects. *Psychiatry Research* **44**, 21–32.

Waldo, M.C., Cawthra, E., Adler, L.E. *et al.* (1994) Auditory sensory gating, hippocampal volume, and catecholamine metabolism in schizophrenics and their siblings. *Schizophrenia Research* **12**, 93–106.

Weinberger, D.R. (1987) Implications of normal brain development for the pathogenesis of schizophrenia. *Archives of General Psychiatry* **44**, 660–669.

Weinberger, D.R., DeLisi, L.E., Neophytides, A.N. & Wyatt, R.J. (1981) Familial aspects of CT scan abnormalities in chronic schizophrenic patients. *Psychiatry Research* **4**, 65–71.

Weinshilboum, R. & Dunnette, J (1981) Thermal stability and the biochemical genetics of erythrocyte catechol-O-methyl-transferase and plasma dopamine-beta-hydroxylase. *Clinical Genetics* **19**, 426–437.

Whicker, L., Abel, L. & Dell'Osso, L. (1985) Smooth pursuit eye movements in the parents of schizophrenics. *Neuro-Ophthalmology* **5**, 1–8.

Williams, G.V. and Goldman-Rakic P.S. (1995) Modulation of memory fields by dopamine D1 receptors in prefrontal cortex. [see comments]. *Nature* **376**, 572–5.

Yee, C.M., Nuechterlein, K.H. & Dawson, M.E. (1998) A longitudinal analysis of eye tracking dysfunction and attention in recent-onset schizophrenia. *Psychophysiology* **35**, 443–451.

Yee, R.D., Baloh, R.W., Marder, S.R. *et al.* (1987) Eye movements in schizophrenia. *Investigative Ophthalmology and Visual Science* **28**, 366–374.

Yurgelun-Todd, D.A. & Kinney, D.K. (1993) Patterns of neuropsychological deficits that discriminate schizophrenic individuals from siblings and control subjects. *Journal of Neuropsychiatry and Clinical Neuroscience* **5**, 294–300.

16 Electrophysiology of schizophrenia

D.F. Salisbury, S. Krljes and R.W. McCarley

The electroencephalogram (EEG) was the first physiological technique used to examine brain activity in schizophrenia and has evolved into a powerful method for studying brain information processing activity. In today's world of multimodal imaging, the EEG is still unsurpassed in providing real-time, millisecond resolution of normal and pathological brain processing, literally at the speed of thought. This chapter discusses the application of this technique to schizophrenia research. The first section begins with an introduction to some basic concepts of electrophysiology.

The electroencephalogram

Cognitive events are subserved by neurones in the brain and this electrical activity may be recorded from the electrodes placed on the surface of the scalp. In general, the EEG derives from summated dendritic inhibitory and excitatory postsynaptic activity in neurones, primarily pyramidal cells in the cortex of the brain. It is important to emphasize that the EEG does not typically reflect neuronal discharges, because they are usually too brief and too asynchronous. (As an aside, we note that blood oxygenation level-dependent (BOLD) functional magnetic resonance imaging (fMRI) 'activation' similarly mainly reflects postsynaptic potential (PSP) activity, which is metabolically most demanding and necessitates the increased blood flow, but not action potential activity, which is metabolically much less demanding.)

The EEG primarily reflects the activity generated in the large dendritic trees of pyramidal cells, with an especially strong representation of activity in dendrites orientated in parallel, perpendicular to the plane of the scalp surface. One of the main limitations of the EEG technique is a difficulty in assessing the source of the recorded activity. For example, generators in different brain locations can produce the same EEG scalp recorded signal. To combat this problem various source localization techniques are employed.

Event-related potentials

The EEG reflects the activity of many groups of neurones, representing brain operations related to a variety of ongoing events, such as breathing, seeing, hearing and thinking, as well as different processing modes of large groups of nerve cells. One of the important advances in EEG-based research was the development of a technique to isolate brain activity related to specific events from the background EEG. Using various averaging techniques, it is possible to visualize small potentials related to one of the many different brain operations reflected in the EEG. Typically, these events are related to the specific processing of certain stimuli in the stimulus field, i.e. the events in the environment impinging upon the individual. Signal averaging isolates the brain activity related to specific events by recording small portions (epochs) of the EEG each time a specific stimulus is presented. The stimulus is presented many times, thus a large number of EEG epochs are recorded. For each epoch, there are two types of activity:

1 the activity specifically related to the stimulus; and
2 the activity related to the other ongoing processes in the brain.

The former activity is said to be time-locked, with all the activity in sensory system relay and processing areas occurring at roughly the same time after each stimulus is presented. Hence, at any specific point in time after the presentation of the stimulus, time-locked event-related activity will be temporally stable from one trial to the next. The latter activity will be, by definition, random with respect to the stimulus. By averaging together all the epochs, the time-locked event-related activity will remain stable, because it occurs at roughly the same time from trial to trial, while the rest of the EEG activity is averaged out. The time-locked brain activity that remains is referred to as the event-related potential (ERP) waveform, and each of the various positive or negative events that comprise it are referred to as event-related potentials. The reader desiring more information regarding EEG and ERP theory and techniques is referred to Regan (1989).

The place of electrophysiology in the neuroimaging spectrum

In recent years many new means of measuring brain structure and function have been developed. Some image the structure of the brain: X-ray-based techniques (e.g. computerized axial tomography or CAT scans) and nuclear magnetic field-based techniques (e.g. magnetic resonance imaging or MRI). These structural techniques have high spatial resolution and provide detailed information about the static structure of the brain. However, they provide little information about brain activity, as they provide only a snapshot of brain tissue rather than a series of measures of brain physiology.

A second class of brain imaging techniques measure brain functional activity. These functional techniques assay brain activity based on blood oxygenation level, an indirect measure of brain activity (BOLD fMRI), or on positron emission tomography (PET), which uses radioactive-labelled substances to measure metabolism ([^{18}]fluorodeoxyglucose or [^{18}F]2DG), blood flow ([^{15}O]water) or receptor occupancy (labelled ligands) as well as single photon emission tomography (SPECT). It is an important point that fMRI haemodynamic signals and [^{15}O]H_2O PET, as well as [^{18}F]2DGPET metabolic measures, all primarily derive from PSP activity and not neuronal discharge, because PSP activity is metabolically most demanding on the neurone and also evokes most of the blood flow changes (Logothetis *et al.* 2001). Thus, 'activation', as is commonly used in neuroimaging, mainly reflects PSPs (often from input to the region) and not neuronal discharge. These techniques provide relatively good spatial resolution (although not as good as structural MRI) but their temporal resolution (in the second range) is at best several thousand-fold less than electrophysiological measures, which provide resolution within a few milliseconds. The interested reader is referred to Raichle (1998) and Rauch and Renshaw (1995) for further information regarding different imaging modalities, as well as to other chapters in this volume.

In contrast with its superior temporal resolution, the EEG's spatial resolution is limited, because the source of the voltage fluctuations at the scalp cannot be precisely identified as coming from particular brain regions. It seems intuitively obvious that 'multimodal' imaging (combining EEG and other modalities with higher spatial resolution) has advantages, particularly when coupled with knowledge of plausible locations of brain activity based on depth EEG recordings in patients being prepared for surgery, and from experimental animal data on the origin of certain potentials.

Event-related potentials in schizophrenia

Overview

This section discusses some key issues in the history of ERP research in schizophrenia, and then focuses on three auditory ERPs of particular relevance to current schizophrenia research (gamma-band oscillations, mismatch negativity and P300). We conclude this section with a brief overview of other ERPs that have been studied in schizophrenia patients, and implications of ERP findings to the overall knowledge on schizophrenia. While we focus on ERP measures in schizophrenia in this chapter, we note that other EEG measures have been studied extensively. For example, measures of resting level EEG and techniques for analysing the data, such as measuring the relative amounts of activity in each constituent frequency band, called quantitative electroencephalography (Q-EEG), have led to interesting findings regarding brain–behaviour relationships in schizophrenia. The interested reader is referred to John *et al.* (1994).

The vast majority of ERP studies in schizophrenia have been conducted on chronically ill patients who have had persistent symptoms for many years. Thus, many studies may be confounded by the fact that chronicity itself may lead to secondary effects on brain physiology because of the possible effects of long-term medication, poor diet, understimulating environment and comorbidity (e.g. use of illicit drugs, poor general health). Such factors could affect the brain independently of any disease process and it is difficult to identify which effects arise from chronicity factors as opposed to those directly related to a schizophrenic disease process.

A physiological abnormality in chronically ill patients that is also present at the onset of the disease cannot be caused by the secondary effects associated with chronicity. Whatever abnormal brain process gives rise to schizophrenia at the time of first overt psychosis should give clues as to the primary brain pathology of schizophrenia, highlighting the importance of research on first episode and unmedicated patients.

History of event-related potential research in schizophrenia

The technique for signal averaging the EEG to reveal ERPs was developed in the late 1950s, and the brain potentials related to the stimulus parameters, the so-called sensory potentials, were recorded in schizophrenia patients as early as 1959 (Shagass 1968). Much of the ERP work in schizophrenia throughout the 1960s and 1970s focused on the evoked potentials – those brain potentials elicited by repetitive stimuli in some sensory modality. The major interest was in N100, a negative-going brain potential arising approximately 100 ms after the onset of a stimulus. N100 amplitude (size) and latency (timing) are tied to stimulus intensity in several different modalities; thus N100 is referred to as a sensory potential. N100 was shown to be of smaller amplitude and greater variability in schizophrenia patients in the auditory modality (Saletu *et al.* 1971), visual modality (Shagass 1977) and the somatosensory modality (Shagass *et al.* 1974). However, results were far from uniform. Some groups reported larger ERP amplitudes in patients (Shagass 1968) while others reported no differences between patients and controls (Domino *et al.* 1979). Studies were motivated in large part by the theory that patients with schizophrenia were unable to filter irrelevant stimuli from the environment and were swamped or overloaded with stimuli seeking access to higher order cognitive processing resources (McGhie & Chapman 1961; Venables 1964). The size of the ERPs was thus thought to reflect either abnormally large signals (either pathological at the sensory channel or abnormally 'augmented') which forced their processing rather than filtration, or abnormally small signals which reflected the active 'reducing' of input by schizophrenics as a defensive adjustment to an abnormal filter (see e.g. Schooler *et al.* 1976). By the late 1970s, it was apparent from controlled methodology and from technological improvements that the signals were, in general, reduced in schizophrenia. Shagass *et al.* also argued, somewhat presciently, that the lateralized pattern of abnormalities in N100 in all modalities indicated a left hemisphere abnormality in schizophrenia.

As the intellectual attractiveness of theories of augmenting and reducing decreased, and the notion that changes in N100 amplitude reflected the operations of selective attention was replaced by the idea that changes in N100 were likely caused by other coincident preattentive signals (e.g. mismatch negativity), interest in these potentials waned in the 1980s, although there has been a recent renaissance of research into basic sensory processing ERPs in schizophrenia, as discussed below. Analysis of sensory evoked potentials was largely replaced by a focus on P300, which was robustly reduced in patients and clearly linked to the operations of selective attention and processing of infrequent stimuli (the reader is referred to reviews of ERP research by Buchsbaum 1977; Roth 1977; Shagass 1979).

Sutton *et al.* (1965), using a prediction paradigm wherein subjects tried to guess which of two stimuli was going to be presented, described a brain potential that was related to the cognitive activity of the subject, rather than directly to the characteristics of the stimulus. This revolutionary finding revealed a brain potential, an objective physiological event, related to the internal operations of the subject. This ERP, eventually termed the P3 or P300 (for the third positive potential or the positive potential at 300 ms after the stimulus, respectively), was found to be intimately tied to the selective attention paid to rare external events by the subjects in tasks where they had to use information about the stimulus. Roth and Cannon (1972), the first to examine P300 in schizophrenia, reported that P300 was reduced relative to controls. Levit *et al.* (1973) also showed a reduction of P300 in schizophrenia. This finding has subsequently been termed the most robust physiological finding of any abnormality in schizophrenia. However, reduction of P300 is not pathognomonic to schizophrenia as it is also reduced in other psychiatric diseases, such as bipolar disorder and Alzheimer's dementia. More specific alterations of the total scalp field, or regionally specific topographic differences, by contrast, may be specifically associated with different psychiatric diseases, as discussed below in the section entitled 'P300'.

Although P300 amplitude varies with the amount of attention paid to a task, there is only moderate improvement in P300 amplitude when there is symptom resolution in schizophrenia (Ford *et al.* 1994; Turetsky *et al.* 1998): the reduction of P300 in schizophrenia is largely trait-like, rather than state-like. Even with improvement in symptoms, the P300 of patients rarely reaches normal levels. Hence, P300 amplitude might reflect abnormalities of an enduring aspect of the disease pathology. By contrast, P300 latency, which is occasionally reported as prolonged in schizophrenia (Blackwood *et al.* 1991), is intimately tied to attention and task performance and may be more state-like in nature (Salisbury *et al.* 1994a).

Current event-related potential research in schizophrenia

Because space limitations preclude discussion of all ERPs currently being investigated in schizophrenia, this section focuses on the three ERPs currently being researched by the authors and also under examination in other laboratories. We briefly discuss other potentials at the end of the section. Each of the three ERPs can be related to an increasingly more complex stage of information processing in the brain. We chose the auditory modality because it is one of the most affected in schizophrenia, as evinced in the primacy of auditory hallucinations and speech/language pathology. It is our hypothesis that schizophrenia involves abnormalities in auditory processing from the most simple to the most complex level, and that the anatomical substrates in the neocortical temporal lobe, most carefully investigated in the superior temporal gyrus, themselves evince reduction in grey matter neuropil volume.

The first ERP we consider is the steady-state gamma-band response. Gamma-band refers to a brain oscillation at and near the frequency of 40 hertz (hz) or 40 times per second, while 'steady state' refers to its being elicited by a stimulus of the same frequency. The second ERP discussed is mismatch negativity (MMN), an ERP related to the automatic sensory memory detection of a stimulus that deviates from a repetitive pattern, regardless of whether the subject is actively trying to detect the deviant stimulus or not. The last potential considered reflects the active, deliberate and conscious detection and processing of a deviant or 'oddball' stimulus by the subject. This ERP is called the P3 or P300, and is one of the most widely studied physiological events in schizophrenia, as well as one of the most robustly abnormal measures of brain activity in that disorder. ERPs provided the first objective physiological measure of brain activity related to mental cognitive events, joined later by PET and regional cerebral blood blow (rCBF) studies, and only recently by fMRI. As previously noted, the temporal resolution of ERPs, in the order of milliseconds, far surpasses the temporal resolution of fMRI (in the order of many seconds). In addition, ERPs are more sensitive to neural activation than is fMRI. The spatial resolution of fMRI surpasses that of ERPs, but combination of MRI and ERPs informed by intracortical recordings provides the greatest accuracy in modelling localized brain activity *in vivo*. This approach is particularly fruitful in brain disorders where abnormalities are thought to be localized to specific areas from which arise certain ERPs. As a case in point, schizophrenia is likely to involve abnormalities in temporal lobe areas that generate P300, and structural abnormalities in these areas are strongly related to abnormalities of the brain activity thought to arise there (see below).

Gamma activity

At the cellular level, gamma-band activity is an endogenous

brain oscillation thought to reflect the synchronizing of activity in several columns of cortical neurones, or between cortex and thalamus, with this synchronization facilitating communication. At the cognitive level, work in humans suggests that gamma activity reflects the convergence of multiple processing streams in cortex, giving rise to a unified percept. A simple example is a 'firetruck', where a particular combination of form perception, motion perception and auditory perception are melded to form this percept. Gamma activity at its simplest, however, involves basic neural circuitry composed of projection neurones, usually using excitatory amino acid (EAA) neurotransmission, linked with inhibitory γ-aminobutyric acid (GABA) interneurones. Studies of gamma activity in schizophrenia aim to determine if there is a basic circuit abnormality present, such as a deficiency in recurrent inhibition, postulated by a number of workers (see review in McCarley *et al.* 1996).

Kwon *et al.* (1999) began the study of gamma in schizophrenia using an exogenous input of 40 Hz auditory clicks, leading to a steady-state gamma response. The magnitude of the brain response was measured by power, the amount of EEG energy at a specific frequency, with the degree of capability of gamma driving being reflected in the power at and near 40 Hz.

As shown in Fig. 16.1, schizophrenia patients had – compared with healthy controls – a markedly reduced power at 40 Hz input, although showing normal driving at slower frequencies which indicated that this was not a general reduction in power, but one specific to the gamma band.

Moreover, the phase–response curve, a description of the relationship between the timing of each stimulus and the EEG response, suggested that it was an intrinsic oscillator that was being driven. This was because the time duration between the stimulus and the EEG response, as the 40 Hz stimulation continued, was reduced to a duration too short to be explained by simple conduction to the auditory cortex. This phase–response curve is very common when an external signal drives a 'tuned oscillator', much as auditory stimuli can set in motion a tuning fork, which oscillates (resonates) at a particular frequency. The abnormal amplitude and phase–response in schizophrenic patients raised the possibility that there was an intrinsic deficit in brain circuitry supporting 40 Hz oscillations. Were this to be

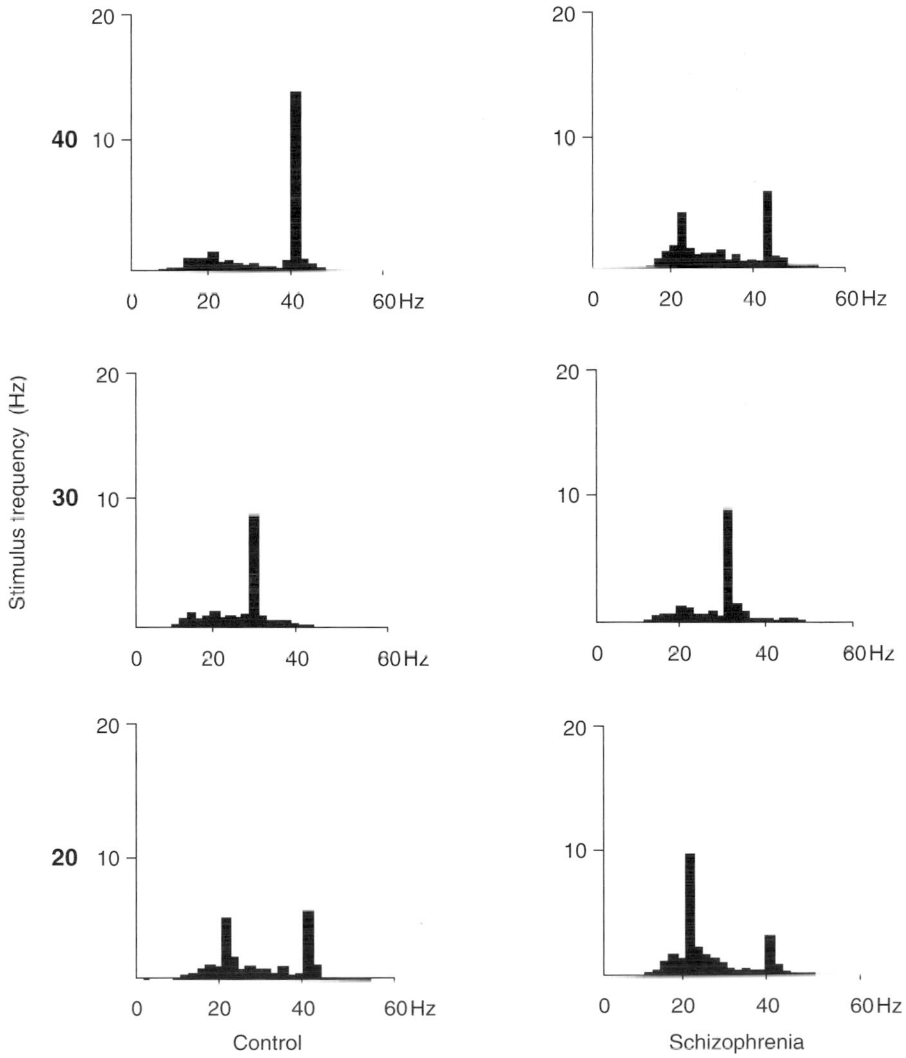

Fig 16.1 Mean power spectra for the EEG recorded to trains of clicks at three different stimulus rates: 40 Hz stimulation (upper); 30 Hz stimulation (middle); and 20 Hz stimulation (lower). The schizophrenic patients ($n = 15$; right column) show decreased power at 40 Hz stimulation compared with control subjects ($n = 15$; left column), but there was no difference between groups at lower frequencies of stimulation. (Adapted from Kwon *et al.* 1999.)

confirmed, it would be an important addition to our knowledge about schizophrenia.

However, it remains to be determined if this deficiency in externally driven gamma implies a deficiency in gamma-band synchronization which occurs endogenously in the course of perception as when, for example, a certain pattern of spots embedded in a field of spots is suddenly perceived to be a Dalmatian dog. Thus, the next phase of gamma research in schizophrenia will be evaluating this kind of gamma, also known as evoked gamma. At present, few studies have been conducted. Baldeweg *et al.* (1998) presented evidence of increased gamma-band activity during somatic hallucinations in a case report. Kissler *et al.* (2000) reported reduced gamma activity and reversed hemispheric asymmetry in chronically ill patients during a mental arithmetic task. Clearly, more work needs to be carried out regarding endogenous gamma oscillations in schizophrenia.

Mismatch negativity

MMN is a negative, relatively short-latency (e.g. occurring 150–250 ms after the stimulus onset) auditory ERP elicited when infrequent sounds (deviants) are presented in the sequence of repetitive sounds (standards). In order to elicit MMN, deviant sounds may differ from the standards in a simple physical characteristic such as pitch, duration, intensity or spatial location. In addition, changes in abstract features of auditory stimuli presentation, such as distinct patterns, also elicit MMN. MMN is primarily evoked automatically, preattentively and preconsciously and is thus thought to reflect the operations of sensory memory, a kind of memory of past stimuli used by the auditory cortex in analysis of temporal patterns. MMN has been extensively studied in humans to changes in stimulus parameters, most commonly to tone pitch or tone duration.

Intracranial recordings in animals (Kraus *et al.* 1994; Csepe 1995; Javitt *et al.* 1996), magnetoencephalographic (MEG) recordings and source localization in humans (Hari *et al.* 1984; Alho 1995) have led to the supposition of bilateral generators of MMN in auditory cortices. It has been proposed that MMN is produced in the auditory cortex by a mismatch between the deviant tone and auditory sensory memory representing the features of the standard tone (Naatanen 1992). Recently, a frontal component supposedly related to involuntary attention to the deviant stimulus has been reported (Giard *et al.* 1994), although it remains unclear whether this component should be considered MMN or a separate mechanism such as the N2b originally suggested to be a consequence of the activity of MMN arising from auditory cortex. Furthermore, it remains unclear whether this potential reflects activity in prefrontal cortex or whether it arises in secondary auditory association cortex in the anterior temporal lobe that projects to the anterior portions of the scalp. Although still controversial, the notion of a prefrontal generator has been partially supported by the findings of reduced MMN in patients with prefrontal cortical lesions (Alho *et al.* 1994; Alain *et al.* 1998), as well as selective impairment of MMN at frontal, but not mastoid, sites in patients with schizophrenia (Baldeweg *et al.* 2002).

MMN has been suggested to reflect the activity of *N*-methyl-D-aspartate (NMDA) channel-mediated influx of current flow in supragranular cortical layers. Studies carried out in monkeys showed that deviants elicited MMN-like activity in the supragranular (surface) layers of primary auditory cortex, and further that this activity was obliterated by application of NMDA-specific antagonists (Javitt *et al.* 1996). Umbricht *et al.* (2000) showed reduced MMN in normal subjects following the administration of ketamine, an NMDA receptor antagonist.

Not surprisingly, given the long-standing interest in early sensory gating abnormalities and the more recent interest in NMDA abnormalities in schizophrenia, MMN has been investigated in schizophrenia to determine whether such an index of early stimulus processing was disrupted. Most studies of MMN have shown reductions in chronically ill schizophrenia patients, generally in the order of 40–50% in the study of pitch deviants (Fig. 16.2). Some studies have reported correlations between the severity of negative symptoms and reduced MMN amplitude at a frontal recording site (Catts *et al.* 1995; Javitt *et al.* 2000a). The reduction of MMN in chronically ill schizophrenia patients appears to be trait-like and not ameliorated by either typical (haloperidol) or atypical (clozapine) medication (Umbricht *et al.* 1998). MMN characteristics have only recently been reported in first episode patients. Javitt *et al.* (2000a) reported marginally significant ($P = 0.06$) MMN reductions in outpatients who were within 3 years of their first psychotic episode, although these patients were not necessarily recorded at their first hospitalization.

Salisbury *et al.* (2002) recently reported that pitch MMN was normal very early in the course of schizophrenia, i.e. at the time of first hospitalization (Fig. 16.2) Thus, the reduction in pitch MMN observed in chronically ill patients is not apparent at the first episode (often empirically defined as the first hospitalization). Thus, it may be related to a progressive neurodegenerative effect of the disease, or possibly to some secondary chronicity variable. Umbricht *et al.* (2002) presented preliminary data supporting the finding of Salisbury *et al.* (2002) of a normal MMN amplitude in first-episode schizophrenia (Fig. 16.3). The recent-onset group also showed a reduced MMN, suggesting progressive changes in pathology. Salisbury *et al.* have presented preliminary longitudinal data to suggest that MMN reductions become apparent within the first 2 years of schizophrenia onset in patients who displayed a normal MMN at first episode (Salisbury *et al.* 2001). While their small subject numbers makes any conclusion tentative, it does raise the possibility of MMN as an index of neurodegeneration in the early course of the disorder (Fig. 16.2), although effects secondary to chronicity, such as the onset of an antipsychotic mediation regimen, cannot be ruled out. It is interesting to note that Catts *et al.* (1995) reported an MMN reduction in unmedicated chronic schizophrenia patients, which suggests that disease duration rather than medication may be related to MMN reductions. We note further that there is evidence that tone duration

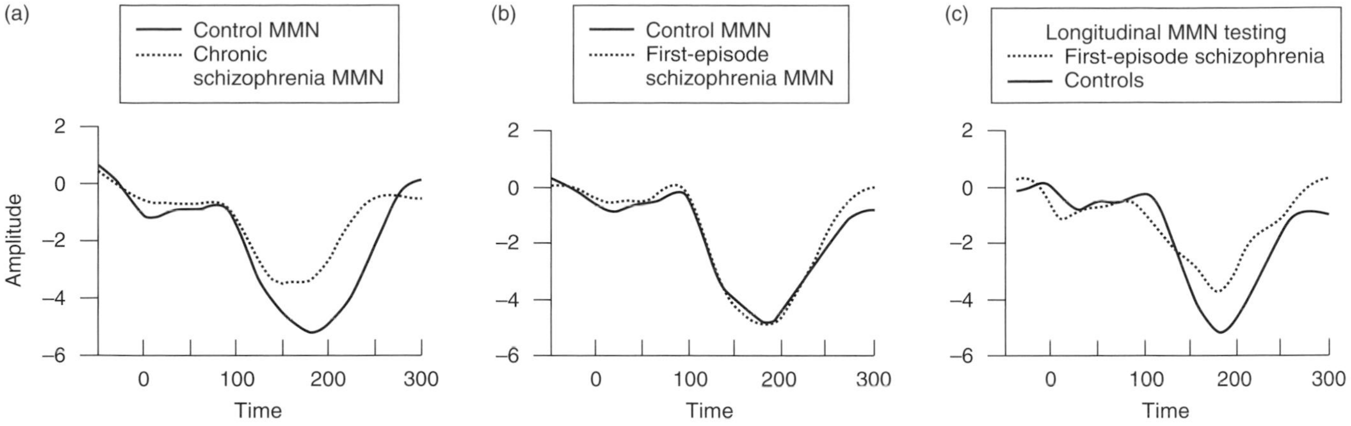

Fig 16.2 (a) Reduced MMN amplitude to pitch deviants in chronic schizophrenia patients. (b) Normal MMN amplitude to pitch deviants in first episode schizophrenia patients. (c) Longitudinal testing of first episode schizophrenia patients 1.5 years later indicates reduction in MMN amplitude to pitch deviants not present at first hospitalization.

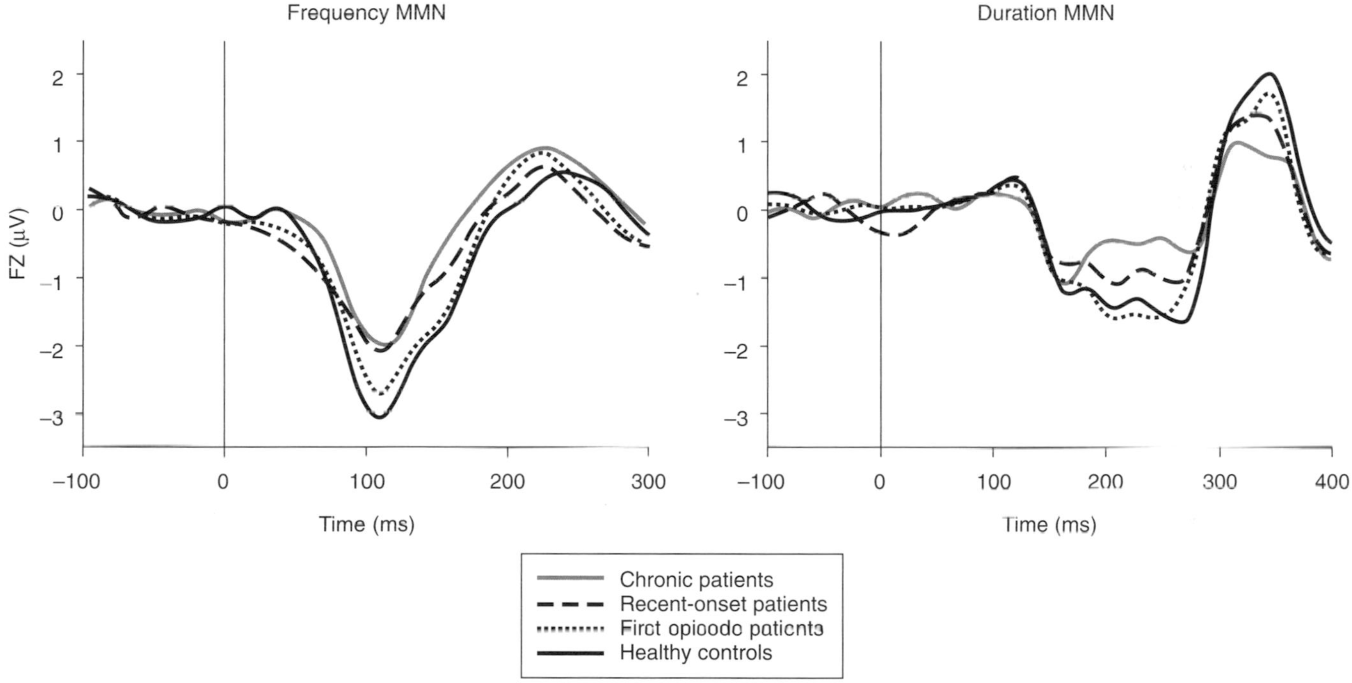

Fig 16.3 Frequency and duration MMN difference waves for chronic patients, recent-onset patients and healthy controls. (Adapted from Umbricht *et al.* 2002.)

MMN may be more sensitive to schizophrenic pathology than pitch MMN.

Reports of normal MMN amplitudes in first episode schizophrenia with an apparent progression of MMN reduction longitudinally suggest that MMN abnormalities develop as a consequence of disease onset. The direct genetic contribution to this reduction remains unclear, given reports of MMN reduction in a small sample of first-degree relatives of schizophrenic patients (Jessen *et al.* 2001). The data from first episode patients indicate a minimal early developmental component, because the MMN in these patients is apparently of normal amplitude at first hospitalization.

Because MMN may reflect, in part, NMDA-mediated activity and this receptor has an important role in cortical excitation and brain development, it is tempting to speculate about an NMDA-related abnormality active during the early course of the illness. If the preliminary data of Salisbury *et al.* (2001) (Fig. 16.2) are supported by subsequent work indicating that MMN undergoes a process of active reduction during the first few years after symptom onset and this is not simply drug-related, then there is the possibility that the MMN, especially the pitch MMN, might serve as an index of disease progression in the superior temporal gyrus. Further, the presence of an active phase of neurodegeneration around the time of first hospitalization would underline the need for pharmacological treatment, especially if the neurodegeneration were dependent on excitatory amino-acid neurotoxicity, as a number of theories suggest (see review in McCarley *et al.* 1996). For example, Olney and Farber (1995) have suggested that schizophrenia may involve postpubertal NMDA-mediated neurodegeneration, and that such effects may be countered most effectively by atypical antipsychotic medications. Recent multimodal imaging (Wible *et al.* 2001) has confirmed the origin of the pitch MMN within Heschl's gyrus and the nearby posterior superior temporal gyrus, and has demonstrated the presence of a deficiency of fMRI activation (BOLD) in schizophrenia to the mismatch stimulus. Preliminary data of Salisbury *et al.* (2001) have also shown that the volume of Heschl's gyrus in first episode schizophrenia patients was significantly correlated with MMN amplitude ($r = -0.68$, $P < 0.05$), even though neither measure was abnormal in the group as a whole. Those patients with the largest Heschl's gyrus volumes had the largest (most negative) MMN amplitudes (Fig. 16.4). It remains to be determined whether the reduction in MMN amplitude over the first few years after first hospitalization for schizophrenia is related to progressive reductions of grey matter in Heschl's gyrus.

P300

The P300 is an ERP that occurs to a stimulus that a subject actively detects and processes. Typically, a low-probability event among another frequently occurring standard stimulus is designated the target. Subjects must actively detect the target stimulus. It differs from the typical MMN paradigm in that the stimuli are presented at a slower rate (typically around 1 per second) and the subject is actively attending the stimuli. P300 is larger when the stimulus is rarer, and thus is typically evoked by 'oddball' stimulus paradigms, much like MMN. Thus, P300 is sensitive to cognitive processes that necessitate selective attention, by contrast with MMN, which reflects automatic orientating responses and is occluded by ERPs reflecting selective attention. Hence, P300 reflects brain activity related to complex cognitive operations on the part of the subject. Where MMN is

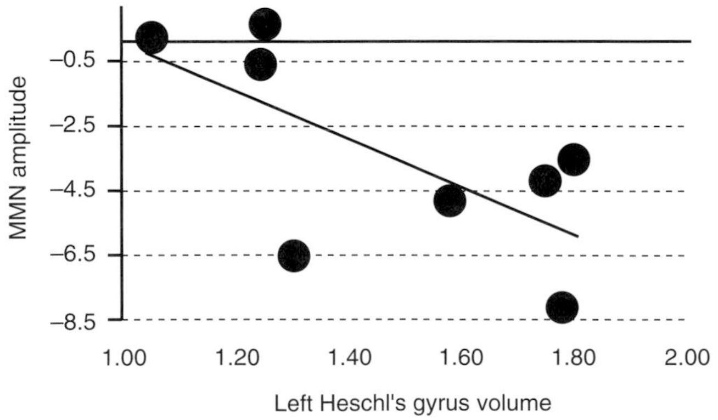

Fig 16.4 MMN amplitude in first episode schizophrenia patients is significantly correlated with the underlying grey matter volume of Heschl's gyrus, which contains primary auditory cortex.

thought to reflect sensory memory, by definition preconscious, P300 is thought to reflect an updating of the conscious information processing stream and of expectancy.

Roth and Cannon (1972) were the first to report a reduction in schizophrenia of P300 amplitude in recording sites over the sagittal midline of the head. Since then, nearly all studies have reported a reduction of P300 amplitude in subjects with schizophrenia. Delays in the onset of P300 are less certain, as most studies have reported similar latencies in patients and controls. The amplitude reduction of P300 is not related to a lack of attention to the task in the patients, as it remains reduced relative to controls even when the patients' performance in detecting the tones is as good as that of controls (Ford *et al.* 1994; Salisbury *et al.* 1994a). Furthermore, the latency of P300 in schizophrenia patients does vary with task difficulty, as in controls, but the amplitude remains reduced. Thus, P300 amplitude is robustly reduced in chronically ill schizophrenia patients. This widespread P300 reduction also appears to be trait-like and an enduring feature of the disease. Ford *et al.* (1994) demonstrated that although P300 showed moderate amplitude increases with symptom resolution, it did not approach normal values during these periods of remission. Umbricht *et al.* (1998) have reported that atypical antipsychotic treatment led to a significant increase of P300 amplitudes in patients with schizophrenia, although this response was not normalized.

In addition to the midline P300 reductions described above and broad reductions of P300 over both left and right hemispheres, chronically ill schizophrenic subjects display an asymmetry in P300 with smaller voltage over the left temporal lobe vs. right (Fig. 16.5). This left temporal P300 amplitude abnormality (from the mid-temporal T3 site) correlates negatively with the extent of psychopathology, as reflected in thought disorder and delusions (McCarley *et al.* 1993).

P300 likely reflects the activity of several different bilateral generators. There is clear evidence for activity in inferior parietal lobule and posterior superior temporal gyrus (STG) that corresponds to the scalp recorded P300. There is less evidence, but suggestive none the less, of a contribution from dorsolateral prefrontal cortex and from anterior cingulate cortex to the scalp-recorded P300. It is likely that many of the deep sources that generate P300-like activity do not propagate to the scalp (e.g. hippocampus).

The left temporal P300 amplitude reduction correlates positively with the grey matter volume of left posterior STG, one of the generator sites of P300, and an area also intimately related to language processing and thinking (McCarley *et al.* 1993). The volume of cortical grey matter in left STG volume is, in turn, correlated negatively with measures of thought disorder (Shenton *et al.* 1992) and the severity of auditory hallucinations (Barta *et al.* 1990). Therefore, abnormal left temporal P300 may reflect underlying STG abnormality and index the severity of psychopathology, and serve as a physiological tie between underlying brain pathology and behavioural psychopathology.

Salisbury *et al.* (1998) showed that the overall P300 reduction across the whole surface of the scalp was present in first episode

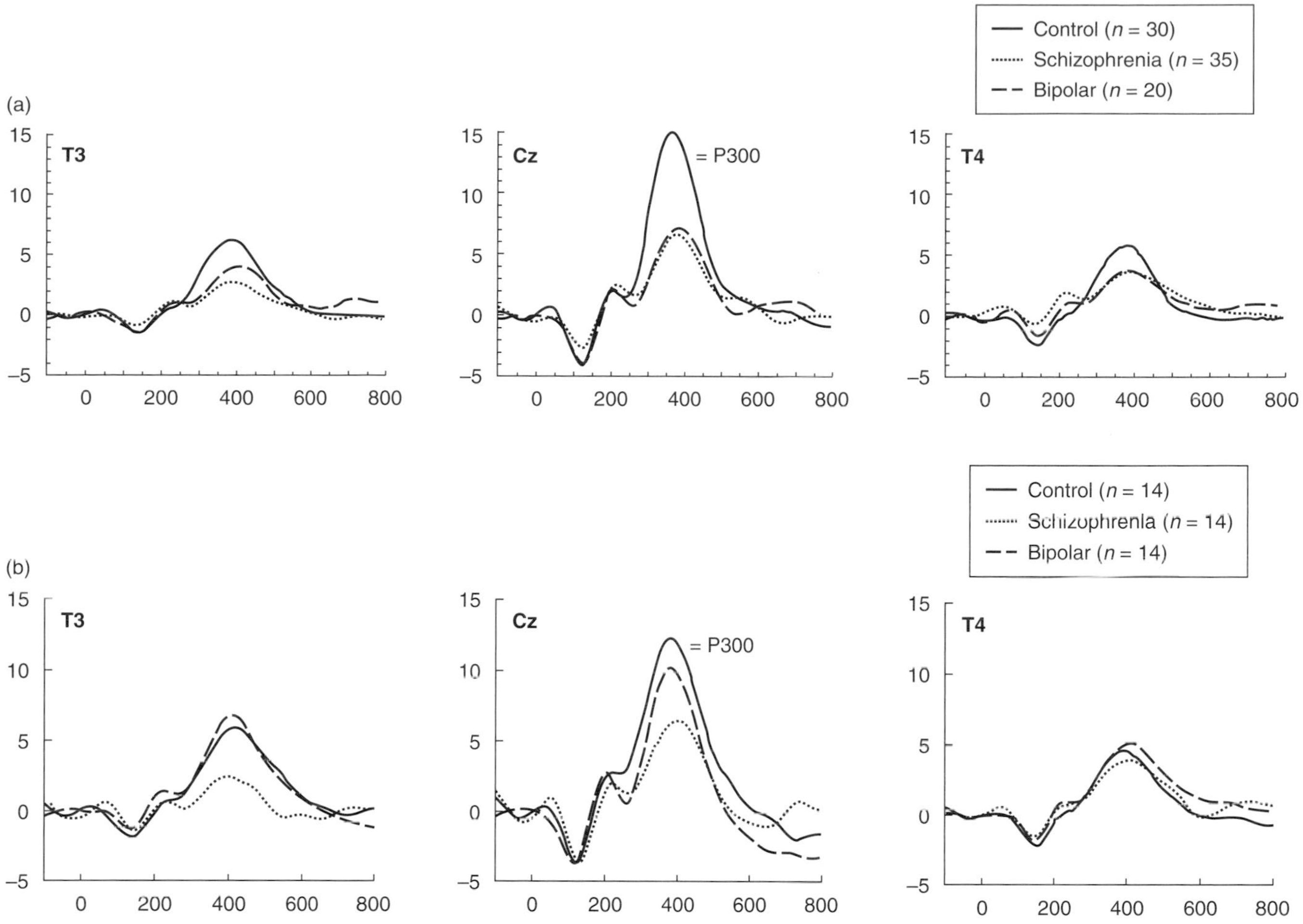

Fig 16.5 (a) P300 is broadly reduced in chronically ill schizophrenia (and psychotic mania) but is asymmetrically reduced on the left only in schizophrenia (T3 site). (b) First episode schizophrenia patients show the same overall and left-sided P300 reductions as do chronically ill patients. Note: T3 site overlies left middle temporal gyrus, T4 overlies right middle temporal gyrus, and Cz overlies sensorimotor cortex at the sagittal and coronal midpoint of the skull (vertex). (Adapted from Salisbury *et al.* 1998; 1999.)

schizophrenia patients, albeit to a lesser degree than in chronically ill patients, as was the same left-hemisphere localized deficit. Both first episode and chronically ill schizophrenia patients show an altered scalp topography of P300, with greater reduction over the left temporal areas (Fig. 16.6). Quantitative volumetric MRI studies have shown that the first episode schizophrenia patients show, in comparison to healthy control and manic first episode patients, a specific reduction in the cortical grey matter volume of posterior superior temporal gyrus, greatest on the left, and of planum temporale, again greatest on the left, as do chronically ill patients compared with controls (Hirayasu *et al.* 1998). Furthermore, as in chronically ill patients, the volumes in posterior STG and planum temporale, which likely contain one of several generators of P3, correlate positively with the left temporal scalp area P3 (McCarley *et al.* 2002). This programme of research has illuminated the specificity of significant left posterior superior temporal lobe involvement in schizophrenia during the early course of the disease, which highlights a possible aetiological role for dysfunction of these cortical areas in the disease. As in this selective illustration, the examination of first episode patients is crucially important in determining whether some pathological findings in chronically ill patients are present at disease onset and thus intrinsic to the disorder, rather than a secondary consequence of chronicity, such as a long exposure to neuroleptic medication.

Other ERPs in schizophrenia

Other ERPs are the focus of intense research in schizophrenia patients, but space limitations preclude extensive discussion of them here. Several of these potentials have been related to the search for an electrophysiological concomitant of an early sensory gating deficit in schizophrenia. These include, for example, the startle response, where the size of a blink to an acoustic probe is measured. Schizophrenia patients appear to be unable to modify their large startle response when forewarned that a probe is coming, by contrast with controls (Braff *et al.* 1978).

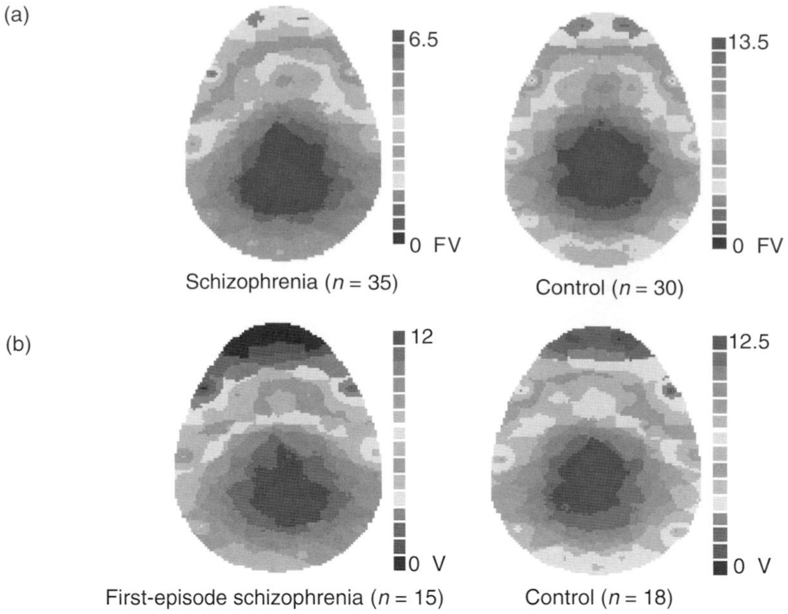

Fig 16.6 Topographic maps of P300 scalp distribution. (a) Chronically ill schizophrenia patients show more oval P300 maxima, skewed to the right relative to controls. (b) The same left-sided reduction and skewed distribution is present in first episode schizophrenia. (Adapted from Salisbury *et al.* 1998; 1999). P300 voltage topography (peak ± 25 ms).

Another ERP thought to be sensitive to an early sensory gating abnormality in schizophrenia is the P50. In the sensory gating paradigm, an auditory click is presented to a subject, eliciting a positive deflection about 50 ms after stimulus onset, the P50 component. After a brief interval (about 500 ms), a second click elicits a much smaller amplitude P50 in normal adult subjects, who are said to show normal gating: the first stimulus inhibits, or closes, the gate to neurophysiological processing of the second stimulus. Patients with schizophrenia, on the other hand, show less reduction in P50 amplitude to the second click, which is referred to as a failure in gating (Freedman *et al.* 1983). This gating deficit occurs in about half of first-degree relatives of a schizophrenic patient, suggesting that it may index a genetic factor in schizophrenia in the absence of overt psychotic symptoms (Waldo *et al.* 1991). While patients with affective disorder may show a gating deficit, the deficit does not persist after successful treatment, whereas in patients with schizophrenia the deficit occurs in both medicated and unmedicated patients and persists after symptom remission (Freedman *et al.* 1983; Adler & Waldo 1991).

The gating effect is thought to take place in temporal lobe structures, possibly the medial temporal lobe (Adler *et al.* 1985). P50 gating is enhanced by nicotinic cholinergic mechanisms, and it is possible that smoking in patients with schizophrenia is a form of self-medication (McCarley *et al.* 1996). Freedman *et al.* (1994) have shown that blockade of the $\alpha 7$ nicotinic receptor, localized to hippocampal neurones, causes loss of the inhibitory gating response to auditory stimuli in an animal model. The failure of inhibitory mechanisms to gate sensory input to higher order processing may result in 'sensory flooding', which Freedman suggests may underlie many of the symptoms of schizophrenia.

The N100 has recently received renewed interest in schizophrenia. The majority of studies using various experimental paradigms have reported a reduction of N100 amplitude in medicated and medication-free schizophrenic patients (Ogura *et al.* 1991; Boutros *et al.* 1997). The underlying basis of this dysfunction was also investigated. Shelley *et al.* (1999) argued that this abnormality was related to a deficit in current flow in underlying neurones. This hypothesis was tested in monkeys, where applications of phencyclidine (PCP), an NMDA receptor antagonist, blocked the normal increase in N100 amplitude with increasing inter-stimulus interval (ISI) (Javitt *et al.* 2000b). Further studies have been interested in the behaviour of the responses as stimulus parameters change. Adler *et al.* (1990) showed that N100 in schizophrenia patients was less influenced by intensity and ISI than N100 in controls. A recent study measured visual evoked potentials in first episode patients, and reported no evidence of reductions in N100 (Katsanis *et al.* 1996). No other study has examined N100 in first episode patients. One other potential, the N200, is thought to relate to the initial categorization of stimuli in the selective attention stream. Studies have reported reduced amplitudes and increased latencies of N200 in schizophrenia (Salisbury *et al.* 1994b; Laurent *et al.* 1999). Unlike the P300, the deficit of the N200 amplitude is not ameliorated by antypsychotic treatment (Umbricht *et al.* 1998). However, the abnormality of N200 in schizophrenia is still not well understood and further studies are needed to address this issue.

Magnetoencephalography – a complement to electroencephalography

Magnetoencephalography (MEG) is the measure of magnetic fields generated by the brain. A key difference in the physical source of the MEG as contrasted to the EEG is that the MEG is sensitive to cells which lie tangential to the brain surface and consequently have magnetic fields orientated tangentially. Cells with a radial orientation (perpendicular to the brain surface) do not generate signals detectable with MEG. The EEG and MEG are complementary in that the EEG is most sensitive to radially orientated neurones and fields. This distinction arises because magnetic fields are generated at right angles to electrical fields. One major advantage that magnetic fields have over electrical potentials is that, once generated, they are relatively invulnerable to intervening variations in the media they traverse (i.e. the skull, grey and white matter, and cerebrospinal fluid), unlike electrical fields, which are 'smeared' by different electrical conductivities. This has made MEG a favourite for use in source localization, where attention has been especially focused on early potentials.

Perhaps because of the expense and non-mobility of the recording equipment needed for MEG, there has been relatively little work using MEG in schizophrenia to replicate and extend the findings of ERPs. A search of Medline revealed only 23 published studies using MEG measures of brain activity in schizophrenia. Studies have shown interesting results. Reite *et al.* (1999) demonstrated that the M100 component (the magnetic analogue to the N100) showed less interhemispheric asymmetry in schizophrenics and had different source orientations in the left hemisphere. The recent review by Reite *et al.* (1999) should be consulted for more details of the work on MEG in schizophrenia.

To summarize the studies to date, most have focused on M100. Results show a great degree of consistency across laboratories. The M100 shows abnormalities, particularly in the left hemisphere, with an altered dipole location (shifted anteriorly), and reduced asymmetry for right-ear stimuli in schizophrenia patients.

Conclusions

ERPs provide the greatest temporal resolution of all current functional imaging techniques. When coupled with information about likely generator sites from intracortical recordings, lesion studies and fMRI, and with spatially accurate measures of brain structure from high-resolution MRI, ERPs greatly contribute to the elucidation of brain function, essentially detecting physiology at the speed of thought. Further, ERPs allow for the elucidation of information processing long before any overt behaviour on the part of the subject. Both exogenous and endogenous ERPs are abnormal in chronically ill schizophrenia patients. These ERPs have help to direct investigations of specific cortical regions, which has identified pathophysiology specific to schizophrenia compared with affective psychosis. The concurrent investigation of ERPs and MRI in chronically ill and first episode patients has allowed for the detection of those abnormalities that are present at disease onset and those that appear to develop with disease course. For the latter abnormalities, such a demonstration immediately suggests the importance of developing psychopharmacological interventions, which might counter at least some of the symptoms that develop with the disease course.

Acknowledgements

This work was supported in part by VA MERIT (R.W.M.) and Schizophrenia Center Awards (R.W.M.) from the Department of Veterans Affairs, the National Institute of Mental Health (MH 40977 R.W.M.), and the National Alliance for Research in Schizophrenia and Depression (D.F.S.).

References

Adler, L.E. & Waldo, M.C. (1991) Counterpoint: sensory gating-hippocampal model of schizophrenia,. *Schizophrenia Bulletin* **17**, 19–24.

Adler, L.E., Waldo, M.C. & Freeman, R. (1985) Neurophysiological studies of sensory gating in schizophrenia: comparison of auditory and visual responses. *Biological Psychiatry* **20**, 1284–1296.

Adler, G., Adler, J., Schenk, M. & Armbruster, B. (1990) Influence of stimulation parameters on auditory stimulus processing in schizophrenia and major depression: an evoked potential study. *Acta Psychiatrica Scandinavica* **81**, 453–458.

Alain, C., Woods, D.L. & Knight, R.T. (1998) A distributed cortical network for auditory sensory memory in humans. *Brain Research* **812**, 23–37.

Alho, K. (1995) Cerebral generators of mismatch negativity (MMN) and its magnetic counterpart (MMNm) elicited by sound changes. *Ear and Hearing* **16**, 38–51.

Alho, K., Woods, D.L., Algazi, A., Knight, R.T. & Naatanen, R. (1994) Lesions of frontal cortex diminish the auditory mismatch negativity. *Electroencephalography and Clinical Neurophysiology* **91**, 353–362.

Baldeweg, T., Spence, S., Hirsch, S.R. & Gruzelier, J. (1998) Gamma-band electroencephalographic oscillations in a patient with somatic hallucinations. *Lancet* **352**, 620–621.

Baldeweg, T., Klugman, A., Gruzelier, J.H. & Hirsch, S.R. (2002). Impairment in frontal but not temporal components of mismatch negativity in schizophrenia. *International Journal of Psychophysiology* **43**, 111–122.

Barta, P.E., Pearlson, G.D., Powers, R.E., Richards, S.S. & Tune, L.E. (1990) Auditory hallucinations and smaller superior temporal gyral volume in schizophrenia. *American Journal of Psychiatry* **147**, 1457–1462.

Blackwood, D.H.R., St. Clair, D.M., Muir, W.J. & Duffy, J.C. (1991) Auditory P300 and eye tracking dysfunction in schizophrenic pedigrees. *Archives of General Psychiatry* **48**, 899–909.

Boutros, N., Nasrallah, H., Leighty, R. *et al.* (1997) Auditory evoked potentials, clinical vs. research applications. *Psychiatry Research* **69**, 183–195.

Braff, D., Stone, C., Callaway, E. *et al.* (1978) Prestimulus effects on human startle reflex in normals and schizophrenics. *Psychophysiology* **15**, 339–343.

Buchsbaum, M. (1977) The middle evoked response components and schizophrenia. *Schizophrenia Bulletin* **3**, 93–104.

Catts, S.V., Shelley, A.M., Ward, P.B. *et al.* (1995) Brain potential evidence for an auditory sensory memory deficit in schizophrenia. *American Journal of Psychiatry* **152**, 213–219.

Csepe, V. (1995) On the origin and development of the mismatch negativity. *Ear Hear* **16**, 91–104.

Domino, E.F., Demetriou, S., Tuttle, T. & Klinge, V. (1979) Comparison of the visually evoked response in drug-free chronic schizophrenic patients and normal controls. *Electroencephalography and Clinical Neurophysiology* **46**, 123–137.

Ford, J.M., White, P.M., Csernansky, J.G. *et al.* (1994) ERPs in schizophrenia: effects of antipsychotic medication. *Biological Psychiatry* **36**, 153–170.

Freedman, R.F., Adler, L., Waldo, M., Oachtman, E. & Franks, R. (1983) Neurophysiological evidence for a defect in inhibitory pathways in schizophrenia: comparison of medicated and drug-free patients. *Biological Psychiatry* **18**, 537–551.

Freedman, R.F., Adler, L.E., Bickford, P. *et al.* (1994) Schizophrenia and nicotinic receptors. *Harvard Review of Psychiatry* **2**, 179–192.

Giard, M.H., Perrin, F., Echallier, J.F. *et al.* (1994) Dissociation of temporal and frontal components in the human auditory N1 wave: a scalp current density and dipole model analysis. *Electroencephalography and Clinical Neurophysiology* **92**, 238–252..

Hari, R., Hamalainen, M., Ilmoniemi, R. *et al.* (1984) Responses of the primary auditory cortex to pitch changes in a sequence of tone pips: neuromagnetic recordings in man. *Neuroscience Letters* **50**, 127–132.

Hirayasu, Y., Shenton, M.E., Salisbury, D.F. *et al.* (1998) Lower left temporal lobe MRI volumes in patients with first-episode schizophrenia compared with psychotic patients with first-episode affective disorder and normal subjects. *American Journal of Psychiatry* **155**, 1384–1391.

Javitt, D.C., Steinschneider, M., Schroeder, C.E. & Arezzo, J.C. (1996) Role of cortical *N*-methyl D-aspartate receptors in auditory sensory memory and mismatch negativity generation: implications for schizophrenia. *Proceedings of the National Academy of Sciences of the USA* **93**, 11962–11967.

Javitt, D.C., Shelley, A.M. & Ritter, W. (2000a) Associated deficits in mismatch negativity generation and tone matching in schizophrenia. *Clinical Neurophysiology* **111**, 1733–1737.

Javitt, D.C., Jayachandra, M., Lindsley, R.W., Specht, C.M. & Schroeder, C.E. (2000b) Schizophrenia-like deficits in auditory P1 and N1 refractoriness induced by the psychotomimetic agenct phencyclidine. *Clinical Neurophysiology* **111**, 833–836.

Jessen, F., Fries, T., Kucharski, C. *et al.* (2001) Amplitude reduction of the mismatch negativity in first-degree relatives of patients with schizophrenia. *Neuroscience Letters* **309**, 185–188.

John, E.R., Prichep, L.S., Alper, K.R. *et al.* (1994) Quantitative electrophysiological characteristics and subtyping of schizophrenia. *Biological Psychiatry* **36**, 801–826.

Katsanis, J., Iacono, W.G. & Beiser, M. (1996) Visual event-related potentials in first-episode psychotic patients and their relatives. *Psychophysiology* **33**, 207–217.

Kissler, J., Muller, M.M., Fehr, T., Rockstroh, B.E. & Bert, T. (2000) MEG gamma band activity in schizophrenia patients and healthy subjects in a mental arithmetic task and at rest. *Clinical Neurophysiology* **111**, 2079–2087.

Kraus, N., McGee, T., Carrell, T. *et al.* (1994) Discrimination of speech-like contrasts in the auditory thalamus and cortex. *Journal of Acoustic Society of America* **96**, 2758–2768.

Kwon, J.S., O'Donnell, B.F., Wallenstein, G.V. *et al.* (1999) Gamma frequency-range abnormalities to auditory stimulation in schizophrenia. *Archives of General Psychiatry* **56**, 1001–1005.

Laurent, A., Garcia-Larréa, L., d'Amato, T. *et al.* (1999) Auditory event-related potentials and clinical scores in unmedicated schizophrenic patients. *Psychiatry Research* **87**, 147–157.

Levit, R.A., Sutton, S. & Zubin, J. (1973) Evoked potential correlated of information processing in psychiatric patients. *Psychological Medicine* **3**, 487–494.

Logothetis, N.K., Pauls, J., Augath, M., Trinath, T. & Oeltermann, A. (2001) Neurophysiological investigation of the basis of the fMRI signal. *Nature* **412**, 150–157.

McCarley, R.W., Shenton, M.E., O'Donnell, B.F. *et al.* (1993) Auditory P300 abnormalities and left posterior superior temporal gyrus volume reduction in schizophrenia. *Archives of General Psychiatry* **50**, 190–197.

McCarley, R.W., Hsiao, J.K., Freedman, R., Pfefferbaum, A. & Donchin, E. (1996) Neuroimaging and the cognitive neuroscience of schizophrenia. *Schizophrenia Bulletin* **22**, 703–725.

McCarley, R.W., Salisbury, D.F., Hirayasu, Y. *et al.* (2002) Association between smaller left posterior superior temporal gyrus MRI volume and smaller left temporal P300 amplitude in first episode schizophrenia. *Archives of General Psychiatry* **59**, 321–331.

McGhie, A. & Chapman, J. (1961) Disorders of attention and perception in early schizophrenia. *British Journal of Medical Psychiatry* **34**, 103–116.

Naatanen, R. (1992) *Attention and Brain Function.* Hillsdale, NJ/ Lawrence Erlbaum, Hove.

Ogura, C., Nageishi, Y., Matsubayashi, M. *et al.* (1991) Abnormalities in event-related potentials, N100, P200, P300 and slow wave in schizophrenia. *Japanese Journal of Psychiatry and Neurology* **45**, 57–65.

Olney, J.W. & Farber, N.B. (1995) Glutamate receptor dysfunction and schizophrenia. *Archives of General Psychiatry* **52**, 998–1007.

Raichle, M. (1998) Behind the scence of functional brain imaging: a historical and physiological perspective. *Proceedings of the National Academy of Sciences of the USA* **95**, 765–772.

Rauch, S. & Renshaw, P. (1995) Clinical neuroimaging in psychiatry. *Harvard Review of Psychiatry* **2**, 297–312.

Regan, D. (1989) Human brain electrophysiology. *Evoked-Potentials and Evoked Magnetic Fields in Science and Medicine.* Elsevier, New York.

Reite, M., Teale, P. & Rojas, D.C. (1999) Magnetoencephalography: applications in psychiatry. *Biological Psychiatry* **45**, 1553–1563.

Roth, W.T. (1977) Late event-related potentials and psychopathology. *Schizophrenia Bulletin* **3**, 105–120.

Roth, W.T. & Cannon, E. (1972) Some features of the auditory evoked response in schizophrenics. *Archives of General Psychiatry* **27**, 466–471.

Saletu, B., Itil, T.M. & Saletu, M. (1971) Auditory evoked response, EEG, and thought process in schizophrenia. *American Journal of Psychiatry* **128**, 336–343.

Salisbury, D.F., O'Donnell, B.F., McCarley, R.W. *et al.* (1994a) Parametric manipulations of auditory stimuli differentially affect P3 amplitude in schizophrenics and controls. *Psychophysiology* **31**, 29–36.

Salisbury, D.F., O'Donnell, B.F., McCarley, R.W., Shenton, M.E. & Benavage, A. (1994b) The N2 event-related potential reflects attention deficit in schizophrenia. *Biological Psychology* **39**, 1–13.

Salisbury, D.F., Shenton, M.E., Sherwood, A.R. *et al.* (1998) First episode schizophrenic psychosis differs from first episode affective psychosis and controls in P300 amplitude over left temporal lobe. *Archives of General Psychiatry* **55**, 173–180.

Salisbury, D.F., Bonner-Jackson, A., Griggs, C.B., Shenton, M.E. & McCarley, R.W. (2001) Mismatch negativity in schizophrenia: does MMN amplitude decline with disease duration? *Biological Psychiatry* **49** (Suppl.), 85S.

Salisbury, D.F., Shenton, M.E., Griggs, C.B., Bonner-Jackson, A. & McCarley, R.W. (2002) Mismatch negativity in chronic schizophrenia and first-episode schizophrenia. *Archives of General Psychiatry* **59**, 686–694.

Schooler, C., Buchsbaum, M.S. & Carpenter, W.T. (1976) Evoked response and kinesthetic measures of augmenting/reducing in schizophrenics: replications and extensions. *Journal of Nervous and Mental Disease* **163**, 221–232.

Shagass, C. (1968) Cerebral evoked responses in schizophrenia. *Conditional Reflex* **3**, 205–216.

Shagass, C. (1977) The early potentials. *Schizophrenia Bulletin* **3**, 80–92.

Shagass, C., Soskis, D.A., Straumanis, J.J. & Overton, D.A. (1974) Symptom patterns related to somatosensory evoked response differences within a schizophrenia population. *Biological Psychiatry* **9**, 25–43.

Shelley, A.M., Silipo, G. & Javitt, D.C. (1999) Diminished responsiveness of ERPs in schizophrenic subjects to changes in auditory stimulation parameters: implications for theories of cortical dysfunction. *Schizophrenia Research* **37**, 65–79.

Shenton, M.E., Kikinis, R., Jolesz, F.A. *et al.* (1992) Abnormalities of the left temporal lobe and thought disorder in schizophrenia: a quantitative magnetic resonance imaging study. *New England Journal of Medicine* **327**, 604–612.

Sutton, S., Braren, M., Zubin, J. & John, E.R. (1965) Evoked potential correlates of stimulus uncertainty. *Science* **150**, 1187–1188.

Turetsky, B., Colbath, E.A. & Gur, R.A. (1998) P300 subcomponent abnormalities in schizophrenia. II. Longitudinal stability and relationship to symptom change. *Biological Psychiatry* **43**, 31–39.

Umbricht, D., Javitt, D., Novak, G. *et al.* (1998) Effects of clozapine on auditory event-related potentials in schizophrenia. *Biological Psychiatry* **44**, 716–725.

Umbricht, D., Schmid, L., Koller, R. *et al.* (2000) Ketamine-induced deficits in auditory and visual context-dependent processing in healthy volunteers. *Archives of General Psychiatry* **57**, 1139–1147.

Umbricht, D.C., Javitt, J., Bates, J., Kane, J.A. & Lieberman (2002) Auditory event-related potentials (ERP): indices of both premorbid and illness-related progressive neuropathology in schizophrenia? *Schizophrenia Research* **53** (3), 18.

Venables, P. (1964) Input dysfunction in schizophrenia. In: *Progress in Experimental Personality Research* (ed. B. Maher), pp. 1–47. Academic Press, New York.

Waldo, M.C., Carey, G., Myles-Worsley, M. *et al.* (1991) Codistribution of a sensory gating deficit and schizophrenia in multi-affected families. *Psychiatry Research* **39**, 257–268.

Wible, C., Kubicki, M., Yoo, S. *et al.* (2001) A functional magnetic resonance imaging study of auditory mismatch in schizophrenia. *American Journal of Psychiatry* **158**, 938–943.

17 Neuropathology of schizophrenia

P.J. Harrison and D.A. Lewis

There is no neuropathology of schizophrenia in the sense that there is a neuropathology of Huntington's disease, neurosyphilis or a glioma. However, this stark statement conceals the fact that significant progress has been made in discovering the existence and nature of histological correlates of schizophrenia, both by ruling out certain processes, as well as by providing some intriguing positive results concerning alterations in cortical architecture which may contribute to the anatomical substrate of the disorder.

The recent upturn of fortunes in this field has come about for several reasons. First, accumulating evidence from computerized tomography (CT) and magnetic resonance imaging (MRI) studies of the past 25 years has shown unequivocally that structural brain abnormalities are present in schizophrenia. There must be a histological and, ultimately, a molecular basis for such alterations, and this simple but fundamental point has stimulated neuropathological research. Secondly, lessons have been learned from the earlier generation of studies, which were inadequate by current standards of study design, methodology and statistical analysis. Thirdly, the resurgence of interest has coincided with the rapid progress in neuroscience and molecular biology. These have increased the sophistication of contemporary studies, and have provided a much more powerful range of tools with which to conduct them.

This chapter summarizes the current understanding of the neuropathology of schizophrenia and its interpretation. We have not attempted a comprehensive or historical review, but emphasize those aspects for which there is a convergence and consistency to the findings in order to highlight the key points and major themes; in anatomical terms we have focused on the hippocampal formation, dorsal prefrontal cortex (DPFC) and the thalamus. (For more detailed coverage, including discussion of brain areas not considered here, see Arnold & Trojanowski 1996; Harrison 1999a; Harrison & Roberts 2000. For review of the now largely disregarded early literature, see David 1957.)

Neurodegeneration in schizophrenia

A critical question concerns the neuropathological nature of schizophrenia. In the most basic (and grossly oversimplified) sense, neuropathological processes are either degenerative or developmental. In the former, there are usually cytopathological inclusions (e.g. neurofibrillary tangles, Lewy bodies) and evidence for neuronal and synaptic loss, accompanied by gliosis (reactive astrocytosis). A degenerative process underlies most dementias, as well as the pathology seen after hypoxia, infection and trauma. In the absence of any evidence for abnormalities of this kind, a neurodevelopmental process, in which something goes awry with normal brain maturation, is by default the likely form of pathology to explain a brain disorder. (Weinberger 1987) Because this distinction – despite its limitations – has such important implications for the nature of the disease, we first review the studies which have sought, and failed, to find consistent positive evidence for neurodegeneration in schizophrenia.

Gliosis

In a paper which heralded the start of the current phase of research, Stevens (1982) described reactive astrocytosis in ~70% of her series of cases with schizophrenia. The gliosis was usually located in periventricular and subependymal regions of the diencephalon or in adjacent basal forebrain structures. This finding supported aetiopathogenic scenarios for schizophrenia involving infective, ischaemic, autoimmune or neurodegenerative processes.

In contrast to Stevens' findings, many subsequent investigations of schizophrenia have not found gliosis (Roberts & Harrison 2000). The study of Bruton *et al.* (1990) was illuminating, finding that gliosis in schizophrenia was only seen in cases exhibiting separate neuropathological abnormalities, such as focal lesions, infarcts and so on, many of which clearly postdated the onset of psychosis. This suggested strongly that gliosis is not an intrinsic feature of the disease, but is a sign of coincidental or superimposed pathological changes (which occur in a significant minority of cases; Riederer *et al.* 1995). This view, although now broadly accepted, is subject to qualifications. First, the recognition and definition of gliosis is not as straightforward as sometimes assumed (Stevens *et al.* 1988, 1992; Da Cunha *et al.* 1993). Secondly, most studies have focused on the cerebral cortex rather than on the diencephalic regions where the gliosis of Stevens (1982) was concentrated, although the recent study of Falkai *et al.* (1999) overcomes this limitation. Thirdly, there could be pathological heterogeneity, with a proportion of cases being 'neurodegenerative'; however, the cumulative data suggest that this proportion would have to be small.

The gliosis debate has been stimulated by its implications for the nature of schizophrenia. The gliotic response is said not to occur until the end of the second trimester *in utero* (Friede 1989). Hence, an absence of gliosis, in the context of other pathological abnormalities, is considered strong evidence for an early neurodevelopmental origin of schizophrenia. However, timing of the developmental onset of the glial response has not been well investigated and so absence of gliosis should not be used to time the pathology of schizophrenia with any certainty. For example, gliotic reactions have been clearly described after amniocentesis needle injury occurring at 16–18 weeks' gestation (Squier *et al.* 2000). Moreover, gliosis is not always demonstrable or permanent (Kalman *et al.* 1993). Neither is it thought to accompany programmed cell death (apoptosis) of neurones, which has been hypothesized to be relevant to schizophrenia. Furthermore, it is a moot point whether the subtle kinds of morphometric disturbance to be described, whenever and however they occurred, would be sufficient to trigger detectable gliosis. Thus, the lack of gliosis does not mean, in isolation, that schizophrenia must be a neurodevelopmental disorder of prenatal origin; it is merely one argument in favour of that conclusion (Roberts & Harrison 2000). Certainly, in isolation, an absence of gliosis does not negate models of schizophrenia which include aberrant plasticity and perhaps mild neurotoxic processes in addition to a classically neurodevelopmental process (DeLisi 1997; Lieberman 1999). Addressing this possibility will require study of other glial cell populations, particularly microglia, which provide complementary information about immune and inflammatory processes (Bayer *et al.* 1999).

Alzheimer's disease

The other area of controversy regarding neurodegenerative processes in schizophrenia concerns the neuropathological explanation for the cognitive deficits of the disorder, and the supposedly greater prevalence of Alzheimer's disease in schizophrenia.

The belief that Alzheimer's disease is more common in schizophrenia originated in the 1930s (Corsellis 1962) and was bolstered by a large, although uncontrolled, study (Prohovnik *et al.* 1993), and by data implying that antipsychotic drugs might promote Alzheimer-type changes (Wisniewski *et al.* 1994). However, a meta-analysis (Baldessarini *et al.* 1997) and several subsequent studies, which have used sophisticated staining techniques and careful experimental designs, show conclusively that Alzheimer's disease is not more common than expected in schizophrenia (Arnold *et al.* 1998; Murphy *et al.* 1998; Purohit *et al.* 1998; Jellinger & Gabriel 1999). This even applies amongst elderly schizophrenics with moderate to severe dementia and in whom there is no other neurodegenerative disorder apparent (Arnold *et al.* 1996, 1998; Purohit *et al.* 1998). Moreover, the evidence does not support the view that antipsychotic drugs predispose to neurofibrillary or amyloid-related pathology (Baldessarini *et al.* 1997; Harrison 1999b).

The only known neuropathological correlate of dementia in schizophrenia is a small increase in the number of glial fibrillary acidic protein (GFAP)-positive astrocytes, with no change in other immunocytochemical indices of gliosis (Arnold *et al.* 1996). Apart from this, the severe cognitive impairment observed in chronically hospitalized elderly subjects with schizophrenia remains unexplained. It may just be a more severe manifestation of whatever pathology underlies the disorder itself, or perhaps the brain in schizophrenia is rendered more vulnerable to cognitive impairment in response to a normal age-related amount of neurodegeneration.

The hippocampal formation

In the absence of degenerative changes, attention is now focused on alterations in the neural cytoarchitecture (the morphology and arrangement of neurones), in tandem with studies of synapses and dendrites. The majority of these studies of schizophrenia have been in the hippocampal formation and prefrontal cortex, and the data in these two areas are considered in turn.

The hippocampal formation (hippocampus and parahippocampal gyrus) in the medial temporal lobe has been studied in schizophrenia for three reasons. First, when the current renaissance began 20 years ago, it was the hippocampal formation wherein several of the most striking initial findings were described, and this has continued to be the case (Arnold 1997; Weinberger 1999). The search for histological changes has been encouraged by the demonstration *in vivo* that hippocampal volume is decreased in first episode (Velakoulis *et al.* 1999) as well as chronic (Nelson *et al.* 1998) cases – although the latter has not been consistently shown postmortem. Furthermore, hippocampal proton resonance spectroscopy shows a reduced hippocampal *N*-acetyl aspartate (NAA) signal, suggestive of a neuronal pathology (Bertolino *et al.* 1998). Parenthetically, the NAA decrease is also present in first episode schizophrenia, providing some encouragement that complementary morphometric findings to be described below, although made in chronic cases, may also have been present at this time. Secondly, abnormal metabolic activity of the medial temporal lobe is seen in functional imaging studies of schizophrenia, related both to psychotic symptoms (Friston *et al.* 1992; Tamminga *et al.* 1992) and attentional/cognitive aspects (Heckers *et al.* 1998).

Neuropsychological data also implicate hippocampal dysfunction (Saykin *et al.* 1994). Thirdly, the relatively precise circuitry of the hippocampal formation lends itself to studies seeking to investigate neural connectivity, a concept which has become central to pathophysiological theories of schizophrenia (Friston & Frith 1995; Harrison 1999a; Benes 2000); this question is much more difficult to address in most other regions.

Hippocampal morphometric findings

The first influential morphometric abnormality reported in the hippocampus in schizophrenia was that of neuronal disarray. Normally, pyramidal neurones in Ammon's horn are aligned, as in a pallisade, with the apical dendrite orientated towards the stratum radiatum. Kovelman and Scheibel (1984) reported that this orientation was more variable and even reversed in schizophrenia, hence the term neuronal disarray. The disarray was present at the boundaries of CA1 with CA2 and subiculum. They suggested that a developmental migrational disturbance might be responsible. Qualified support for a greater variability of hippocampal neuronal orientation came in subsequent studies from the same group (Altshuler *et al.* 1987; Conrad *et al.* 1991). However, several other groups, using computerized image analysis-assisted measurements of neuronal orientation, have not replicated the observation (Christison *et al.* 1989; Benes *et al.* 1991b; Arnold *et al.* 1995a; Zaidel *et al.* 1997b). It is therefore unlikely that hippocampal neuronal disarray is associated with schizophrenia.

The second oft-cited feature of the hippocampal formation in schizophrenia is that of misplaced and aberrantly clustered neurones in lamina II (pre-α cells) and lamina III of the entorhinal cortex (anterior parahippocampal gyrus), described by Jakob and Beckmann (1986) and replicated by Arnold *et al.* (1991a, 1997). This finding was also interpreted as being developmental in origin and resulting from aberrant neuronal migration; certainly it is difficult to think of another plausible mechanism by which a cell population could show this kind of abnormality. However, other studies, with larger samples, better control groups or methodologies which take into account the significant intrinsic and interindividual heterogeneity of the entorhinal cortex, have not found clear differences (Heinsen *et al.* 1996; Akil & Lewis 1997; Krimer *et al.* 1997; Bernstein *et al.* 1998). Nevertheless, the situation remains controversial. Falkai *et al.* (2000) have recently reported quantitative evidence of abnormally located and smaller sized clusters of neurones in the entorhinal cortex, using a different form of analysis in the same brain series as that of Bernstein *et al.* (1998). It is essential to explain these discrepancies and establish if such abnormalities are or are not seen in the disorder, because their presence would be strong evidence in favour of an early neurodevelopmental origin of schizophrenia (Roberts 1991).

A loss of hippocampal neurones is a third finding sometimes described as a feature of schizophrenia. In fact, only two studies have found reductions in neuronal density (Jeste & Lohr 1989; Jonsson *et al.* 1997) and one reported a lower number of pyramidal neurones (Falkai & Bogerts 1986). In contrast, several have found no change in neuronal density (Falkai &Bogerts 1986; Benes *et al.* 1991b; Arnold *et al.* 1995) and one found a right-sided increase (Zaidel *et al.* 1997a). As well as being contradictory, none of these studies were stereological and so their value is limited by the inherent weaknesses of neuronal counts made in this way. The fact that the single stereological study which has been carried out found no difference in neuronal number or density in any subfield (Heckers *et al.* 1991) supports the view that there is no overall change in neuronal content of the hippocampus in schizophrenia. In this context, single reports of altered neuronal density restricted to a specific neuronal type (Benes *et al.* 1998), subfield or hemisphere (Zaidel *et al.* 1997b) must be replicated before discussion is warranted.

Computerized image analysis made it relatively straightforward to measure the size of neurones, either by tracing around the cell body or by measuring the smallest circle within which it fits, although neither of these approaches produces unbiased estimates of somal size now available with stereological techniques. Three studies, each counting large numbers of neurones, have identified a smaller mean size of hippocampal pyramidal neurones (Benes *et al.* 1991b; Arnold *et al.* 1995; Zaidel *et al.* 1997a). Although different individual subfields reached significance in the latter two studies, the same downward trend was present in all CA fields and in the subiculum. The non-replications comprise Christison *et al.* (1989) and Benes *et al.* (1998), perhaps because measurements were limited to a restricted subset of neurones. Smaller neuronal size has also been reported in DPFC, as discussed below. A degree of anatomical specificity is apparent, because cell size is unchanged in visual cortex (Rajkowska *et al.* 1998) and in motor cortex (Benes *et al.* 1986; Arnold *et al.* 1995). Finally, Zaidel *et al.* (1997a) found that pyramidal neurones were more elongated (as well as being smaller) in some hippocampal subfields in schizophrenia, which might relate to the abnormalities in dendritic arborization described in the next section.

Hippocampal synaptic and dendritic abnormalities

Changes in neuronal cell body parameters are likely to be a sign and a consequence of alterations in other neuronal compartments and the cytoarchitecture in which they are situated. Neuronal size is related to axonal diameter and other parameters of axodendritic arborization (Gilbert & Kelly 1975; Lund *et al.* 1975; Pierce & Lewin 1994; Hayes & Lewis 1996; Esiri & Pearson 2000), because the vast majority of a neurone's total volume is in its processes (especially axons in the case of projection neurones), and the size of the soma reflects the cellular machinery necessary to support them. Somal size varies normally within as well as between neuronal populations; it also changes (in both directions) in response to altered afferent and efferent connectivity (e.g. shrinkage after retrograde degeneration).

Investigation of synapses in schizophrenia has used various proteins, which are concentrated in presynaptic terminals, to serve as markers (Honer *et al.* 2000; Eastwood & Harrison

2001). First applied to Alzheimer's disease, using the protein synaptophysin, this approach has been validated in various neuropathological and experimental situations (Eastwood *et al.* 1994). Dendrites can also be investigated in an analogous fashion using dendritically located proteins, notably microtubule-associated protein-2 (MAP-2). In addition, the rapid Golgi method can be used, despite limitations, to study dendritic parameters (e.g. spine density, shape analysis) in postmortem material.

Key synaptic and dendritic findings in the hippocampal formation in schizophrenia are as follows (Harrison & Eastwood 2001). Decreased expression of synaptophysin has been found in several studies, with decrements also in other synaptic proteins such as SNAP-25, the synapsins and the complexins (Eastwood & Harrison 1995, 1999; for review see Honer *et al.* 2000). Data in degenerative disorders indicate that these decreases are likely to be a reflection of a lowered density of synapses; however, decreases in synaptic activity, synaptic plasticity (Eastwood & Harrison 1998) or the turnover of these gene products might also contribute to the observations. The affected circuits involve intrinsic hippocampal neurones (in addition to any involvement of neurones projecting into the hippocampal formation), because the level of the encoding messenger RNAs (mRNAs) is also reduced. Some data suggest that excitatory neurones and their synapses may be more affected than inhibitory ones (Harrison & Eastwood 1998), but other data indicate the reverse pattern (Benes *et al.* 1998; Benes 2000) or a similar involvement of both (Eastwood & Harrison 2000). There are complementary data showing hippocampal dendritic alterations in schizophrenia, with decreased immunoreactivity for MAP-2, a dendritic marker (Arnold *et al.* 1991b), as well as reduced density of dendritic spines in subicular neurones (Rosoklija *et al.* 2000). In summary, there is good evidence for synaptic pathology in the hippocampal formation, but the specific characteristics of the alterations remain to be established. These issues are discussed in more detail after description of the main findings in the prefrontal cortex.

The prefrontal cortex

Although studies by Alzheimer identified the dorsal prefrontal cortex (DPFC) as a possible site of pathological alterations in schizophrenia, this brain region did not become a major focus of postmortem studies until the early 1990s. As such, they have lagged behind those of the hippocampal formation, although noteworthy similarities, as well as differences, are becoming apparent between the two areas. The hippocampal findings were described above by taking each type of morphometric alteration in turn; in contrast, the DPFC studies are considered here within the context of how they may contribute to an overall picture of aberrant connectivity. The latter approach represents the prevailing view as to the nature of the anatomical basis of schizophrenia (Lewis 1997; Harrison 1999a).

Investigations of the DPFC in schizophrenia have been motivated by observations that subjects with schizophrenia exhibit both a relative hypometabolism of the DPFC, and impaired performance on cognitive tasks, such as those involving working memory, which are known to depend upon the integrity of DPFC circuitry. The idea that this dysfunction might be attributable to structural abnormalities in the DPFC has been supported by MRI studies which have revealed subtle reductions in grey matter volume of the DPFC in subjects with schizophrenia (McCarley *et al.* 1999). The failure to detect such abnormalities in all studies has been hypothesized to be a consequence of several factors, including volume reductions that approach the level of sensitivity of MRI and the restriction of volumetric changes to certain DPFC regions or gyri (McCarley *et al.* 1999). Consistent with this view, postmortem studies have frequently revealed a 3–12% decreased in cortical thickness in the DPFC in subjects with schizophrenia (Pakkenberg 1993; Daviss & Lewis 1995; Selemon *et al.* 1995; Woo *et al.* 1997a), although these changes were not always statistically significant. In addition, some (Bertolino *et al.* 1996, 2000; Deicken *et al.* 1997), but not all (Stanley *et al.* 1996), *in vivo* proton spectroscopy studies indicate that subjects with schizophrenia have reduced concentrations of DPFC NAA, a putative marker of neuronal and/or axonal integrity. Interestingly, the magnitude of these NAA changes in the DPFC has been correlated with the degree of impaired activation in other brain regions during working memory tasks, raising the possibility that a neuronal abnormality in the DPFC could account for distributed functional disturbances in the working memory network (Bertolino *et al.* 2000).

Other lines of evidence suggest that these changes may reflect disturbances in the synaptic connectivity of the DPFC. Observations by phosphorus-31 spectroscopy that never-medicated schizophrenic subjects have decreased phosphomonoesters and/or increased phosphodiesters in the DPFC have been interpreted as evidence of decreased synthesis and increased breakdown of membrane phospholipids, and consequently of a decreased number of synapses (Keshavan *et al.* 2000). In addition, DPFC levels of synaptophysin, an integral membrane protein of small synaptic vesicles, have been reported to be reduced in subjects with schizophrenia in many (Perrone-Bizzozero *et al.* 1996; Glantz & Lewis 1997; Davidsson *et al.* 1999; Honer *et al.* 1999; Karson *et al.* 1999) but not all studies (Gabriel *et al.* 1997; Eastwood *et al.* 2000). Alterations in other synapse-related proteins have also been described in the DPFC, although these observations are fewer in number and less consistent across studies and prefrontal cortex regions (Thompson *et al.* 1998; Davidsson *et al.* 1999; Karson *et al.* 1999). Finally, reports of increased cell packing density (Daviss & Lewis 1995; Selemon *et al.* 1995, 1998) have been interpreted as evidence that the DPFC neuropil, which is composed of the axon terminals and dendritic spines and shafts that form most cortical synapses, is reduced in schizophrenia (Selemon & Goldman-Rakic 1999).

Thus, various lines of evidence support the hypothesis that schizophrenia is associated with a decrease in the synaptic connectivity of the DPFC, although alternative explanations for these observations need to be considered. For example, some of the data cited above could be explained by a decrease in the number of DPFC neurones. However, the total number of prefrontal cortex neurones was not decreased in subjects with schizophrenia in a study that used an unbiased approach to address this question (Thune *et al.* 1998). In addition, postmortem studies have tended to find either a normal or, as noted above, increased cell packing density in the DPFC (Daviss & Lewis 1995; Selemon *et al.* 1995, 1998; Rajkowska *et al.* 1998). One limitation of these studies is that they may have lacked adequate sensitivity to detect reduced neuronal number or density of small subpopulations of DPFC neurones. Thus, the possibility that schizophrenia is associated with decrements in certain subsets of neurones, such as small neurones in layer 2 (Benes *et al.* 1991a) or the parvalbumin-containing subpopulation of γ-aminobutyric acid (GABA) neurones (Beasley & Reynolds 1997), cannot be excluded. However, the latter abnormality was not observed in another study (Woo *et al.* 1997a), and it should be noted that a reduction in neuronal density when using immunocytochemical markers may reflect an alteration in abundance or antigenicity of the target protein rather than in the number of neurones.

The reduction in DPFC grey matter in schizophrenia could also be caused, at least in part, by smaller neuronal cell bodies. The somal volume of pyramidal cells in deep layer 3 of DPFC area 9 has been reported in two studies to be decreased in subjects with schizophrenia (Rajkowska *et al.* 1998; Pierri *et al.* 2001). As discussed in the section on the hippocampal formation, this reduction may be associated with a decrease in total length of the basilar dendrites of these neurones (Glantz & Lewis 2000; Kalus *et al.* 2000), as well as with the decreased synaptophysin levels mentioned above. In contrast, the size of DPFC GABA neurones does not appear to be reduced in schizophrenia (Benes *et al.* 1986; Woo *et al.* 1997a). In summary, although a reduction in neurone number cannot be completely excluded, the subtle reduction in DPFC grey matter in schizophrenia appears more attributable to a combination of smaller neurones and a decrease in the axon terminals, distal dendrites and dendritic spines (see below) that represent the principal components of cortical synapses.

Synaptic abnormalities and the connections of the dorsal prefrontal cortex

Alterations in DPFC synaptic connectivity in schizophrenia may involve synapses formed by intrinsic axon terminals arising from neurones within the DPFC and/or from extrinsic axon terminals projecting to the DPFC from other cortical regions, the brainstem or the thalamus.

The reduced somal volume of DPFC layer 3 pyramidal cells (Rajkowska *et al.* 1998; Pierri *et al.* 2001), which give rise to a substantial number of intrinsic excitatory synapses (Levitt *et al.* 1993; Pucak *et al.* 1996), suggests that the synapses furnished by the intrinsic axon collaterals of these neurones may be reduced in number in schizophrenia. The results of a recent study using complementary DNA (cDNA) microarray profiling of the expression of over 7000 genes in DPFC area 9 of subjects with schizophrenia (Mirnics *et al.* 2000) may also be consistent with a disturbance in intrinsic connectivity. For example, among 250 functional gene groups, the most marked changes in expression were found in the group that encode for proteins involved in the regulation of presynaptic neurotransmitter release. Although these findings very likely indicate a general impairment of synaptic transmission within the DPFC in schizophrenia, it remains to be determined whether they represent a 'primary' abnormality intrinsic to the DPFC or a 'secondary' response to deficient inputs from other brain regions. Furthermore, because the specific genes within this group with the most altered levels of expression differed between subjects, it seems unlikely that these findings can be attributed solely to a downregulation of transcription secondary to a diminished number of intrinsic DPFC synapses. Consistent with this interpretation, synaptophysin mRNA levels do not appear to be reduced in the DPFC in schizophrenia (Karson *et al.* 1999; Eastwood *et al.* 2000; Glantz *et al.* 2000), suggesting that the reduced amount of synaptophysin protein in the DPFC may have an extrinsic source. The reduction of synaptophysin mRNA levels in other brain areas in schizophrenia, such as the hippocampal formation, may also be consistent with this view (Eastwood & Harrison 1999). However, whether these transcriptional changes occur in neurones that project to the DPFC, and if so whether they result in reduced levels of synaptophysin protein in the terminal fields of these neurones, has not been assessed.

In terms of subcortical inputs to the DPFC, the dopamine (DA) projections from the mesencephalon may be reduced in number in schizophrenia. The densities of axons immunoreactive for tyrosine hydroxylase, the rate-limiting enzyme in catecholamine synthesis, and the DA membrane transporter, are both decreased in DPFC area 9 of subjects with schizophrenia (Akil *et al.* 1999). In addition, an *in vivo* neuroimaging study reported a reduced density of D_1 receptors in the DPFC of unmedicated subjects with schizophrenia (Okubo *et al.* 1997). Thus, these findings may be in line with other data supporting a hypodopaminergic state in the DPFC in schizophrenia (Weinberger *et al.* 1988; Davis *et al.* 1991). However, the following caveats must be considered:

1 these observations may reflect merely a change in protein markers, and do not necessarily mean that the number of DPFC DA axons is decreased;

2 the reductions in markers of DA axons were confined to the deep cortical layers; and

3 DA axons are estimated to contribute < 1% of cortical synapses (Lewis & Sesack 1997).

Thus, these findings could not alone account for the observed reductions in grey matter volume, or synaptophysin levels, in the DPFC of subjects with schizophrenia.

Thalamic projections to the prefrontal cortex

Various lines of evidence suggest that altered inputs from the thalamus may be one of the major contributors to decreased

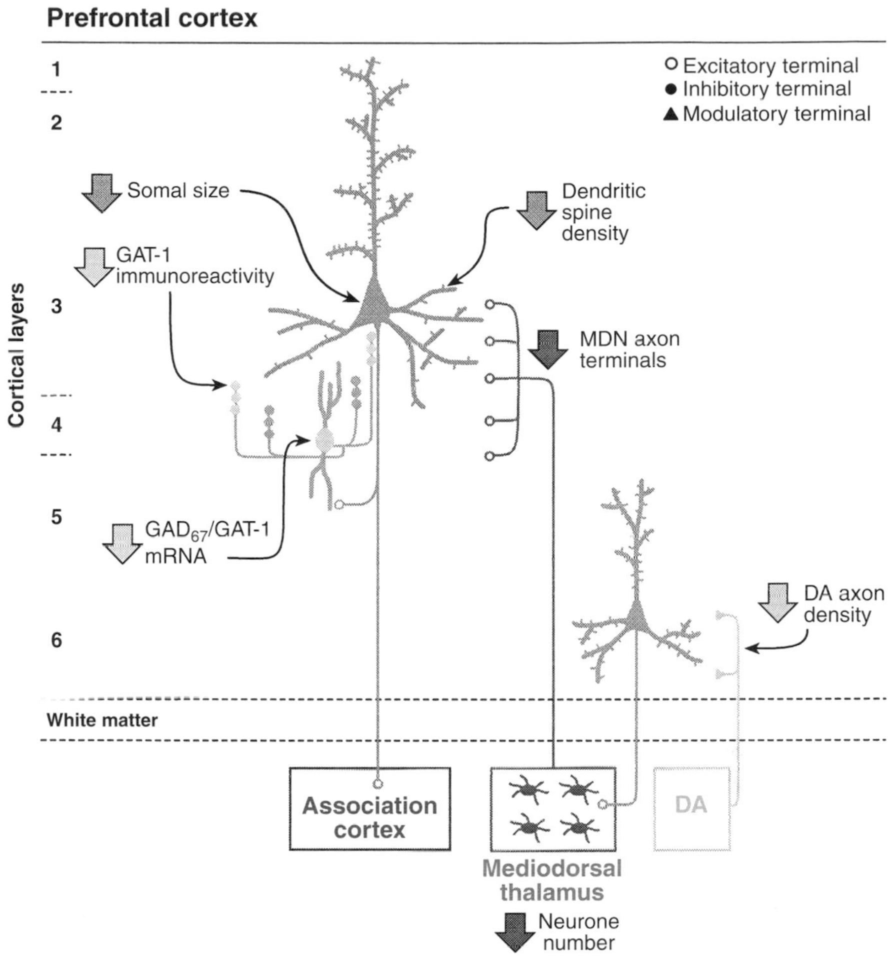

Fig 17.1 Schematic diagram summarizing disturbances in the connectivity between the mediodorsal nucleus of the thalamus (MDN) and the dorsal prefrontal cortex (PFC) in schizophrenia. Postmortem studies have reported that subjects with schizophrenia have:
1 decreased number of neurones in the mediodorsal thalamic nucleus;
2 diminished density of parvalbumin-positive varicosities, a putative marker of thalamic axon terminals, selectively in deep layers 3–4, the termination zone of MDN projections to the PFC;
3 preferential reduction in spine density on the basilar dendrites of deep layer 3 pyramidal neurones, a principal synaptic target of the excitatory projections from the MDN;
4 reduced expression of the mRNAs for glutamic acid decarboxylase (GAD_{67}), the synthesizing enzyme for GABA, and the GABA transporter (GAT-1) in a subset of PFC GABA neurones;
5 decreased density of GAT-1-immunoreactive axon cartridges, the distinctive, vertically arrayed axon terminals of GABAergic chandelier neurones, which synapse exclusively on the axon initial segment of pyramidal neurones;
6 decreased dopamine (DA) innervation of layer 6, the principal location of pyramidal neurones that provide corticothalamic feedback projections (see Lewis 2000b for additional details and references). (Adapted from Lewis & Lieberman 2000.)

synaptic connectivity within the DPFC (Fig. 17.1). Total thalamic volume is decreased, as determined by a meta-analysis of MRI data (Konick & Friedman 2001), with the reduction also seen in never-medicated subjects (Buchsbaum *et al.* 1996). Thalamic volume correlates with prefrontal white matter volume in schizophrenic subjects (Portas *et al.* 1998), suggesting that a reduction in thalamic volume may be associated with fewer axonal projections to the prefrontal cortex. Consistent with these observations, three postmortem studies, all stereologically based, have found that the mediodorsal thalamic nucleus (MDN), the principal source of thalamic projections to the prefrontal cortex, is reduced by 17–25% in volume and by 27–40% in total neurone number in schizophrenia (Pakkenberg 1990; Popken *et al.* 2000; Young *et al.* 2000; see also Byne *et al.* 2001). The available data also suggest that these abnormalities may be specific for projections to the prefrontal cortex and related cortical regions. For example, reduced cell numbers have also been reported in the anterior thalamic nuclei (which project to the prefrontal cortex and anterior cingulate cortex), whereas the ventral posterior medial nucleus, a sensory relay nucleus, appears unaffected (Popken *et al.* 2000; Young *et al.* 2000). In addition, within the MDN, neurone number is reportedly reduced to a greater extent in the parvocellular and densocellular subdivisions (which project principally to the DPFC) than in the magnocellular subdivision (which projects principally to the orbital and medial prefrontal cortex; Popken *et al.* 2000). Finally, studies in patients who had never received antipsychotics (Pakkenberg 1992) and in monkeys treated for 1 year with haloperidol (Pierri *et al.* 1999a) suggest that these medications do not account for the reduction in MDN neurone number. Despite this weight and convergence of data, a reduction in MDN size and neurone number in schizophrenia must still be considered a provisional finding, partly because there is one large negative study (Cullen *et al.* 2000) and because potentially important confounds, such as comorbid alcoholism (which is associated with prominent MDN pathology), have not been adequately assessed.

Nevertheless, several additional lines of evidence are consistent with a thalamic role in diminished DPFC connectivity in schizophrenia. For example, the density of neurones in the anterior thalamic nuclei that contain parvalbumin (Danos *et al.* 1998), a calcium-binding protein present in thalamic projection neurones (Jones & Hendry 1989), is reported to be reduced in schizophrenia. This observation suggests that it is thalamic neurones, that project to the cortex, and not just thalamic interneurones that are affected. In addition, subjects with

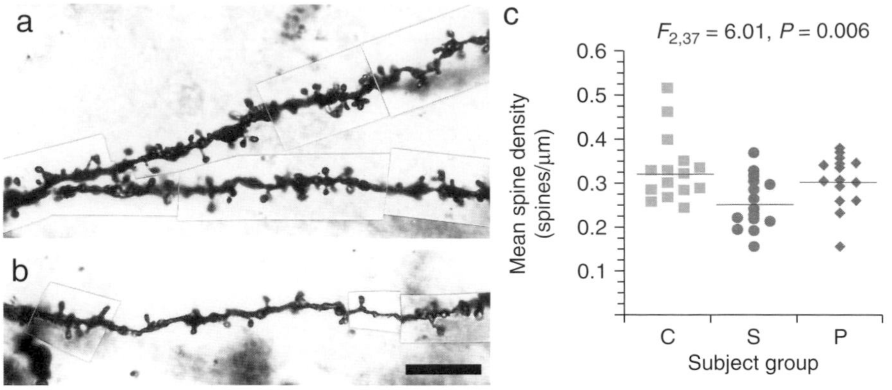

Fig 17.2 Brightfield photomicrographs illustrating Golgi-impregnated basilar dendrites and spines on PFC layer 3 pyramidal neurones from: (a) a normal control subject; and (b) a subject with schizophrenia. Calibration bar = 10 μm. (c) Scatter plot illustrating mean spine densities for 15 pyramidal neurones per subject in the deep portion of layer 3 in PFC area 46. Horizontal lines indicate group means for control (C), schizophrenic (S) and non-schizophrenic psychiatric (P) subjects. (Adapted from Glantz & Lewis 2000.)

schizophrenia, but not those with major depression, have a decreased density of parvalbumin-labelled varicosities (putative axon terminals) selectively in deep layers 3–4, the principal termination zone of thalamic projections to the prefrontal cortex (Cruz *et al.* 2000). However, whether these reductions represent an actual loss of thalamic neurones and their axon terminals, as opposed to a decrease in parvalbumin expression (perhaps because of decreased neuronal activity), is not known.

The dendritic spines of pyramidal neurones are the major target of thalamic projections to the prefrontal cortex (Melchitzky *et al.* 1999). In experimental animals, the elimination of presynaptic axon terminals leads to a resorption of the postsynaptic dendritic spine (Parnavelas *et al.* 1974). Thus, a reduction in MDN projection neurones in schizophrenia would be expected to be associated with a decrease in dendritic spine density in the DPFC. Both studies that have examined this issue found decreased spine density on the basilar dendrites of DPFC layer 3 pyramidal neurones (Garey *et al.* 1998; Glantz & Lewis 2000) (Fig. 17.2). This decrease was most marked for pyramidal neurones whose cell bodies were located in deep layer 3 (Glantz & Lewis 2000), and whose basilar dendrites extend through the laminar zone of termination of projections from the thalamus (Giguere & Goldman-Rakic 1988). These observations are consistent with a reduction in MDN–DPFC connectivity in schizophrenia. However, the presence of more modest reductions in spine density on pyramidal neurones in cortical layers and regions that do not directly receive MDN input suggest that decreased spine density in deep layer 3 may reflect the combined effect of a deficient number of thalamic *and* cortical synapses (Garey *et al.* 1998; Glantz & Lewis 2000). Furthermore, the size of deep layer 3 pyramidal neurones is reported to be reduced in the DPFC of subjects with schizophrenia. Although the possible relationship of these findings to a decrease in MDN inputs is less clear, studies in animals have provided evidence of denervation atrophy of layer 3 pyramidal cells following the loss of other afferent inputs (Wellman *et al.* 1995).

Dorsal prefrontal cortex interneurones and their connections

In the primate visual system, monocular deprivation, which results in reduced afferent drive from the thalamus, is associated with a decline in markers of activity in cortical GABA neurones (Hendry & Jones 1988), including decreased expression of glutamic acid decarboxylase (GAD_{67}), the synthesizing enzyme for GABA (Benson *et al.* 1994). Although this experimental manipulation of the visual system did not involve a partial reduction in thalamic neurone number, if these findings in the visual cortex can be generalized to a deficient number of MDN projections to the DPFC, then a reduction in GAD_{67} in the DPFC of schizophrenic subjects might be expected. Consistent with this prediction, both GAD_{67} mRNA and protein levels have been reported to be reduced in the DPFC of schizophrenic subjects (Akbarian *et al.* 1995; Guidotti *et al.* 2000; Volk *et al.* 2000). These observations are supported by other evidence of reduced GABA neurotransmission in the cerebral cortex of subjects with schizophrenia, such as a decrease in GABA release and uptake and an increase in the binding of muscimol, but not benzodiazepines, to $GABA_A$ receptors (see Lewis *et al.* 1999 for review). However, rather than a consequence of decreased input from the MDN, the reduction in GAD_{67} levels might also be attributable to other factors, such as a deficiency in reelin expression in schizophrenia (Guidotti *et al.* 2000).

The possibility that these alterations in GABA neurotransmission are a result of a disturbance in cortical circuitry is supported by observations that only a subpopulation of GABA neurones are affected. For example, decreased GAD_{67} mRNA expression in schizophrenia appears to be restricted to approximately 25–30% of DPFC GABA neurones, especially those located in the middle cortical layers (Volk *et al.* 2000). Other studies suggest that the affected subpopulation of GABA neurones includes the chandelier subclass of GABA neurones. The axon terminals of chandelier cells form distinctive vertical arrays (termed cartridges) which synapse exclusively on the axon initial segment of pyramidal neurones (Lewis 1998). Interestingly, expression of the mRNA for the GABA membrane transporter (GAT-1) is also undetectable in approximately 25–30% of DPFC GABA neurones, which have a laminar distribution similar to the neurones with undetectable GAD_{67} mRNA expression (Volk *et al.* 2001). In addition, the density of GAT-1 immunoreactive chandelier neurone axon cartridges is decreased in the DPFC of schizophrenic subjects, with the reduction most evident in the middle cortical layers (Woo *et al.* 1998; Pierri *et al.* 1999b). Together, these findings suggest that chandelier cells contain reduced levels of two proteins critical for GABA neurotransmission, although a morphological alteration in their axon terminals cannot be excluded.

Thus, given the powerful inhibitory control that chandelier neurones exert over pyramidal cell output, decreased excitatory thalamic drive to the DPFC may be partially compensated for by a reduction in chandelier cell-mediated inhibition at the axon initial segment of layer 3 pyramidal cells. This effect could occur via the local axon collaterals of layer 3 pyramidal cells, approximately 50% of which target the dendritic shafts of GABA neurones (Melchitzky *et al.* 2001). However, other potential causes and consequences of the observed alterations in chandelier neurones have not been excluded (see Volk *et al.* 2000 for further discussion).

Prefrontal cortex projections to the thalamus

Together, the data summarized in the preceding two sections converge on the hypothesis that schizophrenia is associated with abnormalities in the projection from the MDN to the DPFC. As in other cortical regions, the connections between the MDN and DPFC are reciprocal, which raises the question of whether abnormalities in thalamocortical projections are paralleled by alterations in corticothalamic projections. Studies which have examined DPFC neurones in layer 6, the principal location of corticothalamic projection neurones, have generally not found evidence of a decrease in neurone size or number (Benes *et al.* 1991a; Selemon *et al.* 1995; Rajkowska *et al.* 1998), although one study (Benes *et al.* 1986) did report decreased neuronal density in layer 6. A reduced density of markers of DA axons was observed selectively in DPFC layer 6 of schizophrenic subjects (Akil *et al.* 1999). Interestingly, the dendritic shafts and spines of pyramidal cells are the principal synaptic targets of DA axon terminals in layer 6, and DA appears to play a critical part in regulating the influence of other inputs on pyramidal cell activity (Goldman-Rakic *et al.* 1989). Thus, a shift in DA neurotransmission in DPFC layer 6 could reflect a change in the modulation of corticothalamic feedback in response to abnormal thalamocortical drive (Akil *et al.* 1999).

Neuropathological interpretations

Having reviewed the major themes in the neuropathology of schizophrenia (summarized in Table 17.1), we end with a brief consideration of some of the diverse, broader interpretational issues raised by these data.

How are the hippocampal and dorsal prefrontal cortex changes related?

Experimental studies in rodents and monkeys show that dysfunction of the DPFC may appear postpubertally following perinatal lesions of the hippocampus (Weinberger & Lipska 1995; Saunders *et al.* 1998), perhaps because of age-related maturation of hippocampal–frontal pathways. In this respect, the hippocampal pathology of schizophrenia might be considered primary to that in the DPFC, a view supported indirectly in patients by correlations between hippocampal volume and DPFC activity (Weinberger *et al.* 1992). Equally, however, the direction of causality might be reversed, or there may be an independent pathological event which underlies the changes in both regions.

Table 17.1 Key neurohistopathological findings in schizophrenia.

General
Absence of gliosis
Absence of Alzheimer's disease or other recognized degenerative pathologies
Morphometric findings in hippocampal formation and DPFC
Smaller pyramidal neuronal cell bodies
Increased neuronal packing density (only replicated in DPFC)
Decreased presynaptic protein markers (e.g. SNAP-25, synaptophysin)
Lower density of dendritic spines
Decreased markers of inhibitory neurones and their synaptic terminals (in DPFC)
No overall loss of neurones
Other areas
Mediodorsal thalamic nucleus: decreased volume and neuronal number

For more detailed listings and citations, see text and Harrison (1999a). DPFC, dorsal prefrontal cortex.

Is there an asymmetry of neuropathology?

A number of postmortem studies, notably of the temporal lobe (Crow *et al.* 1989; Zaidel *et al.* 1997a,b; McDonald *et al.* 2000), and also of the thalamus (Blennow *et al.* 1996), have shown lateralized changes in schizophrenia, as do some of the results from other research modalities (Holinger *et al.* 2000). In this respect there is some neuropathological support for an interaction between cerebral asymmetry and schizophrenia (Crow 1990). However, many other studies find bilateral alterations, or have not been designed to address the question – the latter includes most investigations of the DPFC. Overall, it remains unclear whether the neuropathology of schizophrenia is asymmetrical in some way.

How are the pathology and the symptoms related?

The question of clinicopathological correlations in a broad sense is a basic but neglected issue in the literature. It has several facets.

A neural circuitry-based model of schizophrenia requires an appreciation of the mechanistic relationships between the various abnormalities observed in different components of the circuitry. Specifically, understanding the pathophysiology of schizophrenia (or any other psychiatric disorder) depends ultimately on knowledge of how abnormalities in one brain region or circuitry component produce and/or result from disturbances in others, a task that involves a consideration of cause, consequence and compensation (Lewis 2000a). Does a given abnormality represent a primary pathogenetic event (cause), does it reflect a secondary deleterious event (consequence) or does it reveal a homeostatic response intended to restore normal brain function (compensation)? Distinguishing among these three possibilities for each component of a neural network will be necessary for understanding the pathophysiology of the disease as well as for developing novel therapies designed to correct causes and consequences and/or to augment compensatory responses.

A related issue concerns the correspondence between clinical symptoms and pathological findings. For example, which aspects of the clinical syndrome are most closely related to the pathological findings? To date, the clinical information available and the sample sizes used in postmortem research have been inadequate to allow this issue to be addressed. However, it may be hypothesized that the nature and distribution of pathological changes suggest that they might be particularly related to the cognitive deficits rather than necessarily with the psychotic symptoms (Harrison 1999a). Similarly, based on the current data, it is more parsimonious to postulate a single pathological process which varies in severity between patients with schizophrenia – as is the case with the structural imaging findings – rather than invoking multiple pathologies. Across subjects, there may also be different molecular pathways leading to a common final functional and structural disturbance in brain circuitry (Mirnics *et al.* 2000). This view does not preclude a different conclusion as new data emerge (e.g. the possibility of a different pathological phenotype in late-onset schizophrenia).

The temporal relationship between neuropathology and the onset of symptoms is unknown, because postmortem studies of first episode patients are impossible in practice. It is only by extrapolation (e.g. from the decreased NAA seen in first episode cases; the lack of correlation of postmortem findings with duration of illness) that the suggestion can be made that the alterations, at least partly, are present at or before the onset of illness and therefore may have a direct causal role. Equally, however, even if some of the neuropathological changes occur later in the illness, this does not negate their importance or imply that they are epiphenomenal. Rather, if this were the case, it might mean that their development was a factor contributing to the course of the illness.

Do the neuropathological data support a neurodevelopmental origin of schizophrenia?

Although the idea that schizophrenia is a late consequence of an early developmental lesion has many merits, it has proven difficult to obtain direct *positive* evidence for a brain abnormality that necessarily supports such a model (i.e. which can confidently be timed to the second trimester, perinatal period, adolescence, etc.). To date, it remains the lack of evidence *against* there being a progressive or degenerative disease process that, by default, is the strongest pointer towards a neurodevelopmental origin.

The dearth of positive neuropathological support has already been mentioned with regard to the failure to confirm the initial reports of entorhinal dysplasia and hippocampal neurone disarray. Another conceptually attractive finding was the altered distribution of interstitial neurones in the subcortical white matter, because it also strongly suggested an early developmental lesion affecting neuronal migration and/or programmed cell death (Akbarian *et al.* 1993a,b). However, it is not a feature in the majority of schizophrenic subjects (Akbarian *et al.* 1996; Anderson *et al.* 1996; Kirkpatrick *et al.* 1999; see also Dwork 1997). Instead, the changes which are more robustly demonstrable – smaller neuronal size, loss of synaptic proteins and dendritic spines – affect parameters which are dynamically regulated, and mean that the alterations could arise at any timepoint. For example, synaptic proteins and dendritic spines can be altered by many experimental situations, including neuronal activity, seizures, environmental complexity and hypoxia–ischaemia, as well as by ageing (e.g. Masliah *et al.* 1993; Saito *et al.* 1994; Marti *et al.* 1998; Bravin *et al.* 1999; Harris 1999). Thus, developmental interpretations of alterations of this kind observed in schizophrenia should be made with due caution.

On the other hand, one should not neglect the corroborative and circumstantial evidence which, complementing the lack of gliosis, supports a developmental basis for the pathological findings in schizophrenia. There are three aspects to consider:

1 The demonstration that the neural pathways implicated in the pathology of schizophrenia show marked developmental changes at relevant time periods. One example is in the hippocampal formation (Benes *et al.* 1994); another is the circuitry of the primate DPFC. For example, after rising dramatically during the main phase of synaptogenesis in prenatal and early postnatal life, the number of excitatory, but not inhibitory, synapses in the DPFC declines by 50% during adolescence in both monkeys and humans (Huttenlocher 1979; Bourgeois *et al.* 1994). During this time period, dendritic spine densities decrease (Anderson *et al.* 1995), but pyramidal neurone size and total dendritic length increase (Lambe *et al.* 2000). These maturational changes may differ according to the neuronal and synaptic population being considered. For example, there are substantial changes to excitatory, inhibitory and modulatory inputs to pyramidal neurones in deep layer 3 of primate DPFC. The terminals of intrinsic axon collaterals from DPFC layer 3 pyramidal cells may be more extensively pruned than associational cortical projections (Woo *et al.* 1997b), while serotonergic synapses upon these neurones develop much more rapidly than catecholaminergic ones (Lambe *et al.* 2000). The apparent laminar specificity of at least some of these changes supports the observations that circuits involving these pyramidal neurones may be preferentially affected in schizophrenia (Lewis 1997). Knowing whether projections from the MDN are particularly vulnerable to this process might provide critical information for

hypotheses regarding the mechanisms underlying disturbances in MDN–DPFC circuitry in schizophrenia.

2 There are studies in schizophrenia of molecules known to be important in one or other aspect of brain maturation (e.g. neuronal migration, synaptogenesis, apoptosis). Reported alterations of reelin, *Wnt* and glycogen synthase kinase 3b expression in schizophrenia exemplify this approach, and there will no doubt be many more as other key developmental genes are investigated (Weickert & Weinberger 1998). The assumption behind these studies is that the altered gene expression seen in schizophrenia is a persistent sign of aberrant neurodevelopment. This interpretation may well be true, but the very fact that a given gene continues to be expressed in the adult brain may also indicate that it has other, non-developmental, functions and therefore a similarly non-developmental implication for schizophrenia. As with morphometric alterations, a convergence and consistency of results will be needed to allow confidence in the developmental explanation.

3 The neuropathological findings in known neurodevelopmental disorders, although far from conclusive in their own right, provide another form of circumstantial support for a developmental interpretation of the schizophrenia data. For example, dendritic arborizations, dendritic proteins and dendritic spine densities are decreased in the cortex in Rett's syndrome and Williams' syndrome (Kaufmann & Moser 2000), dendritic spines are abnormal in fragile X syndrome (Irwin *et al.* 2000) and neuronal size is reduced in Rett's syndrome and autism (Kemper & Bauman 1998). Parenthetically, because these disorders may be considered 'cognitive' rather than 'psychotic', the data are consistent with the suggestion made earlier that the pathological features in schizophrenia might be related to the cognitive aspects of the syndrome.

Are the changes specific to schizophrenia?

The overlap with the morphometric findings reported in several neurodevelopmental disorders raises the issue of diagnostic specificity. Most neuropathological studies of schizophrenia have not included a comparison group comprised of patients with other psychiatric disorders, and so the specificity of many alterations is uncertain.

Of the DPFC findings mentioned, some have been examined for diagnostic specificity, whereas others have not. The reduction in DPFC dendritic spine density on deep layer 3 pyramidal neurones was not found in subjects with major depressive disorders (Glantz & Lewis 2000), and the reduction in density of GAT-1 immunoreactive axon cartridges was not apparent in subjects with non-schizophrenic psychiatric disorders (Pierri *et al.* 1999b). However, other results show a considerable similarity in bipolar disorder and in schizophrenia (Eastwood & Harrison 2000; Guidotti *et al.* 2000), suggesting that there may be overlaps at least in some aspects of pathology between the disorders. At this stage it is impossible to determine whether neuropathology will ultimately support the continuum or the dichotomy view of the functional psychoses. Such clarification will be aided by the brain series collected by the Stanley Foundation, which comprises matched groups of brains from patients with schizophrenia, bipolar disorder and major depression, as well as controls (Torrey *et al.* 2000).

Are the changes brought about by medication?

Antipsychotic drugs, and other treatments received by patients, are often suspected as contributing to, or even causing, the neuropathological features reported in schizophrenia. Certainly, given that very few subjects in postmortem studies were medication-free at death, and virtually none were medication-naive, it is a difficult possibility to eliminate entirely. However, various experimental and statistical strategies are available, and the data are in fact reassuring: the morphological alterations caused by antipsychotics are largely limited to the basal ganglia, and their characteristics are different from those reported in schizophrenia (Harrison 1999b).

The absence of demonstrable antipsychotic effects on cortical cytoarchitecture is exemplified by findings in the DPFC and MDN. Globally, the increase in DPFC cell packing density seen in subjects with schizophrenia was not found in monkeys treated for 6 months with a variety of antipsychotics (Selemon *et al.* 1999). In addition, treatment of monkeys for 12 months with haloperidol and benzatropine at blood levels known to be therapeutic in humans was not associated with a reduction in the size or total neurone number of the MDN (Pierri *et al.* 1999a). The decreased dendritic spine density also appears to be specific to schizophrenia, in that it was not observed in a psychiatric disorder control group who had received antipsychotics (Glantz & Lewis 2000; Fig. 17.2). The potential influence of antipsychotic drugs on GAT-1-labelled axon cartridges has been examined in several ways (Pierri *et al.* 1999b). Interestingly, the density of labelled cartridges was greater in schizophrenic subjects who were on than off antipsychotic medications at the time of death (although both groups showed reduced levels compared to normal controls). In addition, compared to matched control animals, the density of GAT-1-positive cartridges was elevated in monkeys treated for 1 year with haloperidol. Together, these findings suggest that the pathophysiology of schizophrenia may actually be associated with more marked reductions in GAT-1-immunoreactive cartridge density than those seen in postmortem studies, illustrating that antipsychotic drugs may even attenuate some neuropathological alterations.

There are fewer data on the pathological consequences of other treatments sometimes used in schizophrenia, such as antidepressants and electroconvulsive therapy, but those that exist do not suggest that they are likely to be major confounders (Harrison 1999b).

Will schizophrenia ever be diagnosable down a microscope?

It is quite clear that the existing neuropathological data do not allow this question to be answered. Nevertheless, comparison with Alzheimer's disease is relevant for illustrating the kinds of conditions which would need to be met if it is ever to be answered in the affirmative.

1 In Alzheimer's disease there are reliably identifiable lesions (neurofibrillary tangles, amyloid plaques) that are qualitatively different from normal cytological and histological parameters.

2 These diagnostic lesions have a quantitative relationship to the presence and severity of the clinical syndrome, and their distribution and effect on the cortical circuitry gives a convincing explanation for the features of the syndrome.

3 Key aspects of Alzheimer's disease pathology can now be reproduced in transgenic mice, which develop cognitive impairment; recent data even suggest that the pathology can be reversed, with corresponding improvement in memory performance.

4 The neuropathological picture is clearly different from that of other dementias, and in this sense it is diagnostically specific (although this becomes a circular argument once the disorder is defined by the neuropathology and not the clinical features).

Ultimately, schizophrenia might become, like Alzheimer's disease, a disorder – or disorders – in which neuropathological features are necessary and sufficient for diagnostic purposes. Like Alzheimer's disease, it may also become possible to link the pathology directly to the aetiology, as illustrated by the mice carrying mutations in the causative genes. Alternatively, new approaches, such as gene expression profiling or proteomic strategies, may provide molecular signatures in postmortem tissue that are diagnostic of schizophrenia(s). However, the value of the next generation of postmortem studies of schizophrenia may not rest in the realm of a 'gold standard' for diagnosis, but in the types of pathogenetic or pathophysiological insights that reveal novel targets for pharmacological interventions.

Conclusions

Several histological features have now been observed and replicated in the hippocampal formation and DPFC in schizophrenia (Table 17.1): pyramidal neurones are smaller, dendrites show a lower density of spines and have less extensive arborizations, and presynaptic indices are also decreased. These features together strongly suggest that neural circuits are altered and perhaps 'wired differently' in both of these areas in schizophrenia. In the hippocampal formation, the identity of the affected circuits is unclear, whereas in DPFC there is increasing evidence that it includes thalamocortical afferent connections as well as intrinsic connections between inhibitory interneurones and pyramidal neurones. Changes in the MDN are consistent with the DPFC findings. The spatial distribution of pathological features in schizophrenia beyond these areas remains unclear, although there are many positive findings, not mentioned here, which deserve further study (Arnold & Trojanowski 1996; Harrison 1999a; Benes 2000). The cytoarchitectural findings as a whole, in the absence of any evidence of a degenerative process, support but do not prove a neurodevelopmental origin. Other important questions remain regarding the specificity, molecular characteristics and interpretation of the pathology. Nevertheless, many of the findings are now reasonably robust and, as such, the main focus of attention is no longer whether there is any neuropathology in schizophrenia, but what its details are and how it relates to the aetiology and clinical features of the syndrome.

References

Akbarian, S., Bunney, W.E. Jr, Potkin, S.G. *et al.* (1993a) Altered distribution of nicotinamide-adenine dinucleotide phosphate-diaphorase cells in frontal lobe of schizophrenics implies disturbances of cortical development. *Archives of General Psychiatry* **50**, 169–177.

Akbarian, S., Viñuela, A., Kim, J.J. *et al.* (1993b) Distorted distribution of nicotinamide-adenine dinucleotilde phosphate-diaphorase neurons in temporal lose of schizophrenic implies anomalous cortical development. *Archives of General Psychiatry* **50**, 178–187.

Akbarian, S., Kim, J.J., Potkin, S.G. *et al.* (1995) Gene expression for glutamic acid decarboxylase is reduced without loss of neurons in prefrontal cortex of schizophrenics. *Archives of General Psychiatry* **52**, 258–266.

Akbarian, S., Kim, J.J., Potikin, S.G. *et al.* (1996) Maldistribution of interstitial neurons in prefrontal white matter of the brains of schizophrenic patients. *Archives of General Psychiatry* **53**, 425–436.

Akil, M. & Lewis, D.A. (1997) The cytoarchitecture of the entorhinal cortex in schizophrenia. *American Journal of Psychiatry* **154**, 1010–1012.

Akil, M., Pierri, J.N., Whitehead, R.E. *et al.* (1999) Lamina-specific alteration in the dopamine innervation of the prefrontal cortex in schizophrenic subjects. *American Journal of Psychiatry* **156**, 1580–1589.

Altshuler, L.L., Conrad, A., Kovelman, J.A. & Scheibel, A.B. (1987) Hippocampal pyramidal cell orientation in schizophrenia: a controlled neurohistologic study of the Yakovlev collection. *Archives of General Psychiatry* **44**, 1094–1098.

Anderson, S.A., Classey, J.D., Condé, F., Lund, J.S. & Lewis, D.A. (1995) Synchronous development of pyramidal neuron dendritic spines and parvalbumin-immunoreactive chandelier neuron axon terminals in layer III of monkey prefrontal cortex. *Neuroscience* **67**, 7–22.

Anderson, S.A., Volk, D.W. & Lewis, D.A. (1996) Increased density of microtubule-associated protein 2-immunoreactive neurons in the prefrontal white matter of schizophrenic subjects. *Schizophrenia Research* **19**, 111–119.

Arnold, S.E. (1997) The medial temporal lobe in schizophrenia. *Journal of Neuropsychiatry and Clinical Neuroscience* **9**, 460–470.

Arnold, S.E. & Trojanowski, J.Q. (1996) Recent advances in defining the neuropathology of schizophrenia. *Acta Neuropathologica* **92**, 217–231.

Arnold, S.E., Hyman, B.T., Van Hoesen, G.W. & Damasio, A.R. (1991a) Some cytoarchitectural abnormalities of the entorhinal cortex in schizophrenia. *Archives of General Psychiatry* **48**, 625–632.

Arnold, S.E., Lee, V.M.Y., Gur, R.E. & Trojanowski, J.Q. (1991b) Abnormal expression of two microtubule-associated proteins (MAP2 and MAP5) in specific subfields of the hippocampal formation in schizophrenia. *Proceedings of the National Academy of Sciences of the USA* **88**, 10850–10854.

Arnold, S.E., Franz, B.R., Gur, R.C. *et al.* (1995) Smaller neuron size in schizophrenia hippocampal subfields that mediate cortical–

hippocampal interactions. *American Journal of Psychiatry* **152**, 738–748.

Arnold, S.E., Franz, B.R., Trojanowski, J.Q., Moberg, P.J. & Gur, R.E. (1996) Glial fibrillary acidic protein-immunoreactive astrocytosis in elderly patients with schizophrenia and dementia. *Acta Neuropathologica* **91**, 269–277.

Arnold, S.E., Ruscheinsky, D.D. & Han, L.Y. (1997) Further evidence of abnormal cytoarchitecure of the entorhinal corex in schizophrenia using spatial point pattern analysises. *Biological Psychiatry* **42**, 639–647.

Arnold, S.E., Trojanowski, J.Q., Gur, R.E. *et al.* (1998) Absence of neurodegeneration and neural injury in the cerebral cortex in a sample of elderly patients with schizophrenia. *Archives of General Psychiatry* **55**, 225–232.

Baldessarini, R.J., Hegarty, J., Bird, E.D. & Benes, F.M. (1997) Meta-analysis of postmortem studies of Alzheimer's disease-like neuropathology in schizophrenia. *American Journal of Psychiatry* **154**, 861–863.

Bayer, T.A., Busiei, R., Havas, L. & Falkai, P. (1999) Evidence for activation of microglia in patients with psychiatric illnesses. *Neuroscience Letters* **271**, 126–128.

Beasley, C.L. & Reynolds, G.P. (1997) Parvalbumin-immunoreactive neurons are reduced in the prefrontal cortex of schizophrenics. *Schizophrenia Research* **24**, 349–355.

Benes, F.M. (2000) Emerging principles of altered neural circuitry in schizophrenia. *Brain Research Reviews* **31**, 251–269.

Benes, F.M., Davidson, J. & Bird, E.D. (1986) Quantitative cytoarchitectural studies of the cerebral cortex of schizophrenics. *Archives of General Psychiatry* **43**, 31–35.

Benes, F.M., McSparren, J., Bird, E.D., SanGiovanni, J.P. & Vincent, S.L. (1991a) Deficits in small interneurons in prefrontal and cingulate cortices of schizophrenic and schizoaffective patients. *Archives of General Psychiatry* **48**, 996–1001.

Benes, F.M., Sorensen, I. & Bird, E.D. (1991b) Reduced neuronal size in posterior hippocampus of schizophrenic patients. *Schizophrenia Bulletin* **17**, 597–608.

Benes, F.M., Turtle, M., Khan, Y. & Farol, P. (1994) Myelination of a key relay zone in the hippocampal formation occurs in the human brain during childhood, adolescence, and adulthood. *Archives of General Psychiatry* **51**, 477–484.

Benes, F.M., Kwok, E.W., Vincent, S.L. & Todtenkopf, M.S. (1998) Reduction of non-pyramidal cells in section CA2 of schizophrenics and manic depressives. *Biological Psychiatry* **44**, 88–97.

Benson, D.L., Huntsman, M.M. & Jones, E.G. (1994) Activity-dependent changes in GAD and preprotachykinin mRNAs in visual cortex of adult monkeys. *Cerebral Cortex* **4**, 40–51.

Bernstein, H.-G., Krell, D., Baumann, B. *et al.* (1998) Morphometric studies of the entorhinal cortex in neuropsychiatric patients and controls: clusters of heterotopically displaced lamina II neurons are not indicative of schizophrenia. *Schizophrenia Research* **33**, 125–132.

Bertolino, A., Nawroz, S., Mattay, V.S. *et al.* (1996) Regionally specific pattern of neurochemical pathology in schizophrenia as assessed by multislice proton magnetic resonance spectroscopic imaging. *American Journal of Psychiatry* **153**, 1554–1563.

Bertolino, A., Callicott, J.H., Elman, I. *et al.* (1998) Regionally specific neural pathology in untreated patients with schizophrenia: a proton magnetic resonance spectroscopic imaging study. *Biological Psychiatry* **43**, 641–648.

Bertolino, A., Esposito, G., Callicott, J.H. *et al.* (2000) Specific relationship between prefrontal neuronal *N*-acetylaspartate and activation of the working memory cortical network in schizophrenia. *American Journal of Psychiatry* **157**, 26–33.

Blennow, K., Davidsson, P., Gottfries, C.-G., Ekman, R. & Heilig, M. (1996) Synaptic degeneration in thalamus in schizophrenia. *Lancet* **348**, 692–693.

Bourgeois, J.-P., Goldman-Rakic, P.S. & Rakic, P. (1994) Synaptogenesis in the prefrontal cortex of rhesus monkeys. *Cerebral Cortex* **4**, 78–96.

Bravin, M., Morando, L., Vercelli, A., Rossi, F. & Strata, P. (1999) Control of spine formation by electrical activity in the adult rat cerebellum. *Proceedings of the National Academy of Sciences of the USA* **96**, 1704–1709.

Bruton, C.J., Crow, T.J., Frith, C. *et al.* (1990) Schizophrenia and the brain: a prospective cliniconeuropathological study. *Psychological Medicine* **20**, 285–304.

Buchsbaum, M.S., Someya, T., Teng, C.Y. *et al.* (1996) PET and MRI of the thalamus in never-medicated patients with schizophrenia. *American Journal of Psychiatry* **153**, 191–199.

Byne, W., Buchsbaum, M.S., Kemether, E. *et al.* (2001) Magnetic resonance imaging of the thalamic mediodorsal nucles and pulvinar in schizophrenia and schizotypal personality disorder. *Archives of General Psychiatry* **58**, 133–140.

Christison, G.W., Casanova, M.F., Weinberger, D.R., Rawlings, R. & Kleinman, J.E. (1989) A quantitative investigation of hippocampal pyramidal cell size, shape, and variability of orientation in schizophrenia. *Archives of General Psychiatry* **46**, 1027–1032.

Conrad, A.J., Abebe, T., Austin, R., Forsythe, S. & Scheibel, A.B. (1991) Hippocampal pyramidal cell disarray in schizophrenia as a bilateral phenomenon. *Archives of General Psychiatry* **48**, 413–417.

Corsellis, J.A.N. (1962) Mental illness and the ageing brain. *Institute of Psychiatry Maudsley Monographs No. 9.* Oxford University Press, London.

Crow, T.J. (1990) Temporal lobe asymmetries as the key to the etiology of schizophrenia. *Schizophrenia Bulletin* **16**, 433–443.

Crow, T.J., Ball, J., Bloom, S. *et al.* (1989) Schizophrenia as an anomaly of development of cerebral asymmetry. *Archives of General Psychiatry* **46**, 1145–1150.

Cruz, D.A., Melchitzky, D.S., Pierri, J.N. & Lewis, D.A. (2000) Decreased density of putative thalamic axon terminals in the prefrontal cortex in schizophrenia: effect of antipsychotic medication and diagnostic specificity. *Society of Neuroscience Abstracts* **26**, 1564.

Cullen, T.J., Walker, M.A., Roberts, H. *et al.* (2000) The mediodorsal nucleus of the thalamus in schizophrenia: a post-mortem study. *Schizophrenia Research* **41**, 5.

Da Cunha, A., Jefferson, J.J., Tyor, W.R. *et al.* (1993) Gliosis in human brain: relationship to size but not other properties of astrocytes. *Brain Research* **600**, 161–165.

Danos, P., Baumann, B., Bernstein, H.-G. *et al.* (1998) Schizophrenia and anteroventral thalamic nucleus: selective decrease of parvalbumin-immunoreactive thalamocortical projection neurons. *Psychiatry Research: Neuroimaging* **82**, 1–10.

David, G.B. (1957) The pathological anatomy of the schizophrenias. In: *Schizophrenia: Somatic Aspects.* (ed. D. Richter), pp. 93–130. Pergamon, Oxford.

Davidsson, P., Gottfries, J., Bogdanovic, N. *et al.* (1999) The synaptic-vesicle-specific proteins rab3a and synaptophysin are reduced in thalamus and related cortical brain regions in schizophrenic brains. *Schizophrenia Research* **40**, 23–29.

Davis, K.L., Kahn, R.S., Ko, G. & Davidson, M. (1991) Dopamine in schizophrenia: a review and reconceptualization. *American Journal of Psychiatry* **148**, 1474–1486.

Daviss, S.R. & Lewis, D.A. (1995) Local circuit neurons of the prefrontal cortex in schizophrenia: selective increase in the density of calbindin-immunoreactive neurons. *Psychiatry Research* **59**, 81–96.

Deicken, R.F., Zhou, L., Corwin, F., Vinogradov, S. & Weiner, M.W. (1997) Decreased left frontal lobe *N*-acetylaspartate in schizophrenia. *American Journal of Psychiatry* **154**, 688–690.

DeLisi, L.E. (1997) Is schizophrenia a lifetime disorder or brain plasticity, growth and aging. *Schizophrenia Research* **23**, 119–129.

Dwork, A.J. (1997) Postmortem studies of the hippocampal formation in schizophrenia. *Schizophrenia Bulletin* **23**, 385–402.

Eastwood, S.L. & Harrison, P.J. (1995) Decreased synaptophysin in the medial temporal lobe in schizophrenia demonstrated using immunoautoradiography. *Neuroscience* **69**, 339–343.

Eastwood, S.L. & Harrison, P.J. (1998) Hippocampal and cortical growth-associated protein-43 messenger RNA in schizophrenia. *Neuroscience* **86**, 437–448.

Eastwood, S.L. & Harrison, P.J. (1999) Detection and quantification of hippocampal synaptophysin messenger RNA in schizophrenia using autoclaved, formalin-fixed paraffin wax-embedded sections. *Neuroscience* **93**, 99–106.

Eastwood, S.L. & Harrison, P.J. (2000) Hippocampal synaptic pathology in schizophrenia bipolar disorder and major depression: a study of complexin mRNAs. *Molecular Psychiatry* **5**, 425–432.

Eastwood, S.L. & Harrison, P.J. (2001) Synaptic pathology in the anterior cingulate cortex in schizophrenia and mood disorders: an immunoblotting study of synaptophysin, gap-43 and the complexins and a review. *Brain Research Bulletin* **55**, 569–578.

Eastwood, S.L., Burnet, P.W.J., McDonald, B., Clinton, J. & Harrison, P.J. (1994) Synaptophysin gene expression in human brain: a quantitative *in situ* hybridization and immunocytochemical study. *Neuroscience* **59**, 881–892.

Eastwood, S.L., Cairns, N.J. & Harrison, P.J. (2000) Synaptophysin gene expression in schizophrenia: investigation of synaptic pathology in the cerebral cortex. *British Journal of Psychiatry* **176**, 236–242.

Esiri, M.M. & Pearson, R.C.A. (2000) Perspectives from other diseases and lesions. In: *The Neuropathology of Schizophrenia: Progress and Interpretation* (eds P.J. Harrison & G.W. Roberts), pp. 257–276. Oxford University Press, Oxford.

Falkai, P. & Bogerts, B. (1986) Cell loss in the hippocampus of schizophrenics. *European Archives of Psychiatry and Neurological Science* **236**, 154–161.

Falkai, P., Honer, W.G., David, S. *et al.* (1999) No evidence for astrogliosis in brains of schizophrenic patients: a post-mortem study. *Neuropathology and Applied Neurobiology* **25**, 48–53.

Falkai, P., Schneider-Axmann, T. & Honer, W.G. (2000) Entorhinal cortex pre-alpha cell cluster in schizophrenia: quantitative evidence of a developmental abnormality. *Biological Psychiatry* **47**, 937–943.

Friede, R.J. (1989) *Developmental Neuropathology*. Springer Verlag, Berlin.

Friston, K.J. & Frith, C.D. (1995) Schizophrenia: a disconnection syndrome. *Clinical Neuroscience* **3**, 89–97.

Friston, K.J., Liddle, P.F., Frith, C.D., Hirsch, S.R. & Frackowiak, R.S. (1992) The left medial temporal region and schizophrenia. *Brain* **115**, 367–382.

Gabriel, S.M., Haroutunian, V., Powchik, P. *et al.* (1997) Increased concentrations of presynaptic proteins in the cingulate cortex of subjects with schizophrenia. *Archives of General Psychiatry* **54**, 559–566.

Garey, L.J., Ong, W.Y., Patel, T.S. *et al.* (1998) Reduced dendritic spine density on cerebral cortical pyramidal neurons in schizophrenia. *Journal of Neurology, Neurosurgery and Psychiatry* **65**, 446–453.

Giguere, M. & Goldman-Rakic, P.S. (1988) Mediodorsal nucleus: areal, laminar, and tangential distribution of afferents and efferents in the frontal lobe of rhesus monkeys. *Journal of Comparative Neurology* **277**, 195–213.

Gilbert, C.D. & Kelly, J.P. (1975) The projections of cells in different layers of the cat's visual cortex. *Journal of Comparative Neurology* **63**, 81–106.

Glantz, L.A. & Lewis, D.A. (1997) Reduction of synaptophysin immunoreactivity in the prefrontal cortex of subjects with schizophrenia: regional and diagnostic specificity. *Archives of General Psychiatry* **54**, 943–952.

Glantz, L.A. & Lewis, D.A. (2000) Decreased dendritic spine density on prefrontal cortical pyramidal neurons in schizophrenia. *Archives of General Psychiatry* **57**, 65–73.

Glantz, L.A., Austin, M.C. & Lewis, D.A. (2000) Normal cellular levels of synaptophysin mRNA expression in the prefrontal cortex of subjects with schizophrenia. *Biological Psychiatry* **48**, 389–397.

Goldman-Rakic, P.S., Leranth, C., Williams, S.M., Mons, N. & Geffard, M. (1989) Dopamine synaptic complex with pyramidal neurons in primate cerebral cortex. *Proceedings of the National Academy of Sciences of the USA* **86**, 9015–9019.

Guidotti, A., Auta, J., Davis, J.M. *et al.* (2000) Decrease in reelin and glutamic acid decarboxylase$_{67}$ (GAD_{67}) expression in schizophrenia and bipolar disorder. *Archives of General Psychiatry* **57**, 1061–1069.

Harris, K.M. (1999) Structure, development, and plasticity of dendritic spines. *Current Opinion in Neurobiology* **9**, 343–348.

Harrison, P.J. (1999a) The neuropathology of schizophrenia: a critical review of the data and their interpretation. *Brain* **122**, 593–624.

Harrison, P.J. (1999b) The neuropathological effects of antipsychotic drugs. *Schizophrenia Research* **40**, 87–99.

Harrison, P.J. & Eastwood, S.L. (1998) Preferential involvement of excitatory neurons in medial temporal lobe in schizophrenia. *Lancet* **352**, 1669–1673.

Harrison, P.J. & Eastwood, S.L. (2001) Neuropathological studies of synaptic connectivity in the hippocampal formation in schizophrenia. *Hippocampus* **11**, 508–519.

Harrison, P.J. & Roberts, G.W. (2000) *The Neuropathology of Schizophrenia: Progress and Interpretation*. Oxford University Press, Oxford.

Hayes, T.L. & Lewis, D.A. (1996) Magnopyramidal neurons in the anterior motor speech region: dendritic features and interhemispheric comparisons. *Archives of Neurology* **53**, 1277–1283.

Heckers, S., Heinsen, H., Geiger, B. & Beckmann, H. (1991) Hippocampal neuron number in schizophrenia: a stereological study. *Archives of General Psychiatry* **48**, 1002–1008.

Heckers, S., Rauch, S.L., Goff, D.C. *et al.* (1998) Impaired recruitment of the hippocampus during conscious recollection in schizophrenia. *Nature Neuroscience* **1**, 318–323.

Heinsen, H., Gössmann, E., Rüb, U. *et al.* (1996) Variability in the human entorhinal region may confound neuropsychiatric diagnoses. *Acta Anatomica* **157**, 226–237.

Hendry, S.H.C. & Jones, E.G. (1988) Activity-dependent regulation of GABA expression in the visual cortex of adult monkeys. *Neuron* **1**, 701–712.

Holinger, D., Galaburda, A.M. & Harrison, P.J. (2000) Cerebral asymmetry. In: *The Neuropathology of Schizophrenia: Progress and Interpretation* (eds P.J. Harrison & G.W. Roberts), pp. 151–171. Oxford University Press, Oxford.

Honer, W.G., Falkai, P., Chen, C. *et al.* (1999) Synaptic and plasticity-associated proteins in anterior frontal cortex in severe mental illness. *Neuroscience* **91**, 1247–1255.

Honer, W.G., Young, C. & Falkai, P. (2000) Synaptic pathology. In: *The Neuropathology of Schizophrenia: Progress and Interpretation* (eds P.J. Harrison & G.W. Roberts), pp. 105–136. Oxford University Press, Oxford.

Huttenlocher, P.R. (1979) Synaptic density in human frontal cortex: developmental changes and effects of aging. *Brain Research* **163**, 195–205.

Irwin, S.A., Galvez, R. & Greenough, W.T. (2000) Dendritic spine structural anomalies in fragile X mental retardation syndrome. *Cerebral Cortex* **10**, 1038–1044.

Jakob, H. & Beckmann, H. (1986) Prenatal developmental disturbances in the limbic allocortex in schizophrenics. *Journal of Neural Transactions* **65**, 303–326.

Jellinger, K.A. & Gabriel, E. (1999) No increased incidence of Alzheimer's disease in elderly schizophrenics. *Acta Neuropathologica* **97**, 165–169.

Jeste, D.V. & Lohr, J.B. (1989) Hippocampal pathologic findings in schizophrenia: a morphometric study. *Archives of General Psychiatry* **46**, 1019–1024.

Jones, E.G. & Hendry, S.H.C. (1989) Differential calcium binding protein immunoreactivity distinguishes classes of relay neurons in monkey thalamic nuclei. *European Journal of Neuroscience* **1**, 222–246.

Jonsson, S.A.T., Luts, A., Guldberg-Kjaer, N. & Brun, A. (1997) Hippocampal pyramidal cell disarray correlates negatively to cell number: implications for the pathogenesis ofschizophrenia. *European Archives of Psychiatry and Neurological Science* **247**, 120–127.

Kalman, M., Csillag, A., Schleicher, A. *et al.* (1993) Long-term effects of anterograde degeneration on astroglial reaction in the rat geniculo-cortico system as revealed by computerized image analysis. *Anatomical Embryology* **187**, 1–7.

Kalus, P., Muller, T.J., Zuschratter, W. & Senitz, D. (2000) The dendritic architecture of prefrontal pyramidal neurons in schizophrenic patients. *Neuroreport* **11**, 3621–3625.

Karson, C.N., Mrak, R.E., Schluterman, K.O. *et al.* (1999) Alterations in synaptic proteins and their encoding mRNAs in prefrontal cortex in schizophenia: a possible neurochemical basis for 'hypofrontality'. *Molecular Psychiatry* **4**, 39–45.

Kaufmann, W.E. & Moser, H.W. (2000) Dendritic anomalies in disorders associated with mental retardation. *Cerebral Cortex* **10**, 981–991.

Kemper, T.L. & Bauman, M. (1998) Neuropathology of infantile autism. *Journal of Neuropathology and Experimental Neurology* **57**, 645–652.

Keshavan, M.S., Stanley, J.A. & Pettegrew, J.W. (2000) Magnetic resonance spectroscopy in schizophrenia: methodological issues and findings – Part II. *Biological Psychiatry* **48**, 369–380.

Kirkpatrick, B., Conley, R.C., Kakoyannis, A., Reep, R.L. & Roberts, R.C. (1999) Insterstitial cells of the white matter in the inferior parietal cortex in schizophrenia: an unbiased cell-counting study. *Synapse* **34**, 95–102.

Konick, L.C. & Friedman, L. (2001) Meta-analysis of thalamic size in schizophrenia. *Biological Psychiatry* **49**, 28–38.

Kovelman, J.A. & Scheibel, A.B. (1984) A neurohistological correlate of schizophrenia. *Biological Psychiatry* **19**, 1601–1621.

Krimer, L.S., Herman, M.M., Saunders, R.C. *et al.* (1997) A qualitative and quantitative analysis of the entorhinal cortex in schizophrenia. *Cerebral Cortex* **7**, 732–739.

Lambe, E.K., Krimer, L.S. & Goldman-Rakic, P.S. (2000) Differential postnatal development of catecholamine and serotonin inputs to identified neurons in prefrontal cortex of rhesus monkey. *Journal of Neuroscience* **20**, 8780–8787.

Levitt, J.B., Lewis, D.A., Yoshioka, T. & Lund, J.S. (1993) Topography of pyramidal neuron intrinsic connections in macaque monkey prefrontal cortex (areas 9 and 46). *Journal of Comparative Neurology* **338**, 360–376.

Lewis, D.A. (1997) Development of the prefrontal cortex during adolescence: insights into vulnerable neural circuits in schizophrenia. *Neuropsychopharmacology* **16**, 385–398.

Lewis, D.A. (1998) Chandelier cells: shedding light on altered cortical circuitry in schizophrenia. *Molecular Psychiatry* **3**, 468–471.

Lewis, D.A. (2000a) Distributed disturbances in brain structure and function in schizophrenia. *American Journal of Psychiatry* **157**, 1–2.

Lewis, D.A. (2000b) Is there a neuropathology of schizophrenia? Recent findings converge on altered thalamic–prefrontal cortical connectivity. *Neuroscientist* **6**, 208–218.

Lewis, D.A. & Lieberman, J.A. (2000) Catching up on schizophrenia: natural history and neurobiology. *Neuron* **28**, 325–334.

Lewis, D.A. & Sesack, S.R. (1997) Dopamine systems in the primate brain. In: *Handbook of Chemical Neuroanatomy* (eds F.E. Bloom, A. Björklund & T. Hökfelt), pp. 261–373. Elsevier Science, Amsterdam.

Lewis, D.A., Pierri, J.N., Volk, D.W., Melchitzky, D.S. & Woo, T.-U. (1999) Altered GABA neurotransmission and prefrontal cortical dysfunction in schizophrenia. *Biological Psychiatry* **46**, 616–626.

Lieberman, J.A. (1999) Is schizophrenia a neurodegenerative disorder? A clinical and neurobiological perspective. *Biological Psychiatry* **46**, 729–739.

Lund, J.S., Lund, R.D., Hendrickson, A.E., Bunt, A.H. & Fuchs, A.F. (1975) The origin of efferent pathways from the primary visual cortex, area 17, of the macaque monkey as shown by retrograde transport of horseradish peroxidase. *Journal of Comparative Neurology* **164**, 287–304.

Marti, E., Ferrer, I., Ballabriga, J. & Blasi, J. (1998) Increase in SNAP-25 immunoreactivity in mossy fibers following transient forebrain ischemia in the gerbil. *Acta Neuropathologica* **95**, 254–260.

Masliah, E., Mallory, M., Hansen, L., DeTeresa, R. & Terry, R.D. (1993) Quantitative synaptic alterations in the human neocortex during normal aging. *Neurology* **43**, 192–197.

McCarley, R.W., Wible, C.G., Frumin, M. *et al.* (1999) MRI anatomy of schizophrenia. *Biological Psychiatry* **45**, 1099–1119.

McDonald, B., Highley, J.R., Walker, M.A. *et al.* (2000) Anamalous asymmetry of fusiform and parahippocampal gyrus gray matter in schizophrenia: a postmortem study. *American Journal of Psychiatry* **157**, 40–47.

Melchitzky, D.S., Sesack, S.R. & Lewis, D.A. (1999) Parvalbumin-immunoreactive axon terminals in monkey and human prefrontal cortex: Laminar, regional and target specificity of Type I and Type II synapses. *Journal of Comparative Neurology* **408**, 11–22.

Melchitzky, D.S., Gonzalez-Burgos, G., Barrionuevo, G. & Lewis, D.A. (2001) Synaptic targets of the intrinsic axon collaterals of supragranular pyramidal neurons in monkey prefrontal cortex. *Journal of Comparative Neurology* **430**, 209–221.

Mirnics, K., Middleton, F.A., Marquez, A., Lewis, D.A. & Levitt, P. (2000) Molecular characterization of schizophrenia viewed by microarray analysis of gene expression in prefrontal cortex. *Neuron* **28**, 53–67.

Murphy, G.M. Jr, Lim, K.O., Wieneke, M. *et al.* (1998) No neuropathologic evidence for an increased frequency of Alzheimer's disease among elderly schizophrenics. *Biological Psychiatry* **43**, 205–209.

Nelson, M.D., Saykin, A.J., Flashman, L.A. & Riordan, H.J. (1998) Hippocampal volume reduction in schizophrenia as assessed by nagnetic resonance imaging: a meta-analytic study. *Archives of General Psychiatry* **55**, 433–440.

Okubo, Y., Suhara, T., Suzuki, K. *et al.* (1997) Decreased prefrontal dopamine D_1 receptors in schizophrenia revealed by PET. *Nature* **385**, 634–636.

Pakkenberg, B. (1990) Pronounced reduction of total neuron number in mediodorsal thalamic nucleus and nucleus accumbens in schizophrenics. *Archives of General Psychiatry* **47**, 1023–1028.

Pakkenberg, B. (1992) The volume of the mediodorsal thalamic nucleus in treated and untreated schizophrenics. *Schizophrenia Research* 7, 95–100.

Pakkenberg, B. (1993) Total nerve cell number in neocortex in chronic schizophrenics and controls estimated using optical disectors. *Biological Psychiatry* **34**, 768–772.

Parnavelas, J.G., Lynch, G., Brecha, N., Cotman, C.W. & Globus, A. (1974) Spine loss and regrowth in hippocampus following deafferentation. *Nature* **248**, 71–73.

Perrone-Bizzozero, N.I., Sower, A.C., Bird, E.D. *et al.* (1996) Levels of the growth-associated protein GAP-43 are selectively increased in association cortices in schizophrenia. *Proceedings of the National Academy of Sciences of the USA* **93**, 14182–14187.

Pierce, J.P. & Lewin, G.R. (1994) An ultrastructural size principle. *Neuroscience* **58**, 441–446.

Pierri, J.N., Melchitzky, D.S. & Lewis, D.A. (1999a) Volume and neuronal number of the primate mediodorsal thalamic nucleus: effects of chronic haloperidol administration. *Society for Neuroscience Abstracts* **25**, 1833.

Pierri, J.N., Chaudry, A.S., Woo, T.-U. & Lewis, D.A. (1999b) Alterations in chandelier neuron axon terminals in the prefrontal cortex of schizophrenic subjects. *American Journal of Psychiatry* **156**, 1709–1719.

Pierri, J.N., Volk, C.L.E., Auh, S., Sampson, A. & Lewis, D.A. (2001) Decreased somal size of deep layer 3 pyramidal neurons in the prefrontal cortex in subjects with schizophrenia. *Archives of General Psychiatry* **58**, 466–473.

Popken, G.J., Bunney, W.E. Jr, Potkin, S.G. & Jones, E.G. (2000) Subnucleus-specific loss of neurons in medial thalamus of schizophrenics. *Proceedings of the National Academy of Sciences of the USA* **97**, 9276–9280.

Portas, C.M., Goldstein, J.M., Shenton, M.E. *et al.* (1998) Volume tric evaluation of the thalamus in schizophrenic male patients using magnetic resonance imaging. *Biological Psychiatry* **43**, 649–659.

Prohovnik, I., Dwork, A.J., Kaufman, M.A. & Wilson, N. (1993) Alzheimer-type neuropathology in elderly schizophrenia patients. *Schizophrenia Bulletin* **19**, 805–816.

Pucak, M.L., Levitt, J.B., Lund, J.S. & Lewis, D.A. (1996) Patterns of intrinsic and associational circuitry in monkey prefrontal cortex. *Journal of Comparative Neurology* **376**, 614–630.

Purohit, D.P., Peri, D.P., Haroutunian, V. *et al.* (1998) Alzheimer disease and related neurodegenerative diseases in elderly patients with schizophrenia: a portmortem neuropathologic study of 100 cases. *Archives of General Psychiatry* **55**, 205–211.

Rajkowska, G., Selemon, L.D. & Goldman-Rakic, P.S. (1998) Neuronal and glial somal size in the prefrontal cortex: a postmortem morphometric study of schizophrenia and Huntington disease. *Archives of General Psychiatry* **55**, 215–224.

Riederer, P., Gsell, W., Calza, L. *et al.* (1995) Consensus on minimal criteria of clinical and neuropathological diagnosis of schizophrenia and affective disorders for post mortem research. Report from the European Demential and Scizophrenia Network (BIOMED 1). *Journal of Neural Transmission* **102**, 255–264.

Roberts, G.W. (1991) Schizophrenia: a neuropathological perspective. *British Journal of Psychiatry* **158**, 8–17.

Roberts, G.W. & Harrison, P.J. (2000) Gliosis and its implications for the disease process. In: *The Neuropathology of Schizophrenia: Progress and Interpretation* (eds P.J. Harrison & G.W. Roberts), pp. 137–150. Oxford University Press, Oxford.

Rosoklija, G., Toomayan, G., Ellis, S.P. *et al.* (2000) Structural abnormalities of subicular dendrites in subjects with schizophrenia and mood disorders: preliminary findings. *Archives of General Psychiatry* **57**, 349–356.

Saito, S., Kobayashi, S., Ohashi, Y. *et al.* (1994) Decreased synaptic density in aged brains and its prevention by rearing under enriched environment as revealed by synaptophysin contents. *Journal of Neuroscience Research* **39**, 57–62.

Saunders, R.C., Kolachana, B.S., Bachevalier, J. & Weinberger, D.R. (1998) Neonatal lesions of the medial temporal lobe disrupt prefrontal regulation of striatal dopamine. *Nature* **393**, 169–171.

Saykin, A.J., Shtasel, D.L., Gur, R.E. *et al.* (1994) Neuropsychological deficits in neuroleptic naive patients with first-episode schizophrenia. *Archives of General Psychiatry* **51**, 124–131.

Selemon, L.D. & Goldman-Rakic, P.S. (1999) The reduced neuropil hypothesis: a circuit based model of schizophrenia. *Biological Psychiatry* **45**, 17–25.

Selemon, L.D., Rajkowska, G. & Goldman-Rakic, P.S. (1995) Abnormally high neuronal density in the schizophrenic cortex: a morphometric analysis of prefrontal area 9 and occipital area 17. *Archives of General Psychiatry* **52**, 805–818.

Selemon, L.D., Rajkowska, G. & Goldman-Rakic, P.S. (1998) Elevated neuronal density in prefrontal area 46 in brains from schizophrenic patients: application of a three-dimensional, stereologic counting method. *Journal of Comparative Neurology* **392**, 402–412.

Selemon, L.D., Lidow, M.S. & Goldman-Rakic, P.S. (1999) Increased volume and glial density in primate prefrontal cortex associated with chronic antipsychotic drug exposure. *Biological Psychiatry* **46**, 161–172.

Squier, M., Chamberlain, P., Zaiwalla, Z. *et al.* (2000) Five cases of brain injury following amniocentesis in mid-term pregnancy. *Developmental Medicine and Child Neurology* **42**, 554–560.

Stanley, J.A., Williamson, P.C., Drost, D.J. *et al.* (1996) An *in vivo* proton magnetic resonance spectroscopy study of schizophrenia patients. *Schizophrenia Bulletin* **22**, 597–609.

Stevens, C.D., Altshuler, L.L., Bogerts, B. & Falkai, P. (1988) Quantitative study of gliosis in schizophrenia and Huntington's chorea. *Biological Psychiatry* **24**, 697–700.

Stevens, J.R. (1982) Neuropathology of schizophrenia. *Archives of General Psychiatry* **39**, 1131–1139.

Stevens, J.R., Casanova, M.F., Poltorak, M. & Buchan, G.C. (1992) Comparison of immunocytochemical and Holzer's methods for detection of acute and chronic glioses in human post-mortem material. *Journal of Neuropsychiatry and Clinical Neuroscience* **4**, 168–173.

Tamminga. C.A., Thaker. G.K., Buchanan, R. *et al.* (1992) Limbic system abnormalities identified in schizophrenia using positron emission tomography with fluorodeoxyglucose and neocortical alterations with deficit syndrome. *Archives of General Psychiatry* **49**, 522–530.

Thompson, P.M., Sower, A.C. & Perrone-Bizzozero, N.I. (1998) Altered levels of the synaptosomal associated protein SNAP-25 in schizophrenia. *Biological Psychiatry* **43**, 239–243.

Thune, J.J., Hofsten, D.E., Uylings, H.B.M. & Pakkenberg, B. (1998) Total neuron numbers in the prefrontal cortex in schizophrenia. *Society for Neuroscience Abstracts* **24**, 985.

Torrey, E.F., Webster, M., Knable, M., Johnston, N. & Yoken, R.H. (2000) The Stanley Foundation brain collection and Neuropathology Consortium. *Schizophrenia Research* **44**, 151–155.

Velakoulis, D., Panetelis, C., McGorry, P.D. *et al.* (1999) Hippocampal volume in first-episode psychosis and chronic schizophrenia: a high-resolution magnetic resonance imaging study. *Archives of General Psychiatry* **56**, 133–141.

Volk, D.W., Austin, M.C., Pierri, J.N., Sampson, A.R. & Lewis, D.A. (2000) Decreased GAD_{67} mRNA expression in a subset of prefrontal cortical GABA neurons in subjects with schizophrenia. *Archives of General Psychiatry* **57**, 237–245.

Volk, D.W., Austin, M.C., Pierri, J.N., Sampson, A.R. & Lewis, D.A. (2001) GABA transporter-1 mRNA in the prefrontal cortex in schizophrenia: decreased expression in a subset of neurons. *American Journal of Psychiatry* **158**, 256–265.

Weickert, C. & Weinberger, D.R. (1998) A candidate molecular approach to defining the developmental pathology in schizophrenia. *Schizophrenia Bulletin* **24**, 303–316.

Weinberger, D.R. (1987) Implications of normal brain development for the pathogenesis of schizophrenia. *Archives of General Psychiatry* **44**, 660–669.

Weinberger, D.R. (1999) Cell biology of the hippocampal formation in schizophrenia. *Biological Psychiatry* **45**, 395–402.

Weinberger, D.R. & Lipska, B.K. (1995) Cortical maldevelopment, anti-psychotic drugs, and schizophrenia: a search for common ground. *Schizophrenia Research* **16**, 87–110.

Weinberger, D.R., Berman, K.F. & Illowsky, B.P. (1988) Physiological dysfunction of dorsolateral prefrontal cortex in schizophrenia. III. A new cohort and evidence for a monoaminergic mechanism. *Archives of General Psychiatry* **45**, 609–615.

Weinberger, D.R., Berman, K.F., Suddath, R. & Torrey, E.F. (1992) Evidence of dysfunction of a prefrontal-limbic network in schizophrenia: a magnetic resonance imaging and regional cerebral blood flow study of discordant monozygotic twins. *American Journal of Psychiatry* **149**, 890–897.

Wellman, C.L., Logue, S.F. & Sengelaub, D.R. (1995) Maze learning and morphology of frontal cortex in adult and aged basal forebrain-lesioned rats. *Behavioral Neuroscience* **109**, 837–850.

Wisniewski, H.M., Constantinidis, J., Wegiel, J., Bobinski, M. & Tarnawski, M. (1994) Neurofibrillary pathology in brains of elderly schizophrenics treated with neuroleptics. *Alzheimer Disease and Associated Disorders* **8**, 211–227.

Woo, T.-U., Miller, J.L. & Lewis, D.A. (1997a) Parvalbumin-containing cortical neurons in schizophrenia. *American Journal of Psychiatry* **154**, 1013–1015.

Woo, T.-U., Pucak, M.L., Kye, C.H., Matus, C.V. & Lewis, D.A. (1997b) Peripubertal refinement of the intrinsic and associational circuitry in monkey prefrontal cortex. *Neuroscience* **80**, 1149–1158.

Woo, T.-U., Whitehead, R.E., Melchitzky, D.S. & Lewis, D.A. (1998) A subclass of prefrontal gamma-aminobutyric acid axon terminals are selectively altered in schizophrenia. *Proceedings of the National Academy of Sciences of the USA* **95**, 5341–5346.

Young, K.A., Manaye, K.F., Liang, C.-L., Hicks, P.B. & German, D.C. (2000) Reduced number of mediodorsal and anterior thalamic neurons in schizophrenia. *Biological Psychiatry* **47**, 944–953.

Zaidel, D.W., Esiri, M.M. & Harrison, P.J. (1997a) The hippocampus in schizophrenia: lateralized increase in neuronal density and altered cytoarchitectural asymmetry. *Psychological Medicine* **27**, 703–713.

Zaidel, D.W., Esiri, M.M. & Harrison, P.J. (1997b) Size, shape and orientation of neurons in the left and right hippocampus: investigation of normal asymmetries and alterations in schizophrenia. *American Journal of Psychiatry* **154**, 812–818.

18 Schizophrenia as a neurodevelopmental disorder

D.R. Weinberger and S. Marenco

The idea that schizophrenia has its origins in early development dates back at least to the modern classification of the syndrome by Kraepelin and Bleuler, both of whom noted abnormal neurological and behavioural signs in the childhood histories of adult patients. Some of the neuropathological findings reported in the early part of the twentieth century were interpreted as evidence of abnormal brain development (e.g. Southard 1915). Bender (1947), in her landmark study of cases of childhood schizophrenia, argued that the condition was likely to be a developmental encephalopathy. In studies of children of schizophrenic mothers, Fish and Hagin (1972) described a constellation of apparent lags and disruptions in neurological development, which predicted the later emergence of schizophrenia spectrum symptoms; they also proposed abnormal brain development as the cause. Other investigators had emphasized the early childhood social abnormalities of individuals with adult-onset schizophrenia (Watt 1972), also potentially implicating abnormal brain development. In spite of this diverse literature, the general view among psychiatrists and researchers during much of the twentieth century was that schizophrenia occurs principally because of a biological process that happens or is expressed around early adult life, and that clinical remission is related to reversal of this pathological process, while progression of the clinical condition is an expression of continuing progression of the pathology. This view echoed aspects of Kraepelin's codification of schizophrenia as an early dementia ('dementia praecox') and seemed consistent with the clinical fact that many patients with schizophrenia do not have a clearly abnormal premorbid history.

Beginning in the mid-1980s, a broad conceptual shift in thinking about the neurobiology of schizophrenia began to gather momentum, as the possibility of abnormal brain development again became a popular idea and a neurodevelopmental hypothesis of schizophrenia was elaborated and embraced by both the clinical and research communities. A convergence of factors accounted for this conceptual shift: in particular, a growing body of indirect evidence of abnormal brain development in individuals with schizophrenia and the failure of older formulations to capture the meaning and complexity of new data. For example, several longitudinal outcome studies (Bleuler 1941; Tsuang *et al.* 1979; Harding *et al.* 1992) demonstrated that considerable recovery was well within the bounds of schizophrenia, thus undermining the Kraepelinian concept of schizophrenia as a degenerative disease of early adulthood. Even in patients who did not have good outcomes, the pattern of neuropsychological impairment was not a progressively deteriorating one (Aylward *et al.* 1984). The advent of neuroimaging technologies permitted direct *in vivo* brain studies and led to the archival finding of increased cerebral ventricle size – the first unequivocal neurobiological marker of the illness (Johnstone *et al.* 1976; Weinberger *et al.* 1979, 1982a). The fact that this biological abnormality was present from the onset of the illness (Weinberger *et al.* 1982a), that it did not correlate with duration of illness (Weinberger *et al.* 1979) or advance with continuing illness in most longitudinal studies (Illowsky *et al.* 1988) strengthened further the assumption that a neurodegenerative process was not responsible. Evidence that ventricular enlargement was associated with poor premorbid social adjustment during childhood and that ventricular enlargement existed at the time of the first break was interpreted to indicate that the determining biology was present long before the typical clinical onset and was likely to be developmental in origin (Weinberger *et al.* 1980, 1982a). Meanwhile, postmortem histopathology studies were unable to demonstrate evidence of neurodegeneration, and the long-recognized absence of astrogliosis in the schizophrenic brain was now interpreted as further potential evidence that changes in the brain were of developmental origin and thus would not be associated with a gliotic reaction (Weinberger *et al.* 1983; Weinberger 1987).

By the end of the 1980s, a detailed formulation of the neurodevelopmental hypothesis emerged (Weinberger 1986, 1987), which included educated guesses on the distinct roles of cortical and subcortical dopaminergic systems in the brain, and the relationship of limbic and prefrontal cortical pathology to the manifest psychopathology. It was proposed that subtle abnormalities of cortical development, particularly involving limbic and prefrontal cortices and their connectivities, increase risk for the adult emergence of the schizophrenia syndrome.

Dopamine innervation of prefrontal cortex was considered an important factor in prefrontal cortical function related to negative symptoms and cognitive deficits in schizophrenia and to stress-related symptomatic exacerbation. Impaired dopamine function at the prefrontal cortical level also was seen as a factor in upregulating subcortical dopamine activity, perhaps accounting for psychotic symptoms and response to neuroleptic drugs. Moreover, it was proposed that the triggering of the emergence of the syndrome depended on an interaction of the early developmental abnormalities with normal maturation events of early adult life, such as the maturation of intracortical connectivities and of the cortical dopamine system. Neurodevelopmental changes during adulthood were considered as a possible factor in the clinical evolution of the syndrome, as progression of negative symptoms and even some cognitive deficits might represent normal age-related changes in prefrontal cortex, and the tendency for positive symptoms to attenuate with ageing might reflect normal age-related involution of the dopamine system.

The basic concepts elaborated at that time have remained largely relevant to our current state of knowledge, and in fact considerable evidence has accrued to bolster their credibility. Indeed, the heuristic impact of this paradigm shift in thinking about schizophrenia is illustrated by the many new areas of clinical and basic investigation it has spawned, including:

1 epidemiological studies about prenatal, behavioural and developmental factors associated with the illness, which have provided the most compelling evidence in support of the neurodevelopmental hypothesis (see below and Chapters 12 and 13);

2 the elaboration of a spectrum of developmental animal models which have confirmed the neurobiological plausibility of the hypothesis (see Chapter 21);

3 the search for molecular markers of abnormal cortical development in schizophrenic brain tissue (see Chapter 17); and

4 a quest for genes that might increase susceptibility by affecting brain development (see Chapters 14 and 15).

Numerous authors and investigators have made brain development and schizophrenia a centrepiece of their theoretical approach to the disorder (Murray & Lewis 1987; Bogerts 1989; Crow *et al.* 1989a; Waddington & Youssef 1990; Mednick 1991; Bloom 1993; Cannon *et al.* 1993; Keshavan & Hogarty 1999).

In the first edition of this book, the chapter on neurodevelopment and schizophrenia reviewed the available evidence supporting the hypothesis and speculated about possible developmental mechanisms of pathogenesis (Weinberger 1995). It focused on four areas:

1 basic aspects of normal brain development, with particular reference to how and when putative abnormalities associated with schizophrenia might occur;

2 neuroimaging and postmortem research data interpreted to represent cerebral maldevelopment;

3 evidence for abnormal environmental factors impacting on early brain development; and

4 mechanisms that might explain how the onset of the illness could be delayed until long after the early pathology occurred.

In this revised edition, we focus on new clinical information that has emerged about brain development and schizophrenia since the early 1990s and consider in detail the implications of these new data on the neurodevelopmental hypothesis. This chapter is not intended as a comprehensive summary of the recent literature, which is also surveyed in other chapters in this volume (specifically, Chapters 12, 13 and 22). In contrast to these chapters, we highlight the problems and inconsistencies in this literature as they relate to the potential neurodevelopmental origins of schizophrenia. As we note, some of the evidence for a neurodevelopmental abnormality has become stronger, e.g. environmental adversity *in utero*, while other evidence has come under challenge, e.g. from neuroimaging and neuropathology studies.

Evidence of developmental neuropathology

In the past decade, literally hundreds of studies in many countries have been undertaken in the search for evidence of abnormal brain development in patients with schizophrenia. While there is substantial indication that the brains of such patients are not normal and that their developmental histories are not normal, the evidence that abnormal brain development is a risk factor for schizophrenia remains indirect and circumstantial. Thus, numerous *in vivo* neuroimaging studies have revealed compelling evidence of morphometric changes in the schizophrenic brain (see Chapter 22) and many postmortem studies (see Chapter 17) have found replicable cellular and molecular abnormalities; however, none of the findings can be definitively attributed to a developmental origin. Large epidemiological cohort studies in several countries have confirmed that increased frequency of obstetric complications and abnormal social, motor and cognitive maturation during childhood are associated with emergence of schizophrenia during adulthood (see Chapter 13). However, a direct causative link between these phenomena and abnormal brain development is lacking. We consider now some of the indirect evidence for abnormal early brain development. More detailed discussions of this evidence have appeared in earlier reviews (Marenco & Weinberger 2000; Marenco & Weinberger 2003).

Obstetric abnormalities

The most extensively studied of the early developmental markers are obstetric complications (OCs; see Chapter 13). Beginning in the 1930s (Rosanoff *et al.* 1934), reports that adult patients with schizophrenia had increased frequency of OCs appeared and, as the neurodevelopmental hypothesis became more popular, the frequency of these reports in the literature has increased dramatically. Many obstetric risk factors have been linked with schizophrenia in one study or another, including pre-eclampsia (Kendell *et al.* 1996; O'Dwyer 1997), small head circumference (McNeil *et al.* 1993; Kunugi *et al.* 1996), low birth weight (Lane & Albee 1970; Torrey 1977; Jones *et al.* 1998), Rhesus factor incompatibility (Hollister *et al.* 1996), fetal distress (O'Callaghan *et al.* 1992), weight heavy for length (Hultman *et al.* 1997), multiparity, maternal bleeding during pregnancy (Hultman *et al.* 1999), abnormal presentations (Parnas *et al.* 1982; Gunthergenta *et al.* 1994; Verdoux *et al.* 1997) and increased prepregancy body weight (Susser *et al.* 2000). While most of this evidence is based on case–control comparisons, several recent large cohort epidemiological studies are especially noteworthy. Most impressive of these is a study of 500 000 births in Sweden (Dalman *et al.* 1999). It was reported in this study that the relative risk for schizophrenia was increased up to 2.5 times by pre-eclampsia, gestational age below 33 weeks, inertia of labour, vacuum extraction, respiratory illness and low birth weight. Pre-eclampsia, an indicator of fetal malnutrition, emerged after logistical regression as the strongest risk factor, increasing the risk for schizophrenia between 2 and 2.5 times. Extreme prematurity also increased risk for schizophrenia by more than twice. In spite of the impressive statistical results, the absolute number of cases involved was quite small. Out of a total sample of 238 cases of schizophrenia, only 11 had a history of pre-eclampsia, five extreme prematurity and two very low birth weight.

Two large cohort studies were conducted in Finland: one based on a 1960s cohort of 11 000 pregnancies (Jones *et al.* 1998) and another based on 7840 births in Helsinki in 1955 (Rosso *et al.* 2000). Only low birth weight and short gestation conferred increased risk in the first study, while increased scores on an inventory of abnormalities loosely linked to 'hypoxia' (including prematurity, but not birth weight and gestational age) were found to increase risk in the second study, but only after the cases were divided into those with age of onset before age 22. In the group with age of onset after 22, there was no association with OCs. The authors of the first study also noted the curious finding that mothers of patients with schizophrenia reported being depressed during pregnancy more frequently than mothers of probands without the disorder.

Finally, Cannon *et al.* (2000) examined birth records of 9236 births at an inner city hospital in Philadelphia who were followed as part of the US National Collaborative Perinatal Project. They again reported an increased risk associated with their 'hypoxia' scale only in so-called early-onset cases. Several studies, including those of Rosso *et al.* (2000) and Cannon *et al.* (2000), report an apparent dose relationship between number of OCs and risk for schizophrenia (Hultman *et al.* 1997), as if greater intrauterine or perinatal distress accounts for greater brain involvement and ultimate risk for illness. Indeed, earlier clinical correlation studies have tended to find that adult patients with a history of OCs have other evidence associated with poorer outcome, such as a more chronic course (Wilcox & Nasrallah 1987), predominant negative symptoms (Cannon *et al.* 1990), younger age at onset (Smith *et al.* 1998) and more structural abnormalities on magnetic resonance imaging (MRI) scan (McNeil *et al.* 2000).

Notwithstanding the impressive number of positive reports of an association of OCs with risk for schizophrenia, there are important inconsistencies. In particular, there are two recent large case–control studies based on contemporaneous birth records. Byrne *et al.* (2000) found that OCs were more frequent and more severe only in males presenting for psychiatric treatment before the age of 30. Kendell *et al.* (2000) found almost no association between OCs and schizophrenia in an even larger (almost 500 cases) case–control study. These results were in conflict with those obtained 4 years earlier on the same group of subjects (Kendell *et al.* 1996), when fewer schizophrenia cases had passed through the age of risk. Kendell *et al.* (2000) identified a case–control matching algorithm in the earlier positive study that erroneously depressed the frequency of OCs in controls. There are also negative reports among older cohort studies also based on obstetric records (Done *et al.* 1991; Buka *et al.* 1993). Interestingly, a reanalysis of the data in Done *et al.* (1991) by Sacker *et al.* (1995) found that schizophrenia was associated with a higher likelihood of risk behaviour during pregnancy by the mothers, including smoking, drinking, poorer prenatal care, etc. Perhaps such behaviours should qualify as OCs, although they are not included in the scales used in most studies. It should also be noted that later reanalysis after more prolonged follow-up of the cohort originally studied by Buka *et al.* (1993) did show an association of schizophrenia and OCs related to hypoxia (Zornberg *et al.* 2000).

It is likely that the inconsistencies in the literature reflect the relative weakness of the effect size of OCs on risk for schizophrenia. Meta-analyses of this literature have found that, in general, OCs increase risk from 1.3- to twofold (Geddes *et al.* 1999); thus, they account for a relatively small numbers of cases, analogous to estimates of risk attributable to a single genetic locus (Risch 1990). Nevertheless, it is difficult to escape the conclusion that OCs, of various sorts, depending probably on cohort and record-keeping variations, do slightly increase risk for the emergence of schizophrenia in late life. This means that abnormalities of the intrauterine environment can affect fetal development in a manner that has implications for the expression of schizophrenia. However, this broad conclusion may be as far as the association with OCs will ultimately go in clarifying the specific developmental mechanisms related to schizophrenia.

There are a number of problems in interpreting the biological implications of the OC data. In most studies, the assessment of OCs has tended to lump together those occurring at different times during gestation, delivery and the neonatal period. There has been no agreement on what scales to use and whether multiple OCs should be considered as independent measures related to increasing severity of prenatal or perinatal abnormality (McNeil *et al.* 1997). The attribution of specific OCs to specific pathophysiological mechanisms, e.g. prematurity to hypoxia, is suspect. Certainly, OCs are not specific for schizophrenia, and have been associated with increased risk for bipolar disorder (Lewis & Murray 1987; Done *et al.* 1991; Guth *et al.* 1993; Kinney *et al.* 1998; Marcelis *et al.* 1998), although probably less clearly so than with schizophrenia (Verdoux & Bourgeois 1993;

Bain *et al.* 2000), disruptive behaviour in adolescents (Allen *et al.* 1998), antisocial behaviours (Szatmari *et al.* 1986), autism (Bolton *et al.* 1997) and 'minimal brain dysfunction' (Rao 1990) and cerebral palsy (Nelson & Ellenberg 1984; Eschenbach 1997). Why the same pattern of OCs would result in such diverse conditions is unknown. It may well be that many psychiatric disorders have this antecedent and that OCs are generic risk factors for many behavioural complications.

Another confusing aspect of the OC literature that complicates a mechanistic formulation is that the evidence is inconsistent in terms of timing of OCs during pregnancy. It is difficult to understand how causes acting in the second or third trimester or in the perinatal period result in a similar outcome as a disruption in brain development at different times might be expected to result in different outcomes. Indeed, one of the perplexing aspects of the OC literature is the variability from one study to another of which OC confers increased risk. It is also surprising that OCs tend *not* to correlate with other aspects of premorbid abnormal development, such as motor and cognitive function (Cannon 2000). It would be reasonably expected that if OCs relate to schizophrenia in adulthood because of their impact on brain development, they should relate even more strongly to childhood maturational antecedents that are more proximate to the effects of OCs.

It is also unclear why OCs affect some individuals adversely and appear to have no impact in others, probably the majority of people. Several studies have considered the possibility that OCs interact with genetic risk factors. Cannon *et al.* (1993) reported that a relationship with CT abnormalities and OCs was found only in patients with a family history of schizophrenia. However, several other groups have reported the tendency for OCs to segregate with cases lacking a family history (Lewis *et al.* 1989; Cantor-Graae *et al.* 1994). The question of whether the occurrence of OCs *per se* is related to genetic risk for schizophrenia, i.e. whether risk genes for schizophrenia might also be risk genes for causing OCs, has been addressed in several recent studies, with largely negative results (Marcelis *et al.* 1998; Cannon *et al.* 2000). However, it is also clear that schizophrenic mothers, perhaps because of prenatal behavioural risk factors such as smoking and poor prenatal care, have increased frequencies of OCs (Sacker *et al.* 1996; Bennedsen *et al.* 2001).

Finally, a striking omission in almost all of the OC literature is consideration of environmental risk factors such as smoking and drug/alchohol use on pregnancy outcome. It is clear that tobacco and alcohol use affect the frequency of OCs and brain development (Frank *et al.* 2001). The possibility that an association of such behaviours in the mothers of schizophrenic offspring would provide a potential causative mechanism for OCs needs to be considered in future studies. The implications for prevention are also apparent.

In conclusion, while the OC literature does not provide a mechanistic account of how OCs biologically translate into risk for schizophrenia, it does add substantial evidence of a role of a neurodevelopmental abnormality *per se*, and of the plausibility of the neurodevelopmental hypothesis.

Intrauterine infection and abnormal nutrition

While the causes of OCs associated with schizophrenia are unknown, evidence that potential aetiological factors, such as intrauterine infection and abnormal nutrition, may increase risk for schizophrenia provide further support for the neurodevelopmental hypothesis (see also Chapters 12 and 13). Several studies have linked schizophrenia to evidence of adverse maternal nutrition during pregnancy (e.g. Susser *et al.* 1996; Rosso *et al.* 2000; Wahlbeck *et al.* 2001), although the timing of the putative nutritional adversity has been either unspecified or varied. The data related to famine (Susser *et al.* 1996) have not been independently replicated. A more consistent association has been found between some influenza epidemics, especially the one in Europe in 1957, and an excess of births that would later develop schizophrenia (Mednick *et al.* 1988, 1990). This observation has been replicated in several countries, both in the northern (Kendell & Kemp 1989; O'Callaghan *et al.* 1991; Kunugi *et al.* 1995) and the southern hemispheres (McGrath *et al.* 1994). According to these studies, the fetus, judging from its date of birth, should have been in the second trimester of pregnancy when exposed to the virus. However, Crow *et al.* (1992), using the British birth cohort of 1957, found no evidence of such an effect, and other studies have failed to support an association of intrauterine influenza and schizophrenia (Torrey *et al.* 1988; Selten & Slaets 1994; Susser *et al.* 1994; Morgan *et al.* 1997; Westergaard *et al.* 1999). There are only a few studies where an attempt was made to verify whether mothers had actually suffered from a viral infection during their second trimester (Crow *et al.* 1992; Mednick *et al.* 1994; Cannon *et al.* 1996) and the results of these studies are controversial. Moreover, the mechanism by which influenza *in utero* might produce schizophrenia is unclear, as there is little evidence for direct cytotoxicity of the influenza virus in the fetus (Cotter *et al.* 1995) and influenza viral markers have not been found in cerebrospinal fluid or in postmortem brain tissue of patients with schizophrenia (Sierrahonigmann *et al.* 1995; Taller *et al.* 1996). In addition, possible influenza exposure *in utero* has also been linked to affective disorders in the same population of cases exposed to the 1957 epidemic in Finland that generated the initial data for schizophrenia (Machon *et al.* 1997).

In studies that reviewed the effect of influenza epidemics other than the one in 1957, there is even less consistency and preliminary evidence for a causative role of other potential infectious aetiological agents has emerged, including diptheria and pneumonia (Watson *et al.* 1984), measles, polio, varicella and zoonoses (Torrey *et al.* 2000), rubella (Brown *et al.* 2001) and non-specific upper respiratory infections (Brown *et al.* 2000). The data supporting these recent additional associations are discussed in greater detail elsewhere (see Chapter 13; Marenco & Weinberger 2003).

Schizophrenia has been linked in several large unbiased epidemiological studies to urban birth (Marcelis *et al.* 1999; Mortensen *et al.* 1999) and to late winter–early spring season of birth (Mortensen *et al.* 1999; Suvisaari *et al.* 2000, 2001). The evidence for urban birth is particularly intriguing because it is where an individual was born, not raised or lived, that appears to convey the greatest risk. This implicates indirectly obstetric factors, although the specific variables have not been identified. Multiple studies have found evidence of the so-called season of birth effect (Bradbury & Miller 1985; Hafner *et al.* 1987; Kendell & Kemp 1987; Kendell & Adams 1991; O'Callaghan *et al.* 1991; Torrey *et al.* 1993; Mortensen *et al.* 1999) and the most popular explanation has been increased likelihood of infection during the winter, possibly at a critical period of gestation. However, there are few data directly linking infection rates and season of birth in the same population and fluctuations in epidemic infection rates are unlikely to account for the whole effect (Sham *et al.* 1992). While O'Callaghan *et al.* (1991) reported an interaction between the seasonal variation of schizophrenia births and urban births, this was not replicated in a much larger sample (Suvisaari *et al.* 2000). In general, the seasonality of birth phenomena has been difficult to interpret. There is no consensus in the literature regarding the correlates of seasonal variation in schizophrenia births in terms of other evidence of infection, intrauterine adversity, OCs, later development or manifest symptomatology (for review see Cotter *et al.* 1996). Moreover, seasonal variation in birth may be present in the population as a whole (Russell *et al.* 1993) and in other central nervous system conditions such as bipolar disorder, autism, dyslexia and epilepsy (Cotter *et al.* 1996). There are also unexplained geographical discrepancies in the degree of seasonal variation in birth, with similar data in Japan (Kunugi *et al.* 1997) and Finland (Suvisaari *et al.* 2000), but a quite different pattern in Scotland (Eagles *et al.* 1995).

Several recent studies have explored the possibility that stressful environments experienced by the mother could impact biologically on the developing fetus and increase risk for schizophrenia. For example, Van Os and Selten (1998) have found an association between exposure to aerial bombardment during World War II during the first trimester of pregnancy and subsequent development of schizophrenia. Similarly, Selten *et al.* (1999) found weak evidence for exposure to a flood in the Netherlands to increase the risk for the development of schizophrenia in offspring. However, these studies did not control for other potential deprivations that may accompany such catastrophes and do not implicate a mechanism for the effect. Nevertheless, it has become popular in psychiatry research almost to the point of faddism to attribute structural changes in brain during development and even later in life to the cellular and molecular sequelae of stress, although the evidence for this possibility is limited.

In summary, over the past decade there has been a dramatic accumulation of data that OCs and intrauterine adversity slightly but significantly increase the risk for adult emergence of schizophrenia. Because these factors are likely to reflect phenomena linked to aspects of brain development, they represent the most substantial evidence that abnormal brain development increases the risk for schizophrenia. However, it is also clear from this extensive literature that there is no specific or consistent developmental factor, nor does there appear to be a specific time or stage in human intrauterine development. This makes it difficult to implicate a specific biological mechanism, or a spe-cific developmental defect, at least across the general population of affected patients. The second trimester may be a particularly vulnerable period of development and the 1957 influenza epidemic might have conferred a particularly clear risk but, at most, this event accounts for a very small minority of patients with the illness. Non-specific insults to the brain (from drug exposure to head trauma to epilepsy) also are sometimes thought to cause schizophrenia-like syndromes in adulthood, which appears to be a particularly vulnerable period of life for the expression of psychotic symptoms regardless of the manner of brain insult (Weinberger 1987; Hyde *et al.* 1992). Moreover, the same developmental causes that increase risk for schizophrenia may also increase risk for other disorders, including affective psychosis. These results invite reflection upon the notion of specificity of causation and pathogenesis with respect to schizophrenia. It is reasonable to assume that such diverse environmental factors that disrupt the normal programmes of early human brain development have individually varying clinical effects depending on other modifying and protecting factors, including genetic background and environmental aspects of postnatal development.

Minor physical anomalies

The data reviewed thus far suggest that OCs associated with the later development of schizophrenia are quite non-specific. Given this apparent fact, we would expect that the development of other organs might also be affected. Some evidence exists for the occurrence of an excess of physical anomalies outside the brain in patients with schizophrenia (see Chapter 12; Green *et al.* 1994). These generally range from webbed toes to altered craniofacial morphometry. These putative abnormalities have been interpreted as evidence that brain development also is abnormal.

The physical anomalies that seem to differentiate most clearly patients with schizophrenia from other patient groups are primarily craniofacial. According to Lane *et al.* (1996), these include palate height, bifid tongue, ear protrusion, supraorbital ridges, eye fissure inclination, epicanthus and widened helix. Interestingly, Kraepelin (1919) cited high palate and low set ears as being over-represented in his patients with schizophrenia. A more recent study (Lane *et al.* 1997) found that the combination of 12 variables, all related to cranial morphology, allowed a correct classification of 90% of patients with schizophrenia and 80% of a matched sample of controls.

Another interesting putative physical anomaly involves the development of finger and hand print patterns. Altered dermatoglyphic patterns have been reported in patients with schizophrenia, based on quantitative assessment of ridge counts and patterns (Lane *et al.* 1996; Fearon *et al.* 2001), including in discordant monozygotic twins (Davis & Bracha 1996). Because such dermatoglyphic patterns are thought to cease development by the third trimester of pregnancy, the variations reported in schizophrenia have been interpreted as further evidence of fetal adversity.

The major limitation of interpreting the physical anomaly data is that their frequency in healthy subjects is sometimes surprisingly high (up to 50% for some craniofacial abnormalities; Lane *et al.* 1997), raising the question of whether they are truly anomalies at all. It should also be noted that subtle effects of medication, including parkinsonism or dyskinesias, which may impact on facial features, have not been ruled out as a possible confounder. Moreover, and perhaps most critical, the interpretation of these studies is based on the assumption that because classical developmental syndromes (e.g. Down's syndrome) are associated with marked qualitative deviations in facial and dermatoglyphic features, quantitative physical deviance, if present in schizophrenia, must also be developmental in origin. This assumption may not be valid for such quantitative measures that vary considerably in the normal population. Thus, minor physical anomalies, if they were valid effects of abnormal organ development, would represent direct evidence of disturbed intrauterine development. We believe that the jury is still out on the interpretation of the minor physical anomaly data.

Premorbid neurological and behavioural abnormalities

If the brains of individuals at risk to manifest schizophrenia have not developed normally, it might be expected that some evidence of subtle abnormalities of nervous system function would be apparent during their childhood before they become clinically ill. In fact, the data from case–control and especially from large epidemiological cohorts are unequivocal that such evidence exists. This evidence includes delayed motor and speech milestones during the first year of life, various deficits in motor and cognitive development throughout childhood and consistent social and educational abnormalities. This evidence is reviewed in detail elsewhere (see Chapters 12 and 13; Marenco & Weinberger 2000). A remarkable aspect to the results, of the large epidemiological studies especially, is their consistency. Virtually every study has found evidence of deficits – subtle but significant – in the premorbid development of individuals who manifest schizophrenia during adulthood. The deficits are especially clear in school performance and other signs of cognitive development, although this may reflect in part that such skills are consistently sampled as outcome measures. Clearly, schizophrenia, as it is currently defined and diagnosed, is a disorder of early adult life, but antecedent abnormalities of cognitive and psychological function are part of the syndrome. Thus, it can be concluded that such antecedents reflect malfunction of certain brain systems from relatively early in life. However, because social and psychological deprivations also can affect cognitive and social development, the specific aetiology of these antecedents of schizophrenia cannot be specified from these studies.

Evidence of brain tissue abnormalities

Neuroimaging

The current incarnation of the neurodevelopmental hypothesis was originally proposed based on some unexpected results from computerized axial tomography (CAT) scan studies of adult patients with schizophrenia. Beginning in 1976 with an *in vivo* study of cerebral ventricular size using the novel method of CAT scanning (Johnstone *et al.* 1976), literally hundreds of reports have appeared of subtle variations in cerebral anatomy associated with schizophrenia, especially enlarged cerebral ventricles. Recent applications of MRI, which allow much more detailed measurements of cortical and subcortical brain structures, have confirmed that volumes of various structures in the brain in schizophrenia are slightly smaller and cerebrospinal fluid spaces are larger than found in comparison control groups (see Chapter 22 for a survey of this literature). Weinberger *et al.* (1979) reported, to their surprise, that ventricular size measured on a CAT scan did not correlate with duration of illness, as would have been expected if the neuropathological process responsible for ventricular enlargement advanced as the illness progressed. They raised the possibility that the underlying process was no longer active, i.e. was non-degenerative. The lack of a correlation between ventricular size and duration of illness has been widely replicated (Raz & Raz 1990), and its interpretation appeared to be supported by the results of several longitudinal studies that followed the same patients for up to 10 years (e.g. Jaskiw *et al.* 1994). Shortly after the initial reports in chronic patients, ventricular enlargement was reported in patients at the onset of psychosis in early adulthood (Weinberger *et al.* 1982a), a finding which also has been frequently confirmed (DeLisi *et al.* 1991; Lieberman *et al.* 1993; Gur *et al.* 1998). Moreover, ventricular enlargement has been shown to correlate with early childhood social adjustment and with OCs (Weinberger *et al.* 1980b; Reveley *et al.* 1984; McNeil *et al.* 2000). Together, these various findings led to the conclusions that ventricular enlargement reflects changes in the brain that predate the adult emergence of the clinical syndrome, appear to be relatively stable during the course of the illness, and may reflect early developmental pathology. These conclusions appeared to support the neurodevelopmental hypothesis, as neurodevelopmental changes in brain anatomy would be expected to be present at the onset of the illness, would correlate with antecedents and, unlike degenerative changes, would remain relatively stable during adulthood.

However, a recent review (Woods 1998) and a new series of longitudinal MRI studies have called into question this assumption, by arguing that changes in extracerebral cerebrospinal fluid could not be developmental in origin (Woods 1998), and by revealing changes in measurements of brain structures (e.g. ventricles, hippocampus) over relatively short periods in patients who have been ill for varying periods of time and at various stages of life (reviewed in Weinberger & McClure 2002). Indeed, these recent MRI studies offer a serious challenge to the

Table 18.1 *Continued.*

Investigators	Average age at first scan (years)	Average length follow up (years)	Brain region showing progressive change	Maximum percentage change (per year)	Brain region showing no change or opposite change	Correlation with clinical change
Gur *et al.* (1998)	29.2	2.5	Frontal lobe (left > right) Temporal lobe (left > right)	(–) 4.2 (left) (–) 3.4 (left)	Whole brain Cerebral spinal fluid spaces	Improvement in most symptoms correlated with decreased frontal and temporal lobe volumes in previously previously treated patients Overall, symptoms improved in patients
Davis *et al.* (1998)	39.5	5.1	VBR (left > right) in Kraepelinian patients	(+) 3.3	None	No significant correlation between change in VBR and negative symptoms in non-Kraepelinian patients
Lieberman *et al.* (2001)	26	1.5	Cerebral cortex in poor outcome patients Total ventricles in poor outcome patients	(–) 0.42 (females) (–) 5.4 (females)	Caudate nuclei in all patients Hippocampus in all patients Cerebral cortex in all patients Total ventricles in all patients Total ventricles in good outcome patients Cerebral cortex in good outcome patients Hippocampus in poor outcome patients	Total ventricle and cerebral cortex increase correlates with poor outcome Cerebral cortex and hippocampus increase correlates with good outcome
Mathalon *et al.* (2001)	39.4	3.3	Prefrontal sulcii Right prefrontal grey Right frontal sulcii Left frontal grey Posterior superior temporal sulcii Posterior superior temporal grey Left lateral ventricle	(+) 6.63 (left) (–) 2.12 (–) 2.71 (–)1.72 (+) 9.65 (left) (–) 3.35 (right) (+) 12.96	Left prefrontal grey Left frontal sulcii Right frontal grey Anterior superior temporal sulcii Right anterior superior temporal grey	Overall, symptoms improved in patients

VBR, ventricle-to-brain ratio.

illness is to examine healthy relatives of patients. Presumably, these individuals share risk factors that may operate at the level of brain development, but do not share illness-related epiphenomena. Several studies of family members, especially siblings, have suggested that slightly enlarged ventricles and reduced cortical volumes are found in healthy siblings (see Chapter 15; Weinberger *et al.* 1980b; Seidman *et al.* 1997; Cannon *et al.* 1998). In a recent study of 29 pairs of twins discordant for schizophrenia (15 MZ pairs and 14 DZ pairs) and 29 normal MZ pairs, Baare *et al.* (2001) found evidence of risk and illness-related changes. Slightly smaller intracranial volumes (2%) and larger ventricles were found in the unaffected twin from the discordant MZ pairs but not from the DZ pairs, suggesting that smaller brain growth was related to genetic risk for schizophrenia. Illness was associated with larger changes in brain volume measurements and with reduction in size of other cortical regions (e.g. parahippocampal cortex), suggesting that illness was associated with epigenetic changes affecting brain volume. Because intracranial volume is largely determined early in life, the twin data argue for abnormal brain development being related to genetic risk factors. These data in twins will require replication in larger samples.

While MRI volume measurements are difficult to interpret as evidence for or against pathological brain development, other approaches to analysing MRI scan data may be more informative. For example, several studies have looked at aspects of cortical gyral development. In principle, anomalous gyral patterns would be unequivocal evidence of cortical maldevelopment, as such patterns are almost completely established before birth. However, the results have been inconsistent (Kikinis *et al.* 1994; Kulynych *et al.* 1995a, 1997; Noga *et al.* 1996), and clearly most patients with schizophrenia do not have obvious gyral anomalies (e.g. microgyria, distorted gyri, etc.). Bullmore *et al.* (1998) and Friston and Frith (1995) used statistical methods to analyse the patterns of intercorrelated regional signal intensities on MRI in an effort to test for evidence of dysconnectivity. They reported differences in the intraregional correlation patterns between patients and controls, interpreting their results as evidence of pathological connectivity and presumably abnormal development. The validity of this interpretation of the MRI data is unclear. Several groups have examined the shape of various structures, particularly involving the temporal lobe, arguing that shape may more directly reflect structural development than would volume (Casanova *et al.* 1990; Csernansky *et al.* 1998). While abnormal shape of temporal lobe structures (e.g. hippocampus) was reported in these studies, the validity of the claim that changes in shape are more likely to reflect developmental change than is volume is untested.

Another neuroimaging observation that has been interpreted as reflecting abnormal brain development involves asymmetries of various regional volumes. In some studies, evidence of pathological changes appears to favour the left side of the brain. This has been especially true for the size of the ventricles (Crow *et al.* 1989a,b) and for the volume of the superior temporal gyrus (Shenton *et al.* 1992). Reports of relatively greater reductions in other regions of left temporal cortex have also appeared (Suddath *et al.* 1990; Shenton *et al.* 2001). Indeed, when asymmetric findings have been reported, they usually involve the left hemisphere. This has prompted some to suggest that this lateralization tendency is consistent with a putative delay in the development of the left hemisphere during the second trimester, leaving it more vulnerable to adverse events that might otherwise affect the brain diffusely (Crow *et al.* 1989a; Roberts 1991). Whether the slight delay in the appearance of surface gyri means that the left hemisphere is developing slower or that it is more vulnerable to injury or vulnerable for a longer period is unknown. Moreover, most of the morphometric studies, even those that report unilateral findings (Crow *et al.* 1989a; Shenton *et al.* 1992), have also observed bilateral changes.

Studies of lateralized cerebral function, such as handedness, dichotic listening asymmetries and lateralized cognitive tasks, have suggested that patients with schizophrenia may be less completely lateralized than normal individuals. Some evidence from positron emission tomography (PET) studies even indicates reversed functional cerebral asymmetries in schizophrenia (Gur & Chin 1999). If these functional asymmetries are related to mechanisms of the development of normal anatomical asymmetries, the findings may have implications for abnormal cerebral development in schizophrenia. In a sense, anatomical asymmetries are closer to the issue of intrauterine development than are other morphometric assessments. They inherently control for individual differences in state variables and other artefacts that can confound measurements of *in vivo* and postmortem specimens, presumably because such variables should not be lateralized. In contrast to asymmetric findings (referred to above), findings of anomalous asymmetries are potentially more understandable as developmental in origin. The research question involved is not whether a pathological process is distributed or affects the brain asymmetrically, but whether the normal programmes that determine healthy asymmetry are disrupted. Because the times of origin of many of the well-characterized normal anatomical asymmetries are known, the time of disruption might be inferred. For instance, normal asymmetries of the Sylvian fissures (Chi *et al.* 1977), of the planum temporale (Wada *et al.* 1975), of the frontal operculum (Chi *et al.* 1977) and of the frontal and occipital lobes (Weinberger *et al.* 1982b) appear during the second trimester of gestation. Therefore, if variations in the appearance of such asymmetries are seen in patients with schizophrenia, this might provide further evidence of adverse development during that period. In general, there have been both positive and negative studies in assessments of various asymmetries, and the reasons for the inconsistencies are uncertain (Luchins *et al.* 1979; Bullmore *et al.* 1995; Kulynych *et al.* 1995b; Kwon *et al.* 1999; Shapleske *et al.* 2001). Even the advent of more sophisticated promising methods of image analysis (Thompson *et al.* 1997) has not resulted in extremely convincing findings. For example, Narr *et al.* (2001a) showed no effect of diagnosis on asymmetries of temporal sulci when comparing 28 patients with schizophrenia and 25 normal controls. On the other hand, they ther discussion). Furthermore, the sine qua non of apoptosis is cell death, and diminished populations of cortical neurones are generally not found in schizophrenic tissue, even in elderly patients who have suffered psychotic symptoms all of their adult lives (Pakkenberg 1993; Selemon *et al.* 1995; Arnold *et al.* 1998; Harrison 1999).

These negative results leave unanswered the question of why some patients appear to deteriorate over time. Many unfortunate human circumstances and behaviours appear to get worse in some individuals during their lifetime (e.g. joblessness and homelessness), without necessarily implicating degeneration of brain tissue. While chronic unemployment may in fact be associated with dynamic changes in synaptic architecture, just as learning new behaviours and habits may involve changes in the connections made between cells, these presumably are *plastic* modifications (i.e. potentially reversible), not toxic degenerations (which usually imply irreversibility). It has become increasingly clear from studies in experimental animals that numerous environmental factors have an impact on neuronal plasticity and can be associated with regression of dendrites and spines. However, these non-degenerative adaptations are potentially reversible – part of how a brain does molecular business with its environment – in contrast to the implications of changes that reflect neurodegeneration.

In summary, while the course of schizophrenia implicates progressive processes in some individuals, the evidence that such processes reflect irreversible degeneration of neuronal elements, analogous to a neurotoxic process, are circumstantial and improbable. In terms of cognitive function and the capacity for clinical recovery, and at the level of cellular and molecular analysis, there is virtually no objective evidence for abnormal neurodegeneration in schizophrenia.

Mechanisms of delayed onset

The possibility that schizophrenia is related to an abnormality of early brain development poses yet another interesting theoretical challenge, for the clinical expression of the illness is delayed typically for about two decades after birth. If a neurological abnormality is present at birth, why is the illness itself not manifested earlier in life and what accounts for its predictable clinical expression in early adulthood? Speculation about the answers to these questions has come primarily from two perspectives:

1 the possibility of an additional pathological process occurring around the time of onset of the clinical illness; and

2 an interaction between a developmental defect and developmental programmes or events that occur in early adult life.

As the foremost proponent of the first perspective, Feinberg (1982) focused on the age of onset of schizophrenia as a clue to neurodevelopmental abnormalities that might explain the illness. He posited that schizophrenia is caused by a defect in adolescent synaptic reorganization, because 'too many, too few, or the wrong synapses are eliminated'. In effect, he argued for a second pathological process, a specific pathology of synaptic elimination not necessarily related to possible maldevelopment *in utero*. His hypothesis does not take into account the neuropathological database (most of which did not exist at the time of his original proposal), and he does not address the biological mechanisms that might be responsible for this putative disorder of synaptic elimination. In light of the extensive database that implicates early developmental abnormalities, this hypothesis requires the occurrence of a second primary pathology. It is also unclear what this pathology would be, in the sense of what would be abnormal about the pruning process. As pruning is presumed to reflect a negative state, i.e. the end result of an absence of sustaining molecular and physiological processes that are required to support a synapse, the pathology would not likely be in the pruning *per se*, but in the mechanisms of synaptic sustenance. Numerous electrophysiological and molecular factors, involving classic neurotransmitters and trophic molecules, participate in the process of synaptic survival and plasticity. Another problem with this hypothesis is that it is unclear how one could directly test it, especially because it accommodates all potential variations (i.e. too much, too little, or the 'wrong' pruning). Nevertheless, the abnormal pruning hypothesis has become very popular over the past decade as an explanation for a variety of clinical phenomena, including cortical thinning on MRI scans (Rapoport *et al.* 1999; Mathalon *et al.* 2001), psychotic psychopathology (McGlashan & Hoffman 2000) and metabolic abnormalities (Keshavan 1999).

Other mechanisms for delayed onset that emphasize a new pathology around the time of clinical onset have been proposed. These include abnormalities of myelination (Benes 1989), of neuronal sprouting (Stevens 1992) and of adverse effects of stress-related neural transmission (Bogerts 1989). Each of these involves a variation on the theme of another abnormality taking place in early adult life. In essence, they are dual pathology hypotheses, either positing that maldevelopment is not sufficient pathology, or is coincidental, or that it is only one of two relatively independent pathologies that characterize the illness.

It is possible that abnormalities of pruning or of other processes related to the formation and maintenance of neuronal connections (e.g. myelination) could be abnormal without implicating a 'second hit' hypothesis. Early maldevelopment may set the stage for secondary synaptic disorganization that has its greatest neurobiological and clinical impact in adolescence. Neuronal circuitry that is anomalous from early in development may have particularly profound implications for eventual connectivity (Schwartz & Goldman-Rakic 1990; Marin-Padilla 1997). It is conceivable therefore that primary developmental defects may lead to the creation of abnormal circuits which compete successfully for survival, while certain normal circuits either do not form or are structurally disadvantaged so that they cannot avoid elimination. This modification of the two-hit hypotheses verges on aspects of the second theoretical perspective on mechanisms of delayed onset.

The second theoretical perspective begins with evidence of abnormal brain development and applies the principle of Occam's razor to accommodate delayed emergence of the syndrome without implicating a second pathology during adolescence. This perspective involves an interaction between cortical maldevelopment *in utero* and normal developmental processes that occur much later (Weinberger 1986, 1987). This view rests on several assumptions: that the clinical implications of a developmental defect vary with the maturational state of the brain; that the neural systems disrupted by the defect in early brain development in schizophrenia are normally late maturing neural systems; and that a defect in the function of these neural systems will not be reliably apparent until their normal time of functional maturation. In other words, it is posited that certain neural systems are primed from early development to have the capacity to malfunction in a manner that accounts for the illness but, until a certain state of postnatal brain development, they either do not malfunction to a clinically significant degree, or their malfunctioning can be compensated for by other systems. The first of these assumptions has been repeatedly validated in developmental neurobiology. Indeed, a fundamental principle of the clinical impact of developmental neuropathology, as exemplified by the landmark work of Kennard (1936), is that in general brain damage is apparent early and tends to become less so over time. The young brain has a greater capacity for functional compensation than does the old brain (Kolb & Whishaw 1989), presumably because immature pathways and connections that are normally transient can be recruited and maintained in order to subserve the functions lost by the damaged circuits (Huttenlocher 1990). It is also a fundamental principle of paediatric neurology that in some cases congenital brain damage can have delayed or varying clinical effects if the neural systems involved are neurologically immature at birth (Adams & Lyons 1982).

In the case of schizophrenia, the 'Kennard principle' appears to be inverted, in that the impact of putative early damage is less apparent early and more apparent late. In this respect, the other two assumptions of this perspective are much more speculative. It is not known whether the principle of clinical effects being delayed until the affected neural systems reach functional maturity applies to those neural systems implicated in schizophrenia. More data are needed about the neural systems that develop abnormally in schizophrenia and about their normal course of functional maturation. However, this has been explored over the past decade in a series of experiments in animal models. Animal models based on a variety of neonatal and prenatal perturbations in cortical connectivity, analogous to what is implicated in schizophrenia, have been created (see Chapter 21; for review see Lipska & Weinberger 2000). These animals, especially those with disconnections involving hippocampal–prefrontal circuits, manifest abnormalities in a number of behaviours and pharmacological responses but not until they reach early adulthood. These results in animals support the biological plausibility of the notion that early developmental changes in cortical circuitry can have a delayed impact on complex behaviours and not become manifest until early adult life.

Data from studies of cortical function in patients with schizophrenia, including neuropsychological testing results (see Chapter 10) and studies of cortical physiology using functional brain imaging techniques (see Chapter 22), indicate that cortical dysfunction is a prominent characteristic of the illness and that prefrontal–temporal functional connectivity is especially affected. Even if cortical maldevelopment is widespread, the functional neural systems that appear to be particularly relevant to the clinical characteristics of schizophrenia are those involved in prefrontal–temporal cortical connectivity (Weinberger *et al.* 1992; Weinberger & Lipska 1995; Friston 1998). If the functional maturation of such connectivity is relatively late, as a number of lines of evidence in human and non-human primates suggest (Bachevalier & Mishkin 1984; Chelune & Baer 1986; Thatcher *et al.* 1987; Buchsbaum *et al.* 1992), then this would fit this delayed-onset model. The molecular events that account for the functional maturation of these systems are complex, and involve stabilization of synapses, growth and modification of dendritic arbors, myelination of intracortical pathways and other processes related to the refinement of cortical connectivity, all of which seem to plateau in early adult life.

Interestingly, while it has been popular in the psychiatric literature to emphasize synaptic pruning as a critical maturational event in adolescent brain development, progressive synaptic events, involved in dendritic and spine elaboration, are probably at least if not even more prominent during adolescence. Synaptic pruning is a relatively circumscribed process in early adulthood in the primate, involving so-called asymmetric synapses, which are presumably excitatory and glutamatergic. GABA-ergic inhibitory connections are not pruned at this time. However, despite evidence for synaptic pruning of certain excitatory inputs in cortical neurones, at least in prefrontal cortex, the overall growth of dendrites and of dendritic spines of pyramidal neurones, which are the postsynaptic targets of excitatory, glutamatergic inputs, actually increase in size and density quite remarkably in early adult life (Lambe *et al.* 2000). This dramatic increase in pyramidal dendritic arborization, combined with continuing myelination of cortical–cortical projections during adolescence, probably accounts for the fact that neuropil actually increases in thickness during this period. It is tempting to conclude from these data that the processes of pruning and of synaptic elaboration, which are clearly occurring in parallel during adolescence, dynamically shape the synaptic landscape into a more mature, efficient and environmentally adapted system. This is consistent with the notion that it is the stabilization of dynamic processes involved in postnatal cortical differentiation that signals the functional maturation of cortex (Rakic *et al.* 1986; Lidow & Rakic 1992). In addition to progressive events at the level of dendritic and spine abundance, cortical inputs from subcortical projection neuronal systems also undergo progressive changes during early adulthood. Recent evidence indicates that in the primate prefrontal cortex, dopamine inputs show a dramatic postnatal developmental elaboration culminating in early adult life (Lambe *et al.* 2000). A similar developmental trajectory is not seen with serotonergic inputs, which appear to reach their adult density level much earlier in development.

In a more psychological vein, prefrontal–temporal connectivity has been viewed as facilitating the use of past experience to guide purposeful behaviour when environmental cues are inadequate or maladaptive (Goldman-Rakic 1987; Weinberger 1993). The stresses of independent adult living might be especially likely to place a premium on this manner of neural function. If the neural systems that permit such highly evolved behaviours are developmentally defective, their malfunction might be occult until either they alone are meant to subserve such functions and other systems can no longer compensate, or until the environmental demands for such behaviour overwhelm their diminished capacity. It is important to note that this view does not predict that illness is inevitable, simply because of the existence of early pathology and of the inevitable maturation of relevant brain systems in early adulthood. Clearly, catalytic events may be critical for many individuals, including environment adversity, stress or substance abuse (Lewis & Gonzalez-Burgos 2000).

These alternative perspectives on mechanisms of delayed onset, although differing on the question of whether neurodevelopmental processes of adolescence are abnormal, share an emphasis on cortical connectivity being abnormal, as do the *in vivo* imaging, neuropsychological and postmortem data (Bunney & Bunney 2000). This raises an additional problem for the explanatory power of neurodevelopmental models of schizophrenia, in that the diagnostic symptoms of the illness, i.e. hallucinations and delusions, have not been classically imputed to cortical dysfunction (Jaskiw & Weinberger 1992). Moreover, it is unclear how this apparent inconsistency could be resolved by the added complexity of the neurodevelopmental frame of reference. Studies of animal models based on developmental cortical injury have helped illustrate at least the biological plausibility of cortical maldevelopment impacting on brain functions thought to be related to psychosis (e.g. dopamine activity). To the extent that hallucinations and delusions respond to antidopaminergic drugs, dysfunction of the dopamine system has been a target outcome measure for the animal studies. In general, this work has demonstrated that such developmental cortical abnormalities impact on the regulation of dopamine activity during adulthood, even in the non-human primate (Bertolino *et al.* 1997; Saunders *et al.* 1998), and that this occurs in a manner analogous to what has been described in patients with schizophrenia.

Further support for the model that developmental pathology can be a primary event underlying secondary emergent psychotic phenomena related to adolescent onset comes from studies of various neurological conditions involving subtle developmental abnormalities of intracortical connections. Psychosis is not uncommon in many such conditions, including developmental epilepsies, mental retardation of various types and cerebral malformations. A hemi-deletion of the long arm of chromosome 22, the so-called velocardiofacial syndrome (VCFS), has been the subject of much interest in relation to schizophrenia, because a large portion (perhaps as much as 50%) of such cases develop psychiatric disorders, especially psychosis, and because linkage studies of families segregating schizophrenia have identified a potential genetic susceptibility locus in the hemi-deletion region of chromosome 22 (Bassett & Chow 1999). VCFS cases have subtle cerebral malformations and mild mental retardation (Eliez *et al.* 2001). The interesting aspect of this syndrome in terms of the present discussion is that while the changes in the brain are present at birth, and presumably reflect early abnormal brain development, the psychotic symptoms do not emerge until adolescence or early adulthood (Shprintzen *et al.* 1992; Arnold *et al.* 2001). In fact, the same pattern exists for epilepsy and for many other congenital brain disorders associated with psychosis (Weinberger 1987). This suggests, again, that there is an interaction of the developmental changes in the brain with other processes that are critical for the full expression of the behavioural abnormalities and that these processes are expressed or reach a critical stage around early adulthood. The fact that many neurological and developmental syndromes show the same chronological pattern with respect to the onset of psychosis argues that the factors leading to the manifestation of psychosis are generic and not specific to a particular condition. If they are specific to anything, it appears to be to early adult life.

Metachromatic leucodystrophy (MLD), a rare disorder of aryl sulphatase deficiency, is another informative example of this age association and also of the potential importance of functional 'dysconnection' of cortical regions. Hyde *et al.* (1992) have demonstrated that when MLD presents between the ages of 13 and 30, it presents in the majority of cases as a schizophrenia-like illness. Moreover, the clinical presentation is probably more similar to schizophrenia than is seen in any other neurological disease. Patients have disorganized thinking, act bizarrely, have complex delusions and, when hallucinated, invariably have complex Schneiderian-type auditory hallucinations. The condition is often misdiagnosed as schizophrenia, sometimes for years, before neurological symptoms appear. Interestingly, MLD is a pure connectivity disorder in that the neuropathological changes involve white matter. In its early neuropathological stages, when it is most likely to present with psychosis, the changes are especially prominent in subprefrontal white matter. This suggests that a neural dysfunction with a high valence for producing psychotic symptoms is failure of some aspects of prefrontal connectivity, analogous functionally to what has been implicated in schizophrenia.

In the case of MLD, however, this functional 'dysconnection' does not appear to be enough. When MLD presents outside of this critical age range, it almost never presents with psychosis, even though the location of the neuropathology is not age dependent. In other words, the involvement of critical neural systems is not by itself sufficient for the expression of psychosis. An age-related factor that appears to be independent of the illness is also required. Again, because this age association is seen in other diseases and thus transcends specific illness boundaries, it is probably a function of normal postnatal brain maturation.

The MLD example, like the VCFS example, provides another potential insight into how cortical maldevelopment might be a crucial factor in schizophrenia. The distribution of white matter pathology in MLD is not unique to this illness. For example, a similar distribution of changes was produced by prefrontal leucotomies which did not worsen psychosis, and is seen in some other leucoencephalopathies, such as multiple sclerosis (MS). However, MS plaques and leucotomy lesions spare intracortical fibres which are affected in MLD, suggesting that intracortical 'dysconnection' is closer to the source of psychosis. It also suggests, particularly with reference to leucotomy, that 'dysconnection' is more problematic than no connection. The developmental neuropathology described in association with schizophrenia is much more consistent with the possibility of dysconnection than of no connection. Further support for this possibility comes from studies of epilepsy and psychosis in which congenital malformations of the mesial temporal lobe are more likely to be associated with psychosis than are sclerotic lesions (Roberts *et al.* 1990). The former are also more consistent with the possibility of dysconnection than are the latter. Moreover, temporal lobectomy does not cure psychosis associated with epilepsy, further suggesting that the source of the psychosis is represented as a distributed abnormality.

Candidate maturational processes and clinical onset

Finally, it is of interest to speculate on the critical maturational processes that might interact with the subtle brain developmental abnormalities implicated in schizophrenia. The foregoing discussion militates towards processes involving synaptic plasticity during development and during postnatal life. While schizophrenia may involve genetic variations that impact on the biology of synaptic plasticity (Weinberger 1999), and developmental adversity may disrupt the formation of normal cortical circuitry, the convergence of these risk factors on the processes that hone intracortical connectivity during early adulthood would seem to be the final common pathway for the emergence of the syndrome. We believe that both the genetic risk factors, which may themselves impact on brain development, and environmental adversity during brain development bias the normal molecular processes of postnatal synaptic plasticity towards abnormal connectivity during the early adult years. This biasing effect could operate purely at a cellular and molecular level, i.e. connections that are anomalous do not process signals normally and do not form normal secondary and tertiary connectivities. On the other hand, this biasing effect could also operate at the level of neuronal experience, i.e. anomalous circuits experience (perceive and process) environmental stimuli abnormally, and develop and maintain connections that are normal in terms of their cellular and molecular machinery, but are based on abnormal perception and processing of environmental events. These biasing effects, we surmise, are the proximate causes of the various emergent behavioural and biological phenomena that ultimately result in the diagnosis of schizophrenia (Weinberger *et al.* 2001).

The recent demonstration of a genetic mechanism of risk for schizophrenia is consistent with and extends much of this speculation. Egan *et al.* (2001a) recently showed that a functional polymorphism in the gene for *COMT* slightly increases risk for schizophrenia because the high-risk allele is associated with poorer prefrontal cortical function. This allele appears to lead to more rapid inactivation of prefrontal dopamine and to less efficient prefrontal dopamine signalling and prefrontal cortical function (for detailed discussion see Weinberger *et al.* 2001). The role of prefrontal function in the expression of the schizophrenic syndrome is presumed to be a biological mechanism through which this genetic effect operates. However, because prefrontal function also impacts adversely on subcortical dopamine regulation, which is implicated in psychosis, the high-risk allele may also act through this process. Consistent with this possibility, Akil *et al.* (2001) showed that the high-risk *COMT* allele also is associated with upregulation of tyrosine hydroxylase gene expression in brainstem dopamine neurones in brain tissue of normal subjects. These findings indicate that *COMT* genotype is one of the inherited factors controlling dopamine neuronal activity and prefrontal cortical function. Thus, an allele of this gene that impacts adversely on both of these processes increases risk for the expression of schizophrenia at the levels of both prefrontal cortical dysfunction and subcortical dopamine dysregulation. The fact that dopaminergic innervation of the prefrontal cortex reaches a peak in early adulthood (Lambe *et al.* 2000) and that, as shown in the animal models, prefrontal cortical regulation of mesencephalic dopaminergic function also emerges in early adulthood, would suggest that the impact of this genetic factor on these biological mechanisms related to schizophrenia is likely to be clearest on the phenotype of schizophrenia at this time of life. It might also be hypothesized that if the effects of *COMT* on prefrontal dopamine signalling and subcortical dopamine regulation interact with the cortical elaboration of the dopamine system in early adulthood, then the high-risk *COMT* allele would predict an earlier age of onset. There is preliminary evidence in support of this prediction (Karayiorgou *et al.* 1998).

Conclusions

The neurodevelopmental hypothesis of schizophrenia offers a framework for investigation that prompts us to focus on early antecedents and, in particular, on biological events during pregnancy and during early adolescence. It has obvious public health implications in that prevention should start early and include interventions at multiple ages. A vast body of research data supports this contention, but evidence of a 'smoking gun' is lacking and evidence of specificity for schizophrenia is limited.

The extensive data concerning premorbid developmental abnormalities and the remarkable lack of tissue evidence of neuronal loss or of neuronal degeneration allow us to dismiss a purely degenerative hypothesis of schizophrenia. While much evidence points to the last months of gestation as a critical period for vulnerability to potential causes of schizophrenia, there is no clear evidence against a cause operating across infancy and adolescence and possibly through the initial phases of the illness. On the other hand, the evidence in favour of such a postnatal pathological process is meagre. The most parsimonious reduction of the available evidence argues that early developmental abnormalities subtly alter intracortical connectivity which biases postnatal development towards further abnormalities of synaptic maturation and organization in critical cortical circuits and in their subcortical projections, which together increase the risk that schizophrenia will be manifest in early adult life.

While not fully demonstrated, the neurodevelopmental hypothesis remains the most heuristic conceptual framework, with the broadest health policy implications and the most evidence in its favour. Moreover, the neurodevelomental hypothesis provides a theoretical structure that has made it possible to bridge between molecular biology and genetics, systems neuroscience, and clinical psychology. One of the weaknesses of the hypothesis, however, is that it is difficult to disprove. Sparing convincing evidence of a degenerative process or of some other mechanism of pathogenesis that excludes brain development as a factor, the neurodevelopmental hypothesis cannot be easily dismissed. In order to translate the hypothesis into a definitive understanding of schizophrenia pathogenesis, it will be necessary to elaborate the genetic and molecular mechanisms governing brain growth and connectivity and to evaluate the evolution of these processes in individuals who manifest this illness.

References

Adams, R.D. & Lyons, G. (1982) *Neurology of Hereditary Metabolic Diseases of Children*. McGraw-Hill, New York.

Akbarian, S., Vinuela, A., Kim, J.J. *et al.* (1993) Distorted distribution of nicotinamide-adenine dinucleotide phosphate diaphorase neurons in temporal-lobe of schizophrenics implies anomalous cortical development. *Archives of General Psychiatry* **50**, 178–187.

Akbarian, S., Kim, J.J., Potkin, S.G. *et al.* (1996) Maldistribution of interstitial neurons in prefrontal white matter of the brains of schizophrenic patients. *Archives of General Psychiatry* **53**, 425–436.

Akil, M. & Lewis, D.A. (1997) Cytoarchitecture of the entorhinal cortex in schizophrenia. *American Journal of Psychiatry* **154**, 1010–1012.

Akil, M. Rothmond, D.A., Kolachana, B.S. *et al.* (2001) Effect of COMT genotype on tyrosine hydroxylase gene expression in the human mesencephalon. *Society for Neuroscience Abstracts*. http://sfn.scholarone.com/itin2001/

Allen, N.B., Lewinsohn, P.M. & Seeky, J.R. (1998) Prenatal and perinatal influences on risk for psychopathology in childhood and adolescence. *Developmental Psychopathology* **10**, 513–529.

Anderson, S.A., Volk, D.W. & Lewis, D.A. (1996) Increased density of microtubule associated protein 2- immunoreactive neurons in the prefrontal white matter of schizophrenic subjects. *Schizophrenia Research* **19**, 111–119.

Arnold, P.D., Siegel-Bartelt, J., Cytrynbaum, C., Teshima, I. & Schachar, R. (2001) Velocardiofacial syndrome: implications of microdeletion 22q11 for schizophrenia and mood disorders. *American Journal of Medical Genetics* **105**, 354–362.

Arnold, S.E., Trojanowski, J.Q. , Gur, R.E. *et al.* (1998) Absence of neurodegeneration and neural injury in the cerebral cortex in a sample of elderly patients with schizophrenia. *Archives of General Psychiatry* **55**, 225–232.

Aylward, E., Walker, E. & Bettes, B. (1984) Intelligence in schizophrenia: meta-analysis of the research. *Schizophrenia Bulletin* **10**, 430–459.

Baare, W.F., van Oel, C.J., Hulshoff Pol. H.E. *et al.* (2001) Volumes of brain structures in twins discordant for schizophrenia. *Archives of General Psychiatry* **58**, 33–40.

Bachevalier, J. & Mishkin, M. (1984) An early and a late developing system for learning and retention in infant monkeys. *Behavioral Neuroscience* **98**, 770–778.

Bain, M., Juszczak, E., McInneny, K. & Kendell, R.E. (2000) Obstetric complications and affective psychoses: two case–control studies based on structured obstetric records. *British Journal of Psychiatry* **176**, 523–526.

Barbeau, D., Liang, J.J., Robitaille, Y. Quirion, R. & Srivastava, L.K. (1995) Decreased expression of the embryonic form of the neural cell-adhesion molecule in schizophrenic brains. *Proceedings of the National Academy of Sciences of the USA* **92**, 2785–2789.

Bartley, A.J., Jones, D.W., Torrey, E.F. Zigun, J.R. & Weinberger, D.R. (1993) Sylvian fissure asymmetries in monozygotic twins: a test of laterality in schizophrenia. *Biological Psychiatry* **34**, 853–863.

Bassett, A.S. & Chow, E.W. (1999) 22q11 Deletion syndrome: a genetic subtype of schizophrenia. *Biological Psychiatry* **46**, 882–891.

Bender, L. (1947) Childhood schizophrenia: clinical study of 100 schizophrenic children. *American Journal of Orthopsychiatry* **17**, 40–56.

Benes, F.M. (1989) Myelination of cortical–hippocampal relays during late adolescence. *Schizophrenia Bulletin* **15**, 585–593.

Bennedsen, B.E., Mortensen, P.B., Olesen, A.V. Henriksen, T.B. & Frydenberg, M. (2001) Obstetric complications in women with schizophrenia. *Schizophrenia Research* **47**, 167–175.

Bernstein, H.G., Krell, D., Baumann, B. *et al.* (1998) Morphometric studies of the entorhinal cortex in neuropsychiatric patients and controls: clusters of heterotopically displaced lamina II neurons are not indicative of schizophrenia. *Schizophrenia Research* **33**, 125–132.

Bertolino, A., Saunders, R.C., Mattay, V.S. *et al.* (1997) Altered development of prefrontal neurons in rhesus monkeys with neonatal mesial temporo-limbic lesions: a proton magnetic resonance spectroscopic imaging study. *Cerebral Cortex* **7**, 740–748.

Bleuler, M. (1941) *Krankheitsverlauf, Persoenlichkeit und Verwandtschaft Schizophrener und Ihre Gegenseitigen Beziehungen*. Georg Thieme, Leipzig.

Bloom, F.E. (1993) Advancing a neurodevelopmental origin for schizophrenia. *Archives of General Psychiatry* **50**, 224–227.

Bogerts, B. (1989) The role of limbic and paralimbic pathology in the etiology of schizophrenia. *Psychiatry Research* **29**, 255–256.

Bolton, P.F., Murphy, M., Macdonald, H. *et al.* (1997) Obstetric complications in autism: consequences or causes of the condition? *Journal of the American Academy of Child and Adolescent Psychiatry* **36**, 272–281.

Bradbury, T.N. & Miller, G.A. (1985) Season of birth in schizophrenia: a review of evidence, methodology, and etiology. *Psychological Bulletin* **98**, 569–594.

Brown, A.S., Schaefer, C.A., Wyatt, R.J. *et al.* (2000) Maternal exposure to respiratory infections and adult schizophrenia spectrum disorders: a prospective birth cohort study. *Schizophrenia Bulletin* **26**, 287–295.

Brown, A.S., Cohen, P., Harkavy-Friedman, J., *et al.* (2001) Prenatal rubella, premorbid abnormalities, and adult schizophrenia. *Biological Psychiatry* **49**, 473–486.

Buchsbaum, M.S., Mansour, C.S. Teng, D.G. *et al.* (1992) Adolescent developmental change in topography of EEG amplitude. *Schizophrenia Research* **7**, 101–107.

Buka, S.L., Tsuang, M.T. & Lipsitt, L.P. (1993) Pregnancy/delivery complications and psychiatric diagnosis: a prospective study. *Archives of General Psychiatry* **50**, 151–156.

Bullmore, E., Brammer, M., Harvey, I. Murray, R. & Ron, M. (1995) Cerebral hemispheric asym-metry revisited: effects of handedness, gender and schizophrenia measured by radius of gyration in magnetic resonance images. *Psychological Medicine* **25**, 349–363.

Bullmore, E.T., Woodruff, P.W.R., Wright, I.C. *et al.* (1998) Does dysplasia cause anatomical dysconnectivity in schizophrenia?. *Schizophrenia Research* **30**, 127–135.

Bunney, W.E. & Bunney, B.G. (2000) Evidence for a compromised dorsolateral prefrontal cortical parallel circuit in schizophrenia. *Brain Research Brain Research Review* **31**, 138–146.

Byrne, M., Browne, R., Mulryan, N. *et al.* (2000) Labour and delivery complications and schizophrenia: case–control study using contemporaneous labour ward records. *British Journal of Psychiatry* **176**, 531–536.

Cannon, M., Cotter, D., Coffey, V.P. *et al.* (1996) Prenatal exposure to the 1957 influenza epidemic and adult schizophrenia: a follow-up study. *British Journal of Psychiatry* **168**, 368–371.

Cannon, T.D., Mednick, S.A. & Parnas, J. (1990) Antecedents of predomi-nantly negative-symptom and predominantly positive-symptom schizophrenia in a high-risk population. *Archives of General Psychiatry* **47**, 622–632.

Cannon, T.D., Mednick, S.A., Parnas, J. *et al.* (1993) Developmental brain abnormalities in the offspring of schizophrenic mothers. I. Contributions of genetic and perinatal factors. *Archives of General Psychiatry* **50**, 551–564.

Cannon, T.D., van Erp, T.G.M., Huttumen, M. *et al.* (1998) Regional gray matter, white matter, and cerebrospinal fluid distributions in schizophrenic patients, their siblings, and controls. *Archives of General Psychiatry* **55**, 1084–1091.

Cannon, T.D., Rosso, I.M., Hollister, J.M. *et al.* (2000) A prospective cohort study of genetic and perinatal influences in the etiology of schizophrenia. *Schizophrenia Bulletin* **26**, 351–366.

Cantor-Graae, E., McNeil, T.F., Sjostrman, K. Nordstrom, L.G. & Rosenlund, T. (1994) Obstetric complications and their relationship to other etiological risk factors in schizophrenia: case–control study. *Journal of Nervous and Mental Disease* **182**, 645–650.

Casanova, M.F., Goldberg, T.E. Suddath, R.L. *et al.* (1990) Quantitative shape analysis of the temporal and prefrontal lobes of schizophrenic patients: a magnetic resonance image study. *Journal of Neuropsychiatry and Clinical Neuroscience* **2**, 363–372.

Chelune, G.J. & Baer, R.A. (1986) Developmental norms for the Wisconsin Card Sorting test. *Journal of Clinical and Experimental Neuropsychology* **8**, 219–228.

Chi, J.G., Dooling, E.C. & Gilles, F.H. (1977) Left-right asymmetries of the temporal speech areas of the human fetus. *Archives of Neurology* **34**, 346–348.

Cotter, D., Takei, N., Farrell, M. *et al.* (1995) Does prenatal exposure to influenza in mice induce pyramidal cell disarray in the dorsal hippocampus. *Schizophrenia Rese arch* **16**, 233–241.

Cotter, D., Larkin, C., Waddington, J.L. & O'Callaghan, E. (1996) Season of birth in schizophrenia: clue or cul-de-sac? *The Neurodevelopmental Basis of Schizophrenia* (eds J.L. Waddington & P.F. Buckley), pp. 17–30. R.G. Landes, Georgetown, TX.

Craig, T.J., Bromet, E.J., Fennig, S. *et al.* (2000) Is there an association between duration of untreated psychosis and 24-month clinical outcome in a first-admission series?. *American Journal of Psychiatry* **157**, 60–66.

Crow, T.J., Ball, J., Bloom, S. R. *et al.* (1989a) Schizophrenia as an anomaly of development of cerebral asymmetry: a postmortem study and a proposal concerning the genetic basis of the disease. *Archives of General Psychiatry* **46**, 1145–1150.

Crow, T.J., Colter, N., Frith, C.D., Johnstone, E.C. & Owens, D.G. (1989b) Developmental arrest of cerebral asymmetries in early onset schizophrenia. *Psychiatry Research* **29**, 247–253.

Crow, T.J., Done, D.J. & Johnstone, E.C. (1992) Schizophrenia is not due to maternal influenza in the second (or other) trimester of pregnancy. *Schizophrenia Research* **6**, 99–99.

Crow, T.J., Done, D.J. & Sacker, A. (1996) Cerebral lateralization is delayed in children who later develop schizophrenia. *Schizophrenia Research* **22**, 181–185.

Csernansky, J.G., Joshi, S., Wang, L. *et al.* (1998) Hippocampal morphometry in schizophrenia by high dimensional brain mapping. *Proceedings of the National Academy of Sciences of the USA* **95**, 11406–11411.

Dalman, C., Allebeck, P., Cullberg, J. Grunnewald, C. & Koster, M. (1999) Obstetric complications and the risk of schizophrenia: a longitudinal study of a national birth cohort. *Archives of General Psychiatry* **56**, 234–240.

Davis, J.O. & Bracha, H.S. (1996) Prenatal growth markers in schizophrenia: a monozygotic co-twin control study. *American Journal of Psychiatry* **153**, 1166–1172.

Davis, K.L., Buchsbaum, M.S., Shihebuddin, L. *et al.* (1998) Ventricular enlargement in poor-outcome schizophrenia. *Biological Psychiatry* **43**, 783–793.

DeCarli, C., Kay, J.A., Horowitz, B. & Rapoport, S.I. (1990) Critical analysis of the use of computerized assisted axial tomography to study human brain in aging and dementia of the Alzheimer type. *Neurology* **40**, 872–883.

DeLisi, L. (1997) Is schizophrenia a lifetime disorder of brain plasticity, growth, and aging? *Schizophrenia Research* **23**, 119–129.

DeLisi, L.E., Stritzke, P.H., Holan, V. *et al.* (1991) Brain morphological-changes in first episode cases of schizophrenia: are they progressive. *Schizophrenia Research* **5**, 206–208.

DeLisi, L., Hoff, A.L., Kushner, M., Calev, A. & Stritzke, P. (1992) Left ventricular enlargement associated with diagnostic outcome of schizophreniform disorder. *Biological Psychiatry* **32**, 199–201.

DeLisi, L.E., Tew, W., Xie, S.H. *et al.* (1995) A prospective follow-up-study of brain morphology and cognition in first-episode schizophrenic-patients: preliminary findings. *Biological Psychiatry* **38**, 349–360.

DeLisi, L.E., Sakuma, M., Tew, W. *et al.* (1997) Schizophrenia as a chronic active brain process. a study of progressive brain structural change subsequent to the onset of schizophrenia. *Psychiatry Research:Neuroimaging* **74**, 129–140.

DeLisi, L.E., Sakuma, M., Ge, S. & Kushner, M. (1998) Association of brain structural change with the heterogeneous course of schizophrenia from early childhood through 5 years subsequent to a first hospitalization. *Psychiatry Research: Neuroimaging* **84**, 75–88.

Done, D.J., Johnstone, E.C., Frith, C.D. *et al.* (1991) Complications of pregnancy and delivery in relation to psychosis in adult life: data from the British Perinatal-Mortality Survey sample. *British Medical Journal* **302**, 1576–1580.

Eagles, J.M., Hunter, D. & Geddes, J.R. (1995) Gender-specific changes since 1900 in the season-of-birth effect in schizophrenia. *British Journal of Psychiatry* **167**, 469–472.

Egan, M.F., Goldberg, T.E., Kolachana, B.S. *et al.* (2001a) Effect of

COMT Val108/158 Met genotype on frontal lobe function and risk for schizophrenia. *Proceedings of the National Academy of Sciences of the USA* **98**, 6917–6922.

Egan, M.F., Goldberg, T.E., Gscheidle, T. *et al.* (2001b) Relative risk for cognitive impairments in siblings of patients with schizophrenia. *Biological Psychiatry* **50**, 98–107.

Eliez, S., Antonarakis, S.E. *et al.* (2001) Parental origin of the deletion 22q11.2 and brain development in velocardiofacial syndrome: a preliminary study. *Archives of General Psychiatry* **58**, 64–68.

Elvevåg, B. & Weinberger, D.R. (1997) Commentary: schizophrenia and autism considered as the products of an agnosic right shift gene. *Cognitive Neuropsychiatry* **2**, 221–225.

Eschenbach, D.A. (1997) Amniotic fluid infection and cerebral palsy: focus on the fetus. *Journal of the American Medical Association* **278**, 247–248.

Fearon, P., Lane, A., Airie, M. *et al.* (2001) Is reduced dermatoglyphic a-b ridge count a reliable marker of developmental impairment in schizophrenia?. *Schizophrenia Research* **50**, 151–157.

Feinberg, I. (1982) Schizophrenia: caused by a fault in programmed synaptic elimination during adolescence? *Journal of Psychiatric Research* **17**, 319–334.

Fish, B. & Hagin, R. (1972) Visual-motor disorders in infants at risk for schizophrenia. *Archives of General Psychiatry* **27**, 594–598.

Fix, A., Horn, J.W., Wightman, K.A. *et al.* (1993) Neuronal vacuolization and necrosis induced by the non-competitive *N*-methyl-D-aspartate (NMDA) antagonist MK(+) 801 (dizocilpine maleate): a light and electron microscopic evaluation of the rat retrosplenial cortex. *Experimental Neurology* **123**, 204–215.

Frank, D.A., Augustyn, M., Knight, W.G., Pell, T. & Zuckerman, B. (2001) Growth, development, and behavior in early childhood following prenatal cocaine exposure: a systematic review. *Journal of the American Medical Association* **285**, 1613–1625.

Friston, K.J. (1998) The disconnection hypothesis. *Schizophrenia Research* **30**, 115–125.

Friston, K.J. & Frith, C.D. (1995) Schizophrenia: a disconnection syndrome? *Clinical Neuroscience* **3**, 89–97.

Garver, D., Nair, T.R., Chrisensen, J.D., Holcomb, J.A. & Kingsbury, S.L. (2000) Brain and ventricular instability during psychotic episodes of the schizophrenias. *Schizophrenia Research* **44**, 11–23.

Geddes, J.R., Verdoux, H., Takei, N. *et al.* (1999) Schizophrenia and complications of pregnancy and labor: an individual patient data meta-analysis. *Schizophrenia Bulletin* **25**, 413–423.

Goldman-Rakic, P.S. (1987) Development of cortical circuitry and cognitive function. *Child and Development* **58**, 601–622.

Green, M.F., Satz, P. & Christenson, C. (1994) Minor physical anomalies in schizophrenia patients, bipolar patients, and their siblings. *Schizophrenia Bulletin* **20**, 433–440.

Gunthergenta, F., Bovet, P. & Hohlfeld, P. (1994) Obstetric complications and schizophrenia: a case–control study. *British Journal of Psychiatry* **164**, 165–170.

Gur, R.E. & Chin, S. (1999) Laterality in functional brain imaging studies of schizophrenia. *Schizophrenia Bulletin* **25**, 141–156.

Gur, R.E., Cowell, P., Turetsky, B.I. *et al.* (1998) A follow-up magnetic resonance imaging study of schizophrenia: relationship of neuroanatomical changes to clinical and neurobehavioral measures. *Archives of General Psychiatry* **55**, 145–152.

Guth, C., Jones, P. & Murray, R. (1993) Familial psychiatric illness and obstetric complications in early-onset affective-disorder: a case–control study. *British Journal of Psychiatry* **163**, 492–498.

Hafner, H., Haas, S., Pfeifer-Kurda M, Eichhorn, S. & Michitsuji, S. (1987) Abnormal seasonality of schizophrenic births: a specific finding? *European Archives of Psychiatry Neurological Science* **236**, 333–342.

Harding, C.M., Zubin, J. & Strauss, J.S. (1992) Chronicity in schizophrenia: revisited. *British Journal of Psychiatry* **161**, 27–37.

Harrison, P. (1999) The neuropathology of schizophrenia: a critical review of the data and their interpretation. *Brain* **122**, 593–624.

Heaton, R.K., Gladsjo, J.A., Palmer, B.W. *et al.* (2001) Stability and course of neuropsychological deficits in schizophrenia. *Archives of General Psychiatry* **58**, 24–32.

Heinsen, H., Gossmann, E., Rub, U. *et al.* (1996) Variability in the human entorhinal region may confound neuropsychiatric diagnoses. *Acta Anatomica* **157**, 226–237.

Ho, B.C., Andreasen, N.C., Flaum, M., Nopoulos P. & Miller, D. (2000) Untreated initial psychosis: its relation to quality of life and symptom remission in first-episode schizophrenia. *American Journal of Psychiatry* **157**, 808–815.

Hoff, A.L., Sakuma, M., Razi, K. *et al.* (2000) Lack of association between duration of untreated illness and severity of cognitive and structural brain deficits at the first episode of schizophrenia. *American Journal of Psychiatry* **157**, 1824–1828.

Hollister, J.M., Laing, P. & Mednick, S.A. (1996) Rhesus incompatibility as a risk factor for schizophrenia in male adults. *Archives of General Psychiatry* **53**, 19–24.

Honer, W.G., Bassett, A.S., Squires-Wheeler, E. *et al.* (1995) The temporal lobes, reversed asymmetry and the genetics of schizophrenia. *Neuroreport* **7**, 221–224.

Hultman, C.M., Ohman, A., Cnattingius, S. Wieselgren, I.M. & Lindstrom, L.H. (1997) Prenatal and neonatal risk factors for schizophrenia. *British Journal of Psychiatry* **170**, 128–133.

Hultman, C.M., Sparen, P., Takei, N., Murray, R.M. & Cnattingius, S. (1999) Prenatal and perinatal risk factors for schizophrenia, affective psychosis, and reactive psychosis of early onset: case–control study. *British Medical Journal* **318**, 421–426.

Huttenlocher, P.R. (1990) Morphometric study of human cerebral cortex development. *Neuropsychologia* **28**, 517–527.

Hyde, T.M., Ziegler, J.C. & Weinberger, D.P. (1992) Psychiatric disturbances in metachromatic leukodystrophy: insights into the neurobiology of psychosis [see comments]. *Archives of Neurology* **49**, 401–406.

Hyde, T.M., Bachus, S.E., Levitt, P. *et al.* (1997) Reduction in hippocampal limbic system associated protein (LAMP) mRNA in schizophrenia. Society for Neuroscience Abstracts, 2200.

Illowsky, B.P., Juliano, D.M., Bigelow, L.B. & Weinberger, D.R. (1988) Stability of CT scan findings in schizophrenia: results of an 8 year follow-up study. *Journal of Neurology, Neurosurgery and Psychiatry* **51**, 209–213.

Impagnatiello, F., Guidotti, A.R., Pesold, C. *et al.* (1998) A decrease of reelin expression as a putative vulnerability factor in schizophrenia. *Proceedings of the National Academy of Sciences of the USA* **95**, 15718–15723.

Jacobsen, L., Giedd, J.N., Castellanos, F.X. *et al.* (1998) Progressive reduction of temporal lobe structures in childhood-onset schizophrenia. *American Journal of Psychiatry* **155**, 678–685.

Jakob, H. & Beckmann, H. (1986) Prenatal developmental disturbances in the limbic allocortex in schizophrenics. *Journal of Neural Transmission* **65**, 303–326.

Jaskiw, G.E. & Weinberger, D.R. (1992) Ibotenic acid lesions of medial prefrontal cortex augment swim-stress-induced locomotion. *Pharmacological Biochemistry and Behavior* **41**, 607–609.

Jaskiw, G.E., Juliano, D.M., Goldberg, T.E. *et al.* (1994) Cerebral ventricular enlargement in schizophreniform disorder does not progress: a 7 year follow-up study. *Schizophrenia Research* **14**, 23–28.

Johnstone, E.C., Crow, T.J., Frith, C.D., Husband, J. & Kreel L. (1976)

Cerebral ventricular size and cognitive impairment in chronic schizophrenia. *Lancet* **2**, 924–926.

Jones, P.B., Rantakallio, P., Hartikainen, A.L., Isohanni, M. & Sipila, P. (1998) Schizophrenia as a long-term outcome of pregnancy, delivery, and perinatal complications: a 28-year follow-up of the 1966 North Finland general population birth cohort. *American Journal of Psychiatry* **155**, 355–364.

Karayiorgou, M., Gogos, J.A., Galke, B.L. *et al.* (1998) Identification of sequence variants and analysis of the role of the catechol-O-methyltransferase gene in schizophrenia susceptibility. *Biological Psychiatry* **43**, 425–431.

Kendell, R.E. & Adams, W. (1991) Unexplained fluctuations in the risk for schizophrenia by month and year of birth. *British Journal of Psychiatry* **158**, 758–763.

Kendell, R.E. & Kemp, I.W. (1987) Winter-born vs. summer-born schizophrenics. *British Journal of Psychiatry* **151**, 499–505.

Kendell, R.E. & Kemp, I.W. (1989) Maternal influenza in the etiology of schizophrenia. *Archives of General Psychiatry* **46**, 878–882.

Kendell, R.E., Juszczak, E. & Cole, S.K. (1996) Obstetric complications and schizophrenia: a case–control study based on standardised obstetric records. *British Journal of Psychiatry* **168**, 556–561.

Kendell, R.E., McInneny, K., Juszczak, E. & Bain, M. (2000) Obstetric complications and schizophrenia: two case–control studies based on structured obstetric records. *British Journal of Psychiatry* **176**, 516–522.

Kennard, M.A. (1936) Age and other factors in motor recovery from precentral lesions in monkeys. *American Journal of Physiology* **115**, 138–146.

Keshavan, M.S. (1999) Development, disease and degeneration in schizophrenia: a unitary pathophysiological model. *Journal of Psychiatric Research* **33**, 513–521.

Keshavan, M.S. & Hogarty, G.E. (1999) Brain maturational processes and delayed onset in schizophrenia. *Developmental Psychopathology* **11**, 525–543.

Kikinis, R., Shenton, M.E., Gerig, G. *et al.* (1994) Temporal-lobe sulcogyral pattern anomalies in schizophrenia: an *in vivo* MR 3-dimensional surface rendering study. *Neuroscience Letters* **182**, 7–12.

Kinney, D.K., Yurgelun-Todd, D.A., Tohen, M. & Tramer, S. (1998) Pre- and perinatal complications and risk for bipolar disorder: a retrospective study. *Journal of Affective Disorders* **50**, 117–124.

Kolb, B. & Whishaw, I.Q. (1989) Plasticity in the neocortex: mechanisms underlying recovery from early brain damage. *Progress in Neurobiology* **32**, 235–276.

Kraepelin, E. (1919) *Dementia Praecox and Paraphrenia*. Livingstone, Edinburgh.

Krimer, L.S., Hyde, T.M., Herman, M.M. & Saunders, R.C. (1997) The entorhinal cortex: an examination of cyto- and myeloarchitectonic organization in humans. *Cerebral Cortex* **7**, 722–731.

Kulynych, J.J., Foundas, A.L. & Weinberger, D.R. (1995a) Abnormal cortical gyrification in schizophrenia. *Schizophrenia Research* **15**, 89–89.

Kulynych, J.J., Vladar, K., Fantie, B.D., Jones, D.W. & Weinberger, D.R. (1995b) Normal asymmetry of the planum temporale in patients with schizophrenia: 3-dimensional cortical morphometry with MRI. *British Journal of Psychiatry* **166**, 742–749.

Kulynych, J.J., Luevano, L.F., Jones, D.W. & Weinberger, D.R. (1997) Cortical abnormality in schizophrenia: an *in vivo* application of the gyrification index. *Biological Psychiatry* **41**, 995–999.

Kunugi, H., Nanko, S., Takei, N. *et al.* (1995) Schizophrenia following *in utero* exposure to the 1957 influenza epidemics in Japan. *American Journal of Psychiatry* **152**, 450–452.

Kunugi, H., Takei, N., Murray, R.M., Saito, K. & Nanko, S. (1996) Small head circumference at birth in schizophrenia. *Schizophrenia Research* **20**, 165–170.

Kunugi, H., Nanko, S., Hayashi, N. *et al.* (1997) Season of birth of schizophrenics in a recent Japanese sample. *Psychiatry Clinical Neuroscience* **51**, 213–216.

Kwon, J.S., McCarley, R.W., Hirayasu, Y. *et al.* (1999) Left planum temporale volume reduction in schizophrenia. *Archives of General Psychiatry* **56**, 142–148.

Laakso, M.P., Lehtovirta, M. Partanen, K. Riekkinen, P.J. & Soininen, H. (2000) Hippocampus in Alzheimer's disease: a 3-year follow-up MRI study. *Biological Psychiatry* **47**, 557–561.

Laakso, M.P., Tiihonen, J. Syvalahti, E. *et al.* (2001) A morphometric MRI study of the hippocampus in first episode, neuroleptic-naive schizophrenia. *Schizophrenia Research* **50**, 3–7.

Lambe, E.K., Krimer, L.S. & Goldman-Rakic, P.S. (2000) Differential postnatal development of catecholamine and serotonin inputs to identified neurons in prefrontal cortex of rhesus monkey. *Journal of Neuroscience* **20**, 8780–8787.

Lane, A., Larkin, C., Waddington, J.L. & O'Callaghan, E. (1996) Dysmorphic features and schizophrenia. In: *The Neurodevelopmental Basis of Schizophrenia* (eds J.L. Waddington & P.F. Buckley), pp. 79–94. R.G. Landes, Georgetown, TX.

Lane, A., Kinsella, A., Murphy, P. *et al.* (1997) The anthropometric assessment of dysmorphic features in schizophrenia as an index of its developmental origins. *Psychological Medicine* **27**, 1155–1164.

Lane, E.A. & Albee, G.W. (1970) The birth weight of children born to schizophrenic women. *Journal of Psychology* **74**, 157–160.

Lewis, D.A. & Gonzalez-Burgos, G. (2000) Intrinsic excitatory connections in the prefrontal cortex and the pathophysiology of schizophrenia. *Brain Research Bulletin* **52**, 309–317.

Lewis, D.A. & Lieberman, J.A. (2000) Catching up on schizophrenia: natural history and neurobiology. *Neuron* **28**, 325–334.

Lewis, S.W. & Murray, R.M. (1987) Obstetric complications, neurodevelopmental deviance, and risk of schizophrenia. *Journal of Psychiatric Research* **21**, 413–421.

Lewis, S.W., Owen, M.J. & Murray, R.M. (1989) Obstetric complications and schizophrenia: methodology and mechanisms. *Schizophrenia: Scientific Progress* (eds S.C. Schultz & C.A. Tamminga), pp. 56–68. Oxford University Press, New York.

Lidow, M.S. & Rakic, P. (1992) Scheduling of monoaminergic neurotransmitter receptor expression in the primate neocortex during postnatal development. *Cerebral Cortex* **2**, 401–416.

Lieberman, J. (1999) Is schizophrenia a neurodegenerative disorder? A clinical and neurobiological perspective. *Biological Psychiatry* **46**, 729–739.

Lieberman, J., Chakos M.A., Wu, H. *et al.* (2001) Longitudinal study of brain morphology in first episode schizophrenia. *Biological Psychiatry* **49**, 487–499.

Lieberman, J.A., Jody, D., Alvir, J.M.J. *et al.* (1993) Brain morphology, dopamine, and eye-tracking abnormalities in first-episode schizophrenia: prevalence and clinical correlates. *Archives of General Psychiatry* **50**, 357–368.

Lieberman, J.A., Koreen, A.R., Chakos, M. *et al.* (1996) Factors influencing treatment response and outcome of first-episode schizophrenia: implications for understanding the pathophysiology of schizophrenia. *Journal of Clinical Psychiatry* **57** (Suppl. 9), 5–9.

Lipska, B.K. & Weinberger, D.R. (2000) To model a psychiatric disorder in animals: schizophrenia as a reality test. *Neuropsychopharmacology* **23**, 223–239.

Luchins, D.J., Weinberger, D.R. & Wyatt, R.J. (1979) Schizophrenia: evidence of a subgroup with reversed cerebral asymmetry. *Archives of General Psychiatry* **36**, 1309–1311.

McGlashan, T.H. & Hoffman, R.E. (2000) Schizophrenia as a disorder of developmentally reduced synaptic connectivity. *Archives of General Psychiatry* **57**, 637–648.

McGrath, J.J., Pemberton, M.R., Welham, J.L. & Murray, R.M. (1994) Schizophrenia and the influenza epidemics of 1954, 1957 and 1959: a southern-hemisphere study. *Schizophrenia Research* **14**, 1–8.

McNeil, T.F., Cantorgraae, E. & Cardenal, S. (1993) Prenatal cerebral development in individuals at genetic risk for psychosis: head size at birth in offspring of women with schizophrenia. *Schizophrenia Research* **10**, 1–5.

McNeil, T.F., Cantor-Graae, E., Nordstrom, L.G. & Rosenlund, T. (1997) Does choice of scale for scoring obstetric complications influence their relationship to other etiological risk factors in schizophrenia? *Journal of Nervous and Mental Disease* **185**, 27–31.

McNeil, T.F., Cantor-Graae, E. & Weinberger, D.R. (2000) Relationship of obstetric complications and differences in size of brain structures in monozygotic twin pairs discordant for schizophrenia. *American Journal of Psychiatry* **157**, 203–212.

Machon, R.A., Mednick, S.A. & Huttunen, M.O. (1997) Adult major affective disorder after prenatal exposure to an influenza epidemic. *Archives of General Psychiatry* **54**, 322–328.

Marcelis, M., van Os, J., Sham, P. *et al.* (1998) Obstetric complications and familial morbid risk of psychiatric disorders. *American Journal of Medical Genetics* **81**, 29–36.

Marcelis, M., Takei, N. & van OS, J. (1999) Urbanization and risk for schizophrenia: does the effect operate before or at the time of illness onset?. *Psychological Medicine* **29**, 1197–1203.

Marenco, S. & Weinberger, D.R. (2000) The neurodevelopmental hypothesis of schizophrenia: following a trail of evidence from cradle to grave. *Developmental Psychopathology* **12**, 501–527.

Marenco, S. & Weinberger, D.R. (2003) Following Ariadne's double stranded thread through early development: will we ever get out of the labirynth? In: *Early Clinical Intervention and Prevention in Schizophrenia* (eds W.S. Stone, S.V. Faraone & M.T. Tsuang). Humana Press, Totowa, NJ, in press.

Marin-Padilla, M. (1997) Developmental neuropathology and impact of perinatal brain damage. II. White matter lesions of the neocortex. *Journal of Neuropathology and Experimental Neurology* **56**, 219–235.

Mathalon, D.H., Sullivan, E.V., Lim, K.O. & Pfefferbaum, A. (2001) Progressive brain volume changes and the clinical course of schizophrenia in men: a longitudinal magnetic resonance imaging study. *Archives of General Psychiatry* **58**, 148–157.

Matsumoto, H., Simmons, A., Williams, S. *et al.* (2001) Structural magnetic imaging of the hippocampus in early onset schizophrenia. *Biological Psychiatry* **49**, 824–831.

Mednick, S.A. (1991) Fetal neural development and adult schizophrenia. *Fetal Neural Development and Adult Schizophrenia* (eds S.A. Mednick, T.D. Cannon, C.E. Barr & M. Lyon) Cambridge University Press, Cambridge.

Mednick, S.A., Machon, R.A. *et al.* (1988) Adult schizophrenia following prenatal exposure to an influenza epidemic. *Archives of General Psychiatry* **45**, 189–192.

Mednick, S.A., Machon, R.A. Huttunen, M.O. & Barr, C.E. (1990) Influenza and schizophrenia: Helsinki vs. Edinburgh. *Archives of General Psychiatry* **47**, 875–876.

Mednick, S.A., Huttunen, M.O. & Machon, R.A. (1994) Prenatal influenza infections and adult schizophrenia. *Schizophrenia Bulletin* **20**, 263–267.

Miller, R. (1989) Schizophrenia as a progressive disorder: relations to EEG, CT, neuropathological and other evidence. *Progress in Neurobiology* **33**, 17–44.

Morgan, V., Castle, D., Page, A. *et al.* (1997) Influenza epidemics and incidence of schizophrenia, affective disorders and mental retardation in Western Australia: no evidence of a major effect. *Schizophrenia Research* **26**, 25–39.

Mortensen, P.B., Pedersen, C.B., Westergaard, T. *et al.* (1999) Effects of family history and place and season of birth on the risk of schizophrenia. *New England Journal of Medicine* **340**, 603–608.

Murray, R.M. & Lewis (1987) Is schizophrenia a neurodevelopmental disorder? *British Medical Journal* **295**, 681–682.

Nair, T.R., Christensen, J.D., Kingsbury, S.J. *et al.* (1997) Progression of cerebroventricular enlargement and the subtyping of schizophrenia. *Psychiatry Research* **74**, 141–150.

Narr, K., Thompson, P., Sharma, T. *et al.* (2001a) Three-dimensional mapping of gyral shape and cortical surface asymmetries in schizophrenia: gender effects. *American Journal of Psychiatry* **158**, 244–255.

Narr, K.L., Thompson, P.M., Sharma, T. *et al.* (2001b) Three-dimensional mapping of temporo-limbic regions and the lateral ventricles in schizophrenia: gender effects. *Biological Psychiatry* **50**, 84–97.

Nelson, K.B. & Ellenberg, J.H. (1984) Obstetric complications as risk factors for cerebral palsy or seizure disorders. *Journal of the American Medical Association* **251**, 1843–1848.

Noga, J.T., Bartley, A.J., Jones, D.W., Torrey, E.F. & Weinberger, D.R. (1996) Cortical gyral anatomy and gross brain dimensions in monozygotic twins discordant for schizophrenia. *Schizophrenia Research* **22**, 27–40.

O'Callaghan, E., Sham, P., Takei, N., Glover, G.R., Murray, R.M. (1991) Schizophrenia after prenatal exposure to 1957, A2 influenza epidemic. *Lancet* **337**, 1248–1250.

O'Callaghan, E., Gibson, T., Colohan, H.A. *et al.* (1992) Risk of schizophrenia in adults born after obstetric complications and their association with early onset of illness: a controlled study. *British Medical Journal* **305**, 1256–1259.

O'Dwyer, J.M. (1997) Schizophrenia in people with intellectual disability: the role of pregnancy and birth complications. *Journal of Intellectual Disability Research* **41**, 238–251.

Olney, J.W. & Farber, N.B. (1995) Glutamate receptor dysfunction and schizophrenia. *Archives of General Psychiatry* **52**, 998–1007.

Orr, K.G., Cannon, M., Giluarry, C.M., Jones, P.B. & Murrary, R.M. (1999) Schizophrenic patients and their first-degree relatives show an excess of mixed-handedness. *Schizophrenia Research* **39**, 167–176.

Pakkenberg, B. (1993) Total nerve cell number in neocortex in chronic schizophrenics and controls estimated using optical dissectors. *Biological Psychiatry* **34**, 768–772.

Parnas, J., Schulsinger, F., Teasdak, T.W. *et al.* (1982) Perinatal complications and clinical outcome within the schizophrenia spectrum. *British Journal of Psychiatry* **140**, 416–420.

Perrone-Bizzozero, N.I., Sower, A.C., Bird, E.D. *et al.* (1996) Levels of the growth-associated protein GAP-43 are selectively increased in association cortices in schizophrenia. *Proceedings of the National Academy of Sciences of the USA* **93**, 14182–14187.

Rakic, P., Bourgeois, J.P., Eckenhoff, M.F., Zecevic, N. & Goldman-Rakic, P.E. (1986) Concurrent overproduction of synapses in diverse regions of the primate cerebral cortex. *Science* **232**, 232–235.

Rao, J.M. (1990) A population-based study of mild mental handicap in children: preliminary analysis of obstetric associations. *Journal of Mental Deficiency Research* **34**, 59–65.

Rapoport, J., Giedd, J., Kumra, S. *et al.* (1997) Childhood-onset: progressive ventricular change during adoloescence. *Archives of General Psychiatry* **54**, 897–903.

Rapoport, J.L., Giedd, J.N., & Murrary, R.M. *et al.* (1999) Progressive cortical change during adolescence in childhood-onset schizophrenia: a longitudinal magnetic resonance imaging study. *Archives of General Psychiatry* **56**, 649–654.

Raz, S. & Raz, N. (1990) Structural brain abnormalities in the major psychoses: a quantitative review of the evidence from computerized imaging. *Psychological Bulletin* **108**, 93–108.

Reveley, A.M., Reveley, M.A. & Murrary, R.M. (1984) Cerebral ventricular enlargement in non-genetic schizophrenia: a controlled twin study. *British Journal of Psychiatry* **144**, 89–93.

Risch, N. (1990) Genetic linkage and complex diseases, with special reference to psychiatric disorders. *Genetics Epidemiology* **7**, 3–16; discussion 17–45.

Roberts, G.W. (1991) Schizophrenia: a neuropathological perspective. *British Journal of Psychiatry* **158**, 8–17.

Roberts, G.W., Done, D.J., Bruton, C. & Crow, T.J. (1990) A 'mock up' of schizophrenia: temporal lobe epilepsy and schizophrenia-like psychosis. *Biological Psychiatry* **28**, 127–143.

Robinson, D., Woerner, M.G., Alvir, J.M.J. *et al.* (1999a) Predictors of relapse following response from a first episode of schizophrenia or schizoaffective disorder. *Archives of General Psychiatry* **56**, 241–247.

Robinson, D.G., Woerner, M.G., Alvir, J.M.J. *et al.* (1999b) Predictors of treatment response from a first episode of schizophrenia or schizoaffective disorder. *American Journal of Psychiatry* **156**, 544–549.

Rosanoff, A.J., Handy, L.M., Rosanoff-Plesset, I.R. & Brush, S. (1934) The etiology of so-called schizophrenic psychoses. *American Journal of Psychiatry* **91**, 247–286.

Rosso, I.M., Cannon, T.D., Huttunen, T. *et al.* (2000) Obstetric risk factors for early-onset schizophrenia in a Finnish birth cohort. *American Journal of Psychiatry* **157**, 801–807.

van Rossum, D. & U.K. Hanisch (1999) Cytoskeletal dynamics in dendritic spines: direct modulation by glutamate receptors?. *Trends in Neuroscience* **22**, 290–295.

Rund, B.R. (1998) A review of longitudinal studies of cognitive functions in schizophrenia patients. *Schizophrenia Bulletin* **24**, 425–435.

Russell, D., Douglas, A.S. & Allan, T.M. (1993) Changing seasonality of birth: a possible environmental effect. *Journal of Epidemiology and Community Health* **47**, 362–367.

Sacker, A., Done, D.J. *et al.* (1995) Antecedents of schizophrenia and affective illness: obstetric complications. *British Journal of Psychiatry* **166**, 734–741.

Sacker, A., Done, D.J., Crow, T.J. & Golding, J. (1996) Obstetric complications in children born to parents with schizophrenia: a meta-analysis of case–control studies. *Psychological Medicine* **26**, 279–287.

Saunders, R.C., Kolachana, B.S., Bachevalier, J. & Weinberger, D.R. (1998) Neonatal lesions of the medial temporal lobe disrupt prefrontal cortical regulation of striatal dopamine. *Nature* **393**, 169–171.

Schwartz, M.L. & Goldman-Rakic, P. (1990) Development and plasticity of the primate cerebral cortex. *Clinical Perinatology* **17**, 83–102.

Segal, M. (2001) Rapid plasticity of dendritic spine: hints to possible functions? *Progress in Neurobiology* **63**, 61–70.

Seidman, L.J., Faraone, S.V., Goldstein, J.M. *et al.* (1997) Reduced subcortical brain volumes in non-psychotic siblings of schizophrenic patients: a pilot magnetic resonance imaging study. *American Journal of Medical Genetics* **74**, 507–514.

Selemon, L.D., Rajkowska, G. & Goldman-Rakic, P.S. (1995) Abnormally high neuronal density in the schizophrenic cortex: a morphometric analysis of prefrontal area-9 and occipital area-17. *Archives of General Psychiatry* **52**, 805–818.

Selten, J. & Slaets, J.P.J. (1994) Evidence against maternal influenza as a risk factor for schizophrenia. *British Journal of Psychiatry* **164**, 674–676.

Selten, J.P., van der Graaf, Y., van Duursen, R., Gispen-delvied, C.C., & Kahn, R.S. (1999) Psychotic illness after prenatal exposure to the 1953 Dutch flood disaster. *Schizophrenia Research* **35**, 243–245.

Sham, P.C., O'Callaghan, E., Takei, N. (1992) Schizophrenia following prenatal exposure to influenza epidemics between 1939 and 1960. *British Journal of Psychiatry* **160**, 461–466.

Shannon-Weickert, C., Webster, M.J., Hyde, T.M. *et al.* (2001) Reduced GAP-43 mRNA in dorsolateral prefrontal cortex of patients with schizophrenia. *Cerebral Cortex* **11**, 136–147.

Shapleske, J., Rossell, S.L., Simmons, A., David, A.S. & Woodruff, P.W. (2001) Are auditory hallucinations the consequence of abnormal cerebral lateralization? A morphometric MRI study of the sylvian fissure and planum temporale. *Biological Psychiatry* **49**, 685–693.

Shenton, M.E., Kikinis, R., Jolesz, F.A. *et al.* (1992) Abnormalities of the left temporal lobe and thought disorder in schizophrenia: a quantitative magnetic resonance imaging study. *New England Journal of Medicine* **327**, 604–612.

Shenton, M.E., Dickey, C.C., Frumin, M. & McCarley, R.W. (2001) A review of MRI findings in schizophrenia. *Schizophrenia Research* **49**, 1–52.

Shprintzen, R.J., Goldberg, R. Golding-Kushner, K.J. & Marion, R.W. (1992) Late-onset psychosis in the velocardiofacial syndrome. *American Journal of Medical Genetics* **42**, 141–142.

Sierrahonigmann, A.M., Carbone, K.M., & Yolken, R.H. (1995) Polymerase chain-reaction (PCR) search for viral nucleic-acid sequences in schizophrenia. *British Journal of Psychiatry* **166**, 55–60.

Smith, G.N., Kopala, L.C., Lapointe, J.S. *et al.* (1998) Obstetric complications, treatment response and brain morphology in adult onset and early-onset males with schizophrenia. *Psychological Medicine* **28**, 645–653.

Southard, E.E. (1915) On the topographical distribution of cortex lesions and anamolies in dementia praecox, with some account of their functional significance. *American Journal of Insanity* **71**, 603–671.

Stevens, J.R. (1992) Abnormal reinnervation as a basis for schizophrenia: a hypothesis. *Archives of General Psychiatry* **49**, 238–243.

Suddath, R.L., Christison, G.W., Torrey, E.F., Csanova, M.F. & Weinberger, D.R. (1990) Anatomical abnormalities in the brains of monozygotic twins discordant for schizophrenia. *New England Journal of Medicine* **322**, 789–794.

Susser, E., Lin, S.P., Brown, A.S. *et al.* (1994) No relation between risk of schizophrenia and prenatal exposure to influenza in Holland. *American Journal of Psychiatry* **151**, 922–924.

Susser, E., Neugebauer, R., Hoek, H.W. *et al.* (1996) Schizophrenia after prenatal famine: further evidence. *Archives of General Psychiatry* **53**, 25–31.

Susser, E.S., Schaefer, C.A., Brown, A.S., Begg, M.D. & Wyatt, R.J. (2000) The design of the prenatal determinants of schizophrenia study. *Schizophrenia Bulletin* **26**, 257–273.

Suvisaari, J.M., Haukka, J.K., Tanskanen, A.J. & Lonnquist, J.K. (2000) Decreasing seasonal variation of births in schizophrenia. *Psychological Medicine* **30**, 315–324.

Suvisaari, J.M., Haukka, J.K. & Lonnquist, J.K. (2001) Season of birth among patients with schizophrenia and their siblings: evidence for the procreational habits hypothesis. *American Journal of Psychiatry* **158**, 754–757.

Szatmari, P., Reitsma-Street, M. & Offord, D.R. (1986) Pregnancy and birth complications in antisocial adolescents and their siblings. *Canadian Journal of Psychiatry* **31**, 513–516.

Taller, A.M., Asher, D.M., Pomeroy, K.L. *et al.* (1996) Search for viral nucleic acid sequences in brain tissues of patients with schizophrenia using nested polymerase chain reaction. *Archives of General Psychiatry* **53**, 32–40.

Thatcher, R.W., Walker, R.A. & Giudice, S. (1987) Human cerebral hemispheres develop at different rates and ages. *Science* **236**, 1110–1113.

Thompson, P.M., MacDonald, D. Mega, M.S. *et al.* (1997) Detection and mapping of abnormal brain structure with a probabilistic atlas of cortical surfaces. *Journal of computer Assisted Tomography* **21**, 567–581.

Thompson, P.M., Vidal, C. Giedd, J.N. *et al.* (2001) From the cover: mapping adolescent brain change reveals dynamic wave of accelerated gray matter loss in very early-onset schizophrenia. *Proceedings of the National Academy of Sciences of the USA* **98**, 11650–11655.

Toni, N., Buchs, P.A., Nikonenko, I., Bron, C.R. & Muller, D. (1999) LTP promotes formation of multiple spine synapses between a single axon terminal and a dendrite. *Nature* **402**, 421–425.

Torrey, E.F. (1977) Birth weights, perinatal insults, and HLA types: return to 'original din'. *Schizophrenia Bulletin* **3**, 347–351.

Torrey, E.F., Rawlings, R. & Waldman, I.N. (1988) Schizophrenic births and viral diseases in two states. *Schizophrenia Research* **1**, 73–77.

Torrey, E.F., Bowler, A.E., Rawlings, R. & Terrazas, A. (1993) Seasonality of schizophrenia and stillbirths. *Schizophrenia Bulletin* **19**, 557–562.

Torrey, F.E., Rawlings, R. & Yolken, R.H. (2000) The antecedents of psychoses: a case–control study of selected risk factors. *Schizophrenia Research* **46**, 17–23.

Tsuang, M.T., Woolson, R.F. & Fleming, J.A. (1979) Long-term outcome of major psychoses. I. Schizophrenia and affective disorders compared with psychiatrically symptom-free surgical conditions. *Archives of General Psychiatry* **36**, 1295–1301.

Van Os, J. & Selten, J.P. (1998) Prenatal exposure to maternal stress and subsequent schizophrenia: the May 1940 invasion of the Netherlands. *British Journal of Psychiatry* **172**, 324–326.

Vawter, M.P., Cannon-Spoor, H.E., Hemperly, J.J. *et al.* (1998) Abnormal expression of cell recognition molecules in schizophrenia. *Experimental Neurology* **149**, 424–432.

Verdoux, H. & Bourgeois, M. (1993) A comparative study of obstetric history in schizophrenics, bipolar patients and normal subjects. *Schizophrenia Research* **9**, 67–69.

Verdoux, H., Geddes, J.R., Takei, N. *et al.* (1997) Obstetric complications and age at onset in schizophrenia: an international collaborative meta-analysis of individual patient data. *American Journal of Psychiatry* **154**, 1220–1227.

Verdoux, H., Liraud, F., Bergey, C. *et al.* (2001) Is the association between duration of untreated psychosis and outcome confounded? A 2 year follow-up study of first-admitted patients. *Schizophrenia Research* **49**, 231–241.

Wada, J.A., Clarke, R. & Hamm, A. (1975) Cerebral hemispheric asymmetry in humans: cortical speech zones in 100 adults and 100 infant brains. *Archives of Neurology* **32**, 239–246.

Waddington, J.L. & Youssef, H.A. (1990) The lifetime outcome and involuntary movements of schizophrenia never treated with neuroleptic drugs: four rare cases in Ireland. *British Journal of Psychiatry* **156**, 106–108.

Wahlbeck, K., Forsen, T., Osmond, C., Barker, D.J. & Eriksson, J.G. (2001) Association of schizophrenia with low maternal body mass index, small size at birth, and thinness during childhood. *Archives of General Psychiatry* **58**, 48–52.

Watson, C.G., Kucala, T., Tilleskjor, C. & Jacobs, L. (1984) Schizophrenic birth seasonality in relation to the incidence of infectious diseases and temperature extremes. *Archives of General Psychiatry* **41**, 85–90.

Watt, N.F. (1972) Longitudinal changes in the social behavior of children hospitalized for schizophrenia as adults. *Journal of Nervous and Mental Disease* **155**, 42–54.

Weinberger, D.R. (1986) The pathogenesis of schizophrenia: a neurodevelopmental theory. In: *The Neurology of Schizophrenia* (eds H.A.W. Nasrallah & D.R. Weinberger), pp. 397–406. Elsevier, Amsterdam.

Weinberger, D.R. (1987) Implications of normal brain development for the pathogenesis of schizophrenia. *Archives of General Psychiatry* **44**, 660–669.

Weinberger, D.R. (1993) A connectionist approach to the prefrontal cortex. *Journal of Neuropsychiatry and Clinical Neuroscience* **5**, 241–253.

Weinberger, D.R. (1995) Schizophrenia as a neurodevelopmental disorder. In: *Schizophrenia* (ed. S.R. Hirsch), pp. 293–323. Blackwell Science, Oxford.

Weinberger, D.R. (1999) Schizophrenia: new phenes and new genes. *Biological Psychiatry* **46**, 3–7.

Weinberger, D.R. & Lipska, B.K. (1995) Cortical maldevelopment, anti-psychotic drugs, and schizophrenia: a search for common ground. *Schizophrenia Research* **16**, 87–110.

Weinberger, D.R. & McClure, R.K. (2002) Neurotoxicity, neuroplasticity, and MRI morphometry: what's happening in the schizophrenic brain? *Archives of General Psychiatry* **59**, 553–558.

Weinberger, D.R., Torrey, E.F., Neophytides, A.N. & Wyatt, R.J. (1979) Lateral cerebral ventricular enlargement in chronic schizophrenia. *Archives of General Psychiatry* **36**, 735–739.

Weinberger, D.R., Bigelow, L.B.; Kleiman, J.E. *et al.* (1980a) Cerebral ventricular enlargement in chronic schizophrenia: an association with poor response to treatment. *Archives of General Psychiatry* **37**, 11–13.

Weinberger, D.R., Cannon-Spoor, E., Potkin, S.G. & Wyatt, R.J. (1980b) Poor premorbid adjustment and CT scan abnormalities in chronic schizophrenia. *American Journal of Psychiatry* **137**, 1410–1413.

Weinberger, D.R., DeLisi, L.E., Perman, G.P. *et al.* (1982a) Computed tomography in schizophreniform disorder and other acute psychiatric disorders. *Archives of General Psychiatry* **39**, 778–783.

Weinberger, D.R., Luchins, D.J., Morihisa, J. & Wyatt, R.J. (1982b) Asymmetrical volumes of the right and left frontal and occipital regions of the human brain. *Annals of Neurology* **11**, 97–100.

Weinberger, D.R., Wagner, R.L. & Wyatt, R.J. (1983) Neuropathological studies of schizophrenia: a selective review. *Schizophrenia Bulletin* **9**, 193–212.

Weinberger, D.R., Berman, K.F. Suddath, R. & Torrey, E.F. (1992) Evidence of dysfunction of a prefrontal–limbic network in schizophrenia: a magnetic-resonance-imaging and regional cerebral blood-flow study of discordant monozygotic twins. *American Journal of Psychiatry* **149**, 890–897.

Weinberger, D.R., Egan, M.F., Bertolino, A. *et al.* (2001) Prefrontal neurons and the genetics of schizophrenia. *Biological Psychiatry* **50**, 825–844

Westergaard, T., Mortensen, P.B., Pedersen, C.B. Wohlfahrt, J. & Melbye, M. (1999) Exposure to prenatal and childhood infections and the risk of schizophrenia: suggestions from a study of sibship characteristics and influenza prevalence. *Archives of General Psychiatry* **56**, 993–998.

Wilcox, J.A. & Nasrallah, H.A. (1987) Perinatal distress and prognosis of psychotic illness. *Neuropsychobiology* **17**, 173–175.

Woods, B.T. (1998) Is schizophrenia a progressive neurodevelopmental disorder? Toward a unitary pathogenetic mechanism. *American Journal of Psychiatry* **155**, 1661–1670.

Zornberg, G.L., Buka, S.L. & Tsuang, M.T. (2000) Hypoxic-ischemia-related fetal/neonatal complications and risk of schizophrenia and other non-affective psychoses: a 19-year longitudinal study. *American Journal of Psychiatry* **157**, 196–202.

Zuccato, C., Ciammola, A., Rigamouti, D. *et al.* (2001) Loss of Huntington-mediated BDNF gene transcription in Huntington's disease. *Science* **293**, 493–498.

19 The neurochemistry of schizophrenia

B. Moghaddam and J.H. Krystal

The discovery in the 1950s that drugs such as reserpine and chlorpromazine could influence the expression of some of the symptoms of schizophrenia led to the development of the concept that 'neurochemical' abnormalities may be associated with this disorder. Contrary to the common belief that the 'dopamine hypothesis' was the first neurochemical hypothesis of schizophrenia to follow the discovery of neuroleptics, the 'serotonin deficiency' and 'norepinephrine-depletion' theories (Brodie 1959) were put forth several years before dopamine was implicated in the mechanisms of action of neuroleptics. These theories originated from observations that, in animals, reserpine reduces brain tissue levels of serotonin (and norepinephrine), leading to the postulation that 'liberation' of active serotonin alleviates the serotonin deficiency suspected to occur during active psychosis. While, given our present state of knowledge, this concept appears far-fetched, the inferential line of reasoning used to justify this theory is still applied today to support the two most influential neurotransmitter theories of schizophrenia: the dopamine (hyperactivity) hypothesis and glutamate (deficiency) hypothesis. Fortunately, however, recent advances made in the fields of molecular and cellular neuroscience and brain imaging methodologies have made it possible to move beyond the indirect approach and discover specific abnormalities in neurotransmitter systems in schizophrenia. The goal of this chapter is to provide the reader with an overview of these recent findings on specific neurotransmitter systems which are contributing to our current understanding of the complex abnormal neurotransmitter dynamics that may lead to expression of schizophrenic symptomotology.

Dopamine

The dopamine hypothesis of schizophrenia remains the most studied neurochemical theory relating to schizophrenia. In its simplest form, this hypothesis proposes that dopamine neurotransmission is hyperactive in schizophrenia (Carlsson 1978). This notion is supported by the fact that antipsychotic drugs block central dopamine receptors, and that their effective therapeutic doses correlate with blockade of dopamine D_2 receptors (Seeman *et al.* 1976). Furthermore, chronic exposure to amphetamines, which are indirect dopamine agonists, produces psychosis (Snyder *et al.* 1974a; see Chapter 20 for a review of dopaminergic involvement in schizophrenia).

Glutamate

The notion that glutamate neurotransmission is involved in the pathophysiology of schizophrenia is hardly academic. After all, the most consistent findings in schizophrenia, across all technical disciplines, have involved abnormalities in the function and organization of association cortices, in particular the prefrontal cortices. Considering that *all* cortical efferents – and the majority of cortical afferents including those from the thalamus and limbic structures – are glutamatergic, it is inevitable that glutamate neurotransmission mediates the abnormal cortical connectivity and functioning suspected to occur in schizophrenia. However, evidence for a glutamatergic involvement in schizophrenia has only begun to surface in the last decade.

The first suggestion of glutamatergic abnormality in schizophrenia was put forth by Kim *et al.* (1980). These authors reported reduced glutamate levels in the cerebral spinal fluid (CSF) of schizophrenics compared to controls, and hence postulated that glutamate neurotransmission may be downregulated in schizophrenia. The CSF findings, however, were not replicated by three other groups (Gattaz *et al.* 1982; Perry 1982; Korpi *et al.* 1987). Even if they were, considering that the majority of glutamate found in the brain is involved in intermediary metabolism and other non-neuronal functions, measures of glutamate levels in the CSF would not be considered an accurate index of glutamate-mediated neurotransmission.

About the same time that the CSF studies were being reported, several laboratories were attempting to characterize the mechanism by which the potent 'schizophrenomimetic' drug phencyclidine (PCP) (Luby *et al.* 1959) binds to brain tissue (Zukin & Zukin 1979). The discovery that PCP reduces glutamate neurotransmission at the *N*-methyl-D-aspartate (NMDA) subtype of the glutamate receptor (Lodge & Anis 1982; Anis *et al.* 1983), and is a potent non-competitive antagonist of the NMDA receptor channel, provided compelling, albeit indirect, support for glutamatergic involvement in schizophrenia and led to the speculation that hypoactive glutamate neurotransmission at the NMDA receptor is involved in schizophrenia (Javitt & Zukin 1991). Subsequently, numerous postmortem studies have reported region-specific changes in different subtypes of glutamate receptors in schizophrenic brains (see below) and the glutamate hypothesis has been modified to incorporate more complex mechanisms (Olney & Farber 1995; Tamminga 1998; Krystal *et al.* 1999b; Goff & Coyle 2001).

Glutamate receptor genes and binding

Until two decades ago, it was thought that glutamate exerted its physiological action solely through receptors that act directly as ion channels. Binding of glutamate to these so-called ionotropic receptors stimulates Ca^{2+} entry into neurones through channels formed either by the receptor itself (as is the case with the NMDA receptor subtype) or by opening voltage-sensitive Ca^{2+} channels which are on the cell membrane. Ionotropic glutamate receptors are classified into three broad subtypes according to their preferential agonists as the NMDA, kainate and α-amino-3-hydroxy-5-methyl-isoxazole propionic acid (AMPA) receptors. The AMPA receptors are composed of at least four subunits derived from a family of four genes termed *gluR1–gluR4*. Kainate receptors are thought to be composed of five identical subunits (homomers) derived from genes termed *gluR5–gluR7* and *KA1–KA2*. The NMDA receptor is composed of four or five subunits derived from fives genes *NR1* and *NR2A–NR2D*. The NR1 subunit, which has several isoforms, is an obligate subunit. Nearly all neurones express AMPA and NMDA receptors and it is estimated that glutamate ionotropic receptors mediate nearly 50% of all synaptic transmission in the mammalian central nervous system.

The classical views of glutamate-mediated neurotransmission were changed in the late 1980s when two research groups independently cloned a novel receptor with high affinity for glutamate which had different functional characteristics than other glutamate receptors (Conn & Pin 1997). In contrast to the rapid excitation and opening of ion channels that was the hallmark of ionotropic glutamate receptor activation, stimulation of these so-called metabotropic receptors indirectly regulated electrical signalling by activation of various second messenger cascades. From a clinical point of view, the discovery of these receptors was important because they activated synaptic transduction mechanisms similar to those of the monoamine neurotransmitters such as dopamine and serotonin, which are the site of action of most known psychotherapeutic drugs. At least eight metabotropic glutamate receptors have been cloned (mGlu1–mGlu8). These receptors share no sequence homology with other known receptors in the nervous system, suggesting that they are members of a new receptor gene family. The eight subtypes of mGlu receptors are currently classified into three groups (groups I–III). This classification is primarily based on sequence identity: the amino acid sequence homology between mGluR of the same group is about 70%, while between groups the homology is about 40%. The classification is also based on transduction mechanism: stimulation of group I mGlu receptor activates the enzyme phospholipase C which in turn results in breakdown of membrane phospholipid to the second messengers, inositol triphosphate or diacylglycerol. Activation of group II or III receptors results in downregulation of the enzyme adenylate cyclase, resulting in reduced synthesis of the second messenger cyclic adenosine monophosphate (cAMP).

Unlike the monoamine systems, selective glutamate receptor ligands for clinical imaging studies have not been fully developed for routine use in healthy and patient volunteers (Bressan & Pilowsky 2000). Although studies using proton magnetic resonance spectroscopy (MRS) are beginning to provide some valuable functional data on glutamate abnormalities in schizophrenia (Kegeles *et al.* 2000), the primary focus of research on glutamate and schizophrenia remains on postmortem studies.

As would be expected, numerous studies have examined glutamate receptor binding or expression in cortical, striatal and temporal lobe structures in schizophrenic brain (for a recent review see Meador-Woodruff & Healy 2000). The earliest report in the literature using [^{3}H]MK801 (MK801 is a selective non-competitive antagonist of the NMDA receptor) described increased binding in the putamen, but not in the frontal cortex or temporal lobe (Kornhuber *et al.* 1989). Similar increases were reported using [^{3}H]D-aspartate (Aparicio-Legarza *et al.* 1997) but another study failed to replicate the finding in putamen (Noga *et al.* 1997). Studies using [^{3}H]TCP (which, similar to MK801, binds to the PCP site on the NMDA receptor complex) have also resulted in conflicting observations with either no change (Weissman *et al.* 1991) or an increase in binding in orbitofrontal cortex being reported (Simpson *et al.* 1992).

More recent studies have examined the expression of NMDA receptor subunits in schizophrenic brain and have reported several region-specific results. In the prefrontal cortex, Akbarian *et al.* (1996b) found no major changes in any of the NMDA receptor subunits; however, a higher ratio of NR2D to the other NR2 subunits was noted. In the thalamus, a significant reduction in NR1, NR2B and NR2CR subunits has been reported (Ibrahim *et al.* 2000). In a study of prospectively assessed patients, levels of NR1 subunit was shown to be significantly correlated with several measures of cognitive function (global cognitive deterioration, Mini Mental State examination, and National Adult Learning test) in rapid autopsy samples of schizophrenic patients (Humphries *et al.* 1996). Other reports have also demonstrated a downregulation of NR1 in the superior temporal gyrus and hippocampus (Sokolov 1998; Gao *et al.* 2000) and the thalamus (Ibrahim *et al.* 2000) and upregulation of NR2B subunit in the superior temporal cortex (Grimwood *et al.* 1999).

Findings with the AMPA receptor subunits have been more consistent, suggesting a decrease in the expression of several AMPA receptor subunits as well as a decrease in receptor binding in the medial temporal lobe in schizophrenic brains. Decreases in AMPA receptor binding in CA3 and CA4 subfields of hippocampus was first noted by Harrison and coworkers (Kerwin *et al.* 1990; Harrison *et al.* 1991). These findings are consistent with reduced expression of *gluR1* and *gluR2* reported by several laboratories (Harrison *et al.* 1991; Eastwood *et al.* 1995, 1997; Healy *et al.* 1998). In contrast to the temporal lobe regions, one study reported small changes in frontal cortex and striatal regions (Noga *et al.* 2001).

Several other studies have examined kainate receptor binding or messenger RNA (mRNA) levels (Nishikawa *et al.* 1983; Deakin *et al.* 1989; Noga *et al.* 1997; Porter *et al.* 1997; Sokolov 1998; Meador-Woodruff *et al.* 2001). In general, these studies follow the same pattern of change as in AMPA receptor expression, suggesting reduced levels of expression in temporal lobe regions and small increases or no effect in these cortical areas.

Studies examining the expression of the family of metabotropic glutamate receptor have only recently begun and, although there are only a few published studies in this area (Ohnuma *et al.* 1998; Richardson-Burns *et al.* 2000), this is likely to be an active field of research in the future. So far, an increase in mGluR5 in orbitofrontal cortex has been reported (Ohnuma *et al.* 1998).

In addition to glutamate receptors, Coyle and coworkers (Tsai *et al.* 1995) have reported postmortem abnormalities in the expression of the neuropeptide *N*-acetylaspartyl glutamate (NAAG), which is considered an endogenous ligand for some subtypes of glutamate receptors. This reported increase in the levels of NAAG as well as a decrease in its catabolic enzyme NAALADase in the prefrontal cortex and hippocampus most likely reflects alteration in glutamate neurotransmission in schizophrenia (Coyle 1996).

Despite the above-reported changes in glutamate receptor expression and binding, genetic studies have not yet provided convincing evidence of a functional mutation of glutamate receptor genes in schizophrenia. A linkage study with a genetically isolated African population suggested that an NR1 subunit polymorphism may be associated with predisposition to develop schizophrenia (Riley *et al.* 1997). Other studies, however, have so far reported lack of association with polymorphisms for genes encoding for NR1, NR2B, GluR5, mGluR7 and mGluR8 (Pariseau *et al.* 1994; Bray *et al.* 2000; Nishiguchi *et al.* 2000; Bolonna *et al.* 2001).

Psychopharmacological studies

One of the first 'challenge' studies with schizophrenic subjects involved the use of the drug PCP (Luby *et al.* 1959; Itil *et al.* 1967). PCP (Sernyl) was developed in the 1950s as a general anaesthetic that was devoid of depressant effects on the cardiovascular system. However, intraoperative reactions that included hallucinations and postoperative psychotic states, which in some cases persisted for days, led to its withdrawal from the market in 1965. Luby and several other investigators reported on the effects of subanaesthetic doses of PCP in healthy individuals as well as patients with schizophrenia (Luby *et al.* 1959; Bakker & Amini 1961; Itil *et al.* 1967; Burns & Lerner 1976; Aniline & Pitts 1982). These reports suggested that PCP produces a behavioural syndrome in non-schizophrenics that closely resembles endogenous symptoms of schizophrenia. These symptoms included: positive symptoms such as paranoia, agitation, auditory hallucination; negative symptoms such as apathy, social withdrawal; and cognitive deficits such as impaired attention. More importantly, in patients with schizophrenia, including chronic stabilized patients, a single dose of PCP produced a profound exacerbation of pre-existing symptoms that lasted for days or months.

The 'schizophrenomimetic' effects of PCP engendered a great deal of interest in understanding its biological actions. In 1979, a high-affinity binding site for PCP was described (Vincent *et al.* 1979; Zukin & Zukin 1979). This 'PCP receptor' was later found to be a binding site in the NMDA receptor ion channel (Javitt *et al.* 1987; Sircar *et al.* 1987; Wong *et al.* 1988), consistent with reports that PCP reduces the excitatory effects of glutamate (Anis *et al.* 1983). Based on these findings, and previous clinical reports indicating that PCP intoxication resembles schizophrenia more closely than the acute paranoid psychosis caused by amphetamines, Javitt and Zukin (1991) proposed that a dysfunction in the NMDA receptor-mediated neurotransmission contributes to pathogenesis of schizophrenia.

NMDA receptor-related hypotheses related to the neurobiology of schizophrenia have been the subject of intense research in the past decade. The interest in this model has been, in part, a result of several recent studies that have established the clinical validity of this model using the PCP analogue, ketamine. At subanaesthetic doses, similar to PCP, ketamine is a relatively selective non-competitive antagonist of the NMDA receptor. However, unlike PCP, ketamine is a widely used anaesthetic with an established record of safety in healthy humans. The original human studies with PCP were descriptive and naturalistic, and hence difficult to interpret in the context of present diagnostic criteria. Using ketamine, a new generation of rigorous clinical pharmacological studies has been performed (Krystal *et al.* 1994; Malhotra *et al.* 1996b; Newcomer *et al.* 1999). These studies used validated measures of assessing signs and symptoms of schizophrenia and therefore provided a thorough documentation of the cognitive and other behavioural effects of ketamine in healthy subjects. The features of the ketamine psychosis can be quite striking. The form and content of thought may be altered, resulting in bizarre, disorganized or concrete ideation, which may be indistinguishable from that seen in some schizophrenic patients. Cognitive functions common for schizophrenic patients in attention, abstract reasoning, the shifting of mental set and memory are observed in healthy subjects administered ketamine. Less common for schizophrenia, ketamine alters perception in most perceptual spheres. During ketamine, time may seem to slow; the shape, colour or vividness of objects may be altered; sounds may be distorted in intensity, content or localization; derealization or depersonalization are also common (Krystal *et al.* 1994).

In addition to studies in healthy volunteers, a very limited number of challenge studies administered ketamine to schizophrenic volunteers who were on antipsychotic medication. In these schizophrenic patients, ketamine produced a brief exacerbation of pre-existing psychotic symptoms (Lahti *et al.* 1995; Malhotra *et al.* 1997). Collectively, the human pharmacological studies, albeit not without ethical concerns, have been invaluable for facilitating translational and hypothesis-driven research on the role of NMDA receptors in normal cognitive functioning and in schizophrenia. This line of research has led to the identification of several novel therapeutic approaches which are in various stages of basic laboratory characterization or clinical trials (Javitt *et al.* 1994; Moghaddam & Adams 1998; Goff *et al.* 1999; Anand *et al.* 2000).

It should be emphasized, however, that while animal and human studies with ketamine and PCP have strongly implicated a role for NMDA receptors in the pathophysiology of schizophrenia, the nature of this NMDA involvement remains unclear. The most simplified hypothesis has been that a reduction in glutamate neurotransmission at the NMDA receptor is responsible for aspects of schizophrenic symptomatology (Javitt & Zukin 1991; Olney & Farber 1995; Tamminga 1998). However, as reviewed above, uniform postmortem or genomic evidence for an NMDA receptor dysfunction has been difficult to identify in schizophrenia. An alternative hypothesis is that secondary effects of systemic NDMA blockade may produce conditions that mimic some aspects of schizophrenic pathophysiology. For example, PCP and ketamine produce a prefrontal cortex-specific activation of glutamate efflux (Moghaddam *et al.* 1997), suggesting that a cortical glutamate hyperactivity (at non-NMDA receptors) may produce some of the schizomimetic effects of these drugs (Moghaddam & Adams 1998; Krystal *et al.* 1999b). Consistent with this mechanism, pharmacological pretreatments that reduce glutamate hyperactivity also ameliorate behavioural effects of PCP or ketamine in animals (Moghaddam & Adams 1998) and humans (Anand *et al.* 2000).

Serotonin (5-HT)

Currently, there is no clear evidence that 5-HT neuronal cytopathology contributes to the pathophysiology of schizophrenia, although alterations in 5-HT neuronal function may be features of the symptoms of schizophrenia and its treatment. 5-HT projections arise from the raphe nuclei and project widely, but not randomly, in the brain (Wilson & Molliver 1991). The single study to report on 5-HT neuronal architecture in brain tissue from schizophrenic patients did not find evidence of abnormal morphology of 5-HT axons within the prefrontal cortex (Akil *et al.* 1999). Other postmortem studies did not find altered levels of cortical or striatal 5-HT metabolites (Crow *et al.* 1979; Joseph *et al.* 1979) or evidence of altered monoamine oxidase (MAO) activity in brain tissue from schizophrenic patients (Meltzer *et al.* 1980; Reveley *et al.* 1981). Many other studies have related clinical characteristics of schizophrenia or its treatment to the CSF levels of 5-HT or its metabolites. This topic, reviewed elsewhere (Widerlov 1988), is beyond the scope of this review. In the following section, we consider the possibility that schizophrenia may be associated with alterations in the binding properties of 5-HT-receptors, mutations in 5-HT-related genes.

5-HT-receptor binding and gene expression

Studies of postmortem brain tissue from schizophrenic patients reported alterations in several 5-HT receptors. Several studies report upregulation of the density of 5-HT_{1A}-receptor binding in the prefrontal cortex, but not hippocampus, in tissue from schizophrenic patients, although mRNA levels for this receptor were not changed in either region (Hashimoto *et al.* 1991; Burnet *et al.* 1996; Simpson *et al.* 1996; Sumiyoshi *et al.* 1996; Gurevich & Joyce 1997). So far, only one study failed to find changes in the cortical levels of 5-HT_{1A}-receptors in prefrontal cortex tissue from schizophrenic patients (Dean *et al.* 1999b). A single study found no difference in the levels of mRNA for 5-HT_{1A}-receptors in the prefrontal cortical tissue from patients where increased 5-HT_{1A}-receptor binding was measured (Burnet *et al.* 1996). To date, there are no studies suggesting that polymorphisms of the 5-HT_{1A}- or 5-HT_{1B}-receptor genes are related to the diagnosis of schizophrenia or treatment response in this patient group (Erdmann *et al.* 1995; Kawanishi *et al.* 1998; Bruss *et al.* 1999).

Several studies report reductions in the density of 5-HT_{2A}- or 5-HT_{2C}-receptors in cortical and hippocampal tissue from schizophrenic patients (Bennett *et al.* 1979; Mita *et al.* 1986; Arora & Meltzer 1991; Hashimoto *et al.* 1991; Burnet *et al.* 1996; Dean & Hayes 1996; Gurevich & Joyce 1997; Hernandez & Sokolov 2000). Confusion related to these 5-HT_2-receptor subtypes was introduced by the use of non-selective ligands, such as [^{3}H]lysergic acid diethylamide (LSD), in several of the initial studies (Bennett *et al.* 1979; Whitaker *et al.* 1981; Gurevich & Joyce 1997). As reviewed elsewhere (Abi-Dargham & Krystal 2000), there are mixed findings with postmortem studies of 5-HT_{2A}-preferring ligands, with some studies reporting reductions in cortical receptor density and others not finding diagnosis-related differences. Studies of medicated patients suggest that reported reductions in the density of 5-HT_2-receptors in schizophrenic patients reflect a large and widespread down-regulation related to antipsychotic treatment at the time of death and a more modest reduction that shows greater brain regional restriction described in medication-free patients (Gurevich & Joyce 1997). Another factor complicating postmortem studies is that tissue is often collected from medical examiners (coroners). As a result, they may over-represent the population of patients who die from suicide or violent causes. One study noted that patients who died from suicide did not differ from control groups in the density of cortical 5-HT_{2A}-receptors, while those patients who died from natural causes showed reductions in prefrontal 5-HT_{2A}-receptor density (Laruelle *et al.* 1993). Other potential confounds, such as the impact of comorbid substance abuse, cannot be adequately addressed on the basis of the current postmortem literature. Findings from *in vivo* neuroimaging studies have similarly not provided clear evidence of reductions in cortical 5-HT_2-receptors. One study reported reductions in 5-HT_2 binding (Ngan *et al.* 2000), but no difference was found in four other studies (Trichard *et al.* 1998; Lewis *et al.* 1999b; Okubo *et al.* 2000; Verhoeff *et al.* 2000).

Molecular genetic studies do not yet provide evidence of a functional mutation of 5-HT_2-receptor-related genes and schizophrenia. The most intensively studied polymorphism is a T-to-C substitution at nucleotide 102 of the 5-HT_{2A}-receptor gene that does not alter the amino acid sequence of this protein. Six studies reported associations between alleles of this gene and the diagnosis of schizophrenia (Erdmann *et al.* 1996b; Inayama *et al.* 1996; Williams *et al.* 1996, 1997; Tay *et al.* 1997; Spurlock *et al.* 1998), while nine others failed to find this relationship (Arranz *et al.* 1996; Malhotra *et al.* 1996a; Nimgaonkar *et al.* 1996; Chen *et al.* 1997; Hawi *et al.* 1997; He *et al.* 1999; Lin *et al.* 1999; Ohara *et al.* 1999; Serretti *et al.* 2000). Because the *T102C* polymorphism was silent, interest shifted to other polymorphisms that were in linkage disequilibrium with this site. An A-to-G substitution in the promoter region of the 5-HT_{2A}-receptor gene (*A-1438G*) was also identified, found to have no functional significance and was associated with schizophrenia in one of two studies (Spurlock *et al.* 1998; Ohara *et al.* 1999). Similarly, this polymorphism was not related to the density of 5-HT_{2A}-receptors in the frontal cortex of schizophrenic patients (Kouzmenko *et al.* 1999). Two other mutations of the 5-HT_{2A}-receptor gene (*Thr25Asn*, *His452Tyr*) were not associated with schizophrenia in a population that showed an association between the *T102C* allele and schizophrenia (Erdmann *et al.* 1996b).

5-HT_2-receptor-related genes also have been implicated in the clinical response to atypical neuroleptic agents. An association was reported between *T102C* or *A-1438G* polymorphisms and clozapine response; however, some of the positive reports are of marginal significance or not replicated internally (Arranz *et al.* 1995, 1998a,b, 2000; Joober *et al.* 1999). Other studies fail to find a link between these polymorphisms and response to typical (Nimgaonkar *et al.* 1996) or atypical antipsychotic drugs (Malhotra *et al.* 1996b; Nimgaonkar *et al.* 1996; Masellis *et al.* 1998; Lin *et al.* 1999). Similarly, a *Cys23Ser* polymorphism of the 5-HT_{2C}-receptor gene was not related to clozapine response in schizophrenic patients (Malhotra *et al.* 1996a; Masellis *et al.* 1998).

Several studies have also suggested that the 5-HT transporter (5-HTT) is abnormally expressed in the hippocampus and perhaps other regions in brain tissue from schizophrenic patients. As was recently reviewed (Abi-Dargham & Krystal 2000), several studies report reductions in 5-HTT binding in postmortem tissue in the frontal cortex, although reductions in receptor density were not observed in occipital cortex (Laruelle *et al.* 1993) or hippocampus (Dean *et al.* 1995). A single photon emission computerized tomography (SPECT) study failed to find brainstem alterations in schizophrenic patients using a ligand, [^{123}I]β-CIT, which is not informative in studies of cortical 5-HTT binding (Laruelle *et al.* 2000). New radiotracers are able to provide information about cortical and limbic 5-HTT binding *in vivo* and the data generated using these tracers should enhance our understanding of this 5-HT binding site. Genetic studies have suggested an association between the long variant of the 5-HTT gene and schizophrenia (Malhotra *et al.* 1998), although negative studies exist (Rao *et al.* 1998; Serretti *et al.* 1999).

To date, no significant postmortem findings have emerged for the 5-HT_3- (Abi-Dargham *et al.* 1993) or 5-HT_4-receptors (Dean *et al.* 1999a). Also, no significant associations have emerged between markers related to the 5-HT_3-, 5-HT_{5A}-, 5-HT_6-, or 5-HT_7-receptor genes and the diagnosis of schizophrenia (Erdmann *et al.* 1996a; Birkett *et al.* 2000; Vogt *et al.* 2000; Niesler *et al.* 2001). Although one 5-HT_6-receptor-related marker showed an association with atypical neuroleptic response (Yu *et al.* 1999), no other associations between genes for the 5-HT_3 to 5-HT_7-receptors have yet emerged (Masellis *et al.* 2001).

Psychopharmacological studies

The study of the behavioural effects of the serotonergic hallucinogens was a fundamental step in the appreciation of the neurochemical basis of psychosis and a potent stimulus for the development of modern psychopharmacology (Gouzoulis-Mayfrank *et al.* 1998; Krystal *et al.* 1999a). Albert Hoffman described his accidental discovery of the psychedelic properties of LSD in these terms:

> Last Friday, April 16, 1943, I was forced to interrupt my work in the laboratory in the middle of the afternoon and proceed home, being affected by a remarkable restlessness, combined with a slight dizziness. At home I lay down and sank into a not unpleasant intoxicated-like condition characterized by an extremely stimulated imagination. In a dreamlike state, with eyes closed (I found the daylight to be unpleasantly glaring), I perceived an uninterrupted stream of fantastic pictures, extraordinary shapes with intense, kaleidoscopic play of colours. After some two hours this condition faded away. (from www.macalester.edu/~psych/whathap/UBNRP/LSD/links.htm)

Subsequent careful study of LSD (Rosenbaum *et al.* 1959; Cohen *et al.* 1962; Freedman 1968), mescaline (Hermle *et al.* 1998), psilocybin (Vollenweider *et al.* 1997; Vollenweider 1998) and *N,N*-dimethyltryptamine (DMT) (Strassman *et al.* 1994) yielded a consistent picture. These drugs generally produce, in a dose-related fashion, profound sensory distortions and hallucinations, impairments in attention and concentration, mood instability, depersonalization, derealization and formal thought disorder. Drug administration less consistently produces systematized delusions or auditory hallucinations, but these symptoms may emerge in some individuals. Relative to NMDA antagonists, the psychosis associated with the serotonergic hallucinogens is associated with less blunting of affect and cognitive impairment. However, these comparisons are difficult because these effects are dose-dependent and adequate comparison would require a clear reference point and the comparison of multiple doses of each drug.

Clinical studies of these hallucinogenic agents suggest that drugs that block 5-HT_2-receptors attenuate their cognitive and perceptual effects. For example, the cognitive and perceptual effects of psilocybin were blocked dose-dependently by ketanserin and risperidone, but not by haloperidol (Vollenweider *et al.* 1998). Also, the hallucinogenic effects of DMT were potentiated rather than reduced by pretreatment with the 5-HT_{1A} antagonist pindolol (Strassman 1996). These findings are consistent with preclinical studies implicating 5-HT_2-receptor stimulation in the cognitive and behavioural effects of serotonergic hallucinogens (Aghajanian & Marek 1999).

The capacity of these 5-HT_2 agonists to produce psychosis may have therapeutic implications for schizophrenia. The serotonergic hallucinogens produce psychoses and cognitive impairments that resemble some aspects of schizophrenia, stimulate lasting schizophrenic-like states in a vulnerable subpopulation of individuals exposed to these drugs (Bowers 1987) and may worsen or even reduce symptoms in some schizophrenic patients (Itil *et al.* 1969). The extent to which the psychotogenic or propsychotic effects of these drugs are attributable to 5-HT_2-receptor stimulation suggests a role for 5-HT_2-receptor antagonism in the treatment of schizophrenia. Further, elaboration of the circuitry underlying the actions of 5-HT_2-receptor stimulation within the cortex suggests that drugs that attenuate glutamate release or attenuate its postsynaptic effects might also have a role in the treatment of schizophrenia (Aghajanian & Marek 2000; Marek *et al.* 2000). Similarly, interactions between 5-HT_2 and dopamine systems may contribute to both symptoms and the treatment of schizophrenia (Abi-Dargham *et al.* 1997).

Studies employing the 5-HT agonist *m*-chlorophenylpiperazine (mCPP) supported interest in the contribution of 5-HT systems to the pathophysiology and treatment of this disorder. Although it acts at multiple sites (Hamik & Peroutka 1989; Schoeffter & Hoyer 1989), the behavioural effects of mCPP appear most likely to be mediated by facilitation of 5-HT_{1B}- (Meneses *et al.* 1997; Maurel *et al.* 1998) or 5-HT_{2C}- (Fiorella *et al.* 1995) receptors (reviewed in Abi-Saab *et al.* 2002). While behavioural findings across groups were not consistent (Kahn *et al.* 1992; Owen *et al.* 1993; Maes & Meltzer 1996; Koreen *et al.* 1997), three studies found that mCPP increased psychosis and behavioural activation or anxiety in schizophrenic patients (Iqbal *et al.* 1991; Krystal *et al.* 1993; Abi-Saab *et al.* 2002). In contrast, several studies indicate that mCPP does not produce psychosis in healthy subjects (Charney *et al.* 1987; Kahn & Wetzler 1991; Seibyl *et al.* 1991; Krystal *et al.* 1993). The cause of the differential response to mCPP in schizophrenic patients and healthy control subjects is not clear. However, GABA deficits associated with schizophrenia may play a part. For example, pretreatment of healthy subjects with the benzodiazepine inverse agonist iomazenil resulted in a vulnerability to mCPP-induced psychosis (D'Souza *et al.* 2002). The behavioural and endocrine effects of mCPP in schizophrenic patients were attenuated by treatment with clozapine, but not by haloperidol (Krystal *et al.* 1990; Breier *et al.* 1993; Kahn *et al.* 1993b, 1994; Owen *et al.* 1993). These effects of mCPP were also attenuated by pretreatment with single doses of ritanserin (Abi-Saab *et al.* 2002). The adrenocorticotrophic hormone (ACTH) and cortisol response to mCPP in schizophrenic patients also predicted subsequent treatment response in schizophrenic patients (Kahn *et al.* 1993a; Owen *et al.* 1993). Unlike a preferential 5-HT_2-receptor antagonist in healthy subjects (Seibyl *et al.* 1991), clozapine treatment completely blocked the prolactin response to mCPP in schizophrenic patients (Kahn *et al.* 1994).

There is compelling evidence that 5-HT_2-receptor antagonism or inverse agonism may contribute to the efficacy of atypical neuroleptic medications. Atypical neuroleptics showed greater affinity for serotonin-2A (5-HT_{2A})-receptors relative to their affinity for D_2 receptors (Meltzer *et al.* 1989). More recently, the clinical profile of the atypical neuroleptic class was attributed to relatively higher levels of occupancy of cortical 5-HT_{2A}-receptors relative to their occupancy of striatal D_2 receptors at therapeutic doses (Kapur *et al.* 1999). Recent preclinical data suggest that typical and atypical neuroleptic drugs are inverse agonists at 5-HT_{2A}-receptors (Egan *et al.* 1998), but only atypical neuroleptics cause internalization of these receptors (Willins *et al.* 1999). In addition, atypical neuroleptics, but not typical neuroleptics, show inverse agonist activity at 5-HT_{2C}-receptors (Herrick-Davis *et al.* 2000) and perhaps the 5-HT_6-receptor (Glatt *et al.* 1995; Frederick & Meador-Woodruff 1999; Zhukovskaya & Neumaier 2000).

GABA

There is now substantial evidence that abnormalities in cortical and limbic GABA neuronal populations are a facet of the neurobiology of schizophrenia. The reader is referred to two excellent recent reviews of this topic for more detail (Lewis 2000; Benes & Berretta 2001).

Abnormal number or localization of GABA neurones

After a series of postmortem studies, it remains unclear whether schizophrenia is associated with a reduction in the number of cortical interneurones, most of which contain GABA as their neurotransmitter. If this deficit exists, it is not likely to be specific to schizophrenia. Reductions in the density of non-pyramidal neurones were reported in layers II–VI of the anterior cingulate cortex and in layer II of the prefrontal cortex (Benes *et al.* 1991). Reductions in the number of parvalbumin, presumably GABA, neurones in prefrontal cortex were also reported in another laboratory (Beasley & Reynolds 1997). Subsequent studies have not replicated these findings (Akbarian *et al.* 1995; Arnold *et al.* 1995; Selemon *et al.* 1995, 1998; Woo *et al.* 1997). It is possible that opposing changes in subpopulations of GABA neurones may confound analyses that do not control for these effects. For example, regional reductions in parvalbumin-containing neurones may be accompanied by increases in the density of calretinin-containing neurones (Daviss & Lewis 1995).

Reduction in the density of GABA neurones is found in schizoaffective disorder patients (Benes *et al.* 1991) as well as patients with unipolar and bipolar affective disorder without comorbid schizophrenia (Benes *et al.* 1997; Rajakowska *et al.* 1998). These studies raise the possibility that GABA deficits are a consequence of pathogenic processes related to comorbid mood disorder in schizophrenic patients.

One unresolved issue related to the measurement of GABA neuronal populations is whether there is a disturbance in the migration of GABA neurones within the cortex in early development. There are at least two sources of cortical GABA neurones in development. One population migrates into the cerebral cortex from the lateral ganglionic eminence, a region that becomes the striatum later in development (Anderson *et al.* 1997). A second population, including the Cajal–Retzius cells, is present in layer I. These cells secrete reelin, a substance implicated in the modulation of cellular migration and cortical and hippocampal lamination (Ogawa *et al.* 1995; Del Rio *et al.* 1997). GABAergic abnormalities could arise in schizophrenia as a defect in the secretion of molecules that control the migration of GABA. For example, the reductions in GABA neurones in superficial cortical layers could be consistent with decreases in reelin found in superficial layers of prefrontal cortex in tissue from schizophrenic patients (Impagnatiello *et al.* 1998).

Other interneurone migration abnormalities associated with schizophrenia have less clear aetiologies. For example, two studies suggest that schizophrenia is associated with increased density, 'nests of cells', in the subcortical white matter (Akbarian *et al.* 1993, 1996a). It is conceivable that migration abnormalities contributing to alterations in cell migration contribute to alterations in interneurone density. For example, if the GABA neurones in the deep layers were cells that failed to migrate to positions in more superficial layers, migration deficits could contribute to decreases in GABA neuronal populations that have been reported. However, it is not clear that interneurone migration abnormalities in schizophrenia, if they exist, are specific to this disorder. For example, a growing number of genes have been identified where mutations produce human neural migration disorders (Pilz & Quarrell 1996; Uher & Golden 2000). A neuronal migration disturbance also has been described in the context of velocardiofacial syndrome (22q11 deletion) (Bird & Scambler 2000), a condition associated with schizophrenia. Similarly, environmental insults that may increase risk for schizophrenia may independently produce disturbances in neuronal migration, including prenatal cytomegalovirus infection (Tarantal *et al.* 1998) and prenatal ethanol exposure (Miller 1993; see also Chapter 17).

GABA neurone dysfunction

If GABA neuronal populations were normal in size and in their appropriate locations, abnormalities in the structure or function of GABA neurones might signal abnormalities in the development of the brain and might, in turn, contribute to the dysfunction of neural networks. This section reviews evidence of GABAergic dysfunction in schizophrenia. To our knowledge, published studies have not yet examined whether polymorphisms of genes related to GABA systems are particularly associated with schizophrenia. Therefore, this section focuses on neurobiological studies of postmortem tissue.

Several studies suggest that schizophrenic patients exhibit reductions in the levels of protein or mRNA for glutamate acid decarboxylase (GAD). However, the impact of medication effects on the current findings is not clear. GAD exists in two isoforms, GAD_{65}, primarily localized to axon terminals, and GAD_{67}, which is localized widely within GABA neurones. Most GAD_{67} is active under basal conditions, i.e. present as a holoenzyme saturated with its cofactor pyridoxal phosphate. Only half of GAD_{65} is present in this form (Kaufman *et al.* 1991). Several studies report reductions in GAD_{67} mRNA and protein levels in studies of prefrontal cortex and hippocampal tissue from patients with schizophrenia and bipolar disorder (Akbarian *et al.* 1995; Guidotti *et al.* 2000; Volk *et al.* 2000). In contrast, GAD_{65} protein levels were reported to be reduced in the anterior cingulate in patients with bipolar disorder but not schizophrenia (Todtenkopf & Benes 1998).

Reductions in GAD levels would be expected to reflect a reduction in GAD activity or cortical GABA level. One study failed to find reductions in GAD activity in prefrontal cortex (Bennett *et al.* 1979). However, several studies documented reductions in GABA levels in cortical and subcortical structures (Cross *et al.* 1979; Perry *et al.* 1979). In studies of GAD, neuroleptic effects have received attention as a potential confounding factor. However, mood stabilizing anticonvulsants, commonly prescribed to both schizophrenic and bipolar disorder patients, are of perhaps greater concern as confounding factors. For example, an anticonvulsant that significantly increases synaptic GABA levels by two- to threefold produces up to an 80% drop in cortical GAD_{67} protein levels after a 7-day administration period in animals (Rimvall *et al.* 1993). The effects of long-term anticonvulsant treatment upon GAD mRNA levels are not known. Recent measurements of cortical GABA levels also suggest that benzodiazepine administration reduces cortical GABA level in healthy human subjects (Goddard *et al.* 2002). Thus, additional research is needed to systematically distinguish medication effects from the GAD abnormalities intrinsic to schizophrenia.

Placed in a broader context, GAD_{67} reductions in schizophrenia could reflect an abnormality intrinsic to GABA neuronal terminals, particularly in the chandelier cell subgroup of interneurones. In this regard, several markers associated with GABA terminals are reduced in schizophrenic patients. For example, several studies reported reductions in binding to the GABA transporter (GAT1) in cortical and subcortical structures (Simpson *et al.* 1989; Reynolds *et al.* 1990). Decreases in GAT1 expression show a similar laminar distribution in the prefrontal cortex to reductions in GAD_{67} gene expression (Volk *et al.* 2001). Reductions in cortical GABA content in prefrontal cortex also are associated with reductions in GAT1 mRNA levels (Ohnuma *et al.* 1999). GAT1 labelling was also used to visualize

Akbarian, S., Kim, J.J., Potkin, S.G. *et al.* (1995) Gene expression for glutamic acid decarboxylase is reduced without loss of neurons in prefrontal cortex of schizophrenics. *Archives of General Psychiatry* **52**, 258–266.

Akbarian, S., Kim, J.J., Potkin, S.G. *et al.* (1996a) Maldistribution of interstitial neurons in prefrontal white matter of the brains of schizophrenic patients. *Archives of General Psychiatry* **53**, 425–436.

Akbarian, S., Sucher, N.J., Bradley, D. *et al.* (1996b) Selective alterations in gene expression for NMDA receptor subunits in prefrontal cortex of schizophrenics. *Journal of Neuroscience* **16**, 19–30.

Akil, M., Pierri, J.N., Whitehead, R.E. *et al.* (1999) Lamina-specific alterations in the dopamine innervation of the prefrontal cortex in schizophrenic subjects. *American Journal of Psychiatry* **156**, 1580–1589.

Anand, A., Charney, D.S., Oren, D.A. *et al.* (2000) Attenuation of the neuropsychiatric effects of ketamine with lamotrigine: support for hyperglutamatergic effects of *N*-methyl-D-aspartate receptor antagonists. *Archives of General Psychiatry* **57**, 270–276.

Anderson, S.A., Eisenstat, D.D., Shi, L. & Rubenstein, J.L. (1997) Interneuron migration from basal forebrain to neocortex: dependence on Dlx genes. *Science* **278**, 474–476.

Aniline, O. & Pitts, F.N. Jr (1982) Phencyclidine (PCP): a review and perspectives. *Critical Reviews in Toxicology* **10**, 145–177.

Anis, N.A., Berry, S.C., Burton, N.R. & Lodge, D. (1983) The dissociative anaesthetics, ketamine and phencyclidine, selectively reduce excitation of central mammalian neurones by *N*-methyl-aspartate. *British Journal of Pharmacology* **79**, 565–575.

Aparicio-Legarza, M.I., Cutts, A.J., Davis, B. & Reynolds, G.P. (1997) Deficits of [^{3}H]D-aspartate binding to glutamate uptake sites in striatal and accumbens tissue in patients with schizophrenia. *Neuroscience Letters* **232**, 13–16.

Arnold, S.E., Franz, B.R., Gur, R.C. *et al.* (1995) Smaller neuron size in schizophrenia in hippocampal subfields that mediate cortical–hippocampal interactions. *American Journal of Psychiatry* **152**, 738–748.

Arora, R.C. & Meltzer, H.Y. (1991) Serotonin$_2$ (5-HT$_2$) receptor binding in the frontal cortex of schizophrenic patients. *Journal of Neural Transmission – General Section* **85**, 19–29.

Arranz, M., Collier, D., Sodhi, M. *et al.* (1995) Association between clozapine response and allelic variation in 5-HT$_{2A}$ receptor gene. *Lancet* **346**, 281–282.

Arranz, M.J., Lin, M.W., Powell, J., Kerwin, R. & Collier, D. (1996) 5-HT$_{2A}$ receptor T102C polymorphism and schizophrenia. *Lancet* **347**, 1831–1832.

Arranz, M.J., Munro, J., Owen, M.J. *et al.* (1998a) Evidence for association between polymorphisms in the promoter and coding regions of the 5-HT$_{2A}$ receptor gene and response to clozapine. *Molecular Psychiatry* **3**, 61–66.

Arranz, M.J., Munro, J., Sham, P. *et al.* (1998b) Meta-analysis of studies on genetic variation in 5-HT$_{2A}$ receptors and clozapine response. *Schizophrenia Research* **32**, 93–99.

Arranz, M.J., Munro, J., Birkett, J. *et al.* (2000) Pharmacogenetic prediction of clozapine response. *Lancet* **355**, 1615–1616.

Bakker, C.B. & Amini, F.B. (1961) Observations on the psychotomimetic effects of sernyl. *Comparative Psychiatrics* **2**, 269–280.

Beasley, C.L. & Reynolds, G.P. (1997) Parvalbumin-immunoreactive neurons are reduced in the prefrontal cortex of schizophrenics. *Schizophrenia Research* **24**, 349–355.

Benes, F.M. & Berretta, S. (2001) GABAergic interneurons: implications for understanding schizophrenia and bipolar disorder. *Neuropsychopharmacology* **25**, 1–27.

Benes, F.M., McSparren, J., Bird, E.D., SanGiovanni, J.P. & Vincent, S.L. (1991) Deficits in small interneurons in prefrontal and cingulate cortices of schizophrenic and schizoaffective patients. *Archives of General Psychiatry* **48**, 996–1001.

Benes, F.M., Vincent, S.L., Alsterberg, G., Bird, E.D. & SanGiovanni, J.P. (1992) Increased GABAA receptor binding in superficial layers of cingulate cortex in schizophrenics. *Journal of Neuroscience* **12**, 924–929.

Benes, F.M., Vincent, S.L., Marie, A. & Khan, Y. (1996) Upregulation of GABAA receptor binding on neurons of the prefrontal cortex in schizophrenic subjects. *Neuroscience* **75**, 1021–1031.

Benes, F.M., Wickramasinghe, R., Vincent, S.L., Khan, Y. & Todtenkopf, M. (1997) Uncoupling of GABA (A) and benzodiazepine receptor binding activity in the hippocampal formation of schizophrenic brain. *Brain Research* **755**, 121–129.

Bennett, J.P. Jr, Enna, S.J., Bylund, D.B. *et al.* (1979) Neurotransmitter receptors in frontal cortex of schizophrenics. *Archives of General Psychiatry* **36**, 927–934.

Bird, L.M. & Scambler, P. (2000) Cortical dysgenesis in two patients with chromosome 22q11 deletion. *Clinical Genetics* **58**, 64–68.

Birkett, J.T., Arranz, M.J., Munro, J. *et al.* (2000) Association analysis of the 5-HT$_{5A}$ gene in depression, psychosis and antipsychotic response. *Neuroreport* **11**, 2017–2020.

Bolonna, A.A., Kerwin, R.W., Munro, J., Arranz, M.J. & Makoff, A.J. (2001) Polymorphisms in the genes for mGluR types 7 and 8: association studies with schizophrenia. *Schizophrenia Research* **47**, 99–103.

Bowers, M.B.J. (1987) The role of drugs in the production of schizophreniform psychoses and related disorders. In: *Psychopharmacology: the Third Generation of Progress* (ed. H.Y. Meltzer), pp. 819–823. Raven Press, New York.

Bray, N.J., Williams, N.M., Bowen, T. *et al.* (2000) No evidence for association between a non-synonymous polymorphism in the gene encoding human metabotropic glutamate receptor 7 and schizophrenia. *Psychiatric Genetics* **10**, 83–86.

Breese, C.R., Lee, M.J., Adams, C.E. *et al.* (2000) Abnormal regulation of high affinity nicotinic receptors in subjects with schizophrenia. *Neuropsychopharmacology* **23**, 351–364.

Breier, A., Kirkpatrick, B. & Buchanan, R.W. (1993) Clozapine attenuates *meta*-chlorophenylpiperazine (mCPP)-induced plasma cortisol increases in schizophrenia. *Biological Psychiatry* **34**, 492–494.

Bressan, R.A. & Pilowsky, L.S. (2000) Imaging the glutamatergic system *in vivo*: relevance to schizophrenia. *European Journal of Nuclear Medicine* **27**, 1723–1731.

Brodie, T.M. (1959) Psychopharmacology: an evaluation. In: *Biological Psychiatry* (ed. J.H. Masserman), pp. 264–268. Grune & Stratton, New York.

Bruss, M., Bonisch, H., Buhlen, M. *et al.* (1999) Modified ligand binding to the naturally occurring Cys-124 variant of the human serotonin 5-HT$_{1B}$ receptor. *Pharmacogenetics* **9**, 95–102.

Burnet, P.W., Eastwood, S.L. & Harrison, P.J. (1996) 5-HT$_{1A}$ and 5-HT$_{2A}$ receptor mRNAs and binding site densities are differentially altered in schizophrenia. *Neuropsychopharmacology* **15**, 442 455.

Burns, R. & Lerner, L.S. (1976) Perspectives: acute phencyclidine intoxication. *Clinical Toxicology* **9**, 477–501.

Busatto, G.F., Pilowsky, L.S., Costa, D.C. *et al.* (1997) Correlation between reduced *in vivo* benzodiazepine receptor binding and severity of psychotic symptoms in schizophrenia [see comments]. *American Journal of Psychiatry* **154**, 56–63. [Published erratum appears in *American Journal of Psychiatry* 1997; **154**, 722.]

Carlsson, A. (1978) Antipsychotic drugs, neurotransmitters, and schizophrenia. *American Journal of Psychiatry* **135**, 164–173.

Charney, D.S., Woods, S.W., Goodman, W.K. & Heninger, G.R. (1987) Serotonin function in anxiety. II. Effects of the serotonin agonist MCPP in panic disorder patients and healthy subjects. *Psychopharmacology* **92**, 14–24.

Chen, C.H., Lee, Y.R., Wei, F.C. *et al.* (1997) Lack of allelic association between 102T/C polymorphism of serotonin receptor type 2A gene and schizophrenia in Chinese. *Psychiatric Genetics* **7**, 35–38.

Cohen, B.D., Rosenbaum, G., Luby, E.D. & Gottlieb, J.S. (1962) Comparison of phencyclidine hydrochloride (sernyl) with other drugs: simulation of schizophrenic performance with phencyclidine hydrochloride (sernyl), lysergic acid diethylamide (LSD-25), amobarbital (amytal) sodium. II. Symbolic and sequential thinking. *Archives of General Psychiatry* **6**, 79–85.

Conn, J.P. & Pin, J.-P. (1997) Pharmacology and functions of metabotropic glutamate receptors. *Annual Review of Pharmacology and Toxicology* **37**, 205–237.

Coyle, J. (1996) The glutamatergic dysfunction hypothesis for schizophrenia. *Harvard Review of Psychiatry* **3**, 241–253.

Crook, J.M., Tomaskovic-Crook, E., Copolov, D.L. & Dean, B. (2001) Low muscarinic receptor binding in prefrontal cortex from subjects with schizophrenia: a study of Brodmann's areas 8, 9, 10 and 46 and the effects of neuroleptic drug treatment. *American Journal of Psychiatry* **158**, 918–925.

Cross, A.J., Crow, T.J. & Owen, F. (1979) Gamma-aminobutyric acid in the brain in schizophrenia. *Lancet* **1**, 560–561.

Crow, T.J., Baker, H.F., Cross, A.J. *et al.* (1979) Monoamine mechanisms in chronic schizophrenia: post-mortem neurochemical findings. *British Journal of Psychiatry* **134**, 249–256.

Dalack, G.W., Healy, D.J. & Meador-Woodruff, J.H. (1998) Nicotine dependence in schizophrenia: clinical phenomena and laboratory findings. *American Journal of Psychiatry* **155**, 1490–1501.

Davis, K.L., Berger, P.A., Hollister, L.E. & Defraites, E. (1978) Physostigmine in mania. *Archives of General Psychiatry* **35**, 119–122.

Daviss, S.R. & Lewis, D.A. (1995) Local circuit neurons of the prefrontal cortex in schizophrenia: selective increase in the density of calbindin-immunoreactive neurons. *Psychiatry Research* **59**, 81–96.

Deakin, J., Slater, P., Simpson, M. *et al.* (1989) Frontal cortical and left temporal glutamatergic dysfunction in schizophrenia. *Journal of Neuroscience* **52**, 1781–1786.

Dean, B. & Hayes, W. (1996) Decreased frontal cortical serotonin$_{2A}$ receptors in schizophrenia. *Schizophrenia Research* **21**, 133–139.

Dean, B., Opeskin, K., Pavey, G. *et al.* (1995) [^{3}H]paroxetine binding is altered in the hippocampus but not the frontal cortex or caudate nucleus from subjects with schizophrenia. *Journal of Neurochemistry* **64**, 1197–1202.

Dean, B., Crook, J.M., Opeskin, K. *et al.* (1996) The density of muscarinic M1 receptors is decreased in the caudate–putamen of subjects with schizophrenia [see comments]. *Molecular Psychiatry* **1**, 54–58.

Dean, B., Tomaskovic-Crook, E., Opeskin, K., Keks, N. & Copolov, D. (1999a) No change in the density of the serotonin$_{1A}$ receptor, the serotonin$_4$ receptor or the serotonin transporter in the dorsolateral prefrontal cortex from subjects with schizophrenia. *Neurochemistry International* **34**, 109–115.

Dean, B., Hussain, T., Hayes, W. *et al.* (1999b) Changes in serotonin$_{2A}$ and GABA (A) receptors in schizophrenia: studies on the human dorsolateral prefrontal cortex. *Journal of Neurochemistry* **72**, 1593–1599.

Del Rio, J.A., Heimrich, B., Borrell, V. *et al.* (1997) A role for Cajal–Retzlus cells and reelin in the development of hippocampal connections. *Nature* **385**, 70–74.

D'Souza, D.C., Gil, R., MacDougall, L. *et al.* (2002) GABA–serotonin interactions in healthy subjects: implications for psychosis and dissociation. *Archives of General Psychiatry* in press.

Durany, N., Zochling, R., Boissl, K.W. *et al.* (2000) Human postmortem striatal $\alpha 4\beta 2$ nicotinic acetylcholine receptor density in schizophrenia and Parkinson's syndrome. *Neuroscience Letters* **287**, 109–112.

Eastwood, S.L., McDonald, B., Burnet, P.W. *et al.* (1995) Decreased expression of mRNAs encoding non-NMDA glutamate receptors GluR1 and GluR2 in medial temporal lobe neurons in schizophrenia. *Brain Research – Molecular Brain Research* **29**, 211–223.

Eastwood, S.L., Burnet, P.W. & Harrison, P.J. (1997) GluR2 glutamate receptor subunit flip and flop isoforms are decreased in the hippocampal formation in schizophrenia: a reverse transcriptase-polymerase chain reaction (RT-PCR) study. *Brain Research – Molecular Brain Research* **44**, 92–98.

Edelstein, P., Schultz, J.R., Hirschowitz, J., Kanter, D.R. & Garver, D.L. (1981) Physostigmine and lithium response in the schizophrenias. *American Journal of Psychiatry* **138**, 1078–1081.

Egan, C.T., Herrick-Davis, K. & Teitler, M. (1998) Creation of a constitutively activated state of the 5-hydroxytryptamine$_{2A}$ receptor by site-directed mutagenesis: inverse agonist activity of antipsychotic drugs. *Journal of Pharmacology and Experimental Therapeutics* **286**, 85–90.

Erdmann, J., Shimron-Abarbanell, D., Cichon, S. *et al.* (1995) Systematic screening for mutations in the promoter and the coding region of the 5-HT$_{1A}$ gene. *American Journal of Medical Genetics* **60**, 393–399.

Erdmann, J., Nothen, M.M., Shimron-Abarbanell, D. *et al.* (1996a) The human serotonin 7 (5-HT$_7$) receptor gene: genomic organization and systematic mutation screening in schizophrenia and bipolar affective disorder. *Molecular Psychiatry* **1**, 392–397.

Erdmann, J., Shimron-Abarbanell, D., Rietschel, M. *et al.* (1996b) Systematic screening for mutations in the human serotonin-2A (5-HT$_{2A}$) receptor gene: identification of two naturally occurring receptor variants and association analysis in schizophrenia. *Human Genetics* **97**, 614–619.

Fiorella, D., Rabin, R.A. & Winter, J.C. (1995) The role of the 5-HT$_{2A}$ and 5-HT$_{2C}$ receptors in the stimulus effects of *m*-chlorophenylpiperazine. *Psychopharmacology* **119**, 222–230.

Fisher, C.M. (1991) Visual hallucinations on eye closure associated with atropine toxicity: a neurological analysis and comparison with other visual hallucinations. *Canadian Journal of Neurological Sciences* **18**, 18–27.

Frederick, J.A. & Meador-Woodruff, J.H. (1999) Effects of clozapine and haloperidol on 5-HT$_6$ receptor mRNA levels in rat brain. *Schizophrenia Research* **38**, 7–12.

Freedman, D.X. (1968) On the use and abuse of LSD. *Archives of General Psychiatry* **18**, 330–347.

Freedman, R., Adler, L.E., Bickford, P. *et al.* (1994) Schizophrenia and nicotinic receptors. *Harvard Review of Psychiatry* **2**, 179–192.

Freedman, R., Hall, M., Adler, L.E. & Leonard, S. (1995) Evidence in postmortem brain tissue for decreased numbers of hippocampal nicotinic receptors in schizophrenia. *Biological Psychiatry* **38**, 22–33.

Freedman, R., Coon, H., Myles-Worsley, M. *et al.* (1997) Linkage of a neurophysiological deficit in schizophrenia to a chromosome 15 locus. *Proceedings of the National Academy of Sciences USA* **94**, 587–592.

Gao, X.M., Sakai, K., Roberts, R.C. *et al.* (2000) Ionotropic glutamate receptors and expression of *N*-methyl-D-aspartate receptor subunits in subregions of human hippocampus: effects of schizophrenia. *American Journal of Psychiat* **157**, 1141–1149.

Gattaz, W.F., Gattaz, D. & Beckmann, H. (1982) Glutamate in

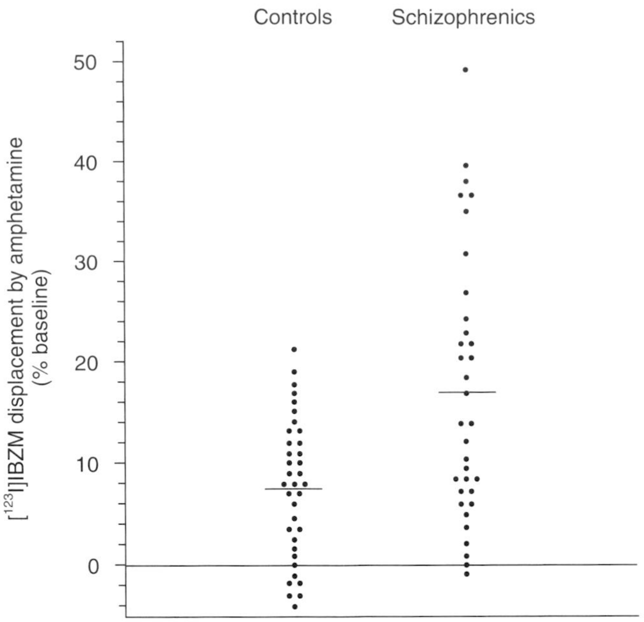

Fig 20.3 Effect of amphetamine (0.3 mg/kg) on [^{123}I]IBZM binding in healthy controls and untreated patients with schizophrenia. The *y*-axis shows the percentage decrease in [^{123}I]IBZM binding potential induced by amphetamine, which is a measure of the increased occupancy of D_2 receptors by DA following the challenge. Increased stimulation of D_2 receptors in schizophrenia was associated with transient worsening or emergence of positive symptoms.

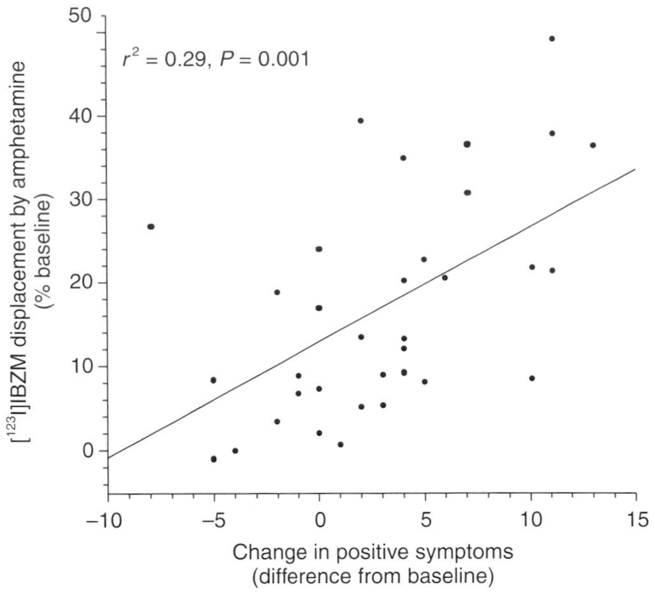

Fig 20.4 Relationship between striatal amphetamine-induced dopamine release (*y*-axis) and amphetamine-induced changes in positive symptoms measured with the positive subscale of the Positive and Negative Symptom Scale (PANSS) in patients with schizophrenia. Stimulation of D_2 receptors was associated with emergence or worsening of positive symptoms and accounted for about 30% of the variance in this behavioural response.

This finding supports the hypothesis that the increased amphetamine effect observed in patients with schizophrenia was not a non-specific consequence of stressful conditions, although it could represent a specific interaction between stress and schizophrenia.

These data are consistent with higher DA output in the striatum of patients with schizophrenia. This phenomenon is probably not a result of increased density of DA terminals. Striatal DA transporters (DATs) are exclusively localized on DA terminals, and the *in vivo* binding of the DAT radioligands [^{123}I]β-CIT (Laruelle *et al.* 2000) or [^{18}F]CFT (Laakso *et al.* 2000) is unaltered in patients with schizophrenia. These *in vivo* observations confirm the postmortem findings of normal DAT density in the striatum of patients with schizophrenia discussed above. In addition, *in vivo* measurement of the vesicular monoamine transporter in the caudate, putamen and ventral striatum with [^{11}C]dihydrotetrabenazine is unaltered in patients with schizophrenia (Taylor *et al.* 2000). We observed no association between amphetamine-induced DA release and DAT density (Laruelle *et al.* 2000). Thus, the increased presynaptic output suggested by the amphetamine studies appears to be associated with a functional dysregulation of DA neurones, rather than an increased number of these neurones.

Imaging baseline DA activity in schizophrenia

A major limitation of the amphetamine studies is that they measured changes in synaptic DA transmission following a non-physiological challenge (i.e. amphetamine) and did not provide any information about 'baseline' synaptic DA levels (i.e. synaptic DA levels in the absence of pharmacological interventions). Several laboratories reported that, in rodents and non-human primates, acute depletion of synaptic DA is associated with an acute increase in the *in vivo* binding of [^{11}C]raclopride or [^{123}I]IBZM to D_2 receptors (Van der Werf *et al.* 1986; Ross & Jackson 1989; Seeman *et al.* 1989; Ross 1991; Young *et al.* 1991; Dewey *et al.* 1992; Ginovart *et al.* 1997). The increased binding was observed *in vivo* but not *in vitro*, indicating that it was not caused by receptor upregulation (Laruelle *et al.* 1997a), but to removal of endogenous DA and unmasking of D_2 receptors previously occupied by DA. Using this acute depletion strategy, baseline occupancy of striatal D_2 receptors by DA was studied in acute patients with schizophrenia (Abi-Dargham *et al.* 2000b). D_2 receptor availability was measured at baseline (i.e. in the absence of any pharmacological intervention) and during acute DA depletion. Acute DA depletion was achieved by administration of high doses of α-MPT for 2 days (Spector *et al.* 1965; Udenfriend *et al.* 1965). Comparing D_2 receptor availability at baseline and in the depleted state provided an indirect measure of the proportion of D_2 receptors occupied by DA in the baseline state. Removal of endogenous DA by α-MPT increased D_2 receptor availability by 9 ± 7% in controls ($n = 18$) and by 19 ± 11% in patients with schizophrenia ($n = 18$, $P = 0.003$). The differential effect of α-MPT between patients and controls was not a result of differences in α-MPT plasma levels. α-MPT effect on D_2 receptor availability was not statistically different between drug-naïve (n = 8, 17 ± 6%) and previously treated patients (n = 10, 20 ± 15%), and both groups were significantly different from controls.

Thus, the results of this study suggest that DA occupies a greater proportion of striatal D_2 receptors in patients with schizophrenia compared with matched control subjects during first episode of illness and subsequent episodes of illness exacerbation. The significance of this result stems from the fact that the paradigm used here reveals D_2 receptor occupancy by DA during the baseline scan, i.e. in the absence of any pharmacological intervention. The result of this study directly supports the classical dopamine hypothesis of schizophrenia, but should be viewed with caution until independently replicated.

The results of the α-MPT study are consistent with results of studies reporting DOPA decarboxylase activity in patients with schizophrenia, using [^{18}F]DOPA (Reith *et al.* 1994; Hietala *et al.* 1995, 1999; Dao-Castellana *et al.* 1997) or [^{11}C]DOPA (Lindstrom *et al.* 1999). Four out of five studies reported increased accumulation of DOPA in the striatum of patients with schizophrenia (Table 20.2), and the combined analysis of these studies yields an effect size of 0.92 ± 0.45, which is significantly different from zero (P = 0.01). While the relationship between DOPA decarboxylase and DA synthesis rate is unclear (DOPA decarboxylase is not the rate-limiting step of DA synthesis), these observations appear consistent with the higher synaptic DA concentration observed in patients with schizophrenia in the α-MPT study.

The term 'baseline' activity used here simply denotes that this study aimed at measuring occupancy of D_2 receptors by DA in the absence of pharmacological challenge. Because patients were studied during an episode of illness exacerbation, the occupancy of D_2 receptors by DA during periods of illness remission remains uncharacterized.

The 'baseline' DA activity studied by the α-MPT paradigm should not be confused with the tonic release described by Grace (1991, 1993) in his model of DA dysregulation associated with schizophrenia. This model rests on the distinction between tonic and phasic DA release. Tonic release refers to the extracellular extrasynaptic DA release, is impulse-independent and regulated by glutamatergic projections from the PFC to DA terminals in striatum. In contrast, the phasic release is the impulse-dependent synaptic DA release. Grace (1991, 1993) speculated that schizophrenia might be associated with low tonic DA activity, resulting from a decreased glutamatergic stimulation. This low DA tonic activity would in turn induce increased phasic DA activity, leading to overstimulation of postsynaptic D_2 receptors and emergence of positive symptoms. The baseline D_2 receptor occupancy by DA measured in the α-MPT study is presumably caused by the temporal and spatial integration of phasic release, as several lines of evidence suggest that the effect measured by these imaging techniques is intra- rather than extrasynaptic (for review and discussion see Laruelle 2000a). Thus, results of the α-MPT are consistent with the Grace (1991, 1993) model.

Importantly, high synaptic DA concentration revealed by the α-MPT paradigm was not associated with global severity of positive symptoms (Abi-Dargham *et al.* 2000b). Among positive symptoms, only severity of suspiciousness was associated at trend level with high synaptic DA levels, an interesting observation because suspiciousness is probably one of the most 'DA-dependent' dimensions of psychosis (Ellinwood *et al.* 1973). One of the important functions of subcortical DA is to signal the 'salience' of environmental stimuli (Schultz *et al.* 1998), and it is relatively easy to comprehend how dysregulation of the DA salience system might lead to suspiciousness, interpretation and paranoia (Ellinwood *et al.* 1973). None the less, the general lack of correlation between synaptic DA excess and severity of positive symptoms guards against simplistic association between positive symptoms and D_2 receptor stimulation.

This negative result might be a result of the limited resolution of the SPECT camera. Rodent studies suggest that antipsychotic drug action is associated with D_2 receptor antagonism in the mesolimbic (nucleus accumbens) rather than the nigrostriatal (dorsostriatal) DA systems (for review see Deutch 1993). This hypothesis derives mainly from the observation that atypical antipsychotic drugs, such as clozapine, are more potent at affecting DA transmission in the nucleus accumbens compared with the striatum (for review see Abi-Dargham *et al.* 1997). The limited resolution of the PET or SPECT cameras used in clinical studies so far did not allow distinguishing the respective contributions of the ventral and dorsal striata to the imaging signal. Studies with the newest high-resolution PET cameras recently demonstrated that the signal from ventral and dorsal striata can be reliably identified (Drevets *et al.* 2001; Mawlawi *et al.* 2001). Thus, the use of this improved technology will enable comparison of ventral and dorsal striatal DA transmission in schizophrenia. Meanwhile, the specific role of the ventral striatum in the psychotic process remains conjectural.

On the other hand, this negative result might indicate that the severity of positive symptoms rated cross-sectionally at a given point in time depends mostly on factors located downstream from the mesolimbic dopaminergic synapses. The dysfunctional neuronal circuits that underlie the experience of positive symptoms are likely to involve dysregulated information processing in the prefrontal–ventrostriatal–ventropallidal–mediodorsal–thalamoprefrontal loops reviewed above, and their regulation by hippocampal and amygdalar afferents (Grace *et al.* 1998; O'Donnell & Grace 1998a). Activity in these putative propsychotic neuronal ensembles is under modulatory influence of subcortical DA. A sudden rise in subcortical DA (such as measured following amphetamine) will exacerbate these symptoms, while a sudden decline in DA (such as measured following α-MPT) will blunt their intensity. Thus, psychotic symptomatology includes both DA-dependent and DA-independent components, with the respective contribution of each component varying from patient to patient (and presumably varying with time within the same patient).

Patients included in the α-MPT study completed 6 weeks of antipsychotic medication as inpatients. High synaptic levels of DA at baseline, measured by the α-MPT effect on D_2 receptor

BP, was significantly associated with greater improvement of positive symptoms following 6 weeks of antipsychotic treatment. Thus, the dysregulation of DA transmission revealed by the imaging study was predictive of better response of positive symptoms to antipsychotic treatment. Schizophrenic patients who experienced positive symptoms in the presence of increased DA stimulation of D_2 receptors showed a remarkable and rapid decline in these symptoms following treatment with antipsychotic drugs. Subjects who experienced positive symptoms in the presence of apparently normal stimulation of D_2 receptors by DA showed little improvement of these symptoms following 6 weeks of antipsychotic treatment. The fact that high levels of synaptic DA at baseline predicted better or faster response to atypical antipsychotic drugs (13 out of 14 patients were treated with atypical drugs) also suggests that the D_2 receptor blockade induced by these drugs remains a key component of their initial mode of action.

Contrary to widely accepted views, antipsychotic drugs have only partial efficacy against positive symptoms. A substantial proportion of schizophrenic patients, possibly one-third, remains actively psychotic despite appropriate and prolonged blockade of D_2 receptors (Huckle & Palia 1993; Weiden *et al.* 1996). The data from the α-MPT study suggest that, in some patients, blockade of D_2 receptors by antipsychotic drugs fails to alter positive symptoms significantly because these symptoms might not be related to excessive stimulation of these receptors by DA.

Discussion

While the studies reviewed above generally confirmed the classical DA hypothesis of schizophrenia, it is important to examine these results in light of the more recent views of schizophrenia as a neurodevelopmental illness, involving dysconnectivity of cortico–subcortical and intracortical networks. In this discussion, we speculate about the possible relationships between the imaging results reviewed above and this contemporary view of schizophrenia. The model proposed here suggests that neurodevelopmental abnormalities of intracortical and corticolimbic connectivity set the stage for the development of intermittent episodes of endogenous sensitization of the mesolimbic DA system that lead to the abnormal gating of information flow in the limbic loops that is underlying the psychotic experience. If sustained, this aberrant gating leads to plastic adaptation and remodelling of these circuits. As a result of these neuroplastic changes, the psychotic symptoms might become independent of sustained DA hyperactivity and resistant to D_2 receptor blockade.

Cortical regulation of subcortical dopamine transmission

While it cannot be definitively ruled out that the DA dysregulation revealed by these studies would stem from a primary abnormality of DA neurones, it seems more likely that these abnormalities are a consequence of cortico–subcortical dysconnectivity. Moreover, given the weight of evidence implicating PFC connectivity as a central deficient node in the schizophrenic brain, it is tempting to speculate that a dysregulation of the firing activity of dopaminergic neurones might stem from a failure of the PFC to regulate this process. In fact, it has long been hypothesized that dysregulation of subcortical DA function in schizophrenia may be secondary to a failure of the PFC to adequately control subcortical dopaminergic function (Weinberger *et al.* 1986; Grace 1991).

In patients with schizophrenia, low *N*-acetyl-aspartate (NAA) concentration in the DLPFC, a marker of DLPFC pathology, is associated with increased amphetamine-induced DA release (Bertolino *et al.* 2000). This result provides direct support to the hypothesis that disinhibition of subcortical DA activity might be secondary to prefrontal pathology in schizophrenia. Yet, the nature of the PFC pathology in schizophrenia and how it might affect subcortical DA function remains to be elucidated.

According to a model introduced by Carlsson *et al.* (1999b), the PFC modulates activity of midbrain DA neurones via both an activating pathway (the 'accelerator') and an inhibitory pathway ('the brake'), allowing fine tuning of dopaminergic activity by the PFC (Fig. 20.5). The activating pathway is provided by direct and indirect glutamatergic projections onto the dopaminergic cells. These indirect projections are likely to involve the pedunculopontine tegmentum (see discussion and reference in Carr & Sesack 2000). The inhibitory pathway is provided by PFC glutamatergic efferents to midbrain GABAergic interneurones and striatomesencephalic GABA neurones.

The inhibition of dopaminergic cell firing following amphetamine is an important feedback mechanism by which the brain reduces the effect of amphetamine on DA release. The inhibition of dopaminergic cell firing induced by amphetamine is mediated both by stimulation of presynaptic D_2 autoreceptors and by stimulation of this inhibitory pathway (Bunney & Aghajanian 1978; Carlsson *et al.* 1999b). Following administration of amphetamine (i.e. under conditions in which the inhibitory pathway should be activated), NMDA receptor blockade results in a failure of activation of the inhibitory pathway, resulting in exaggerated amphetamine-induced DA release (Miller & Abercrombie 1996). Kegeles *et al.* (2000) recently confirmed this mechanism in humans: pretreatment with the NMDA non-competitive antagonist ketamine significantly enhanced amphetamine-induced DA release. The increase in amphetamine-induced DA release induced by ketamine (greater than twofold) was comparable in magnitude to the exaggerated response seen in patients with schizophrenia (Fig. 20.6). These data are consistent with the hypothesis that the alteration of DA release revealed by the amphetamine challenge in schizophrenia results from a disruption of glutamatergic neuronal systems regulating dopaminergic cell activity. Moreover, these data provide a direct link between the DA hypothesis and the NMDA receptor hypofunction hypothesis of schizophrenia (Javitt & Zukin 1991; Olney & Farber 1995; Jentsch & Roth 1999).

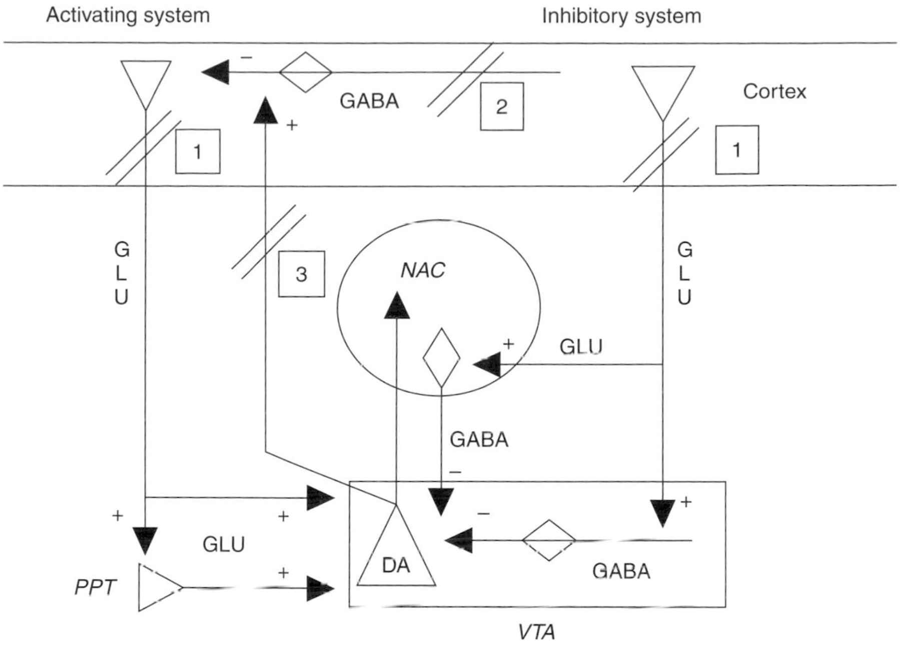

Fig 20.5 Model of modulation of VTA DA cells activity by PFC. Activity of midbrain DA neurones is under dual influence of PFC via activating and inhibitory pathways, allowing fine tuning of dopaminergic activity by the PFC. The activating pathway is provided by glutamatergic projections onto the dopaminergic cells, and the inhibitory pathway is provided by glutamatergic projections to midbrain GABAergic interneurones or striatomesencephalic GABA neurones (see text for description and references). This model predicts that a deficiency in *N*-methyl-D-aspartate (NMDA) transmission [lesion 1] and/or GABA PFC function [lesion 2] and/or DA PFC function [lesion 3] would result in a failure of the PFC to inhibit subcortical DA activity under conditions of excessive stimulation (such as stress or amphetamine challenge). NAC, nucleus accumbens; PPT, pedunculopontine tegmentum; VTA, ventral tegmental area.

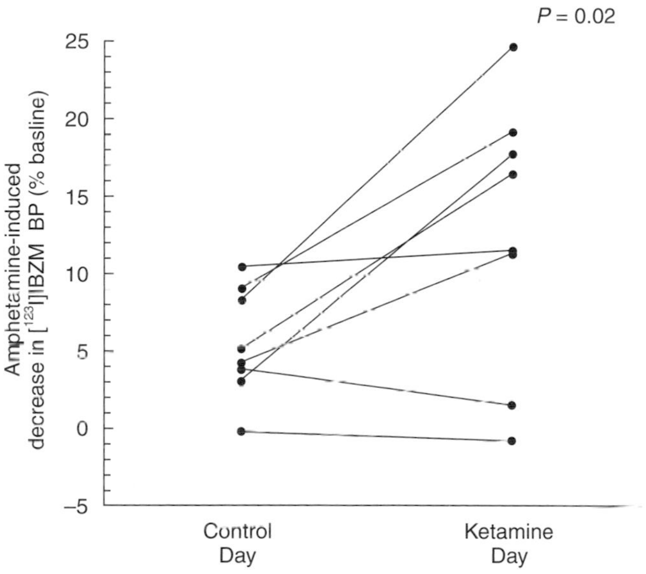

Fig 20.6 Ketamine modulation of striatal amphetamine-induced dopamine release in healthy volunteers, showing a significantly larger release in eight healthy volunteers pretreated with i.v. ketamine compared with control conditions (repeated measures ANOVA, $P = 0.023$). These data indicate that, in humans, amphetamine-induced DA release in the striatum is modulated by glutamatergic circuits involving NMDA transmission.

Alternatively, the failure of PFC control of subcortical DA release might stem from mechanisms other than NMDA hypofunction. For example, glutamatergic projections from the PFC to the VTA are under tonic inhibition by prefrontal GABA (see Karreman & Moghaddam 1996 and references therein). It follows that deficit in GABAergic function in the PFC is also expected to lead to disinhibition of subcortical DA response to amphetamine. Alteration of GABAergic function in the PFC is one of the most consistently noted postmortem abnormalities in schizophrenia. Gene expression for GABA synthetic enzyme glutamic acid decarboxylase-67 ($GABA_{67}$) appears to be reduced in the PFC (Akbarian *et al.* 1995; Volk *et al.* 2000). GABAergic markers in axon terminals of chandelier neurones might be substantially reduced (Woo *et al.* 1998). One study reported decreased density of GABAergic interneurones in PFC in layer II (Benes *et al.* 1991), although this finding has not been replicated (Akbarian *et al.* 1995; Woo *et al.* 1997). Increased binding of the $GABA_A$ receptors was also observed (Hanada *et al.* 1987; Benes *et al.* 1992, 1996), which has been interpreted as a compensatory upregulation induced by GABA deficit.

Since the seminal work of Pycock *et al.* (1980), many laboratories have described the reciprocal and opposite regulations between cortical and subcortical dopaminergic systems: stimulation of cortical DA leads to inhibition of subcortical DA (Kolachana *et al.* 1995; Karreman & Moghaddam 1996), while destruction of cortical DA projections leads to subcortical disinhibition (Deutch *et al.* 1990; Wilkinson 1997). In the cortex, DA has an inhibitory effect on pyramidal neurones that stimulate DA release at the VTA level (Karreman & Moghaddam 1996), an effect mediated in part by DA stimulation of GABAergic interneurones (Deutch 1993). Schizophrenia has been postulated to be associated with a deficit of the prefrontal DA system. Thus, deficits in PFC DA innervation might represent another avenue leading to the disinhibition of subcortical DA revealed by these imaging studies. Figure 20.5 summarizes how these various pathophysiological mechanisms in the PFC might result in disinhibition of subcortical DA neurones.

Moreover, preclinical studies documented that dysregulation of subcortical DA function might be a delayed and enduring consequence of neurodevelopmental abnormalities of limbocortical connectivity. Studies in rodents showed that alteration of corticolimbic development induced by prenatal exposure to the antimitotic agent methylazoxymethanol acetate (MAM) results in increased subcortical DA release in adulthood (Watanabe *et al.* 1998). The increase in subcortical DA transmission in MAM-treated rodents was correlated strongly with the severity of cerebral cortical thinning resulting from altered development. Adult rhesus monkeys with neonatal ablation of the amygdala–hippocampal formation exhibit lower NAA concentration in the PFC and impaired PFC inhibition of subcortical DA functions (Bertolino *et al.* 1997; Saunders *et al.* 1998). Thus, several lines of evidence, both at the preclinical and clinical level, suggest that hyperactivity of subcortical DA release in schizophrenia might be secondary to neurodevelopmental events affecting primarily connectivity within the PFC or between the PFC and the limbic system.

Schizophrenia and endogenous sensitization

While the evidence reviewed above is consistent with the model that dysregulation of subcortical DA function in schizophrenia is an enduring consequence of neurodevelopmental abnormalities involving PFC connectivity, these models *per se* do not account for the apparent episodic nature of this dysregulation. In the imaging studies reviewed above, elevated amphetamine-induced DA release was observed only in patients experiencing a first episode of illness or an episode of illness exacerbation, but not in patients studied during a period of illness remission. To confirm this observation by studying the same subjects during and between episodes is warranted. Nevertheless, this observation, combined with the clinical evidence of the fluctuating nature of positive symptomatology, suggests that subcortical hyperdopaminergia is episodic in the schizophrenic brain.

Neurochemical sensitization of mesolimbic DA systems has been proposed by several authors as one mechanism that might underlie the progression of a 'silent' vulnerability into an overt symptomatology, resulting in further 'toxic' effects on the brain (Robinson & Becker 1986; Lieberman *et al.* 1990, 1997; Glenthoj & Hemmingsen 1997; Pierce & Kalivas 1997). Sensitization is a process whereby exposure to a given stimulus such as a drug or a stressor results in an enhanced response to subsequent exposures. This phenomenon has been well characterized in rodents: repeated exposure to psychostimulants such as amphetamine induces an increase in the behavioural (locomotion) and biochemical (DA release) response to amphetamine, other stimulants, or stressors (for review see Robinson & Becker 1986; Kalivas & Stewart 1991; Kalivas *et al.* 1993; Sorg *et al.* 1994). Under certain conditions, sensitization is a long-lasting adaptation: animals sensitized to stimulants continue to display enhanced response after months of abstinence (Magos 1969; Robinson & Becker 1986). Sensitization is a form of learning behaviour and is essentially a non-homeostatic positive feedback mechanism. Sensitization makes individuals more vulnerable rather than more resistant to a number of pharmacological or environmental stimulations.

Subjects who abused psychostimulants and experienced stimulant-induced psychotic episodes are reported to remain vulnerable to low doses of psychostimulants (Connell 1958; Ellinwood *et al.* 1973; Sato *et al.* 1983). In these subjects, exposure to psychostimulants at doses that do not normally produce psychotic symptoms can trigger recurrence of these symptoms. The similarity between these patients and patients with schizophrenia in terms of vulnerability to the propsychotic effects of psychostimulants has been noted and led to the suggestion that schizophrenia might be associated with an 'endogenous' sensitization process (Lieberman *et al.* 1990; Glenthoj & Hemmingsen 1997).

The brain imaging data reviewed above provide support for the hypothesis that dysfunction of DA systems in schizophrenia results from a process similar to the sensitization phenomenon described following repeated psychostimulant exposure in rodents, because both conditions are associated with increased psychostimulant-induced DA release. In turn, this proposition suggests that neurodevelopmental abnormalities associated with schizophrenia may set the stage for the development of an endogenous sensitization process (Lieberman *et al.* 1997; Laruelle 2000b).

We have reviewed elsewhere (Laruelle 2000b) the preclinical literature suggesting that early brain lesions that affect the development of cortical connectivity might result in enhanced vulnerability to sensitization of mesolimbic DA systems. During late adolescence, alteration in cortical connectivity in schizophrenia might limit the capacity of the brain to modulate stress-related increased activity of mesolimbic DA neurones. This failure of normal homeostatic and buffering mechanisms results in endogenous sensitization of mesolimbic DA neurones, a response not observed in humans under normal circumstances. While increased DA activity is initially associated with environmental stressors, the sensitization process is self-perpetuating and, beyond a given threshold, becomes independent of the environmental factors responsible for its initiation. This positive feedback loop, in which more DA leads to more DA, results ultimately in profound gating alterations in the corticostriatal–thalamocortical loops and expression of positive symptoms.

With treatment, chronic blockade of D_2 receptors and/or neuroleptic-induced depolarization blockade of dopaminergic neurones (Bunney & Grace 1978) might allow a progressive extinction of this sensitized state of the mesolimbic DA system. This proposition is suggested by the failure to detect an increase in amphetamine-induced DA release in currently untreated patients with schizophrenia during periods of illness stabilization. However, the high rate of relapse during prolonged treatment discontinuation suggests that the vulnerability to develop endogenous sensitization remains. Upon environmental, physiological or pharmacological stress, this process might be reactivated, leading to clinical relapse.

Beyond the dopaminergic synapse

The data derived from the brain imaging studies reviewed above are consistent with the hypothesis that subcortical DA transmission mediates the expression of positive symptoms in patients with schizophrenia. However, the data also suggest that a component of the positive symptomatology is independent of increased activity of subcortical DA transmission. First, the increase in DA transmission at striatal D_2 receptors following amphetamine explained only 30% of the variability in the psychotic response to D-amphetamine (Fig. 20.4). Secondly, the severity of positive symptoms was not associated with increased synaptic DA concentration as revealed by the α-MPT challenge (Abi-Dargham *et al.* 2000b). Thus, a simple relationship between intensity of DA transmission at the D_2 receptors and severity of positive symptoms is an oversimplification. In addition, such a simple relationship is not supported by the delay between D_2 receptor blockade and antipsychotic response, or by resistance of positive symptoms to even sustained dopaminergic blockade in about 25% of patients with schizophrenia (Huckle & Palia 1993).

In this context, it is also important to note a critical difference in the propsychotic effects of DA agonists, on one hand, and NMDA antagonists or 5-HT_{2A} agonists, on the other. In healthy individuals, drugs such as ketamine or lysergic acid diethylamide (LSD) induce a psychotic state immediately upon drug exposure, while sustained administration of DA agonists is typically required for the emergence of psychotic symptoms (for review see Krystal *et al.* 1999). This time-dependency of DA agonists' psychotogenic effect suggests that some plasticity or neuroadaptation must take place between the hyperstimulation of D_2 receptors and the psychotic experience.

To account for these data, one might speculate that, with time, increased DA activity triggers neuroplastic adaptation 'downstream' from the mesolimbic dopaminergic synapse and that, once established, these neuroplastic changes become independent of increased DA activity. Positive symptom circuits might become 'hard-wired' in prefrontal–ventrostriatal–ventropallidal–mediodorsal–thalamoprefrontal loops described above (Fig. 20.1). The established role of DA in modulating LTP and LTD of glutamatergic synapses (Arbuthnott *et al.* 2000; Kerr & Wickens 2001) provides a potential cellular mechanism by which sustained excess of DA activity might shape and remodel these circuits. Following this neuroplastic change, excessive DA stimulation maintains the potential to activate these neuronal ensembles (as demonstrated by the relationship between D_2 receptor stimulation and worsening of positive symptoms), but the evidence suggests that, at least in some patients, these symptoms might become independent of continuous DA stimulation (as demonstrated by the observation that some patients exhibit severe positive symptoms in the absence of detectable abnormalities in synaptic DA). Thus, the emergence of treatment-resistant positive symptoms suggests that these symptoms have taken 'a life of their own', i.e. have become independent of DA stimulation. A better understanding of the consequences of sustained dopaminergic activity on the plasticity of prefrontal–striatothalamic loops is needed to further characterize the neurobiological effects of the sustained hyperdopaminergic state.

The ubiquitous role of DA in the creation of these hypothetical psychotic ensembles remains to be established. Whether DA hyperactivity has been present at some point or another in the life of every schizophrenic patient with positive symptoms is quite uncertain. A deficiency in glutamate transmission that would impair appropriate modulation of prefrontal–striatothalamic loops by afferents from the amygdala–hippocampal complex is another mechanism that might induce positive symptoms in the absence of overactivity of DA transmission (Carlsson 1988; Grace *et al.* 1998; O'Donnell & Grace 1998b). In other terms, endogenous sensitization of dopaminergic systems might represent only one avenue among others leading to chronic and/or recurrent psychotic episodes.

This view is supported by the observation that the acute propsychotic effects of NMDA antagonists in humans (or their putative equivalent manifestation in animals) do not appear to be modulated by increased DA activity or markedly affected by D_2 receptor blockade (for review see Lahti *et al.* 1995; Moghaddam & Adams 1998; Carlsson *et al.* 1999a,b; Jentsch & Roth 1999). Clinical and preclinical evidence suggests that NMDA hypofunction, at least acutely, induces psychotic symptoms by mechanisms largely independent of DA. We should note, however, that a DA transmission imbalance (decreased prefrontal activity and increased mesolimbic reactivity) is involved in the effects of prolonged administration of NMDA antagonists such as PCP, effects that more faithfully mimic schizophrenia than the effects of acute NMDA antagonist administration (Jentsch & Roth 1999).

Dopamine in the history of the schizophrenic brain

The general model proposed here predicates that in schizophrenia various clinical and neurobiological periods could be differentiated in relation to subcortical hyperdopaminergia (Fig. 20.7). It might be important to think about DA in schizophrenia within the context of a brain with a history, divided into a predopaminergic, a dopaminergic and a postdopaminergic era. The neurodevelopmental abnormalities associated with schizophrenia do not lead to hyperdopaminergia during childhood, but induce vulnerability to stress-mediated induction of sensitization of mesolimbic DA systems during adolescence. Sustained hyperactivity of DA neurones resulting from this sensitization process leads to neuroplastic changes downstream from the DA synapse. These neuroplastic adaptations underlie the emergence of the psychotic experience. If untreated, activities in these aberrant circuits become 'hard-wired' and independent from increased DA activity. Early treatment will reverse these neuroplastic changes and induce an extinction of the sensitization process. This model clearly supports the rationale for D_2 blockade during periods of illness exacerbation, and for early intervention during prodromal states.

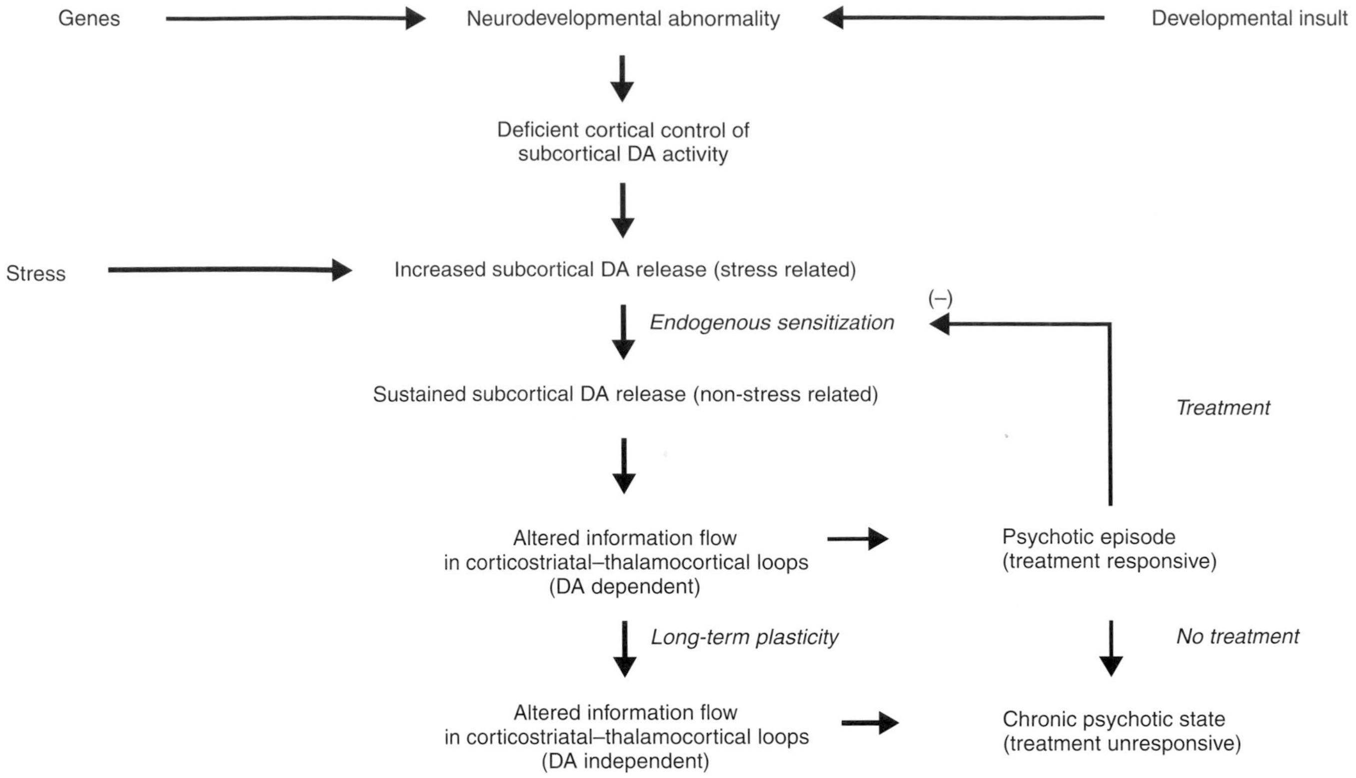

Fig 20.7 Model describing the role of subcortical DA dysregulation in the chain of events leading to clinical expression of positive symptoms in schizophrenia. It is postulated that neurodevelopmental abnormalities, resulting from complex interactions of genetic vulnerability and pre- or perinatal insults, induce, among other consequences, impaired regulation of subcortical DA activity by the prefrontal cortex (see Fig. 20.5). The lack of normal buffering systems results in vulnerability of DA systems to develop a process of endogenous sensitization. Excessive DA activity, initially as a response to stress, initiates a positive feedback loop, in which elevated DA activity becomes self-sustained even in the absence of stressors or other salient stimuli. This excessive DA activity perturbs information flow in corticostriatal–thalamocortical loops (see Fig. 20.1), which results over time in remodelling of these circuits. The hypothetical neuroplastic response to DA hyperactivity mediates alterations of information processing leading to a psychotic episode. D_2 receptor blockade not only recalibrates DA responsivity by interrupting the endogenous DA process, but also reverses the neuroplastic changes that took place downstream from the DA synapse. However, in the absence of treatment, these neuroplastic changes become progressively 'hard-wired', and activity in these re-entrant psychotic ensembles becomes independent of sustained DA activity and unresponsive to D_2 receptor blockade. While this model integrates observations from brain imaging studies of DA synaptic activity in schizophrenia, its speculative nature has to be emphasized. Furthermore, we do not imply that this chain of events is the only avenue leading to emergence of psychotic symptoms in the schizophrenic brain. None the less, it provides a number of testable hypotheses and directions for future research.

This model also calls for new relapse prevention strategies. Currently, pharmacological 'maintenance' during remission phases is based on dopaminergic D_2 receptor blockade. These treatments succeed in preventing the re-emergence of sensitization and in reducing the risk of relapse yet they exert their preventive benefits at the price of inducing a hypodopaminergic state, which is associated with significant adverse effects and lower quality of life. A better understanding of the neurobiological mechanisms that trigger the re-emergence of sensitization might lead to new relapse prevention strategies sparing D_2 receptor function. In other terms, the apparent normality of DA transmission during illness remission might be a more important finding of these imaging studies than the dysregulation during illness exacerbation.

This model also calls for a better understanding of the long-term consequences of exaggerated stimulation of D_2 receptors on cortico–subcortical connectivity. The observation that, in some patients, psychotic symptoms are independent of DA transmission (these symptoms are experienced in the presence of apparently normal levels of synaptic DA and show little or no response to D_2 receptor blockade) is another fundamental observation from these imaging studies. This observation supports the need for the development of new non-dopaminergic therapeutic approaches.

Conclusions

The availability of new imaging methods aiming at measuring presynaptic activity in striatal DA afferents provided data consistent with the view that schizophrenia is associated with hyperactivity of subcortical transmission at D_2 receptors. These results are consistent with the known mode of action of current antipsychotic treatment (D_2 receptor blockade), with the psychotogenic effects of sustained stimulation of DA function by psychostimulants, and with the 'classical' DA hypothesis of schizophrenia derived from these observations. In addition, these results suggest that the DA hyperactivity of subcortical systems is episodic in nature, and accounts for only some aspects of positive symptomatology. These observations have several implications for the development of new treatment strategies.

As a final note, it should be re-emphasized that positive symptoms are only one aspect of the symptomatology presented by these patients. While they might be the most visible expression of the illness, these symptoms are not the most enduring nor the ones associated with most disability, at least in the postneuroleptic era. Cognitive impairments appear to precede and outlive psychotic episodes, and their severity is one of the best predictors of poor outcome (Green 1996). While the brain imaging studies reported here supported the role of subcortical hyperdopaminergic activity in the pathophysiology of positive symptoms, the potential role of prefrontal deficit in DA transmission in the pathophysiology of cognitive impairment remains to be firmly established. The development of new brain imaging techniques enabling the study of prefrontal DA transmission is warranted to explore this other face of the dopaminergic imbalance hypothesis of schizophrenia.

Acknowledgements

Supported by the National Alliance for Research on Schizophrenia and Depression (NARSAD), and the National Institute of Mental Health (K02 MH01603-01).

References

Abi-Dargham, A., Laruelle, M., Aghajanian, G.K., Charney, D. & Krystal, J. (1997) The role of serotonin in the pathophysiology and treatment of schizophrenia. *Journal of Neuropsychology and Clinical Neuroscience* 9, 1–17.

Abi-Dargham, A., Gil, R., Krystal, J. *et al.* (1998) Increased striatal dopamine transmission in schizophrenia: confirmation in a second cohort. *American Journal of Psychiatry* 155, 761–767.

Abi-Dargham, A., Martinez, D., Mawlawi, O. *et al.* (2000a) Measurement of striatal and extrastriatal dopamine D_1 receptor binding potential with [^{11}C]NNC 112 in humans: validation and reproducibility. *Journal of Cerebral Blood Flow Metabolism* 20, 225–243.

Abi-Dargham, A., Rodenhiser, J., Printz, D. *et al.* (2000b) Increased baseline occupancy of D_2 receptors by dopamine in schizophrenia. *Proceedings of the National Academy of Sciences of the USA* 97, 8104–8109.

Akbarian, S., Kim, J.J., Potkin, S.G. *et al.* (1995) Gene expression for glutamic acid decarboxylase is reduced without loss of neurons in prefrontal cortex of schizophrenics. *Archives of General Psychiatry* 52, 258–266.

Akil, M., Pierri, J.N., Whitehead, R.E. *et al.* (1999) Lamina-specific alterations in the dopamine innervation of the prefrontal cortex in schizophrenic subjects. *American Journal of Psychiatry* 156, 1580–1589.

Akil, M., Edgar, C.L., Pierri, J.N., Casali, S. & Lewis, D.A. (2000) Decreased density of tyrosine hydroxylase-immunoreactive axons in the entorhinal cortex of schizophrenic subjects. *Biological Psychiatry* 47, 361–370.

Albin, R.L., Young, A.B. & Penney, J.B. (1989) The functional anatomy of basal ganglia disorders. *Trends in Neuroscience* 12, 366–375.

Alexander, G.E., Delong, M.R. & Stick, P.L. (1986) Parallel organization of functionally segregated circuits linking basal ganglia and cortex. *Annual Review of Neuroscience* 9, 357–381.

Angrist, B. & van Kammen, D.P. (1984) CNS stimulants as a tool in the study of schizophrenia. *Trends in Neuroscience* 7, 388–390.

Arbuthnott, G.W., Ingham, C.A. & Wickens, J.R. (2000) Dopamine and synaptic plasticity in the neostriatum. *Journal of Anatomy* 196, 587–596.

Benes, F.M., McSparren, J., Bird, E.D., Vincent, S.L. & SanGiovani, J.P. (1991) Deficits in small interneurons in schizophrenic cortex. *Archives of General Psychiatry* 48, 996–1001.

Benes, F.M., Vincent, S.L., Alsterberg, G., Bird, E.D. & SanGiovanni, J.P. (1992) Increased GABAa receptor binding in superficial layers of cingulate cortex in schizophrenics. *Journal of Neuroscience* 12, 924–929.

Benes, F.M., Vincent, S.L., Marie, A. & Khan, Y. (1996) Upregulation of GABAA receptor binding on neurons of the prefrontal cortex in schizophrenic subjects. *Neuroscience* 75, 1021–1031.

Benes, F.M., Todtenkopf, M.S. & Taylor, J.B. (1997) Differential distribution of tyrosine hydroxylase fibers on small and large neurons in layer II of anterior cingulate cortex of schizophrenic brain. *Synapse* 25, 80–92.

Bertolino, A., Saunders, R.C., Mattay, V.S. *et al.* (1997) Altered development of prefrontal neurons in rhesus monkeys with neonatal mesial temporolimbic lesions: a proton magnetic resonance spectroscopic imaging study. *Cerebral Cortex* 7, 740–748.

Bertolino, A., Breier, A., Callicott, J.H. *et al.* (2000) The relationship between dorsolateral prefrontal neuronal *N*-acetylaspartate and evoked release of striatal dopamine in schizophrenia. *Neuropsychopharmacology* 22, 125–132.

Blin, J., Baron, J.C., Cambon, H. *et al.* (1989) Striatal dopamine D_2 receptors in tardive dyskinesia: PET study. *Journal of Neurology, Neurosurgery and Psychiatry* 52, 1248–1252.

Breier, A., Su, T.P., Saunders, R. *et al.* (1997) Schizophrenia is associated with elevated amphetamine-induced synaptic dopamine concentrations: evidence from a novel positron emission tomography method. *Proceedings of the National Academy of Sciences of the USA* 94, 2569–2574.

Bunney, B.S. & Aghajanian, G.K. (1978) D-Amphetamine-induced depression of central dopamine neurons: evidence for mediation by both autoreceptors and a striato-nigral feedback pathway. *Naunyn-Schmiedeberg's Archives of Pharmacology* 304, 255–261.

Bunney, B.S. & Grace, A.A. (1978) Acute and chronic haloperidol treatment: comparison of effects on nigral dopaminergic cell activity. *Life Science* 23, 423–435.

Bunzow, J.R., Van Tol, H.H., Grandy, D.K. *et al.* (1988) Cloning and expression of a rat D_2 dopamine receptor cDNA. *Nature* 336, 783–787.

Burt, D.R., Creese, I. & Snyder, S.S. (1977) Antischizophrenic drugs: chronic treatment elevates dopamine receptors binding in brain. *Science* 196, 326–328.

Carlsson, A. (1988) The current status of the dopamine hypothesis of schizophrenia. *Neuropsychopharmacology* 1, 179–186.

Carlsson, A. & Lindqvist, M. (1963) Effect of chlorpromazine or haloperidol on formation of 3-methoxytyramine and normetanephrine in mouse brain. *Acta Pharmacologica Toxicologica* **20**, 140–144.

Carlsson, A., Hansson, L.O., Waters, N. & Carlsson, M.L. (1999a) A glutamatergic deficiency model of schizophrenia. *British Journal of Psychiatry Supplement* **37**, 2–6.

Carlsson, A., Waters, N. & Carlsson, M.L. (1999b) Neurotransmitter interactions in schizophrenia: therapeutic implications. *Biological Psychiatry* **46**, 1388–1395.

Carr, D.B. & Sesack, S.R. (2000) Projections from the rat prefrontal cortex to the ventral tegmental area: target specificity in the synaptic associations with mesoaccumbens and mesocortical neurons. *Journal of Neuroscience* **20**, 3864–3873.

Carson, R.E., Breier, A., deBartolomeis, A. *et al.* (1997) Quantification of amphetamine-induced changes in [C-11]raclopride binding with continuous infusion. *Journal of Cerebral Blood Flow and Metabolism* **17**, 437–447.

Chinaglia, G., Alvarez, F.J., Probst, A. & Palacios, J.M. (1992) Mesostriatal and mesolimbic dopamine uptake binding sites are reduced in Parkinson's disease and progressive supranuclear palsy: a quantitative autoradiographic study using [^{3}H]mazindol. *Neuroscience* **49**, 317–327.

Chiodo, L. & Bunney, B. (1983) Typical and atypical neuroleptics: differential effects of chronic administration on the activity of A9 and A10 midbrain dopaminergic neurons. *Journal of Neuroscience* **3**, 1607–1619.

Connell, P.H. (1958) *Amphetamine Psychosis*. Chapman and Hill, London.

Crawley, J.C., Owens, D.G., Crow, T.J. *et al.* (1986) Dopamine D_2 receptors in schizophrenia studied *in vivo*. *Lancet* **2**, 224–225.

Creese, I., Burt, D.R. & Snyder, S.H. (1976) Dopamine receptor binding predicts clinical and pharmacological potencies of antischizophrenic drugs. *Science* **19**, 481–483.

Cross, A.J., Crow, T.J. & Owen, F. (1981) ^{3}H-Flupenthixol binding in postmortem brains of schizophrenics: evidence for a selective increase in dopamine D_2 receptors. *Psychopharmacology* **74**, 122–124.

Cross, A.J., Crow, T.J., Ferrier, I.N. *et al.* (1983) Dopamine receptor changes in schizophrenia in relation to the disease process and movement disorder. *Journal of Neural Transmission Supplement* **18**, 265–272.

Czudek, C. & Reynolds, G.P. (1989) [^{3}H]GBR 12935 binding to the dopamine uptake site in postmortem brain tissue in schizophrenia. *Journal of Neural Transmission* **77**, 227–230.

Dao-Castellana, M.H., Paillere-Martinot, M.L., Hantraye, P. *et al.* (1997) Presynaptic dopaminergic function in the striatum of schizophrenic patients. *Schizophrenia Research* **23**, 167–174.

Davis, K.L., Kahn, R.S., Ko, G. & Davidson, M. (1991) Dopamine in schizophrenia: a review and reconceptualization. *American Journal of Psychiatry* **148**, 1474–1486.

Dean, B., Pavey, G. & Opeskin, K. (1997) [H-3]raclopride binding to brain tissue from subjects with schizophrenia: methodological aspects. *Neuropharmacology* **36**, 779–786.

Dearry, A., Gingrich, J.A., Falardeau, P. *et al.* (1990) Molecular cloning and expression of the gene for a human D_1 dopamine receptor. *Nature* **347**, 72–76.

DeLong, M.R., Crutcher, M.D. & Georgopoulos, A.P. (1985) Primate globus pallidus and subthalamic nucleus: functional organization. *Journal of Neurophysiology* **53**, 530–543.

Deutch, A.Y. (1993) Prefrontal cortical dopamine systems and the elaboration of functional corticostriatal circuits: implications for schizophrenia and Parkinson's disease. *Journal of Neural Transmission* **91**, 197–221.

Deutch, A., Clark, W.A. & Roth, R.H. (1990) Prefrontal cortical dopamine depletion enhances the responsiveness of the mesolimbic dopamine neurons to stress. *Brain Research* **521**, 311–315.

Deutch, A., Moghadam, B., Innis, R. *et al.* (1991) Mechanisms of action of atypical antipsychotic drugs: implication for novel therapeutic strategies for schizophrenia. *Schizophrenia Research* **4**, 121–156.

Deutch, A., Lee, M.C. & Iadarola, M.J. (1992) Regionally specific effects of atypical antipsychotic drugs on striatal fos expression: the nucleus accumbens shell as a locus of antipsychotic action. *Molecular and Cellular Neurosciences* **3**, 332–341.

Dewey, S.L., Logan, J., Wolf, A.P. *et al.* (1991) Amphetamine induced decrease in [^{18}F]-*N*-methylspiperidol binding in the baboon brain using positron emission tomography (PET). *Synapse* **7**, 324–327.

Dewey, S.L., Smith, G.S., Logan, J. *et al.* (1992) GABAergic inhibition of endogenous dopamine release measured *in vivo* with ^{11}C-raclopride and positron emission tomography. *Journal of Neuroscience* **12**, 3773–3780.

Drevets, W.C., Gautier, C., Price, J.C. *et al.* (2001) Amphetamine-induced dopamine release in human ventral striatum correlates with euphoria. *Biological Psychiatry* **49**, 81–96.

Dunah, A.W. & Standaert, D.G. (2001) Dopamine D_1 receptor-dependent trafficking of striatal nmda glutamate receptors to the postsynaptic membrane. *Journal of Neuroscience* **21**, 5546–5558.

Ellinwood, E.H., Sudilovsky, A. & Nelson, L.M. (1973) Evolving behavior in the clinical and experimental amphetamine model psychosis. *American Journal of Psychiatry* **130**, 1088–1093.

Everitt, B.J., Morris, K.A., O'Brien, A. & Robbins, T.W. (1991) The basolateral amygdala–ventral striatal system and conditioned place preference: further evidence of limbic–striatal interactions underlying reward-related processes. *Neuroscience* **42**, 1–18.

Farde, L., Wiesel, F., Stone-Elander, S. *et al.* (1990) D_2 dopamine receptors in neuroleptic-naive schizophrenic patients: a positron emission tomography study with [^{11}C]raclopride. *Archives of General Psychiatry* **47**, 213–219.

Fauchey, V., Jaber, M., Caron, M.G., Bloch, B. & Le Moine, C. (2000) Differential regulation of the dopamine D_1, D_2 and D_3 receptor gene expression and changes in the phenotype of the striatal neurons in mice lacking the dopamine transporter. *European Journal of Neuroscience* **12**, 19–26.

Ferry, A.T., Ongur, D., An, X. & Price, J.L. (2000) Prefrontal cortical projections to the striatum in macaque monkeys: evidence for an organization related to prefrontal networks. *Journal of Comparative Neurology* **425**, 447–470.

Gerfen, C.R. (1992) The neostriatal mosaic: multiple levels of compartmental organization in the basal ganglia. *Annual Review of Neuroscience* **15**, 285–320.

Ginovart, N., Farde, L., Halldin, C. & Swahn, C.G. (1997) Effect of reserpine-induced depletion of synaptic dopamine on [C-11]raclopride binding to D_2-dopamine receptors in the monkey brain. *Synapse* **25**, 321–325.

Glenthoj, B.Y. & Hemmingsen, R. (1997) Dopaminergic sensitization: implications for the pathogenesis of schizophrenia. *Progress in Neuro-Psychopharmacology and Biological Psychiatry* **21**, 23–46.

Goldman-Rakic, P.S. (1999) The physiological approach: functional architecture of working memory and disordered cognition in schizophrenia. *Biological Psychiatry* **46**, 650–661.

Goldman-Rakic, P.S. & Selemon, L.D. (1997) Functional and anatomical aspects of prefrontal pathology in schizophrenia. *Schizophrenia Bulletin* **23**, 437–458.

Goldman-Rakic, P.S., Muly, E.C. III & Williams, G.V. (2000) D_1 receptors in prefrontal cells and circuits. *Brain Research Review* **31**, 295–301.

Grace, A.A. (1991) Phasic versus tonic dopamine release and the modulation of dopamine system responsivity: a hypothesis for the etiology of schizophrenia. *Neuroscience* **41**, 1–24.

Grace, A.A. (1993) Cortical regulation of subcortical systems and its possible relevance to schizophrenia. *Journal of Neural Transmission* **91**, 111–134.

Grace, A.A. (2000) Gating of information flow within the limbic system and the pathophysiology of schizophrenia. *Brain Research Review* **31**, 330–341.

Grace, A.A., Moore, H. & O'Donnell, P. (1998) The modulation of corticoaccumbens transmission by limbic afferents and dopamine: a model for the pathophysiology of schizophrenia. *Advances in Pharmacology* **42**, 721–724.

Green, M.F. (1996) What are the functional consequences of neurocognitive deficits in schizophrenia? *American Journal of Psychiatry* **153**, 321–330.

Gurevich, E.V., Bordelon, Y., Shapiro, R.M. *et al.* (1997) Mesolimbic dopamine D_3 receptors and use of antipsychotics in patients with schizophrenia: postmortem study. *Archives of General Psychiatry* **54**, 225–232.

Haber, S.N. & Fudge, J.L. (1997) The primate substantia nigra and VTA: integrative circuitry and function. *Critical Reviews in Neurobiology* **11**, 323–342.

Haber, S.N., Fudge, J.L. & McFarland, N.R. (2000) Striatonigrostriatal pathways in primates form an ascending spiral from the shell to the dorsolateral striatum. *Journal of Neuroscience* **20**, 2369–2382.

Hanada, S., Mita, T., Nishino, N. & Tanaka, C. (1987) [^{3}H]muscimol binding sites increased in autopsied brains of chronic schizophrenics. *Life Sciences* **40**, 259–266.

Hersch, S.M., Ciliax, B.J., Gutekunst, C.A. *et al.* (1995) Electron microscopic analysis of D_1 and D_2 dopamine receptor proteins in the dorsal striatum and their synaptic relationships with motor corticostriatal afferents. *Journal of Neuroscience* **15**, 5222–5237.

Hess, E.J., Bracha, H.S., Kleinman, J.E. & Creese, I. (1987) Dopamine receptor subtype imbalance in schizophrenia. *Life Science* **40**, 1487–1497.

Hietala, J., Syvalahti, E., Vuorio, K. *et al.* (1994) Striatal D_2 receptor characteristics in neuroleptic-naive schizophrenic patients studied with positron emission tomography. *Archives of General Psychiatry* **51**, 116–123.

Hietala, J., Syvalahti, E., Vuorio, K. *et al.* (1995) Presynaptic dopamine function in striatum of neuroleptic-naive schizophrenic patients. *Lancet* **346**, 1130–1131.

Hietala, J., Syvalahti, E., Vilkman, H. *et al.* (1999) Depressive symptoms and presynaptic dopamine function in neuroleptic-naive schizophrenia. *Schizophrenia Research* **35**, 41–50.

Hirai, M., Kitamura, N., Hashimoto, T. *et al.* (1988) [^{3}H]GBR-12935 binding sites in human striatal membranes: binding characteristics and changes in parkinsonians and schizophrenics. *Japanese Journal of Pharmacology* **47**, 237–243.

Hoover, J.E. & Strick, P.L. (1993) Multiple output channels in the basal ganglia. *Science* **259**, 819–821.

Huckle, P.L. & Palia, S.S. (1993) Managing resistant schizophrenia. *British Journal of Hospital Medicine* **50**, 467–471.

Innis, R.B., Malison, R.T., Al-Tikriti, M. *et al.* (1992) Amphetamine-stimulated dopamine release competes *in vivo* for [^{123}I]IBZM binding to the D_2 receptor in non-human primates. *Synapse* **10**, 177–184.

Javitt, D.C. & Zukin, S.R. (1991) Recent advances in the phencyclidine model of schizophrenia. *American Journal of Psychiatry* **148**, 1301–1308.

Jentsch, J.D. & Roth, R.H. (1999) The neuropsychopharmacology of phencyclidine: from NMDA receptor hypofunction to the dopamine hypothesis of schizophrenia. *Neuropsychopharmacology* **20**, 201–225.

Joel, D. & Weiner, I. (2000) The connections of the dopaminergic system with the striatum in rats and primates: an analysis with respect to the functional and compartmental organization of the striatum. *Neuroscience* **96**, 451–474.

Joyce, J.N. & Gurevich, E.V. (1999) D_3 receptors and the actions of neuroleptics in the ventral striatopallidal system of schizophrenics. *Annals of New York Academy of Sciences* **877**, 595–613.

Joyce, J.N. & Meador Woodruff, J.H. (1997) Linking the family of D_2 receptors to neuronal circuits in human brain: insights into schizophrenia. *Neuropsychopharmacology* **16**, 375–384.

Joyce, J.N., Lexow, N., Bird, E. & Winokur, A. (1988) Organization of dopamine D_1 and D_2 receptors in human striatum: receptor autoradiographic studies in Huntington's disease and schizophrenia. *Synapse* **2**, 546–557.

Kalivas, P.W. & Duffy, P. (1995) Selective activation of dopamine transmission in the shell of the nucleus accumbens by stress. *Brain Research* **675**, 325–328.

Kalivas, P.W. & Stewart, J. (1991) Dopamine transmission in the initiation and expression of drug- and stress-induced sensitization of motor activity. *Brain Research Review* **16**, 223–244.

Kalivas, P.W., Sorg, B.A. & Hooks, M.S. (1993) The pharmacology and neural circuitry of sensitization to psychostimulants. *Behavioral Pharmacology* **4**, 315–334.

Karlsson, P., Farde, L., Halldin, C. & Sedvall, G. (1997) D_1-dopamine receptors in schizophrenia examined by PET. *Schizophrenia Research* **24**, 179.

Karreman, M. & Moghaddam, B. (1996) The prefrontal cortex regulates the basal release of dopamine in the limbic striatum: an effect mediated by ventral tegmental area. *Journal of Neurochemistry* **66**, 589–598.

Kebabian, J.W. & Calne, D.B. (1979) Multiple receptors for dopamine. *Nature* **277**, 93–96.

Keefe, R.S., Silva, S.G., Perkins, D.O. & Lieberman, J.A. (1999) The effects of atypical antipsychotic drugs on neurocognitive impairment in schizophrenia: a review and meta-analysis. *Schizophrenia Bulletin* **25**, 201–222.

Kegeles, L.S., Zea-Ponce, Y., Abi-Dargham, A. *et al.* (1999) Stability of [^{123}I]IBZM SPECT measurement of amphetamine-induced striatal dopamine release in humans. *Synapse* **31**, 302–308.

Kegeles, L.S., Abi-Dargham, A., Zea-Ponce, Y. *et al.* (2000) Modulation of amphetamine-induced striatal dopamine release by ketamine in humans: implications for schizophrenia. *Biological Psychiatry* **48**, 627–640.

Kerr, J.N. & Wickens, J.R. (2001) Dopamine D_1/D_5 receptor activation is required for long-term potentiation in the rat neostriatum *in vitro*. *Journal of Neurophysiology* **85**, 117–124.

Knable, M.B. & Weinberger, D.R. (1997) Dopamine, the prefrontal cortex and schizophrenia. *Journal of Psychopharmacology* **11**, 123–131.

Knable, M.B., Hyde, T.M., Herman, M.M. *et al.* (1994) Quantitative autoradiography of dopamine-D_1 receptors, D_2 receptors, and dopamine uptake sites in postmortem striatal specimens from schizophrenic patients. *Biological Psychiatry* **36**, 827–835.

Knable, M.B., Hyde, T.M., Murray, A.M., Herman, M.M. & Kleinman, J.E. (1996) A postmortem study of frontal cortical dopamine D_1 receptors in schizophrenics, psychiatric controls, and normal controls. *Biological Psychiatry* **40**, 1191–1199.

Knable, M.B., Egan, M.F., Heinz, A. *et al.* (1997) Altered dopaminergic function and negative symptoms in drug-free patients with schizophrenia. [^{123}I]-iodobenzamide SPECT study. *British Journal of Psychiatry* **171**, 574–577.

Kolachana, B.S., Saunders, R. & Weinberger, D. (1995) Augmentation of prefrontal cortical monoaminergic activity inhibits dopamine release in the caudate nucleus: an *in vivo* neurochemical assessment in the rhesus monkey. *Neurosciences* **69**, 859–868.

Konradi, C. (1998) The molecular basis of dopamine and glutamate interactions in the striatum. *Advances in Pharmacology* **42**, 729–733.

Kramer, M.S., Last, B., Getson, A. *et al.* (1997) The effects of a selective D_4 dopamine receptor antagonist (L-745 870) in acutely psychotic inpatients with schizophrenia. *Archives of General Psychiatry* **54**, 567–572.

Krystal, J.H., Abi-Dargham, A., Laruelle, M. & Moghaddam, B. (1999) In: *Neurobiology of Mental Illness* (eds D. Charney, E.J. Nestler & B. Bunney), pp. 214–224. Oxford University Press, New York.

Kunishio, K. & Haber, S.N. (1994) Primate cingulostriatal projection: limbic striatal versus sensorimotor striatal input. *Journal of Comparative Neurology* **350**, 337–356.

Laakso, A., Vilkman, H., Alakare, B. *et al.* (2000) Striatal dopamine transporter binding in neuroleptic-naive patients with schizophrenia studied with positron emission tomography. *American Journal of Psychiatry* **157**, 269–271.

Lahti, A.C., Koffel, B., LaPorte, D. & Tamminga, C.A. (1995) Subanesthetic doses of ketamine stimulate psychosis in schizophrenia. *Neuropsychopharmacology* **13**, 9–19.

Lahti, R.A., Roberts, R.C., Conley, R.R. *et al.* (1996a) D_2-type dopamine receptors in postmortem human brain sections from normal and schizophrenic subjects. *Neuroreport* **7**, 1945–1948.

Lahti, R.A., Roberts, R.C., Conley, R.R. & Tamminga, C.A. (1996b) Dopamine D_2, D_3 and D_4 receptors in human postmortem brain sections: comparison between normals and schizophrenics. *Schizophrenia Research* **18**, 173.

Lahti, R.A., Roberts, R.C., Cochrane, E.V. *et al.* (1998) Direct determination of dopamine D_4 receptors in normal and schizophrenic postmortem brain tissue: a [H-3]NGD-94-1 study. *Molecular Psychiatrics* **3**, 528–533.

Laruelle, M. (2000a) Imaging synaptic neurotransmission with *in vivo* binding competition techniques: a critical review. *Journal of Cerebral Blood Flow and Metabolism* **20**, 423–451.

Laruelle, M. (2000b) The role of endogenous sensitization in the pathophysiology of schizophrenia: implications from recent brain imaging studies. *Brain Research Review* **31**, 371–384.

Laruelle, M., Casanova, M., Weinberger, D. & Kleinman, J. (1990) Postmortem study of the dopaminergic D_1 receptors in the dorsolateral prefrontal cortex of schizophrenics and controls. *Schizophrenia Research* **3**, 30–31.

Laruelle, M., Abi-Dargham, A., van Dyck, C.H. *et al.* (1996) Single photon emission computerized tomography imaging of amphetamine-induced dopamine release in drug-free schizophrenic subjects. *Proceedings of the National Academy of Sciences of the USA* **93**, 9235–9240.

Laruelle, M.D., Souza, C.D., Baldwin, R.M. *et al.* (1997a) Imaging D_2 receptor occupancy by endogenous dopamine in humans. *Neuropsychopharmacology* **17**, 162–174.

Laruelle, M., Iyer, R.N., Al-Tikriti, M.S. *et al.* (1997b) Microdialysis and SPECT measurements of amphetamine-induced dopamine release in non-human primates. *Synapse* **25**, 1–14.

Laruelle, M., Abi-Dargham, A., Gil, R., Kegeles, L. & Innis, R. (1999) Increased dopamine transmission in schizophrenia: relationship to illness phases. *Biological Psychiatry* **46**, 56–72.

Laruelle, M., Abi-Dargham, A., van Dyck, C. *et al.* (2000) Dopamine and serotonin transporters in patients with schizophrenia: an imaging study with $[^{123}I]\beta$-CIT. *Biological Psychiatry* **47**, 371–379.

Lee, S.P., O'Dowd, B.F., Ng, G.Y. *et al.* (2000) Inhibition of cell surface expression by mutant receptors demonstrates that D_2 dopamine receptors exist as oligomers in the cell. *Molecular Pharmacology* **58**, 120–128.

Lee, T., Seeman, P., Tourtelotte, W.W., Farley, I.J. & Hornykiewicz, O. (1978) Binding of ^{3}H-neuroleptics and ^{3}H-apomorphine in schizophrenic brains. *Nature* **274**, 897–900.

Le Moine, C., Normand, E., Guitteny, A.F. *et al.* (1990) Dopamine receptor gene expression by enkephalin neurons in rat forebrain. *Proceedings of the National Academy of Sciences of the USA* **87**, 230–234.

Le Moine, C., Normand, E. & Bloch, B. (1991) Phenotypical characterization of the rat striatal neurons expressing the D_1 dopamine receptor gene. *Proceedings of the National Academy of Sciences of the USA* **88**, 4205–4209.

Leveque, J.C., Macias, W., Rajadhyaksha, A. *et al.* (2000) Intracellular modulation of NMDA receptor function by antipsychotic drugs. *Journal of Neuroscience* **20**, 4011–4020.

Lieberman, J.A., Kane, J.M. & Alvir, J. (1987) Provocative tests with psychostimulant drugs in schizophrenia. *Psychopharmacology* **91**, 415–433.

Lieberman, J.A., Kinon, B.L. & Loebel, A.D. (1990) Dopaminergic mechanisms in idiopathic and drug-induced psychoses. *Schizophrenia Bulletin* **16**, 97–110.

Lieberman, J.A., Sheitman, B.B. & Kinon, B.J. (1997) Neurochemical sensitization in the pathophysiology of schizophrenia: deficits and dysfunction in neuronal regulation and plasticity. *Neuropsychopharmacology* **17**, 205–229.

Lindstrom, L.H., Gefvert, O., Hagberg, G. *et al.* (1999) Increased dopamine synthesis rate in medial prefrontal cortex and striatum in schizophrenia indicated by L-(β-11C) DOPA and PET. *Biological Psychiatry* **46**, 681–688.

Lindvall, O. & Björklund, A. (1983) In: *Chemical Neuroanatomy* (ed. P. Emson), pp. 229–255. Raven Press, New York.

Mackay, A.V., Iversen, L.L., Rossor, M. *et al.* (1982) Increased brain dopamine and dopamine receptors in schizophrenia. *Archives of General Psychiatry* **39**, 991–997.

Magos, L. (1969) Persistence of the effect of amphetamine on stereotyped activity in rats. *European Journal of Pharmacology* **6**, 200–201.

Martinot, J.-L., Peron-Magnan, P., Huret, J.-D. *et al.* (1990) Striatal D_2 dopaminergic receptors assessed with positron emission tomography and ^{76}Br-bromospiperone in untreated patients. *American Journal of Psychiatry* **147**, 346–350.

Martinot, J.L., Paillère-Martinot, M.L., Loc'h, C. *et al.* (1991) The estimated density of D_2 striatal receptors in schizophrenia: a study with positron emission tomography and ^{76}Br-bromolisuride. *British Journal of Psychiatry* **158**, 346–350.

Martinot, J.L., Paillère-Martinot, M.L., Loch, H.C. *et al.* (1994) Central D_2 receptors and negative symptoms of schizophrenia. *British Journal of Pharmacology* **164**, 27–34.

Marzella, P.L., Hill, C., Keks, N., Singh, R. & Copolov, D. (1997) The binding of both [H-3]nemonapride and [H-3]raclopride is increased in schizophrenia. *Biological Psychiatry* **42**, 648–654.

Mawlawi, O., Martinez, D., Slifstein, M. *et al.* (2001) Imaging human mesolimbic dopamine transmission with positron emission tomography. I. Accuracy and precision of D_2 receptor parameter measurements in ventral striatum. *Journal of Cerebral Blood Flow and Metabolism* **21**, 1034–1057.

Meador-Woodruff, J.H., Damask, S.P., Wang, J. *et al.* (1996) Dopamine receptors mRNA expression in human striatum and neocortex. *Neuropsychopharmacology* **15**, 17–29.

Meador-Woodruff, J.H., Haroutunian, V., Powchik, P. *et al.* (1997) Dopamine receptor transcript expression in striatum and prefrontal and occipital cortex: focal abnormalities in orbitofrontal cortex in schizophrenia. *Archives of General Psychiatry* **54**, 1089–1095.

Meltzer, H. (1989) Clinical studies on the mechanism of action of clozapine: the dopamine–serotonin hypothesis of schizophrenia. *Psychopharmacology* **99**, S18–S27.

Miller, D.W. & Abercrombie, E.D. (1996) Effects of MK-801 on spontaneous and amphetamine-stimulated dopamine release in striatum measured with *in vivo* microdialysis in awake rats. *Brain Research Bulletin* **40**, 57–62.

Missale, C., Nash, S.R., Robinson, S.W., Jaber, M. & Caron, M.G. (1998) Dopamine receptors: from structure to function. *Physiological Review* **78**, 189–225.

Mita, T., Hanada, S., Nishino, N. *et al.* (1986) Decreased serotonin S_2 and increased dopamine D_2 receptors in chronic schizophrenics. *Biological Psychiatry* **21**, 1407–1414.

Mogenson, G.J., Jones, D.L. & Yim, C.Y. (1980) From motivation to action: functional interface between the limbic system and the motor system. *Progress in Neurobiology* **14**, 69–97.

Moghaddam, B. & Adams, B.W. (1998) Reversal of phencyclidine effects by a group II metabotropic glutamate receptor agonist in rats. *Science* **281**, 1349–1352.

Monsma, F. Jr, Mahan, L.C., McVittie, L.D., Gerfen, C.R. & Sibley, D.R. (1990) Molecular cloning and expression of a D_1 dopamine receptor linked to adenylyl cyclase activation. *Proceedings of the National Academy of Sciences of the USA* **87**, 6723–6727.

Mrzljak, L., Bergson, C., Pappy, M. *et al.* (1996) Localization of dopamine D_4 receptors in GABAergic neurons of the primate brain. *Nature* **381**, 245–248.

Murray, A.M., Hyde, T.M., Knable, M.B. *et al.* (1995) Distribution of putative D_4 dopamine receptors in postmortem striatum from patients with schizophrenia. *Journal of Neuroscience* **15**, 2186–2191.

Ng, G.Y., O'Dowd, B.F., Caron, M. *et al.* (1994) Phosphorylation and palmitoylation of the human D_2L dopamine receptor in Sf9 cells. *Journal of Neurochemistry* **63**, 1589–1595.

Ng, G.Y., O'Dowd, B.F., Lee, S.P. *et al.* (1996) Dopamine D_2 receptor dimers and receptor-blocking peptides. *Biochemical and Biophysical Research Communications* **227**, 200–204.

Nguyen, T.V., Kosofsky, B.E., Birnbaum, R., Cohen, B.M. & Hyman, S.E. (1992) Differential expression of c-fos and zif268 in rat striatum after haloperidol, clozapine, and amphetamine. *Proceedings of the National Academy of Sciences of the USA* **89**, 4270–4274.

Nishi, A., Snyder, G.L. & Greengard, P. (1997) Bidirectional regulation of DARPP-32 phosphorylation by dopamine. *Journal of Neuroscience* **17**, 8147–8155.

Nordstrom, A.L., Farde, L., Eriksson, L. & Halldin, C. (1995) No elevated D_2 dopamine receptors in neuroleptic-naive schizophrenic patients revealed by positron emission tomography and [^{11}C] *N*-methylspiperone [see comments]. *Psychiatry Research* **61**, 67–83.

O'Donnell, P. & Grace, A.A. (1998a) Dysfunctions in multiple interrelated systems as the neurobiological bases of schizophrenic symptom clusters. *Schizophrenia Bulletin* **24**, 267–283.

O'Donnell, P. & Grace, A.A. (1998b) Phencyclidine interferes with the hippocampal gating of nucleus accumbens neuronal activity *in vivo*. *Neuroscience* **87**, 823–830.

Okubo, Y., Suhara, T., Suzuki, K. *et al.* (1997) Decreased prefrontal dopamine D_1 receptors in schizophrenia revealed by PET. *Nature* **385**, 634–636.

Olney, J.W. & Farber, N.B. (1995) Glutamate receptor dysfunction and schizophrenia. *Archives of General Psychiatry* **52**, 998–1007.

Owen, F., Cross, A.J., Crow, T.J. *et al.* (1978) Increased dopamine-receptor sensitivity in schizophrenia. *Lancet* **2**, 223–226.

Owen, R., Owen, F., Poulter, M. & Crow, T.J. (1984) Dopamine D_2 receptors in substantia nigra in schizophrenia. *Brain Research* **299**, 152–154.

Palermo-Neto, J. (1997) Dopaminergic systems: dopamine receptors. *Psychiatrics Clinics of North America* **20**, 705–721.

Parent, A. & Hazrati, L.N. (1995a) Functional anatomy of the basal ganglia. I. The corticobasal ganglia–thalamocortical loop. *Brain Research Review* **20**, 91–127.

Parent, A. & Hazrati, L.N. (1995b) Functional anatomy of the basal ganglia. II. The place of subthalamic nucleus and external pallidum in basal ganglia circuitry. *Brain Research Review* **20**, 128–154.

Parsey, R.V., Oquendo, M., Zea-Ponce, Y. *et al.* (2001) Dopamine D_2 receptor availability and amphetamine-induced dopamine release in unipolar depression. *Biological Psychology* **50**, 313–322.

Pearce, R.K., Seeman, P., Jellinger, K. & Tourtellotte, W.W. (1990) Dopamine uptake sites and dopamine receptors in Parkinson's disease and schizophrenia. *European Neurology* **30** (Suppl. 1), 9–14.

Pennartz, C.M., Groenewegen, H.J. & Lopes da Silva, F.H. (1994) The nucleus accumbens as a complex of functionally distinct neuronal ensembles: an integration of behavioural, electrophysiological and anatomical data. *Progress in Neurobiology* **42**, 719–761.

Pierce, R.C. & Kalivas, P.W. (1997) A circuitry model of the expression of behavioral sensitization to amphetamine-like psychostimulants. *Brain Research Review* **25**, 192–216.

Pilowsky, L.S., Costa, D.C., Ell, P.J. *et al.* (1994) D_2 dopamine receptor binding in the basal ganglia of antipsychotic-free schizophrenic patients: an I-123-IBZM single photon emission computerized tomography study. *British Journal of Psychiatry* **164**, 16–26.

Pimoule, C., Schoemaker, H., Reynolds, G.P. & Langer, S.Z. (1985) [^{3}H]SCH 23390 labelled D_1 dopamine receptors are unchanged in schizophrenia and Parkinson's disease. *European Journal of Pharmacology* **114**, 235–237.

Pycock, C.J., Kerwin, R.W. & Carter, C.J. (1980) Effect of lesion of cortical dopamine terminals on subcortical dopamine receptors in rats. *Nature* **286**, 74–77.

Reith, J., Benkelfat, C., Sherwin, A. *et al.* (1994) Elevated dopa decarboxylase activity in living brain of patients with psychosis. *Proceedings of the National Academy of Sciences of the USA* **91**, 11651–11654.

Reynolds, G.P. (1983) Increased concentrations and lateral asymmetry of amygdala dopamine in schizophrenia. *Nature* **305**, 527–529.

Reynolds, G.P. (1989) Beyond the dopamine hypothesis: the neurochemical pathology of schizophrenia. *British Journal of Psychiatry* **155**, 305–316.

Reynolds, G.P. & Czudek, C. (1988) Status of the dopaminergic system in postmortem brain in schizophrenia. *Psychopharmacological Bulletin* **24**, 345–347.

Reynolds, G.P. & Mason, S.L. (1994) Are striatal dopamine D_4 receptors increased in schizophrenia? *Journal of Neurochemistry* **63**, 1576–1577.

Reynolds, G.P., Czudek, C., Bzowej, N. & Seeman, P. (1987) Dopamine receptor asymmetry in schizophrenia. *Lancet* **1**, 979.

Robertson, G.S., Matsumura, H. & Fibiger, H.C. (1994) Induction patterns of Fos-like immunoreactivity in the forebrain as predictors of atypical antipsychotic activity. *Journal of Pharmacology and Experimental Therapy* **271**, 1058–1066.

Robinson, T.E. & Becker, J.B. (1986) Enduring changes in brain and behavior produced by chronic amphetamine administration: a review and evaluation of animal models of amphetamine psychosis. *Brain Research Review* **11**, 157–198.

Ross, S.B. (1991) Synaptic concentration of dopamine in the mouse striatum in relationship to the kinetic properties of the dopamine receptors and uptake mechanism. *Journal of Neurochemistry* **56**, 22–29.

Ross, S.B. & Jackson, D.M. (1989) Kinetic properties of the *in vivo* accumulation of [^{3}H] (–)-*N*-propylnorapomorphine in the mouse brain. *Naunyn-Schmiedeberg's Archives of Pharmacology* **340**, 13–20.

Ruiz, J., Gabilondo, A.M., Meana, J.J. & Garcia-Sevilla, J.A. (1992) Increased [^{3}H] raclopride binding sites in postmortem brains from schizophrenic violent suicide victims. *Psychopharmacology* **109**, 410–414.

Sato, M., Chen, C.C., Akiyama, K. & Otsuki, S. (1983) Acute exacerbation of paranoid psychotic state after long-term abstinence in patients with previous methamphetamine psychosis. *Biological Psychiatry* **18**, 429–440.

Saunders, R.C., Kolachana, B.S., Bachevalier, J. & Weinberger, D.R. (1998) Neonatal lesions of the medial temporal lobe disrupt prefrontal cortical regulation of striatal dopamine. *Nature* **393**, 169–171.

Schoots, O., Seeman, P., Guan, H.C., Paterson, A.D. & Vantol, H.H.M. (1995) Long-term haloperidol elevates dopamine D_4 receptors by 2-fold in rats. *European Journal of Pharmacology: Molecular Pharmacology Section* **289**, 67–72.

Schultz, W., Tremblay, L. & Hollerman, J.R. (1998) Reward prediction in primate basal ganglia and frontal cortex. *Neuropharmacology* **37**, 421–429.

Schwartz, J.C., Diaz, J., Bordet, R. *et al.* (1998) Functional implications of multiple dopamine receptor subtypes: the D_1/D_3 receptor coexistence. *Brain Research Review* **26**, 236–242.

Seamans, J.K., Gorelova, N., Durstewitz, D. & Yang, C.R. (2001) Bidirectional dopamine modulation of GABAergic inhibition in prefrontal cortical pyramidal neurons. *Journal of Neuroscience* **21**, 3628–3638.

Seeman, P. (1988) Brain dopamine receptors in schizophrenia: PET problems. *Archives of General Psychiatry* **45**, 598–560.

Seeman, P. (1992) Dopamine receptor sequences. Therapeutic levels of neuroleptics occupy D_2 receptors, clozapine occupies D_4. *Neuropsychopharmacology* **7**, 261–284.

Seeman, P. & Lee, T. (1975) Antipsychotic drugs: direct correlation between clinical potency and presynaptic action on dopamine neurons. *Science* **188**, 1217–1219.

Seeman, P., Ulpian, C., Bergeron, C. *et al.* (1984) Bimodal distribution of dopamine receptor densities in brains of schizophrenics. *Science* **225**, 728–731.

Seeman, P., Bzowej, N.H., Guan, H.C. *et al.* (1987) Human brain D_1 and D_2 dopamine receptors in schizophrenia, Alzheimer's, Parkinson's, and Huntington's diseases. *Neuropsychopharmacology* **1**, 5–15.

Seeman, P., Guan, H.-C. & Niznik, H.B. (1989) Endogenous dopamine lowers the dopamine D_2 receptor density as measured by [^{3}H] raclopride: implications for positron emission tomography of the human brain. *Synapse* **3**, 96–97.

Seeman, P., Guan, H.C. & Van Tol, H.H.M. (1993) Dopamine D_4 receptors elevated in schizophrenia. *Nature* **365**, 411–445.

Seeman, P., Guan, H.C. & Van Tol, H.H. (1995) Schizophrenia: elevation of dopamine D_4-like sites, using [^{3}H]nemonapride and [^{125}I]epidepride. *European Journal of Pharmacology* **286**, R3–R5.

Smiley, J.F., Levey, A.I., Ciliax, B.J. & Goldman-Rakic, P.S. (1994) D_1 dopamine receptor immunoreactivity in human and monkey cerebral cortex: predominant and extrasynaptic localization in dendritic spines. *Proceedings of the National Academy of Sciences of the USA* **91**, 5720–5724.

Sokoloff, P., Giros, B., Martres, M.-P., Bouthenet, M.-L. & Schwartz, J.-C. (1990) Molecular cloning and characterization of a novel dopamine receptor D_3 as a target for neuroleptics. *Nature* **347**, 146–151.

Sorg, B.A., Hooks, M.S. & Kalivas, P.W. (1994) Neuroanatomy and neurochemical mechanisms of time-dependent sensitization. *Toxicology and Industrial Health* **10**, 369–386.

Spector, S., Sjoerdsma, A. & Udenfriend, S. (1965) Blockade of endogenous norepinephrine synthesis by α-methyl-tyrosine, an inhibitor of tyrosine hydroxylase. *Journal of Pharmacology and Experimental Therapy* **147**, 86–95.

Sumiyoshi, T., Stockmeier, C.A., Overholser, J.C., Thompson, P.A. & Meltzer, H.Y. (1995) Dopamine D_4 receptors and effects of guanine nucleotides on [^{3}H]raclopride binding in postmortem caudate nucleus of subjects with schizophrenia or major depression. *Brain Research* **681**, 109–116.

Sunahara, R.K., Guan, H.-C., O'Dowd, B.F. *et al.* (1991) Cloning of the gene for a human dopamine D_5 receptor with higher affinity for dopamine than D_1. *Nature* **350**, 614–619.

Surmeier, D.J., Eberwine, J., Wilson, C.J. *et al.* (1992) Dopamine receptor subtypes colocalize in rat striatonigral neurons. *Proceedings of the National Academy of Sciences of the USA* **89**, 10178–10182.

Surmeier, D.J., Song, W.J. & Yan, Z. (1996) Coordinated expression of dopamine receptors in neostriatal medium spiny neurons. *Journal of Neuroscience* **16**, 6579–6591.

Tarazi, F.I., Florijn, W.J. & Creese, I. (1997) Differential regulation of dopamine receptors after chronic typical and atypical antipsychotic drug treatment. *Neuroscience* **78**, 985–996.

Taylor, S.F., Koeppe, R.A., Tandon, R., Zubieta, J.K. & Frey, K.A. (2000) *In vivo* measurement of the vesicular monoamine transporter in schizophrenia. *Neuropsychopharmacology* **23**, 667–675.

Tiberi, M., Jarvie, K.R., Silvia, C. *et al.* (1991) Cloning, molecular characterization, and chromosomal assignment of a gene encoding a second D_1 dopamine receptor subtype: differential expression pattern in rat brain compared with the D_{1A} receptor. *Proceedings of the National Academy of Sciences of the USA* **88**, 7491–7495.

Tune, L.E., Wong, D.F., Pearlson, G. *et al.* (1993) Dopamine D_2 receptor density estimates in schizophrenia: a positron emission tomography study with ^{11}C-*N*-methylspiperone. *Psychiatry Research* **49**, 219–237.

Udenfriend, S., Nagatsu, T. & Zaltzman-Nirenberg, P. (1965) Inhibitors of purified beef adrenal tyrosine hydroxylase. *Biochemistry and Pharmacology* **14**, 837–847.

Van der Werf, J.F., Sebens, J.B., Vaalburg, W. & Korf, J. (1986) *In vivo* binding of *N*-propylnorapomorphine in the rat brain: regional localization, quantification in striatum and lack of correlation with dopamine metabolism. *European Journal of Pharmacology* **87**, 259–270.

Van Tol, H.H.M., Bunzow, J.R., Guan, H-C. *et al.* (1991) Cloning of the gene for a human dopamine D_4 receptor with high affinity for the antipsychotic clozapine. *Nature* **350**, 610–614.

Volk, D.W., Austin, M.C., Pierri, J.N., Sampson, A.R. & Lewis, D.A. (2000) Decreased glutamic acid decarboxylase$_{67}$ messenger RNA expression in a subset of prefrontal cortical γ-aminobutyric acid neurons in subjects with schizophrenia. *Archives of General Psychiatry* **57**, 237–245.

Watanabe, M., Nonaka, R., Hagino, Y. & Kodama, Y. (1998) Effects of prenatal methylazoxymethanol treatment on striatal dopaminergic systems in rat brain. *Neuroscience Research* **30**, 135–144.

Weiden, P., Aquila, R. & Standard, J. (1996) Atypical antipsychotic drugs and long-term outcome of schizophrenia. *Journal of Clinical Psychiatry* **57** (S1), 53–60.

Weinberger, D.R. (1987) Implications of the normal brain development for the pathogenesis of schizophrenia. *Archives of General Psychiatry* **44**, 660–669.

Weinberger, D.R., Berman, K.F. & Zec, R.F. (1986) Physiological dysfunction of dorsolateral prefrontal cortex in schizophrenia. I. Regional cerebral blood flow evidence. *Archives of General Psychiatry* **43**, 114–124.

Wickens, J.R. (2000) In: *Brain Dynamics and the Striatal Complex* (eds R. Miller & J.R. Wickens), pp. 65–76. Academic, Harwood.

Wilkinson, L.S. (1997) The nature of interactions involving prefrontal and striatal dopamine systems. *Journal of Psychopharmacology* **11**, 143–150.

Wong, D.F., Wagner, H.N., Tune, L.E. *et al.* (1986) Positron emission tomography reveals elevated D_2 dopamine receptors in drug-naive schizophrenics. *Science* **234**, 1558–1563.

Woo, T.U., Miller, J.L. & Lewis, D.A. (1997) Schizophrenia and the parvalbumin-containing class of cortical local circuit neurons. *American Journal of Psychiatry* **154**, 1013–1015.

Woo, T.U., Whitehead, R.E., Melchitzky, D.S. & Lewis, D.A. (1998) A subclass of prefrontal γ-aminobutyric acid axon terminals are selectively altered in schizophrenia. *Proceedings of the National Academy of Sciences of the USA* **95**, 5341–5346.

Yang, C.R., Seamans, J.K. & Gorelova, N. (1999) Developing a neuronal model for the pathophysiology of schizophrenia based on the nature of electrophysiological actions of dopamine in the prefrontal cortex. *Neuropsychopharmacology* **21**, 161–194.

Young, L.T., Wong, D.F., Goldman, S. *et al.* (1991) Effects of endogenous dopamine on kinetics of [^{3}H]methylspiperone and [^{3}H]raclopride binding in the rat brain. *Synapse* **9**, 188–194.

Zawarynski, P., Tallerico, T., Seeman, P. *et al.* (1998) Dopamine D_2 receptor dimers in human and rat brain. *FEBS Letters* **441**, 383–386.

Zhou, Q.Y., Grandy, D.K., Thambi, L. *et al.* (1990) Cloning and expression of human and rat D_1 dopamine receptors. *Nature* **347**, 76–80.

21 Animal models of schizophrenia

B.K. Lipska and D.R. Weinberger

Animal models are important in exploring the mechanisms underlying human disease and designing new therapies. However, this approach has not been very popular in psychiatric research as modelling of psychiatric disorders in experimental animals has often been regarded as highly controversial. Schizophrenia is an example of a particularly formidable challenge for animal modelling. It is a complex disorder of unknown origin, characterized by abnormalities of uniquely human behaviours in the realms of perception, thinking and the experience of emotions, and whose onset is virtually restricted to young adulthood. Schizophrenia is an inherently human disease, so it is not possible to reproduce in a rodent, or even in a non-human primate, its most prominent symptoms – hallucinations, delusions and thought disorder. However, recent new evidence about the neurobiology of the condition has generated new avenues of animal research. In this chapter, we present recent achievements in the efforts to model the neurobiology of schizophrenia in animals, consider limitations inherent in any heuristic animal model of this and probably other psychiatric disorders, and discuss the usefulness of a new generation of animal models for testing particular hypotheses about aetiology and pathophysiology of schizophrenia. Parts of this chapter appeared in an earlier version (Lipska & Weinberger 2000).

An animal model may represent a disease on three different levels:

1 it may reproduce inducing factor(s) (e.g. a genetic defect and the subsequent pathological processes underlying the disease);
2 it may mimic phenomenology (e.g. an array of symptoms of schizophrenia); and
3 it may predict responsiveness to already available treatments (e.g. antipsychotic drugs).

Thus, the characteristics of an animal model and its faithfulness vary according to the aspects that it aspires to represent. Models that reconstruct the aetiology and pathophysiological mechanisms of the disease are of the highest order of fidelity; they have so-called 'construct validity'. Models with construct validity usually, although not invariably (see below), possess some degree of face and predictive validity (Kornetsky & Markowitz 1978; McKinney & Moran 1981; Ellenbroek & Cools 1990; Rupniak & Iversen 1993; Costall & Naylor 1995). A good illustration of valid and useful models of complex diseases are the genetic models of diabetes and hypertension: for instance, the db/db mice model of diabetes (Kobayashi *et al.* 2000) and the spontaneously hypertensive rat (SHR) (Patel *et al.* 2000). Unlike these models, which faithfully reproduce relatively clear-cut physiological characteristics (e.g. high blood sugar levels or high blood pressure), models of psychiatric disorders face the unique difficulty of simulating much more complex and less easily defined pathophysiology.

Pharmacological dopamine-based animal models

Traditionally, most animal models of schizophrenia have focused on phenomena linked to dopamine, because the dopaminergic system has been strongly implicated in this disorder, as all effective antipsychotic drugs are antagonists of dopamine receptors, and dopamine agonists induce symptoms that resemble psychosis (Kornetsky & Markowitz 1978; McKinney & Moran 1981; Ellenbroek & Cools 1990; Costall & Naylor 1995; see Table 21.1). For instance, some dopamine-based models involve behavioural paradigms that were inspired by antipsychotic (i.e. antidopaminergic) pharmacology but bear no resemblance to schizophrenia (e.g. antagonism of apomorphine-induced emesis). Others reproduce phenomena isomorphic with selected characteristics of schizophrenia such as motor behaviours (e.g. dopamimetic drugs-induced stereotypies) and information processing deficits (e.g. apomorphine-induced prepulse inhibition of startle (PPI) abnormalities; Costall & Naylor 1995). These dopamine-linked behaviours, although not specific for or uniquely prominent in schizophrenia, can at least be detected and precisely quantified in non-human species and have been useful in screening drugs with a predicted mechanism of action (e.g. dopamine blockade). Thus, models based on perturbing dopamine have no construct validity, limited face validity but relatively good predictive validity. The predictive validity is to be expected given that the models are based on changing dopamine function. However, as 'dopamine-in, dopamine-out' models (i.e. models based on direct pharmacological manipulation of

Table 21.1 Clinical aspects of schizophrenia and relevant behavioural changes in animals.

Schizophrenia: clinical phenomena	Animal models: behavioural changes
1 Psychotic symptoms	Behaviours related to increased dopaminergic transmission: (i) Dopamimetic-induced hyperlocomotion (ii) Reduced haloperidol-induced catalepsy
2 Stereotypic behaviours	Dopamimetic-induced stereotypies
3 Worsening of psychotic symptoms by NMDA antagonists	NMDA antagonist-induced locomotion
4 Vulnerability to stress	Stress-induced hyperlocomotion
5 Information processing deficits	Sensorimotor gating (PPI, P50) deficits
6 Attentional deficits	Deficits in latent inhibition
7 Cognitive deficits	Impaired performance in delayed alternation and spatial memory tests
8 Social withdrawal	Reduced contacts with unfamiliar partners

the dopaminergic system and tests of behavioural outcome related to dopamine function), they precluded exploring other than dopamine-based mechanisms of the disease and discovering novel antipsychotic therapies. Drugs that have emerged as a result of such models all exert antidopaminergic efficacy. Antidopaminergic drugs, however, although ameliorative of some of the symptoms of schizophrenia, do not cure the disease. It has become increasingly clear that models based on direct manipulations of the dopamine system may have exhausted their heuristic potential and that new strategies need to be developed to provide novel targets for the development of more effective therapeutic agents.

Novel approaches to modelling schizophrenia

In the context of our current knowledge about schizophrenia, innovative or heuristic models have several goals:

1 to test the plausibility of theories derived from the emerging research data about the disorder;

2 to probe the explanatory power of new biological findings about the disorder;

3 to uncover mechanisms of schizophrenia-like phenomena; and

4 to suggest potential new treatments.

Thus, a heuristic model, in contrast to a traditional dopamine-based model, needs to evince other schizophrenia-like abnormalities besides the feature that it directly manipulates. For instance, a model based on hippocampal injury would be heuristic if it triggered behavioural and/or molecular changes outside the hippocampus that are associated with schizophrenia, enabled testing of the mechanisms underlying the ensuing changes, and predicted novel therapies based on newly discovered mechanisms.

Recently, as interest in schizophrenia research has shifted from a principal focus on dopamine to theories of abnormal neurodevelopment, dysfunction of cortical glutamatergic neurones and genetic susceptibility, animal models have followed a similar trend. The novel models considered below are either non-pharmacological or based on pharmacological manipulation of a neurotransmitter other than dopamine. Thus, they have ventured off the beaten path of 'dopamine-in, dopamine-out' models, and offer the potential of elucidating non-dopamine mechanisms of disease and treatment. All animal models of schizophrenia, however, whether new or old, suffer from a generic problem – lack of a straightforward test of fidelity. This is because there is no valid genotype, cellular phenotype or other biological marker that is characteristic of the disorder, and no animal model can fully reproduce the perceptual, cognitive and emotional features of the human illness. In the absence of a pathognomonic marker, a faithful model is expected to reproduce a constellation of behavioural and biological phenomena relevant to schizophrenia. If a model addresses a cluster of relevant changes ranging from anatomical and neurochemical to behavioural and cognitive features, rather than a single or a few non-specific phenomena, then there is a higher probability that the model is heuristic and isomorphic with biological processes related to the human disorder. As new findings about the pathophysiology of schizophrenia emerge, new models increasingly focus on certain cell or tissue phenotypes and a variety of complex behavioural characteristics, in addition to time-honoured effects on dopamine-related function (see Tables 21.1 and 21.2); unfortunately, as shown in the examples below, rarely are multiple phenomena addressed in a single model.

In this chapter, we examine three approaches to creating animal models related to schizophrenia:

1 neurodevelopmental models;

2 glutamatergic hypofunction models; and

3 genetic models.

The first approach is based on experimentally induced disruption of brain development that becomes evident in an adult

Table 21.2 The neonatal ventral hippocampal (VH) lesion model: schizophrenia-like phenomena.

Neonatal VH lesion model	Schizophrenia
Behavioural changes	
Hyperlocomotion to stress	Stress vulnerability
PPI deficits	PPI deficits
LI deficits	LI deficits
Deficits in delayed alternation tests	Working memory deficits
Reduced social contacts	Social withdrawal
Pharmacological responses	
Amphetamine-induced hyperactivity	Enhanced symptomatic response to dopamimetics
Apomorphine-induced stereotypies	Neuroleptic tolerance enhanced
Reduced catalepsy to haloperidol	Symptomatic response to ketamine
MK-801 and PCP-induced hyperactivity	
Molecular changes in the prefrontal cortex	
NAA levels ↓	NAA levels ↓
GAD_{67} mRNA ↓	GAD_{67} mRNA ↓
BDNF mRNA ↓	BDNF mRNA ↓
Changes in synaptic morphology in the prefrontal cortex	
Spine density ↓	Spine density ↓

BDNF, brain-derived neurotrophic factor; GAD_{67}, glutamate decarboxylase-67; LI, latent inhibition; NAA, *N*-acetylaspartate; PCP, phencyclidine; PPI, prepulse inhibition of startle; ↓ reduced vs. controls.

animal in the form of altered brain neurochemistry and aberrant behaviour (neurodevelopmental models). These models test hypotheses that schizophrenia is caused by a defect in cerebral development (Lillrank *et al.* 1995; Lipska & Weinberger 2000) and, in some instances, test whether the effects of early brain damage could remain inconspicuous until after a considerable delay, as appears to be the case in the human condition (Weinberger 1986, 1987; Murray & Lewis 1987; Bloom 1993). Another popular modelling approach involves pharmacological disruption of brain function and behaviour via *N*-methyl-D-aspartate (NMDA) antagonists. These models test the hypothesis that dysfunction of glutamate neurotransmission accounts for a variety of schizophrenic phenomena (Javitt & Zukin 1991). Still another effort focuses on the search for susceptibility genes employing modern technologies of genetic engineering (genetic models; Erickson 1996). These models test the clinical evidence that susceptibility genes account for risk for illness and, together with epigenetic/environmental factors, for phenotypic variation. Characteristically, a majority of these new models, despite the diversity of their origins, target components of a common neural circuitry implicated in schizophrenia, i.e. the temporolimbic cortices–nucleus accumbens/striatal complex–thalamus–prefrontal cortex. The involvement of this circuitry may account for the overlap in 'schizophrenia-like' phenomena at the anatomical, neurochemical or behavioural level that are common to these various models.

Neurodevelopmental models

Models testing aetiological theories

Many epidemiological and clinical correlational studies have been carried out in search of early developmental factors that may predispose to schizophrenia. There have been reports linking schizophrenia to obstetric complications (Woerner *et al.* 1973; DeLisi *et al.* 1988; McNiel 1988; Hultman *et al.* 1997; Dalman *et al.* 1999), *in utero* exposure to alcohol (Lohr & Bracha 1989) and severe malnutrition (Susser & Lin 1992). A number of animal models have been designed to test the plausibility of specific gestational factors having a role in the origin of this disorder. These 'aetiological' models, none of which directly manipulates dopamine, aspire to construct validity and heuristic value because they reproduce putative causes of the disease and theoretically model putative primary pathological mechanisms.

For instance, a gestational malnutrition model (or, more precisely, prenatal protein deprivation that begins prior to and continues throughout pregnancy) results in severe permanent changes in the development of the rat brain (for reviews see Morgane *et al.* 1993; Brown *et al.* 1996). Malnutrition affects neurogenesis, cell migration and differentiation, and leads to deviations in normal brain development, including disrupted formation of neural circuits and neurotransmitter systems (Lewis *et al.* 1979; Cintra *et al.* 1997). Not suprisingly, malnutrition has been shown to have debilitating effects on cognitive function and learning abilities (Tonkiss & Galler 1990). Thus, to some degree these models mimic certain 'face' features of schizophrenia. In contrast to schizophrenia, however, morphological abnormalities are severe and widespread, and the behavioural consequences are varied and inconsistent, perhaps, at least in part, because the impact of malnutrition on brain development is likely to be quite variable and depend on many factors, which have only been explored to a small degree. As a test of the plausibility of the malnutrition theory of schizophrenia this model has limited validity.

Prenatal exposure to influenza virus, another predisposing factor implicated in schizophrenia by several large epidemiological studies (Mednick *et al.* 1988; Kendell & Kemp 1989; O'Callaghan *et al.* 1991; Adams *et al.* 1993), has been shown to induce pyramidal cell disarray in a small subgroup of mice whose mothers were inoculated with the virus (Cotter *et al.* 1995). This developmental defect is somewhat similar to that reported in two studies in the hippocampi of schizophrenic patients (Scheibel & Kovelman 1981; Conrad *et al.* 1991). Another recent report indicates that infection with human influenza of day 9 pregnant mice results in defective corticogenesis as indicated by reduced thickness of the neocortex and hippocampus and by significant reductions of cortical reelin immunoreactivity in the offspring (Fatemi *et al.* 1999). This model thus reproduces a hypothetical causative factor in schizophrenia and has face validity, at least at the level of reduced reelin expression, a neurobiological finding recently explored in brains of patients with schizophrenia (Impagnatiello *et al.* 1998). These are intriguing observations, but more conclusive data on the involvement of reelin in schizophrenia and on the behavioural phenotype of the animal model are required before conclusions about the relevance of this model for schizophrenia can be made.

The plausibility that other, less common, viruses may induce schizophrenia-like changes has also been investigated (Rott *et al.* 1985; Waltrip *et al.* 1995). *In utero* Borna disease virus (BDV), a neurotropic virus with limbic selectivity, damages the hippocampus and prefrontal cortex and results in complex changes in regional dopamine in rats (Solbrig *et al.* 1994, 1996a,b; Hornig *et al.* 1999). While this model may invite further research into the mechanisms involved, notwithstanding convincing evidence of BDV infection in schizophrenia, its relevance to the pathophysiology of schizophrenia seems remote. Another example of a viral model is neonatal infection with lymphocytic choriomeningitis virus (LCMV) which disrupts in adult rats the integrity of γ-aminobutyric acid (GABA)-ergic neurones and excitatory amino acid systems, both implicated in schizophrenia (Pearce *et al.* 1996, 1999). The potential face validity of this model at a cellular level makes it particularly attractive because it addresses two theories about the pathophysiology of schizophrenia: vulnerability of GABAergic interneurones to developmental insult and adolescent vulnerability to excitotoxic injury (Benes *et al.* 1991, 1992; Olney & Farber 1995). Although conceptually appealing, it has yet to address a broader spectrum of aspects of the disorder and its basic construct, LCMV infection, is of dubious relevance to schizophrenia.

The plausibility of obstetric and birth complications is difficult to explore in animals because their causes in schizophrenia are unknown. Nevertheless, studies of models of caesarean birth and of anoxia during birth in rats report changes in limbic dopamine function of adult animals consistent with hyperresponsiveness of the dopamine system to stimulants (Brake *et al.* 1997a,b; El-Khodor & Boksa 1997, 1998). Surprisingly, animals born by caesarean section and not subject to anoxia seem to be even more affected than anoxic rats (El-Khodor & Boksa 1997). If this has bearing on schizophrenia, it would suggest that caesarean section constitutes a greater risk factor than the more dramatic birth trauma of anoxia. In humans, caesarean section is generally assumed to involve less stress to the fetus and has not been noted as one of the obstetric complications linked to schizophrenia. Clearly, more studies are needed to elucidate the mechanisms underlying the caesarean section-related phenomena in animals.

Until a broader array of schizophrenia-related phenomena is assessed in each of these aetiological models, it is premature to draw firm conclusions about whether any reproduces mechanisms underlying the human disorder. Moreover, the validity of these models is tempered by the lack of convincing evidence for the role of any of these various causative factors in schizophrenia, with the possible exception of influenza. However, these models illustrate that certain early developmental insults may permanently disrupt brain function in ways that are similar to some of the phenomena reported in schizophrenia.

Models of disrupted neurogenesis

Several postmortem studies of schizophrenia have reported variations in cortical cytoarchitecture (Arnold *et al.* 1991; Akbarian *et al.* 1993a,b; Kirkpatrick *et al.* 1999), possibly of developmental nature. These reports have inspired models based on disrupted neurogenesis. These models do not attempt to reproduce specific putative causative factors implicated in schizophrenia, but aspire to face validity at the anatomical level by mimicking cellular aberrations that presumably would follow a disruption of early cortical development analogous to what has been described in some of the human postmortem studies. The heuristic framework of these models is that specific prenatal interruptions of cell maturation would result in relevant biological and behavioural changes as the animal matures. Examples include cortical dysgenesis induced by gestational X-ray irradiation (Rakic 1996; Mintz *et al.* 1997; Selemon *et al.* 2000), *in utero* exposure to a mitotic toxin, methylazoxymethanol acetate (MAM), which destroys populations of rapidly dividing neurones (Johnston *et al.* 1988; Talamini *et al.* 1998), and systemic administration of nitric oxide synthase (NOS) inhibitors, which interfere with maturation of neurones and synaptogenesis (Black *et al.* 1999). Animals that have undergone X-ray or MAM manipulations exhibit morphological changes in a broad array of brain structures implicated in schizophrenia, particularly the hippocampus, and frontal and entorhinal cortices. These animals also demonstrate a variety of behavioural alterations such as locomotor hyperactivity, stereotypies, cognitive impairments and disruption of latent inhibition and PPI, and show electrophysiological abnormalities posited to underlie psychomotor disturbances in schizophrenia (Johnston *et al.* 1988; Moore *et al.* 1998; Talamini *et al.* 1998). Male rats exposed to a NOS inhibitor (L-nitroarginine) between 3 and 5 days of life show in adulthood locomotor hypersensitivity to amphetamine and deficits in PPI, but similarly treated females were not found to be affected on these measures (Black *et al.* 1999). These preliminary results are provocative and invite further research.

Models of aberrant neurogenesis, although the data are limited at this time, appear to have potential heuristic value in discovering mechanisms of specific neural circuit disruptions caused by elimination of maturing neurones. There are a number of areas to be pursued including characterizing critical risk periods (specifically, a period corresponding to the second trimester of gestation in humans), critical neuronal populations, molecular adaptations in remaining neurones, etc. These models demonstrate again that perturbation in cortical development can reproduce some of the behavioural characteristics associated with schizophrenia, including those linked to dopamine systems.

Perinatal stress models

This group of models focuses on the long-lasting consequences of stress for brain development and for shaping adult behavioural responses. They have been variably used as models of depression, anxiety and schizophrenia, diseases in which stress has long been thought to have some role. Stress has been postulated as a factor in so-called 'two hit' models of schizophrenia in which two independent insults (e.g. aberrant genetic trait and stressful experience) are thought to be necessary for the occurrence of the disorder. In rodents, early life exposure to experiential stressors such as maternal separation (Liu *et al.* 1997) and social isolation (Jones *et al.* 1992; Geyer *et al.* 1993; Wilkinson *et al.* 1994) produce numerous hormonal, neurochemical and behavioural changes, including locomotor hyperactivity in a novel environment, maze learning impairments, anxiety, latent inhibition and sensorimotor gating deficits. Of particular interest is that some of these alterations emerge in adult life and can be restored by a wide range of antipsychotics, including various typical and atypical drugs (Varty & Higgins 1995; Bakshi *et al.* 1998; Ellenbroek *et al.* 1998). Importantly, the effects of adverse early life events (e.g. maternal separation) on adult reactivity are strongly influenced by genetic as well as non-genomic factors (Zaharia *et al.* 1996; Anisman *et al.* 1998; Francis *et al.* 1999).

These models provide important evidence for an interaction between genetic predisposition and early life experiences and demonstrate that both are involved in shaping the adult stress response system and adult patterns of behaviour. They might thus represent an interesting approach to study the interactions of these variables in schizophrenia.

Neonatal lesion models

Another series of studies have focused on neonatal damage of restricted brain regions in rats (Lipska *et al.* 1993; Chambers *et al.* 1996; Flores *et al.* 1996a; Wan *et al.* 1996, 1998; Wan & Corbett 1997; Black *et al.* 1998; Becker *et al.* 1999; Brake *et al.* 1999; Grecksch *et al.* 1999; Schroeder *et al.* 1999) and in monkeys (Beauregard & Bachevalier 1996; Bertolino *et al.* 1997; Saunders *et al.* 1998; Bachevalier *et al.* 1999). The main objective of many of these studies is to disrupt development of the hippocampus, a brain area consistently implicated in human schizophrenia (Falkai & Bogerts 1986; Jeste & Lohr 1989; Bogerts *et al.* 1990; Suddath *et al.* 1990; Eastwood & Harrison 1995, 1998; Eastwood *et al.* 1995, 1997; Weinberger 1999), and thus disrupt development of the widespread cortical and subcortical circuitry in which the hippocampus participates. The lesions were intended to involve regions of the hippocampus that directly project to the prefrontal cortex, i.e. ventral hippocampus and ventral subiculum (Jay *et al.* 1989; Carr & Sesack 1996), and that correspond to the anterior hippocampus in humans, a region that shows anatomical abnormalities in schizophrenia (Suddath *et al.* 1990).

Neonatal excitotoxic lesions of the rat ventral hippocampus (VH) lead in adolescence or early adulthood to the emergence of abnormalities in a number of dopamine-related behaviours, which bear close resemblance to behaviours seen in animals sensitized to psychostimulants. When tested as juveniles (postnatal day 35), rats with the neonatal VH lesions are less social than controls (Sams-Dodd *et al.* 1997), but otherwise behave normally in motor tests involving exposure to stress and dopamine agonists. In adolescence and adulthood (postnatal day 56 and older), lesioned animals display markedly changed behaviours thought to be primarily linked to increased mesolimbic/nigrostriatal dopamine transmission (motor hyperresponsiveness to stress and stimulants, enhanced stereotypies). They also show enhanced sensitivity to glutamate antagonists (MK-801 and PCP), deficits in PPI and latent inhibition, impaired social behaviours and working memory problems (Lipska & Weinberger 1993, 1994a,b; Lipska *et al.* 1995a; Becker *et al.* 1999; Grecksch *et al.* 1999; Hori *et al.* 1999; Al-Amin *et al.* 2000, 2001), phenomena showing many parallels with schizophrenia. Emergence of the behavioural changes in adolescence appears not to be related to the surge of gonadal hormones during puberty because a similar temporal pattern of abnormalities is observed in animals depleted of gonadal hormones prior to puberty (Lipska & Weinberger 1994b). Notably, removal of prefrontal neurones in adult animals with the earlier hippocampal lesion restores some of the behaviours (i.e. those modulated by but not critically dependent on the prefrontal cortex, such as hyperlocomotion after amphetamine), suggesting that aberrant development of the prefrontal cortex in the context of early damage to the hippocampus may be a critical factor in the expression of the syndrome (Lipska *et al.* 1998a). In this context, it is important to emphasize that anatomical findings from post-mortem studies and neuropsychological and neuroimaging studies of brain function in patients with schizophrenia have implicated prefrontal cortical maldevelopment and a developmental 'dysconnection' of the temporolimbic and prefrontal cortices (for review see Weinberger & Lipska 1995). Although the exact mechanisms of a seemingly similar 'dysconnection' and malfunction of the prefrontal cortex in the VH lesioned rats need to be elucidated, preliminary findings from molecular and electrophysiological studies (such as reduced cortical levels of *N*-acetylaspartate (NAA), attenuated stress-induced cortical dopamine release, attenuated cortical expression of a membrane glutamate transporter EAAC1 and of a synthetic enzyme for GABA, glutamate decarboxylase-67 (GAD_{67}), reduced brain-derived neurotrophic factor (BDNF) expression, altered cortical expression of transcription factors, c-fos and ΔfosB, as well as altered firing pattern of cortical pyramidal neurones in response to ventral tegmental area (VTA) stimulation) suggest that aberrant cortical dopamine–glutamate–GABA interactions may underlie cortical dysfunction in the neonatally VH lesioned rats (Lipska *et al.* 1995b; Lee *et al.* 1998; Ashe *et al.* 1999; Bertolino *et al.* 1999; O'Donnell *et al.* 1999). We have recently reported that excitotoxic prefrontal cortical lesions in adult animals cause downstream striatal NAA losses and reduced GAD_{67} mRNA expression, and suggested that both changes might reflect transsynaptic pathology (Roffman *et al.* 2000). It is possible that similar transsynaptic events occur in response to the neonatal VH lesion but further work is required to determine if and by what mechanisms molecular changes in prefrontal neurones are linked.

It is interesting to note that many of these changes have been reported in stress- and psychostimulant-sensitization models (Feldpausch *et al.* 1998; Gambarana *et al.* 1999; Vanderschuren *et al.* 1999), as well as in patients with schizophrenia (Akbarian *et al.* 1995; Bertolino *et al.* 1998). Subcortical function in the neonatally lesioned rats is also altered in a fashion consistent with at least some reports on behavioural sensitization (Imperato *et al.* 1996; Nestler & Aghajanian 1997; Steiner & Gerfen 1998; Castner *et al.* 2000), i.e. striatal dopamine release is attenuated in response to stress and amphetamine, midbrain expression of the membrane dopamine transporter (DAT) mRNA is reduced, striatal expression of dynorphin (an opioid peptide colocalized with D_1 receptors) and of ΔfosB (a transcription factor sensitive to persistent stimulation) are enhanced (Lipska *et al.* 1998b; Lee *et al.* 1998). However, it should be noted that enhanced rather than attenuated striatal dopamine release has been observed in other paradigms of sensitization to psychostimulants (for review see Spanagel & Weiss 1999) as well as in a subgroup of schizophrenics as evidenced by recent single photon emission computerized tomography (SPECT) studies (Laruelle *et al.* 1996; Breier *et al.* 1997; Abi-Dargham *et al.* 1998). Similarly discrepant are the findings of synaptic morphology – increased synaptic densities, the number of branches and dendritic length are reported in prefrontal cortex in sensitization models (Robinson & Kolb 1997), whereas these dendritic parameters are decreased in schizophrenia (Glantz & Lewis 2000) and in the neonatal hippocampal lesion model (Lipska *et al.* 2001). Nevertheless, an array of behavioural and molecular changes associated with this model suggest that early developmental insult of the ventral hippocampus may facilitate sensitization of the dopamine system, and thereby account for the adult onset of a maladaptive condition characterized by a variety of dopamine-related abnormalities. Similar pathophysiological mechanisms have been hypothesized to underlie schizophrenia (Lieberman *et al.* 1997; Meng *et al.* 1998; Duncan *et al.* 1999). Unlike psychostimulant sensitization models, however, the neonatal lesion model does not target the dopamine system directly and similar sensitization-like phenomena are not seen following an analogous hippocampal lesion in adult animals. It may be of considerable heuristic interest to determine how the developmental lesion initiates the subsequent behavioural and molecular phenomena associated with sensitization.

In terms of the predictive validity of the neonatal VH lesion model, antipsychotic drugs normalize some lesion-induced behaviours (Lipska & Weinberger 1994a; Sams-Dodd *et al.* 1997). Drugs targeting the glutamate system may also prove beneficial; LY293558, an alpha-amino-3-hydroxy-5-methyl-4-isoxazole propionic acid (AMPA) antagonist, is highly efficient in blocking hyperlocomotion in the neonatally lesioned rats at doses that do not affect locomotor activity in controls (Al-Amin *et al.* 2000). Thus, this model may have predictive validity and heuristic potential to identify drugs with new mechanisms of action. The model also appears to mimic a spectrum of neurobiological and behavioural features of schizophrenia, including functional pathology in presumably critical brain regions interconnected with the hippocampal formation and targeted by antipsychotic drugs – the striatum/nucleus accumbens and the prefrontal cortex (see Table 21.2). It is noteworthy that in the non-human primate, early postnatal damage of the hippocampal region also alters development of the dorsal prefrontal cortex and the mechanisms whereby the dorsal prefrontal cortex regulates subcortical dopamine function, phenomena similar to those described in patients with schizophrenia (Bertolino *et al.* 1997, 2000; Saunders *et al.* 1998). Thus, neonatal damage to the hippocampus of the rat appears to reproduce a broad spectrum of schizophrenia-related phenomena, and establishes the neurobiological plausibility of early damage having a delayed impact on neural functions implicated in schizophrenia.

Developmental lesions of other brain structures implicated in schizophrenia and components of a limbic–neocortical circuit (e.g. thalamus, prefrontal cortex) also have been considered as models. For instance, thalamic excitotoxic lesions in PD7 rats result in adult expression of apomorphine- and amphetamine-induced hyperlocomotion (Rajakumar *et al.* 1996). Intracerebroventricular infusions of kainic acid into neonatal (PD7) rats lead in adulthood to a reduction in neural numbers in the dorsal hippocampus, and are associated with changes in the expression of subpopulations of glutamate receptors and immediate early genes (Csernansky *et al.* 1998; Montgomery *et al.* 1999). Neonatal (PD7) excitotoxic damage of the medial prefrontal cortex was reported to produce delayed behavioural effects accompanied by dopamine receptor changes (Flores *et al.* 1996b), although others did not confirm these data (Lipska *et al.* 1998a). The spectrum of behavioural and cellular parameters examined in these models is rather limited at this time.

Another neonatal insult with intriguing implications is selective depletion of serotonin in neonatal rats (by tryptophan hydroxylase inhibitor parachlorophenylalanine (PCPA) that decreases markers of synaptic density in the adult brain, and results in cognitive deficits; Mazer *et al.* 1997). These effects are somewhat similar to those reported in the postmortem schizophrenic brain (Weinberger 1999), but other schizophrenia-relevant aspects need to be tested in this model.

Although developmental lesion models represent a rather crude technique to study the role of particular brain regions, transmitter systems or the connections between them, they have confirmed the plausibility of neurodevelopmental damage having selected deleterious effects after a prolonged period of relative normalcy. In this respect, they appear to have face validity, not only in terms of behavioural, cellular and pharmacological phenomena, but also in terms of the temporal course of the clinical disorder. As models of developmental pathology they certainly lack construct validity, as the schizophrenic brain does not manifest a 'lesion' analogous to any of these models, but they may have heuristic value in discovering molecular consequences of early brain damage and new treatment prospects.

Pharmacological models of glutamatergic antagonism

In addition to the non-pharmacological non-dopaminergic approaches described above, pharmacological blockade of NMDA receptors in adult animals has gained popularity as a model of schizophrenia. Observations that non-competitive NMDA antagonists, such as phencyclidine (PCP) and ketamine, exacerbate some psychotic symptoms in schizophrenic patients and have psychotomimetic effects in normal humans (Krystal *et al.* 1994; Lahti *et al.* 1995) have encouraged speculation that some aspects of schizophrenia may relate to abnormal glutamatergic function. This has been further supported by postmortem studies in schizophrenia showing a variety of changes in the glutamate system, including altered glutamate metabolism and expression of various glutamate receptors (Javitt & Zukin 1991; Akbarian *et al.* 1996; Jentsch & Roth 1999; Weinberger 1999).

In rodents and monkeys, acute subanaesthetic doses of NMDA antagonists produce a constellation of phenomena potentially relevant to schizophrenic symptomatology, including hyperlocomotion, enhanced stereotyped behaviours, cognitive and sensorimotor gating deficits and impaired social interactions. PCP as well as other NMDA antagonists acutely increase extracellular levels of dopamine and glutamate (as well as norepinephrine and acetylcholine) in the prefrontal cortex, and alter firing patterns of dopaminergic and nucleus accumbens neurones (Verma & Moghaddam 1996; O'Donnell & Grace 1998). Repeated administration of PCP can also induce robust behavioural and neurochemical changes even after long-term withdrawal (Jentsch *et al.* 1997, 1998a,b). Of particular interest is differential dysregulation of the firing patterns of mesolimbic and mesocortical dopaminergic neurones by low behaviourally relevant doses of NMDA antagonists. These changes in dopamine cell firing may render them unresponsive or inappropriately responsive to salient environmental stimuli such as stress and reward (Murase *et al.* 1993; Mathe *et al.* 1998). If a similar process underlies psychotic symptoms and cognitive deficits in schizophrenia, the NMDA antagonist model may offer novel treatment strategies targeting glutamate rather than dopamine. Recently, experimental approaches to reverse NMDA antagonist-induced abnormalities have included pharmacological enhancement of NMDA receptor activity, enhancement of metabotropic glutamate receptor (mGluR2) activity, and blockade of AMPA receptors (Moghaddam *et al.* 1997; Moghaddam & Adams 1998), the latter approach shown to be also effective in the neonatal hippocampal lesion model (see above). Thus, a model based on a primary glutamatergic abnormality appears to show important heuristic properties in terms of identifying potential novel therapies. This model may offer insight into molecular adaptations that follow chronic NMDA blockade, and identify new therapeutic targets. Notably, the repeated non-competitive NMDA blockade model, which had also been intensely investigated from the perspective of behavioural sensitization and its role in drug addiction and reward mechanisms (Wolf *et al.* 1993), shares certain behavioural and neurochemical similarities with the neonatal hippocampal lesion model, including cognitive deficits (in particular, in working memory tasks), reduced frontal dopamine transmission (Jentsch *et al.* 1997, 1998a) and reduced GABA activity as indicated by reduced levels of GAD_{67} (Qin *et al.* 1994; Yonezawa *et al.* 1998), and disrupted social behaviours and augmented locomotor responses to stress and amphetamine (Jentsch *et al.* 1998b). The similarities between the models may reflect a common disruption of cortical glutamate–GABA function which may converge towards a common underlying process of behavioural sensitization. Unlike the aetiological or neonatal lesions models, the NMDA antagonist approach does not, however, address the developmental component of schizophrenia.

Genetic models

Schizophrenia is a highly heritable disorder that probably involves multiple genes with small effects across large populations (Kendler *et al.* 1996). Elucidating the roles of the susceptibility genes for this clinically diverse and probably genetically heterogeneous disorder will require considerable effort and is unlikely to be fully resolved soon. Modern technologies, involving targeted gene deletions or gene transfer techniques that have revolutionized experimental medicine, may provide a new generation of animal models for schizophrenia that may help in this daunting task.

Some genetic models for neurological diseases are almost perfect in terms of construct validity because transgenic animals may be, in a sense, 'humanized' by the introduction of human genes involved in the disease or the mutated animal homologues of such genes (Loring *et al.* 1996). However, transgenic models also illustrate that even a highly accurate model in terms of construct validity may fail the test of face validity in terms of a phenotype analogous to the disorder. For instance, the Duchenne's muscular dystrophy mdx mutation mouse model is hardly symptomatic (Erickson 1996), the PDAPP transgenic mouse model of Alzheimer's disease which overexpresses human amyloid precursor protein (Johnson-Wood *et al.* 1997) does not have an isomorphic behavioural phenotype, and the hypoxanthine-guanine phosphoribosyl-transferase (HPRT) knockout mouse has no recognizable phenotype analogous to Lesch–Nyhan disease (Wu & Melton 1993). Behavioural phenotypes of these models are not isomorphic with the disease, because genetic mutation can have remarkably different phenotypes when placed on different genetic backgrounds. However, despite phenotypic dissimilarity, such models are faithful in terms of certain cellular characteristics and can be very useful in illuminating molecular mechanisms leading to pathological changes and in discovering new treatments. This approach is possible only if the disease can be attributed to specific human genes, and thus seems to have limited application in studying schizophrenia or other psychiatric illnesses at the present time.

In an attempt to test the possibility of involvement of various neurotransmitter receptors relevant to schizophrenia (D_1–D_5 subtypes of dopamine receptors, adenosine A2A receptors, α_2-adrenergic receptors and NMDA receptors) and to elucidate their functional roles, investigators have used genetically altered mice in which expression of these receptors was selectively and usually completely suppressed (Sibley 1999). Probably the most intriguing is a recent attempt at targeting the NR1 subunit of the NMDA receptor in a genetic mouse model (Mohn *et al.* 1999), despite lack of direct evidence that an NMDA receptor gene is abnormal in schizophrenia. Mutant mice expressing only 5% of essential NR1 receptors show increased spontaneous hyperlocomotion that attenuates after a single injection of haloperidol and clozapine, and deficits in social and sexual behaviours that respond to acute clozapine treatment. Although some of these behavioural changes suggest increased dopaminergic tone, dopamine release and turnover are not altered in these animals. However, somewhat contrary to the phenotype expected in a schizophrenia model, NR1 mutant mice do not exhibit enhanced responsiveness to the NMDA antagonists MK-801 and PCP. Continued studies of these mice will provide more information about the consequences of dramatic congenital hypofunction of the glutamatergic system and will shed light on interactions of the glutamatergic system with other neurotransmitter systems, but the relevance of this model to schizophrenia is yet unclear. This example underscores a unique problem of modelling the schizophrenic phenotype in animals that even a genetic model cannot escape – lack of pathognomonic neurobiological markers and validation criteria.

Another promising genetic strategy is identification of predisposing candidate genes by selecting rodent lines or strains for particular behavioural traits. Such candidate genes may then be used to identify homologous human genes potentially involved in the aetiology of schizophrenia. For instance, studies in inbred mice strains with deficits in sensory inhibition have indicated that altered expression and function of the α_7 nicotinic cholinergic receptor may be responsible for some auditory sensory gating deficits (Stevens *et al.* 1998). A defect in the so-called 'P50 auditory-evoked response' is found in patients with schizophrenia and in their unaffected relatives (Freedman *et al.* 1987). This evoked potential defect (but not schizophrenia itself because many individuals showing P50 deficits are clinically unaffected) was subsequently linked to a chromosome 15 locus, near the site of the α_7 nicotinic cholinergic receptor gene (Freedman *et al.* 1997). This linkage finding, which echoed data from the earlier mice experiments, suggested that a genetic defect in the α_7 nicotinic cholinergic receptor might be a predisposing factor in schizophrenia. Sequencing of the α_7 nicotinic cholinergic receptor gene in individuals with this phenotype is currently in progress. Another example involves animals bred for high susceptibility to apomorphine-induced stereotypic behaviours (APO-SUS rats). These animals, in contrast to apomorphine non-responsive (APO-UNSUS) rats, demonstrate various behavioural (e.g. prepulse inhibition and latent inhibition deficits), biochemical (e.g. elevated levels of tyrosine hydroxylase mRNA in the substantia nigra and D_2 receptor binding in the dorsal striatum) and immunological (e.g. reduced sensitivity for rheumatoid arthritis) features implicated in schizophrenia (Ellenbroek *et al.* 1995, 2000). Thus, such behavioural trait-selected animals may be used as models of schizophrenia-prone individuals and provide material for novel gene identification and for candidate gene analyses.

Another model has combined neurodevelopmental and genetic predisposition approaches. Fisher344 rats, a highly stress-responsive inbred strain, show particularly high susceptibility to the behavioural effects of neonatal hippocampal damage. Lewis rats, on the other hand, bred for low stress responsiveness, appear to be resistant to the behavioural consequences of identical lesions (Lipska & Weinberger 1995). This lesion genetic model may be used for identification of candidate genes that mediate behavioural responses to a neonatal hippocampal insult, and that, by extension, might predispose to or modify the expression of schizophrenia.

Because recent data suggest a significant role for neurodevelopmental processes in schizophrenia, another approach to genetic modelling of schizophrenia may focus on manipulating in animals those genes that have a role in neurodevelopment, maintenance of cell–cell connections, and trophic factors (Weickert & Weinberger 1998; see Table 21.3). For instance, in an attempt to alter genes involved in neural migration, neural cell adhesion molecule isoform 180 (*NCAM-180*) gene was deleted in mice. Mice with this selective gene deletion display a marked reduction in the levels of PSA-NCAM (polysialic-acid-rich NCAM), a molecule involved in neuronal regeneration and plasticity, which has also been reported as reduced in the hippocampus of patients with schizophrenia (Barbeau *et al.* 1995). *NCAM-180*-depleted mice are characterized by abnormal migration of neurones within the subventricular zone, altered cytoarchitecture of multiple brain regions, including olfactory bulb, hippocampus and cerebellum, enlarged ventricles and changes in behaviour (PPI deficits) (Tomasiewicz *et al.* 1993; Wood *et al.* 1998). Although some of these changes resemble abnormalities observed in schizophrenia, more thorough phenotypic characterization is needed.

Because the early hippocampal damage models have demonstrated the plausibility of developmental defects in the hippocampus having a delayed impact on other neural circuits and systems (e.g. prefrontal cortex), transgenic models that selectively disrupt development of hippocampal circuitry may turn out to be especially heuristic. In a recent attempt to alter development of the hippocampus, the LIM homeobox *Lhx5* gene was deleted in mice (Zhao *et al.* 1999). The *Lhx5* homozygous mutant embryos showed dramatic defects in hippocampal morphology; however, most of the homozygotes died within a few days after birth. Somewhat less severe changes in hippocampal

Table 21.3 Potential animal models based on genetic manipulation of cellular phenotype.

Molecular changes in schizophrenia	Brain region	Molecular targets for genetic manipulations in animals
Trophic/ECM molecules ↓	Cortex, hippocampus	BDNF, LAMP, PSA-NCAM, reelin[1]
Glutamate function ↓	Cortex, hippocampus	GluR1-4, GluR5-7, NR1-2, KA1-2, GCP II, EAAC1, GLT1, GLAST[2]
GABA function ↓	Cortex, hippocampus	GAD_{67}, GABA(A)[3]
Synaptic markers ↓	Cortex, hippocampus	Synapsin, synaptophysin, SNAP-25, GAT1,3, complexin[4]
Other cellular markers ↓	Cortex, hippocampus	GAP-43, MAPs[5]

BDNF, brain-derived neurotrophic factor; ECM, extracellular matrix; EAAC1, neuronal glutamate transporter; GABA(A), γ-aminobutyric acid A receptors; GAP-43, neuronal growth-associated protein; GAD_{67}, glutamate decarboxylase-67; GAT1,3, GABA transporters; GCP II, glutamate carboxypeptidase II; GLT1, GLAST, glial glutamate transporters; GluR1-4, subunits of AMPA (α-amino-3-hydroxy-5-methyl-4-isoxazolepropionic acid) receptor; GluR5-7 and KA1-2, subunits of kainate receptor; LAMP, limbic system-associated membrane protein, MAP, microtubule-associated protein; NR1-2, subunits of NMDA (*N*-methyl-D-aspartate) receptor; PSA-NCAM, polysialylated neural cell adhesion molecule; SNAP-25, synaptosomal-associated protein of 25 kDa; ↓ decreased expression or compromised function.

Selected references:

1 Vawter *et al.* (1998); Barbeau *et al.* (1995); Impagnatiello *et al.* (1998); Fatemi *et al.* (1999)
2 Ohnuma *et al.* (1998); Eastwood *et al.* (1995, 1997)
3 Benes *et al.* (1996, 1997); Huntsman *et al.* (1998); Dean *et al.* (1999)
4 Eastwood & Harrison (1995); Glantz & Lewis (1997); Young *et al.* (1998); Harrison & Eastwood (1998); Karson *et al.* (1999)
5 Perrone-Bizzozero *et al.* (1996); Eastwood & Harrison (1998)

development, but still often lethal or too damaging to be considered relevant to schizophrenia, have been reported in mice with null deletions of other homeobox genes (e.g. *Emx2* (Pellegrini *et al.* 1996) and *Lhx2* (Porter *et al.* 1997)) as well as genes involved in neural migration during development (e.g. β subunit of platelet-activating factor acetylhydrolase *Pafah1b1* (or *Lis1*) (Hirotsune *et al.* 1998), cycline-dependent kinase 5 (*Cdk5*) (Ohshima *et al.* 1996), *mdab1* (Sheldon *et al.* 1997) and reeler (Goffinet 1995)). More interesting, because of a more subtle pathology, is a model of heterozygous haploinsufficient reeler mouse (HRM) which expresses 50% of the brain reelin content of a wild-type mouse and exhibits many phenotypic traits reminiscent of neurochemical and neuroanatomical characteristics of schizophrenia (Liu *et al.* 2001). These features include: (i) downregulation of prefrontal cortical GAD_{67} mRNA; (ii) an increase of neuronal packing density and a decrease of cortical thickness; and (iii) a reduction in cortical and hippocampal spine density. Some intriguing behavioural changes, such as increased anxiety, disrupted PPI and cognitive deficits in a radial maze, have also been observed in this model. Another promising strategy might involve conditional reduction (or enhancement) of expression of certain genes restricted to critical periods in development, an approach that has recently been used in a drug addiction model that inducibly overexpresses ΔfosB (Kelz *et al.* 1999). Table 21.3 contains other suggestions for novel models based on transgenic approaches to reproduce specific cellular abnormalities that have been implicated in certain brain regions in schizophrenia; not all of these findings, however, have been independently replicated. Such developmental genetic models may provide new candidate genes for assessment in clinical studies and help to model the cell biology of this complex disorder. Candidate genes selected from their chromosomal position near genetic loci linked to schizophrenia might also be future targets for transgenic models.

Conclusions

The approach to studying the aetiology and pathophysiology of schizophrenia at the level of animal neurobiology has become much more sophisticated. In light of mounting evidence linking schizophrenia to certain neuropathological processes in the brain, heuristic animal models may prove to be important tools in testing new theories about the origin and mechanisms of this disorder. In particular, some of the recent models have confirmed the plausibility of neurodevelopmental insults having prolonged effects on the dopamine system and behaviours relevant to schizophrenia, and supported the notion that disruption of glutamatergic neurotransmission may lead to new approaches to treatment. The neonatal lesion model has suggested that the effects of an early ventral hippocampal insult, rather than being compensated for, precipitate a state remarkably similar to stress- or psychostimulant-induced sensitization, associated with long-lasting maladaptive cellular changes that lead to delayed onset of abnormal behaviours. Mechanisms underlying sensitization to stress, amphetamine, cocaine, opioids or non-competitive NMDA antagonists are not well understood and seem to involve complex changes in multiple neurotransmitter systems, including dopamine, glutamate and GABA. If the effects of sensitization following developmental abnormalities of the cortex are, indeed, involved in the adolescent/adult onset of schizophrenia-like changes in this model, and by extension in schizophrenia, this may underscore the importance of preventive treatment strategies directed at reducing the impact of experiential stressors in predisposed individuals. Findings from the neonatal stress models discussed above might provide clues about the mechanisms of such potential interventions.

Modern technologies that have been successfully applied to animal modelling of genetic neurological diseases may one day also open the door to our understanding of the mechanisms underlying psychiatric disorders. The transgenic murine models, in which mutations homologous to mutations in humans are inserted by transgenesis or by stem cell knockouts, may seem superior to any pharmacological, surgical or experiential models, but they have their own limitations. It is clear that most psychiatric disorders, including schizophrenia, are multifactorial (i.e. multiple genes interact with multiple environmental factors to create a particular phenotype; Egan & Weinberger 1997). Theoretically at least, by choosing the right combination of the mutation and modifier genes as well as appropriate environmental influences on their expression, one might be able to create at the cellular level a high fidelity animal model of such a complex human disease as schizophrenia.

References

Abi-Dargham, A., Gil, R., Krystal, J. *et al.* (1998) Increased striatal dopamine transmission in schizophrenia: confirmation in a second cohort. *American Journal of Psychiatry* **155**, 761–767.

Adams, W., Kendell, R.E., Hare, E.H. & Munk-Jorgensen, P. (1993) Epidemiological evidence that maternal influenza contributes to the aetiology of schizophrenia: an analysis of Scottish, English and Danish data. *British Journal of Psychiatry* **163**, 169–177.

Akbarian, S., Bunney, W.E. Jr, Potkin, S.G. *et al.* (1993a) Altered distribution of nicotinamide–adenine dinucleotide phosphate-diaphorase cells in frontal lobe of schizophrenics implies disturbances of cortical development. *Archives of General Psychiatry* **50**, 169–177.

Akbarian, S., Vinuela, A., Kim, J.J. *et al.* (1993b) Distorted distribution of nicotinamide–adenine dinucleotide phosphate–diaphorase neurons in temporal lobe of schizophrenics implies anomalous cortical development. *Archives of General Psychiatry* **50**, 178–187.

Akbarian, S., Kim, J.J., Potkin, S.G. *et al.* (1995) Gene expression for glutamic acid decarboxylase is reduced without loss of neurons in prefrontal cortex of schizophrenics. *Archives of General Psychiatry* **52**, 258–266.

Akbarian, S., Sucher, N.J., Bradley, D. *et al.* (1996) Selective alterations in gene expression for NMDA receptor subunits in prefrontal cortex of schizophrenics. *Journal of Neuroscience* **16**, 19–30.

Al Amin, H.A., Weinberger, D.R. & Lipska, B.K. (2000) Exaggerated MK-801-induced motor hyperactivity in rats with the neonatal lesion of the ventral hippocampus. *Behavioral Pharmacology* **11**, 269–278.

Al-Amin, H.A., Weickert, C.S., Lillrank, S.M., Weinberger, D.R. & Lipska, B.K. (2001) Delayed onset of enhanced MK-801-induced motor hyperactivity after neonatal lesions of the rat ventral hippocampus. *Biological Psychiatry* **49**, 528–539.

Anisman, H., Zaharia, M.D., Meaney, M.J. & Merali, Z. (1998) Do early-life events permanently alter behavioral and hormonal responses to stressors? *International Journal of Developmental Neuroscience* **16**, 149–164.

Arnold, S.E., Hyman, B.T., van Hoesen, G.W. & Damasio, A.R. (1991) Some cytoarchitectural abnormalities of the entorhinal cortex in schizophrenia. *Archives of General Psychiatry* **48**, 625–632.

Ashe, P., Chlan-Fourney, J., Juorio, A.V., Li, X.-M. & Boulton, A.A. (1999) Brain-derived neurotrophic factor mRNA in rats with neonatal ibotenic acid lesions of the ventral hippocampus. *Society of Neuroscience Abstract* **635.11**.

Bachevalier, J., Alvarado, M.C. & Malkova, L. (1999) Memory and socioemotional behavior in monkeys after hippocampal damage incurred in infancy or in adulthood. *Biological Psychiatry* **46**, 329–339.

Bakshi, V.P., Swerdlow, N.R., Braff, D.L. & Geyer, M.A. (1998) Reversal of isolation rearing-induced deficits in prepulse inhibition by Seroquel and olanzapine. *Biological Psychiatry* **43**, 436–445.

Barbeau, D., Liang, J.J., Robitalille, Y., Quirion, R. & Srivastava, L.K. (1995) Decreased expression of the embryonic form of the neural cell adhesion molecule in schizophrenic brains. *Proceedings of the National Academy of Sciences of the USA* **92**, 2785–2789.

Beauregard, M. & Bachevalier, J. (1996) Neonatal insult to the hippocampal region and schizophrenia: a review and a putative animal model. *Canadian Journal of Psychiatry* **41**, 446–456.

Becker, A., Grecksch, G., Bernsteinn, H.-G., Hollt, V. & Bogerts, B. (1999) Social behavior in rats lesioned with ibotenic acid in the hippocampus: quantitative and qualitative analysis. *Psychopharmacology* **144**, 333–338.

Benes, F.M., McSparren, J., Bird, E.D., San Giovanni, J.P. & Vincent, S.L. (1991) Deficits in small interneurons in prefrontal cortex and anterior cingulate cortices of schizophrenic and schizoaffective patients. *Archives of General Psychiatry* **48**, 996–1001.

Benes, F.M., Vincent, S.L., Alsterberg, G., Bird, E.D. & San Giovanni, J.P. (1992) Increased GABA-A receptor binding in superficial laminae in cingulate cortex of schizophrenic brain. *Journal of Neuroscience* **12**, 924–929.

Benes, F.M., Vincent, S.L., Marie, A. & Khan, Y. (1996) Up-regulation of GABAA receptor binding on neurons of the prefrontal cortex in schizophrenic subjects. *Neuroscience* **7**, 1021–1031.

Benes, F.M., Wickramasinghe, R., Vincent, S.L., Khan, Y. & Todtenkopf, M. (1997) Uncoupling of GABA (A) and benzodiazepine receptor binding activity in the hippocampal formation of schizophrenic brain. *Brain Research* **755**, 121–129.

Bertolino, A., Saunders, R.C., Mattay, V.S. *et al.* (1997) Altered development of prefrontal neurons in rhesus monkeys with neonatal mesial temporo-limbic lesions: a proton magnetic resonance spectroscopic imaging study. *Cerebral Cortex* **7**, 740–748.

Bertolino, A., Callicott, J.H., Elman, I. *et al.* (1998) Regionally specific neuronal pathology in untreated patients with schizophrenia: a proton magnetic resonance spectroscopic imaging study. *Biological Psychiatry* **43**, 641–648.

Bertolino, A., Roffman, J.L., Lipska, B.K. *et al.* (1999) Postpubertal emergence of prefrontal neuronal deficits and altered dopaminergic behaviors in rats with neonatal hippocampal lesions. *Society of Neuroscience Abstract* **520.8**.

Bertolino, A., Breier, A., Callicott, J.H. *et al.* (2000) The relationship between dorsolateral prefrontal neuronal *N*-acetylaspartate and evoked release of striatal dopamine in schizophrenia. *Neuropsychopharmacology* **22**, 125–132.

Black, M.D., Lister, S., Hitchcock, J.M., Giersbergen, P. & Sorensen, S.M. (1998) Neonatal hippocampal lesion model of schizophrenia in rats: sex differences and persistence of effects into maturity. *Drug and Developmental Research* **43**, 206–213.

Black, M.D., Selk, D.E., Hitchcock, J.M., Wetttstein, J.G. & Sorensen, S.M. (1999) On the effect of neonatal nitric oxide synthase inhibition in rats: a potential neurodevelopmental model of schizophrenia. *Neuropharmacology* **38**, 1299–1306.

Bloom, F.E. (1993) Advancing a neurodevelopmental origin of schizophrenia. *Archives of General Psychiatry* **50**, 224–227.

Bogerts, B., Ashtar, M., Degreef, G. *et al.* (1990) Reduced temporal limbic structure volumes on magnetic resonance images in first-episode schizophrenia. *Psychiatrics Research: Neuroimaging* **35**, 1–13.

Brake, W., Noel, M.B., Boksa, P. & Gratton, A. (1997a) Influence of perinatal factors on the nucleus accumbens dopamine response to repeated stress during adulthood: an electrochemical study in rat. *Neuroscience* **77**, 1067–1076.

Brake, W., Boksa, P. & Gratton, A. (1997b) Effects of perinatal anoxia on the locomotor response to repeated amphetamine administration in adult rats. *Psychopharmacology* **133**, 389–395.

Brake, W.G., Sullivan, R.M., Flores, G., Srivastava, L. & Gratton, A. (1999) Neonatal ventral hippocampal lesions attenuate the nucleus accumbens dopamine response to stress: an electrochemical study in the rat. *Brain Research* **831**, 25–32.

Breier, A., Su, T.P., Saunders, R. *et al.* (1997) Schizophrenia is associated with elevated amphetamine-induced synaptic dopamine concentrations: evidence from a novel positron emission tomography method. *Proceedings of the National Academy of Sciences of the USA* **94**, 2569–2574.

Brown, A.S., Susser, E.S., Butler, P.D. *et al.* (1996) Neurobiological plausibility of prenatal nutritional deprivation as a risk factor for schizophrenia. *Journal of Nervous and Mental Disease* **184**, 71–85.

Carr, D.B. & Sesack, S.R. (1996) Hippocampal afferents to the rat prefrontal cortex: Synaptic targets and relation to dopaminergic terminals. *Journal of Comparative Neurology* **369**, 1–15.

Castner, S.A., Al-Tikriti, M.S., Baldwin, R.M. *et al.* (2000) Behavioral changes and [^{123}I]IBZM equilibrium SPECT measurement of amphetamine-induced dopamine release in rhesus monkeys exposed to subchronic amphetamine. *Neuropsychopharmacology* **22**, 4–13.

Chambers, R.A., Moore, J., McEvoy, J.P. & Levin, E.D. (1996) Cognitive effects of neonatal hippocampal lesions in a rat model of schizophrenia. *Neuropsychopharmacology* **15**, 587–594.

Cintra, L., Granados, L., Aguilar, A. *et al.* (1997) Effects of prenatal protein malnutrition on mossy fibers of the hippocampal formation in rats of four age groups. *Hippocampus* **7**, 184–191.

Conrad, A.J., Abebe, T., Ron, A., Forsythe, S. & Scheibel, B. (1991) Hippocampal pyramidal cell disarray in schizophrenia as a bilateral phenomenon. *Archives of General Psychiatry* **48**, 413–417.

Costall, B. & Naylor, R.J. (1995) Animal neuropharmacology and its prediction of clinical response. In: *Schizophrenia* (eds S.R. Hirsch & D.R. Weinberger), pp. 401–424. Blackwell Science, Oxford.

Cotter, D., Takei, N., Farrell, M. *et al.* (1995) Does prenatal exposure to influenza in mice induce pyramidal cell disarray in the dorsal hippocampus? *Schizophrenia Research* **16**, 233–241.

Csernansky, J.G., Csernansky, C.A., Kogelman, L., Montgomery, E.M. & Bardgett, M.E. (1998) Progressive neurodegeneration after intracerebroventricular kainic acid administration in rats: implications for schizophrenia? *Biological Psychiatry* **44**, 1143–1150.

Dalman, C., Allebeck, P., Cullberg, J., Grunewald, C. & Koster, M. (1999) Obstetric complications and the risk of schizophrenia: a longitudinal study of a national birth cohort. *Archives of General Psychiatry* **56**, 234–240.

Dean, B., Hussain, T., Hayes, W. *et al.* (1999) Changes in serotonin2A and GABA (A) receptors in schizophrenia: studies on the human dorsolateral prefrontal cortex. *Journal of Neurochemistry* **72**, 1593–1599.

DeLisi, L.E., Dauphinais, I.D. & Gershon, E.S. (1988) Perinatal complications and reduced size of brain limbic structures in afmilial schizophrenia. *Schizophrenia Bulletin* **14**, 185–191.

Duncan, G.E., Sheitman, B.B. & Lieberman, J.A. (1999) An integrated view of pathophysiological models of schizophrenia. *Brain Research Brain Research Review* **29**, 250–264.

Eastwood, S.L. & Harrison, P.J. (1995) Decreased synaptophysin in the medial temporal lobe in schizophrenia demonstrated using immunoautoradiography. *Neuroscience* **69**, 339–343.

Eastwood, S.L. & Harrison, P.J. (1998) Hippocampal and cortical growth-associated protein-43 messenger RNA in schizophrenia. *Neuroscience* **86**, 437–448.

Eastwood, S.L., McDonald, B., Burnet, P.W. *et al.* (1995) Decreased expression of mRNAs encoding non-NMDA glutamate receptors GluR1 and GluR2 in medial temporal lobe neurons in schizophrenia. *Brain Research Molecular Brain Research* **29**, 211–223.

Eastwood, S.L., Burnet, P.W. & Harrison, P.J. (1997) GluR2 glutamate receptor subunit flip and flop isoforms are decreased in the hippocampal formation in schizophrenia: a reverse transcriptase-polymerase chain reaction (RT-PCR) study. *Brain Research Molecular Brain Research* **44**, 92–98.

Egan, M. & Weinberger, D.R. (1997) Neurobiology of schizophrenia. *Current Opinion in Neurobiology* **7**, 701–707.

El-Khodor, B.F. & Boksa, P. (1997) Long-term reciprocal changes in dopamine levels in prefrontal cortex versus nucleus accumbens in rats born by Cesarean section compared to vaginal birth. *Experimental Neurology* **145**, 118–129.

El-Khodor, B.F. & Boksa, P. (1998) Birth insult increases amphetamine induced responses in the adult rat. *Neuroscience* **87**, 893–904.

Ellenbroek, B.A. & Cools, A.R. (1990) Animal models with construct validity for schizophrenia. *Behavioral Pharmacology* **1**, 469–490.

Ellenbroek, B.A., Geyer, M.A. & Cools, A.R. (1995) The behavior of APO-SUS rats in animal models with construct validity for schizophrenia. *Journal of Neuroscience* **11**, 7604–7611.

Ellenbroek, B.A., van den Kroonenberg, P.T. & Cools, A.R. (1998) The effects of an early stressful life event on sensorimotor gating in adult rats. *Schizophrenia Research* **30**, 251–260.

Ellenbroek, B.A., Sluyter, F. & Cools, A.R. (2000) The role of genetic and early environmental factors in determining apomorphine susceptibility. *Psychopharmacology* **148**, 124–131.

Erickson, R.P. (1996) Mouse models of human genetic disease: which mouse is more like a man? *Bioessays* **18**, 993–998.

Falkai, P. & Bogerts, B. (1986) Cell loss in the hippocampus of schizophrenics. *European Archives of Psychiatry and Neurological Science* **236**, 154–161.

Fatemi, S.H., Emamian, E.S., Kist, D. *et al.* (1999) Defective corticogenesis and reduction in Reelin immunoreactivity in cortex and hippocampus of prenatally infected neonatal mice. *Molecular Psychiatry* **4**, 145–154.

Feldpausch, D.L., Needham, L.M., Stone, M.P. *et al.* (1998) The role of dopamine D_4 receptor in the induction of behavioral sensitization to amphetamine and accompanying biochemical and molecular adaptations. *Journal of Pharmacology and Experimental Therapy* **286**, 497–508.

Flores, G., Barbeau, D., Quirion, R. & Srivastava, L.K. (1996a) Decreased binding of dopamine D3 receptors in limbic subregions after neonatal bilateral lesion of rat hippocampus. *Journal of Neuroscience* **16**, 2020–2026.

Flores, G., Wood, G.K., Liang, J.-J., Quirion, R. & Srivastava, L.K. (1996b) Enhanced amphetamine sensitivity and increased expression of dopamine D_2 receptors in postpubertal rats after neonatal excitotoxic lesions of the medial prefrontal cortex. *Journal of Neuroscience* **16**, 7366–7375.

Francis, D., Diorio, J., Liu, D. & Meaney, M.J. (1999) Nongenomic transmission across generations of maternal behavior and stress responses in the rat. *Science* **286**, 1155–1158.

Freedman, R., Adler, L.E., Gerhardt, G.A. *et al.* (1987) Neurobiological studies of sensory gating in schizophrenia. *Schizophrenia Bulletin* **13**, 669–678.

Freedman, R., Coon, H., Myles-Worsley, M. *et al.* (1997) Linkage of a neurophysiological deficit in schizophrenia to a chromosome 15 locus. *Proceedings of the National Academy of Sciences of the USA* **94**, 587–592.

Gambarana, C., Masi, F., Tagliamonte, A. *et al.* (1999) A chronic stress that impairs reactivity in rats also decreases dopaminergic transmission in the nucleus accumbens: a microdialysis study. *Journal of Neurochemistry* **72**, 2039–2046.

Geyer, M.A., Wilkinson, L.S., Humby, T. & Robbins, T.W. (1993) Isolation rearing of rats produces a deficit in prepulse inhibition of acoustic startle similar to that in schizophrenia. *Biological Psychiatry* **34**, 361–372.

Glantz, L.A. & Lewis, D.A. (1997) Reduction of synaptophysin immunoreactivity in the prefrontal cortex of subjects with schizophrenia: regional and diagnostic specificity. *Archives of General Psychiatry* **54**, 943–952.

Glantz, L.A. & Lewis, D.A. (2000) Decreased dendritic spine density on prefrontal cortical pyramidal neurons in schizophrenia. *Archives of General Psychiatry* **57**, 65–73.

Goffinet, A.M. (1995) Developmental neurobiology. A real gene for reeler. *Nature* **374**, 675–676.

Grecksch, G., Bernstein, H.G., Becker, A., Hollt, V. & Bogerts, B. (1999) Disruption of latent inhibition in rats with postnatal hippocampal lesions. *Neuropsychopharmacology* **20**, 525–532.

Harrison, P.J. & Eastwood, S.L. (1998) Preferential involvement of excitatory neurons in medial temporal lobe in schizophrenia. *Lancet* **352**, 1669–1673.

Hirotsune, S., Fleck, M.W., Gambello, M.J. *et al.* (1998) Graded reduction of Pafah1b1 (Lis1) activity results in neuronal migration defects and early embryonic lethality. *Nature Genetics* **19**, 333–339.

Hori, T., Subramaniam, S., Carli, M., Srivastava, L.K. & Quirion, R. (1999) Effects of repeated phencyclidine administration on locomotor activity and forced swimming test in rats with neonatal ventral hippocampal lesions. *Society of Neuroscience Abstract* 635.8.

Hornig, M., Weissenbock, H., Horscroft, N. & Lipkin, W.I. (1999) An infection-based model of neurodevelopmental damage. *Proceedings of the National Academy of Sciences of the USA* **96**, 12102–12107.

Hultman, C.M., Ohman, A., Cnattingius, S., Wieselgren, I.M. & Lindstrom, L.H. (1997) Prenatal and neonatal risk factors for schizophrenia. *British Journal of Psychiatry* **170**, 128–133.

Huntsman, M.M., Tran, B.V., Potkin, S.G., Bunney, W.E. Jr & Jones, E.G. (1998) Altered ratios of alternatively spliced long and short gamma2 subunit mRNAs of the gamma-amino butyrate type A receptor in prefrontal cortex of schizophrenics. *Proceedings of the National Academy of Sciences of the USA* **95**, 15066–15071.

Impagnatiello, F., Guidotti, A.R., Pesold, C. *et al.* (1998) A decrease of reelin expression as a putative vulnerability factor in schizophrenia. *Proceedings of the National Academy of Sciences of the USA* **95**, 15718–15723.

Imperato, A., Obinu, M.C., Carta, G. *et al.* (1996) Reduction of dopamine release and synthesis by repeated amphetamine treatment: role in behavioral sensitization. *European Journal of Pharmacology* **317**, 231–237.

Javitt, D.C. & Zukin, S.R. (1991) Recent advances in the phencyclidine model of schizophrenia. *American Journal of Psychiatry* **148**, 1301–1308.

Jay, T.M., Glowinski, J. & Thierry, A.-M. (1989) Selectivity of the hippocampal projection to the prelimbic area of the prefrontal cortex in the rat. *Brain Research* **505**, 337–340.

Jentsch, J.D. & Roth, R.H. (1999) The neuropsychopharmacology of phencyclidine: from NMDA receptor hypofunction to the dopamine hypothesis of schizophrenia. *Neuropsychopharmacology* **20**, 201–225.

Jentsch, J.D., Tran, A., Le, D., Joungren, K.D. & Roth, R.H. (1997) Subchronic phencyclidine administration reduces mesoprefrontal dopamine utilization and impairs prefrontal cortical-dependent cognition in the rat. *Neuropsychopharmacology* **17**, 92–99.

Jentsch, J.D., Redmond, D.E., Elsworth, J.D. *et al.* (1998a) Enduring cognitive deficits and cortical dopamine dysfunction in monkeys after long-term administration of phencyclidine. *Science* **277**, 953–955.

Jentsch, J.D., Taylor, J.R. & Roth, R.H. (1998b) Subchronic phencyclidine administration increases mesolimbic dopaminergic system responsivity and augments stress- and psychostimulant-induced hyperlocomotion. *Neuropsychopharmacology* **19**, 105–113.

Jeste, D.V. & Lohr, J.B. (1989) Hippocampal pathologic findings in schizophrenia: a morphometric study. *Archives of General Psychiatry* **46**, 1019–1024.

Johnson-Wood, K., Lee, M., Motter, R. *et al.* (1997) Amyloid precursor protein processing and Aβ42 deposition in a transgenic mouse model of Alzheimer disease. *Proceedings of the National Academy of Sciences of the USA* **94**, 1550–1555.

Johnston, M.V., Barks, J., Greenmyre, T. & Silverstein, F. (1988) Use of toxins to disrupt neurotransmitter circuitry in the developing brain. *Progress in Brain Research* **73**, 425–446.

Jones, G.H., Hernandez, T.D., Kendall, D.A., Marsden, C.A. & Robbins, T.W. (1992) Dopaminergic and serotonergic function following isolation rearing in rats: study of behavioral responses and postmortem and *in vivo* neurochemistry. *Pharmacology, Biochemistry and Behavior* **43**, 17–35.

Karson, C.N., Mrak, R.E., Schluterman, K.O. *et al.* (1999) Alterations in synaptic proteins and their encoding mRNAs in prefrontal cortex in schizophrenia: a possible neurochemical basis for 'hypofrontality'. *Molecular Psychiatry* **4**, 39–45.

Kelz, M.B., Chen, J., Carlezon, W.A. Jr. *et al.* (1999) Expression of the transcription factor deltaFosB in the brain controls sensitivity to cocaine. *Nature* **401**, 272–276.

Kendell, R.E. & Kemp, I.W. (1989) Maternal influenza in the etiology of schizophrenia. *Archives of General Psychiatry* **46**, 878–882.

Kendler, K.S., MacLean, C.J., O'Neill, F.A. *et al.* (1996) Evidence for a schizophrenia vulnerability locus on chromosome 8p in the Irish study of high-density schizophrenia families. *American Journal of Psychiatry* **153**, 1534–1540.

Kirkpatrick, B., Conley, R.C., Kakoyannis, A., Reep, R.L. & Roberts, R.C. (1999) Interstitial cells of the white matter in the inferior parietal cortex in schizophrenia: an unbiased cell-counting study. *Synapse* **34**, 95–102.

Kobayashi, K., Forte, T.M., Taniguchi, S. *et al.* (2000) The db/db mouse, a model for diabetic dyslipidemia: molecular characterization and effects of Western diet feeding. *Metabolism* **49**, 22–31.

Kornetsky, C. & Markowitz, R. (1978) Animal models of schizophrenia. In: *Psychopharmacology: a Generation of Progress* (eds M.A. Lipton, A. DiMascio & K.F. Killam), pp. 583–593. Raven Press, New York.

Krystal, J.H., Karper, L.P., Seibyl, J.P. *et al.* (1994) Subanesthetic effects of the noncompetitive NMDA antagonist, ketamine, in humans: psychotomimetic, perceptual, cognitive, and neuroendocrine responses. *Archives of General Psychiatry* **51**, 199–214.

Lahti, A.C., Koffel, B., LaPorte, D. & Tamminga, C.A. (1995) Subanesthetic doses of ketamine stimulate psychosis in schizophrenia. *Neuropsychopharmacology* **13**, 9–19.

Laruelle, M., Abi-Dargham, A., van Dyck, C.H. *et al.* (1996) Single photon emission computerized tomography imaging of amphetamine-induced dopamine release in drug-free schizophrenic subjects. *Proceedings of the National Academy of Sciences of the USA* **93**, 9235–9240.

Lee, C.J., Binder, T., Lipska, B.K. *et al.* (1998) Neonatal ventral hippocampal lesions produce an elevation of Δ-FosB-like protein(s) in the rodent neocortex. *Society of Neuroscience Abstract* **24**, 489.

Lewis, P., Patel, A. & Balazs, R. (1979) Effect of undernutrition on cell generation in the adult rat brain. *Brain Research* **168**, 186–189.

Lieberman, J.A., Sheitman, B.B. & Kinon, B.J. (1997) Neurochemical sensitization in the pathophysiology of schizophrenia: deficits and dysfunction in neuronal regulation and plasticity. *Neuropsychopharmacology* **17**, 205–229.

Lillrank, S.M., Lipska, B.K. & Weinberger, D.R. (1995) Neurodevelopmental animal models of schizophrenia. *Clinical Neuroscience* **3**, 98–104.

Lipska, B.K. & Weinberger, D.R. (1993) Delayed effects of neonatal hippocampal damage on haloperidol-induced catalepsy and apomorphine-induced stereotypic behaviors in the rat. *Developmental Brain Research* **75**, 13–222.

Lipska, B.K. & Weinberger, D.R. (1994a) Subchronic treatment with haloperidol or clozapine in rats with neonatal excitotoxic hippocampal damage. *Neuropsychopharmacology* **10**, 199–205.

Lipska, B.K. & Weinberger, D.R. (1994b) Gonadectomy does not prevent novelty- or drug-induced hyperresponsiveness in rats with neonatal excitototxic hippocampal damage. *Developmental Brain Research* **78**, 253–258.

Lipska, B.K. & Weinberger, D.R. (1995) Genetic variation in vulnerability to the behavioral effects of neonatal hippocampal damage in rats. *Proceedings of the National Academy of Sciences of the USA* **92**, 8906–8910.

Lipska, B.K. & Weinberger, D.R. (2000) To model a psychiatric disorder in animals: schizophrenia as a reality test. *Neuropsychopharmacology* **23**, 223–239.

Lipska, B.K., Jaskiw, G.E. & Weinberger, D.R. (1993) Postpubertal emergence of hyperresponsiveness to stress and to amphetamine after neonatal hippocampal damage: a potential animal model of schizophrenia. *Neuropsychopharmacology* **9**, 67–75.

Lipska, B.K., Swerdlow, N.R., Geyer, M.A. *et al.* (1995a) Neonatal excitotoxic hippocampal damage in rats causes postpubertal changes in prepulse inhibition of startle and its disruption by apomorphine. *Psychopharmacology* **122**, 35–43.

Lipska, B.K., Chrapusta, S.J., Egan, M.F. & Weinberger, D.R. (1995b) Neonatal excitotoxic ventral hippocampal damage alters dopamine response to mild chronic stress and haloperidol treatment. *Synapse* **20**, 125–130.

Lipska, B.K., Al-Amin, H.A. & Weinberger, D.R. (1998a) Excitotoxic lesions of the rat medial prefrontal cortex: effects on abnormal behaviors associated with neonatal hippocampal damage. *Neuropsychopharmacology* **19**, 451–464.

Lipska, B.K., Khaing, Z.Z., Lerman, D.N. & Weinberger, D.R. (1998b) Neonatal damage of the rat ventral hippocampus reduces expression of a dopamine transporter. *Society of Neuroscience Abstract* **24**, 365.

Lipska, B.K., Kolb, B., Halim, N. & Weinberger, D.R. (2001) Synaptic abnormalities in prefrontal cortex and nucleus accumbens of adult rats with neonatal hippocampal damage. *Schizophrenia Research* **49**, 47.

Liu, D., Diorio, J., Tannenbaum, B. *et al.* (1997) Maternal care, hippocampal glucocorticoid receptors, and hypothalamic–pituitary–adrenal responses to stress. *Science* **277**, 1659–1662.

Liu, W.S., Pesold, C., Rodriguez, M.A. *et al.* (2001) Down-regulation of dendritic spine and glutamic acid decarboxylase 67 expressions in the reelin haploinsufficient heterozygous reeler mouse. *Proceedings of the National Academy of Sciences of the USA* **98**, 3477–3482.

Lohr, J.B. & Bracha, S. (1989) Can schizophrenia be related to prenatal exposure to alcohol? Some speculations. *Schizophrenia Bulletin* **15**, 595–603.

Loring, J.F., Paszty, C., Rose, A. *et al.* (1996) Rational design of an animal model for Alzheimer's disease: introduction of multiple human genomic transgenes to reproduce AD pathology in a rodent. *Neurobiological Aging* **17**, 173–182.

McKinney, W.T. & Moran, E.C. (1981) Animal models of schizophrenia. *American Journal of Psychiatry* **138**, 478–483.

McNiel, T.F. (1988) Obstetric factors and perinatal injuries. In: *Handbook of Schizophrenia*, Vol. 3. *Nosology, Epidemiology and Genetic* (eds M.T. Tsuang & J.C. Simpson), pp. 319–344. Elsevier, Amsterdam.

Mathe, J.M., Nomikos, G.G., Schilstrom, B. & Svensson, T.H. (1998) Non-NMDA excitatory amino acid receptors in the ventral tegmental area mediate systemic dizocilpine (MK-801) induced hyperlocomotion and dopamine release in the nucleus accumbens. *Journal of Neuroscience Research* **51**, 583–592.

Mazer, C., Muneyyirci, J., Taheny, K. *et al.* (1997) Serotonin depletion during synaptogenesis leads to decreased synaptic density and learning deficits. I. The adult rat: a possible model of neurodevelopmental disorders with cognitive deficits. *Brain Research* **760**, 68–73.

Mednick, S.A., Machon, R.A., Huttunen, M.O. & Bonett, D. (1988) Adult schizophrenia following prenatal exposure to influenza epidemic. *Archives of General Psychiatry* **45**, 189–192.

Meng, Z.H., Feldpaush, D.L. & Merchant, K.M. (1998) Clozapine and haloperidol block the induction of behavioral sensitization to amphetamine and associated genomic responses in rats. *Brain Research Molecular Brain Research* **61**, 39–50.

Mintz, M., Youval, G., Gigi, A. & Myslobodsky, M.S. (1997) Rats exposed to prenatal gamma-radiation at day 15 of gestation exhibit enhanced persevaration in T-maze. *Society of Neuroscience Abstract* **23**, 1365.

Moghaddam, B. & Adams, B. (1998) Reversal of phencyclidine effects by group II metabotropic glutamate receptor agonist in rats. *Science* **281**, 1349–1352.

Moghaddam, B., Adams, B., Verma, A. & Daly, D. (1997) Activation of glutamatergic neurotransmission by ketamine: a novel step in pathway from NMDA receptor blockade to dopaminergic and cognitive disruptions associated with the prefrontal cortex. *Journal of Neuroscience* **17**, 2921–2927.

Mohn, A.R., Gainetdinov, R.R., Caron, M.G. & Koller, B.H. (1999) Mice with reduced NMDA receptor expression display behaviors related to schizophrenia. *Cell* **98**, 427–436.

Montgomery, E.M., Bardgett, M.E., Lall, B., Csernansky, C.A. & Csernansky, J.G. (1999) Delayed neuronal loss after administration of intracerebroventricular kainic acid to preweanling rats. *Brain Research and Developmental Brain Research* **112**, 107–116.

Moore, H., Ghajarnia, M. & Grace, A.A. (1998) Anatomy and function of prefrontal and limbic corticostriatal circuits in a rodent model of schizophrenia. *37th ACNP Annual Meeting Abstract* **37**, 179.

Morgane, P.J., Austin-LaFrance, R., Bronzino, J. *et al.* (1993) Prenatal malnutrition and development of the brain. *Neuroscience and Biobehaviour Review* **17**, 91–128.

Murase, S., Mathe, J.M., Grenhoff, J. & Svensson, T.H. (1993) Effects of dizocilpine (MK-801) on rat midbrain dopamine cell activity: differential actions on firing pattern related to anatomical localization. *Journal of Neural Transmission: General Section* **91**, 13–25.

Murray, R.M. & Lewis, S.W. (1987) Is schizophrenia a neurodevelopmental disorder? *British Medical Journal* **295**, 681–682.

Nestler, E.J. & Aghajanian, G.K. (1997) Molecular and cellular basis of addiction. *Science* **278**, 58–63.

O'Callaghan, E., Sham, P., Takei, N., Glover, G. & Murray, R.M. (1991) Schizophrenia after prenatal exposure to 1957, A2 influenza epidemic. *Lancet* **337**, 1248–1250.

O'Donnell, P. & Grace, A.A. (1998) Phencyclidine interferes with the hippocampal gating of nucleus accumbens neuronal activity *in vivo*. *Neuroscience* **87**, 823–830.

O'Donnell, P., Lewis, B.L., Lerman, D., Weinberger, D.R. & Lipska, B.K. (1999) Effects of neonatal hippocampal lesions on prefrontal cortical pyramidal cell responses to VTA stimulation. *Society of Neuroscience Abstract* **664.2**.

Ohnuma, T., Augood, S.J., Arai, H., McKenna, P.J. & Emson, P.C. (1998) Expression of the human excitatory amino acid transporter 2 and metabotropic glutamate receptors 3 and 5 in the prefrontal cortex from normal individuals and patients with schizophrenia. *Brain Research Molecular Brain Research* **56**, 207–217.

Ohshima, T., Ward, J.M., Huh, C.G. *et al.* (1996) Targeted disruption of the cyclin-dependent kinase 5 gene results in abnormal corticogenesis, neuronal pathology and perinatal death. *Proceedings of the National Academy of Sciences of the USA* **93**, 11173–11178.

Olney, J.W. & Farber, N.B. (1995) Glutamate receptor dysfunction and schizophrenia. *Archives of General Psychiatry* **52**, 998–1007.

Patel, V.B., Richardson, P.J. & Preedy, V.R. (2000) Non-cardiac nucleic acid composition and protein synthesis rates in hypertension: studies on the spontaneously hypertensive rat (SHR) model. *Clinical Chim Acta* **293**, 167–179.

Pearce, B.D., Steffensen, S.C., Paoletti, A.D., Henriksen, S.J. & Buchmeier, M.J. (1996) Persistent dentate granule cell hyperexcitability following neonatal infection with lymphocytic choriomeningitis virus. *Journal of Neuroscience* **16**, 220–228.

Pearce, B.D., Po, C.L., Pisell, T.L. & Miller, A.H. (1999) Lymphocytic responses and the gradual hippocampal neuron loss following infection with lymphocytic choriomeningitis virus (LCMV). *Journal of Neuroimmunology* **101**, 137–147.

Pellegrini, M., Mansouri, A., Simeone, A., Boncinelli, E. & Gruss, P. (1996) Dentate gyrus formation requires Emx2. *Development* **122**, 3893–3898.

Perrone-Bizzozero, N.I., Sower, A.C., Bird, E.D. *et al.* (1996) Levels of the growth-associated protein GAP-43 are selectively increased in association cortices in schizophrenia. *Proceedings of the National Academy of Sciences of the USA* **93**, 14182–14187.

Porter, F.D., Drago, J., Xu, Y. *et al.* (1997) Lhx2, a LIM homeobox gene, is required for eye, forebrain, and definitive erythrocyte development. *Development* **124**, 2935–2944.

Qin, Z.H., Zhang, S.P. & Weiss, B. (1994) Dopaminergic and glutamatergic blocking drugs differentially regulate glutamic acid decarboxylase mRNA in mouse brain. *Brain Research Molecular Brain Research* **21**, 293–302.

Rajakumar, N., Williamson, P.C., Stoessl, J.A. & Flumerfelt, B.A. (1996) Neurodevelopmental pathogenesis of schizophrenia. *Society of Neuroscience Abstract* **22**, 1187.

Rakic, P. (1996) Experimental deletion of specific cortical neurons: relevance to schizophrenia. *35th ACNP Annual Meeting Abstract* **35**, 91.

Robinson, T.E. & Kolb, B. (1997) Persistent structural modifications in nucleus accumbens and prefrontal cortex neurons produced by previous experience with amphetamine. *Journal of Neuroscience* **17**, 8491–8497.

Roffman, J.L., Lipska, B.K., Bertolino, A. *et al.* (2000) Local and downstream effects of excitotoxic lesions in the rat medial prefrontal cortex on *in vivo* ^{1}H-MRS signals. *Neuropsychopharmacology* **22**, 430–439.

Rott, R., Herzog, S., Fleischer, B. *et al.* (1985) Detection of serum antibodies to Borna disease virus in patients with psychiatric disorders. *Science* **228**, 755–756.

Rupniak, N.M.J. & Iversen, S.D. (1993) Cognitive impairment in schizophrenia: how experimental models using nonhuman primates may assist improved drug therapy for negative symptoms. *Neuropsychologia* **31**, 1133–1146.

Sams-Dodd, F., Lipska, B.K. & Weinberger, D.R. (1997) Neonatal lesions of the rat ventral hippocampus result in hyperlocomotion and deficits in social behaviour in adulthood. *Psychopharmacology* **132**, 303–310.

Saunders, R.C., Kolachana, B.S., Bachevalier, J. & Weinberger, D.R. (1998) Neonatal lesions of the temporal lobe disrupt prefrontal cortical regulation of striatal dopamine. *Nature* **393**, 169–171.

Scheibel, A.B. & Kovelman, J.A. (1981) Disorientation of the hippocampal pyramidal cell and its processes in the schizophrenic patient. *Biological Psychiatry* **16**, 101–102.

Schroeder, H., Grecksch, G., Becker, A., Bogerts, B. & Höllt, V. (1999) Alterations of the dopaminergic and glutamatergic neurotransmission in adult rats with postnatal ibotenic acid hippocampal lesion. *Psychopharmacology* **145**, 61–66.

Selemon, L.D., Castner, S.A., Algan, O., Goldman-Rakic, P.S. & Rakic, P. (2000) Selective deletion of thalamic neurons in early gestation as a primate model of schizophrenia (abstract). *39th ACNP Annual Meeting, Puerto Rico*, p. 44.

Sheldon, M., Rice, D.S., D'Arcangelo, G. *et al.* (1997) Scrambler and yotari disrupt the disabled gene and produce a reeler-like phenotype in mice. *Nature* **389**, 730–733.

Sibley, D.R. (1999) New insights into dopaminergic receptor function using antisense and genetically altered animals. *Annual Review of Pharmacological Toxicology* **39**, 313–341.

Solbrig, M.V., Koob, G.F., Fallon, J.H. & Lipkin, W.I. (1994) Tardive dyskinetic syndrome in rats infected with Borna disease virus. *Neurobiological Disease* **1**, 111–119.

Solbrig, M.V., Koob, G.F., Joyce, J.N. & Lipkin, W.I. (1996a) A neural substrate of hyperactivity in Borna disease: changes in brain dopamine receptors. *Virology* **222**, 332–338.

Solbrig, M.V., Koob, G.F., Fallon, J.H., Reid, S. & Lipkin, W.I. (1996b) Prefrontal cortex dysfunction in Borna disease virus (BDV)-infected rats. *Biological Psychiatry* **40**, 629–636.

Spanagel, R. & Weiss, F. (1999) The dopamine hypothesis of reward: past and current status. *Trends in Neuroscience* **22**, 521–527.

Steiner, H. & Gerfen, C.R. (1998) Role of dynorphin and enkephalin in the regulation of striatal output pathways and behavior. *Experimental Brain Research* **123**, 60–76.

Stevens, K.E., Kem, W.R., Mahnir, V.M. & Freedman, R. (1998) Selective α7-nicotinic agonists normalize inhibition of auditory response in DBA mice. *Psychopharmacology* **136**, 320–327.

Suddath, R.L., Christisin, G.W., Torrey, E.F., Casanova, M. & Weinberger, D.R. (1990) Anatomical abnormalities in the brains of monozygotic twins discordant for schizophrenia. *New England Journal of Medicine* **322**, 789–794.

Susser, E.S. & Lin, S.P. (1992) Schizophrenia after prenatal exposure to the Dutch Hunger Winter of 1944–45. *Archives of General Psychiatry* **49**, 983–988.

Talamini, L.M., Koch, T., Ter Horst, G.J. & Korf, J. (1998) Methylazoxymethanol acetate-induced abnormalities in the entorhinal cortex of the rat; parallels with morphological findings in schizophrenia. *Brain Research* **789**, 293–306.

Tomasiewicz, H., Ono, K., Yee, D. *et al.* (1993) Genetic deletion of a neural cell adhesion molecule variant (N-CAM-180) produces distinct defects in the central nervous system. *Neuron* **11**, 1163–1174.

Tonkiss, J. & Galler, J.R. (1990) Prenatal protein malnutrition and working memory performance in adult rats. *Behavioral Brain Research* **40**, 95–107.

Vanderschuren, L.J., Schmidt, E.D., De Vries, T.J. *et al.* (1999) A single exposure to amphetamine is sufficient to induce long-term behavioral, neuroendocrine, and neurochemical sensitization in rats. *Journal of Neuroscience* **19**, 9579–9586.

Varty, G.B. & Higgins, G.A. (1995) Examination of drug-induced and isolation-induced disruptions of prepulse inhibition as models to screen antipsychotic drugs. *Psychopharmacology* **122**, 15–26.

Vawter, M.P., Hemperly, J.J., Hyde, T.M. *et al.* (1998) VASE-containing N-CAM isoforms are increased in the hippocampus in bipolar disorder but not schizophrenia. *Experimental Neurology* **154**, 1–11.

Verma, A. & Moghaddam, B. (1996) NMDA receptor antagonists impair prefrontal cortex function as assessed via spatial delayed alternation performance in rats: modulation by dopamine. *Journal of Neuroscience* **16**, 373–379.

Waltrip, R.W. II, Buchanan, R.W., Summerfeld, A. *et al.* (1995) Borna disease virus and schizophrenia. *Psychiatrics Research* **56**, 33–44.

Wan, R.Q. & Corbett, R. (1997) Enhancement of postsynaptic sensitivity to dopaminergic agonists induced by neonatal hippocampal lesions. *Neuropsychopharmacology* **16**, 259–268.

Wan, R.-Q., Giovanni, A., Kafka, S.H. & Corbett, R. (1996) Neonatal hippocampal lesions induced hyperresponsiveness to amphetamine: behavioral and *in vivo* microdialysis studies. *Behavioral Brain Research* **78**, 211–223.

Wan, R.Q., Hartman, H. & Corbett, R. (1998) Alteration of dopamine metabolites in CSF and behavioral impairments induced by neonatal hippocampal lesions. *Physiological Behavior* **65**, 429–436.

Weickert, C.S. & Weinberger, D.R. (1998) A candidate molecule approach to defining developmental pathology in schizophrenia. *Schizophrenia Bulletin* **24**, 303–316.

Weinberger, D.R. (1986) The pathogenesis of schizophrenia: a neurodevelopmental theory. In: *The Neurology of Schizophrenia* (eds H.A. Nasrallah & D.R. Weinberger), pp. 397–406. Elsevier, Amsterdam.

Weinberger, D.R. (1987) Implications of normal brain development for the pathogenesis of schizophrenia. *Archives of General Psychiatry* **44**, 660–669.

Weinberger, D.R. (1999) Cell biology of the hippocampal formation in schizophrenia. *Biological Psychiatry* **45**, 395–402.

Weinberger, D.R. & Lipska, B.K. (1995) Cortical maldevleopment, anti-psychotic drugs, and schizophrenia: in search of common ground. *Schizophrenia Research* **16**, 87–110.

Wilkinson, L.S., Killcross, S.S., Humby, T. *et al.* (1994) Social isolation in the rat produces developmentally specific deficits in prepulse inhibition of the acoustic startle response without disrupting latent inhibition. *Neuropsychopharmacology* **10**, 61–72.

Woerner, M.G., Pollack, M. & Klein, D.F. (1973) Pregnancy and birth complications in psychiatric patients: a comparison of schizophrenic and personality disorder patients with their siblings. *Acta Psychiatrica Scandinavica* **49**, 712–721.

Wolf, M.E., White, F.J. & Hu, X.-T. (1993) Behavioral sensitization to MK-801 (dizocilpine): neurochemical and electrophysiological correlates in the mesoaccumbens dopamine system. *Behavioral Pharmacology* **4**, 429–442.

Wood, G.K., Tomasiewicz, H., Rutishauser, U. *et al.* (1998) NCAM-180 knockout mice display increased lateral ventricle size and reduced prepulse inhibition of startle. *Neuroreport* **9**, 461–466.

Wu, C.L. & Melton, D.W. (1993) Production of a model for Lesch–Nyhan syndrome in hypoxanthine phosphoribosyltransferase-deficient mice. *Nature Genetics* **3**, 235–240.

Yonezawa, Y., Kuroki, T., Kawahara, T., Tashiro, N. & Uchimura, H. (1998) Involvement of gamma-aminobutyric acid neurotransmission in phencyclidine-induced dopamine release in the medial prefrontal cortex. *European Journal of Pharmacology* **341**, 45–56.

Young, C.E., Arima, K., Xie, J. *et al.* (1998) SNAP-25 deficit and hippocampal connectivity in schizophrenia. *Cerebral Cortex* **8**, 261–268.

Zaharia, M.D., Kulczycki, J., Shanks, N., Meaney, M.J. & Anisman, H. (1996) The effects of early postnatal stimulation on Morris watermaze acquisition in adult mice: genetic and maternal factors. *Psychopharmacology* **128**, 227–239.

Zhao, Y., Sheng, H.Z., Amini, R. *et al.* (1999) Control of hippocampal morphogenesis and neuronal differentiation by the LIM homeobox gene Lhx5. *Science* **284**, 1155–1158.

22 Brain imaging in schizophrenia

P. Liddle and C. Pantelis

In vivo images of the structure and function of the human brain not only confirm that there are demonstrable brain abnormalities in schizophrenia, but also offer the tantalizing prospect of providing information that could inform diagnosis and guide treatment in individual patients. However, abnormalities of macroscopic structure are small, and often difficult to identify in individuals. For example, although enlargement of the cerebral ventricles is one of the most robust abnormalities in schizophrenia, in the majority of patients ventricular size lies within the normal range (Raz & Raz 1990). In general, abnormalities of function are more substantial, but techniques for imaging brain function present a kaleidoscope of activity that is exquisitely sensitive to a myriad of influences on the external and internal milieu. After a brief review of imaging techniques, we examine the evidence for abnormalities of structure and function in various different brain regions. Finally, we examine the evidence suggesting that the cardinal abnormality in schizophrenia is a disruption of connections between neurones leading to impaired co-ordination of neural activity at spatially remote sites.

Historical overview

The first evidence of abnormal brain structure in schizophrenia, provided by *in vivo* imaging techniques, was the demonstration using pneumoencephalography that the cerebral ventricles, especially the third ventricle, are enlarged in at least some cases (Huber 1964). With the advent of the less invasive technique of X-ray computerized tomography (CT), Johnstone *et al.* (1976) confirmed that patients with severe persistent illness have ventricular enlargement. Subsequent studies using patients who were more representative of the natural range of illness severity have confirmed the existence of ventricular enlargement, but meta-analyses reveal a somewhat smaller effect size than that found in severe chronic cases. Raz and Raz (1990) identified a moderate effect size for both lateral and third ventricular size of 0.7 and 0.66, respectively, while a smaller effect for cortical sulcal cerebrospinal fluid (CSF) space enlargement was also found.

The first functional imaging studies employed techniques involving the injection or inhalation of radioactive xenon to assess local cerebral perfusion, which is an indirect indicator of local neural activity. Using the xenon injection technique, Ingvar and Franzen (1974) demonstrated that medicated patients with chronic schizophrenia have an abnormally low ratio of activity in frontal cortex to that in posterior brain areas, compared with the ratio observed in healthy subjects. However, not all studies have confirmed this hypofrontality. In a study using positron emission tomography (PET) to measure resting state regional oxygen metabolism in a small group of predominantly unmedicated first episode cases, Sheppard *et al.* (1983) failed to find any evidence of reduced frontal metabolism. Subsequent studies, considered in greater detail below, show that resting state blood flow and metabolism depend on phase of illness and symptom profile.

While studies of the resting state blood flow or metabolism are potentially informative about current clinical state, studies of the cerebral activity during the performance of a specific cognitive task can provide information about brain activity associated with task performance. In a seminal study, Weinberger *et al.* (1986) demonstrated that schizophrenic patients produce less activation of the frontal cortex than healthy controls during performance of the Wisconsin Card Sorting Test (WCST), a complex test of executive function. Despite the difficulties of interpretation of cognitive activation studies, because it is not easy to distinguish failure to activate the brain because of failure to engage in the task from a failure to activate a specific region despite adequate engagement in the task, the cognitive activation procedure has proven to be very fruitful in exploring brain function in schizophrenia. The fact that deoxyhaemoglobin is paramagnetic has allowed the development of functional magnetic resonance imaging (fMRI) for the assessment of regional cerebral function without the need to administer radioactive tracer substances, leading to a rapid growth in the use of functional imaging techniques.

Imaging techniques

Structural imaging techniques

The technique of X-ray CT, which was widely employed for studies of brain in schizophrenia in the 15 years following the initial study by Johnstone *et al.* (1976), has now largely been superseded by magnetic resonance imaging (MRI) techniques, which provide better delineation of tissue types. MRI provides images based on the phenomenon of nuclear magnetic resonance (NMR). NMR depends on the fact that atomic nuclei containing unpaired protons or neutrons (e.g. the proton in a hydrogen atom) have a magnetic moment that causes them to precess like spinning tops in an applied magnetic field. If a radiofrequency pulse with frequency matching the rotation frequency is applied, the nuclear particles absorb energy in a way that raises them to a higher energy level and brings the precession into phase. When the radiofrequency pulse is removed they return to the ground state by transferring energy to the environment. This is known as spin–lattice or T1 relaxation. In addition they also lose phase coherence in a process known as spin–spin or T2 relaxation. The T1 and T2 relaxation times differ depending on the tissue type, meaning that they can be used for the generation of contrast in images. Various different protocols for delivering the radiofrequency excitation pulses and for detecting the emitted radiation allow measurement of various aspects of brain structure and function.

Volumetric and morphological measurements using MRI

T1-weighted images, which provide thin slices encompassing the whole brain and extracerebral tissue, provide good contrast between grey and white matter, delineate sulci and gyri and permit the measurement of the volume of specific cortical and subcortical structures. Dual echo sequences provide simultaneous T2-weighted and proton-density images, which allow better differentiation of CSF, grey and white matter and volumetric analysis of these regions, and have been used for semiautomated and automated analyses.

Magnetic resonance spectroscopy

Magnetic resonance spectroscopy (MRS) requires a radiofrequency transmitter and receiver coil focused on a particular nucleus of interest (e.g. ^{31}P, ^{1}H, ^{19}F, ^{13}C), which allows different aspects of *in vivo* neurochemistry to be assessed. A number of reviews examine the methods involved in spectroscopy and summarize the literature in schizophrenia (Keshavan *et al.* 2000; Vance *et al.* 2000). While most MRS studies have had to define a volume of interest (VOI) from which the signal is generated, thereby limiting the areas that can be examined, more recent multislice or chemical shift spectroscopic imaging techniques may be more useful in assessing the relationship between different brain regions (Bertolino *et al.* 1996).

The spectra derived from proton (^{1}H) spectroscopy provide information about *N*-acetylaspartate (NAA), which exists intraneuronally and assesses neuronal mass and integrity, while choline metabolites provide indices of myelin composition and phospholipid metabolism. Other metabolites include: creatine (including phosphocreatine), a general marker of energy metabolism; glutamine, localized mainly in glial cells; and glutamate, an excitatory neurotransmitter found primarily within glutaminergic neurones.

In contrast, phosphorus-31 (^{31}P) MRS provides information about membrane phospholipid metabolism and energy metabolism, and is relevant to assessing the integrity of cell membranes. ^{31}P-MRS allows *in vivo* investigation of phosphomonoesters (PMEs: phospholipid precursors) and phosphodiesters (PDEs: phospholipid breakdown products) which indirectly reflect the rates of cell membrane synthesis and degradation, while phosphocreatine (PCr) and inorganic phosphate (Pi) are indirect indicators of energy metabolism.

T2-relaxometry

T2-relaxometry, which entails the measurement of T2 relaxation time, provides objective (rater-independent) information about brain tissue integrity. For example, increased hydration (e.g. oedema) lengthens T2, while iron deposition reduces T2. T2 relaxation is also prolonged in dysplastic conditions with a neurodevelopmental basis, providing a potentially important method to examine the neurodevelopmental hypothesis of schizophrenia. It has not been extensively used in schizophrenia to date. Hitherto, all studies have been in patients with chronic illness and have generally produced inconsistent findings. However, evidence for frontotemporal abnormalities in schizophrenia (Williamson *et al.* 1992) is consistent with the other recent findings discussed below.

Techniques to assess white matter

The technique of diffusion tensor/weighted imaging (DTI/DWI) assesses the anisotropy of water diffusion and allows the integrity of white matter tracts to be examined, thereby providing a novel means to examine fibre pathways and brain connectivity directly. Initial studies using this technique have identified abnormal fibre pathways in frontostriatal regions diffusely across the brain (Lim *et al.* 1999) and in the corpus callosum (Foong *et al.* 2000). While promising, DTI needs refinement and application in studies of larger samples of patients.

Magnetization transfer imaging (MTI) is another novel technique, which allows the visualization of protons tightly bound to macromolecular structures, such as myelin and cell membranes in white matter. Foong *et al.* (2001) recently used MTI in schizophrenia and identified abnormalities in frontotemporal regions, consistent with other structural and functional imaging literature discussed below. Because myelin content of tissue affects relaxation times, abnormalities of myelination can also be detected by relaxometry.

Novel analysis techniques in structural imaging

Recent innovations in analysis of structural imaging data include semiautomated and automated analysis methods, rather than more laborious manual tracing techniques. These include voxel-based analyses (e.g. Paillere-Martinot *et al.* 2001; Sigmundsson *et al.* 2001; Pantelis *et al.* 2002). While these recent innovations require further validation, they are particularly helpful in examining all brain structures simultaneously, compared with manual tracing techniques which usually target a limited number of regions. However, automated voxel-based methods of estimating tissue volumes may give misleading results if the sulcal/gyral pattern is abnormal. Studies so far have not allowed for this possibility, although there is evidence of anomalous cortical gyrification in schizophrenia (Vogeley *et al.* 2001; Yücel *et al.* 2002a).

Functional imaging techniques

Several techniques, including PET, single photon emission computerized tomography (SPECT) and fMRI provide indirect measurements of the spatial variation in neural activity associated with mental activity. To understand the information provided by these techniques, it is necessary to summarize some features of neural activity and the way regional cerebral blood flow (rCBF) is regulated to support that activity.

The resting state

In the resting state, neural firing is not random and grey matter is not uniformly active. Blood flow and metabolism in healthy subjects are greatest in frontal cortex and medial parietal cortex, regions that are engaged during internally generated mental activity. Abnormalities of self-generated mental activity play an important part in schizophrenia, and studies of resting state brain activity are informative, provided that the clinical state of the patients is assessed with sufficient care. Many studies of the resting state (reviewed by Andreasen *et al.* 1992) reveal underactivity of the frontal cortex, especially in chronic cases, but other studies, especially those of acutely ill patients, reveal resting-state hyperfrontality. At least some of this variability between patients in the patterns of resting state cerebral activity can be attributed to differences in symptom profile. Liddle *et al.* (1992) demonstrated that each of three major groups of persistent schizophrenic symptoms is associated with a distinct pattern of abnormal function of brain regions normally engaged in the types of mental process implicated in the relevant symptoms. In particular, they found that reality distortion (delusions and hallucinations) and disorganization symptoms were associated with overactivity at different frontal loci, while psychomotor poverty (comprising core negative symptoms) was associated with frontal underactivity. Subsequent studies (reviewed by Liddle 2000) have confirmed all the major features of these findings, although it should be noted that some studies of acutely psychotic patients (Erkwoh *et al.* 1997) provide a more complex picture, presumably because of additional mental processes in acute psychosis. Antipsychotic medication also produces changes in resting brain activity. Ngan *et al.* (2002) found that a single dose of risperidone produced decreases in lateral and medial frontal lobe activity, but that the changes in medial frontal activity were associated with subsequent reduction in severity of psychotic symptoms.

Haemodynamic response to neural stimulation

Increased neural firing during mental activity produces an increase in local perfusion that exceeds the immediate need for oxygen. Consequently, measurement of changes in rCBF, using either PET or SPECT with a radioactive tracer that accumulates in brain tissue in proportion to local perfusion, provides a sensitive index of neural activity. Unfortunately, the use of radioactive tracers limits the number of scans that can be performed in a single subject. However, paramagnetic properties of deoxyhaemoglobin provide a non-invasive way to detect local neural activity, using fMRI. Following a magnetizing pulse that aligns the protons in tissue, the magnetic resonance signal decays rapidly owing to processes that cause dephasing of the spinning protons. The dephasing of protons arises not only from interactions with other nuclei (the spin–spin interactions responsible for T2 relaxation) but also from the effects of local magnetic field inhomogeneities (T2* relaxation). One source of inhomogeneity is paramagnetic deoxyhaemoglobin in capillaries. In the vicinity of active neurones, increased perfusion removes deoxyhaemoglobin, and the strength of the magnetic resonance signal decays less rapidly. This enhancement of signal in the vicinity of active neurones is known as the blood oxygen level-dependent (BOLD) effect.

This haemodynamic response can be imaged using various 'single-shot' techniques, in which the information required to construct an image is obtained following application of a single pulse of magnetization. Using the technique known as echoplanar imaging, a slice of brain can be imaged in 40 ms, and the entire brain can be imaged within 2–3 s. In a typical fMRI study, several hundred brain images are collected during 10–20 min. In block-design studies, the mental state of interest is maintained for 20–30 s. Blocks of the mental state of interest alternate with blocks in which an appropriate baseline mental state is maintained. In event-related designs, the haemodynamic response to individual mental events is compared with a sustained baseline state.

Whole brain volume and cerebrospinal fluid spaces

Intracranial and whole brain changes

Assessment of intracranial volume (ICV) and whole brain volume (WBV) provides information about the impact of premorbid and morbid factors on overall brain structure in schizophrenia. Because cranial vault size is determined by age 6, comparison of abnormalities in ICV with abnormalities in WBV provides an indication of the developmental stage at which the abnormalities might have arisen (for discussion see Woods 1998). Also, accounting for global measures provides information about whether changes in particular brain structures are local or part of a more global change.

Meta-analyses indicate that WBV is smaller (by about 2%) in schizophrenia compared with controls (Ward *et al.* 1996; Wright *et al.* 2000), while intracranial volume (ICV) may show a smaller reduction (Ward *et al.* 1996). These differences are more consistently seen in chronic patients. The majority of studies that have examined grey and white matter compartments separately have found that it is grey matter volume that is reduced, although some studies of regional brain volume have reported white matter deficits (Breier *et al.* 1992; Cannon *et al.* 1998). Reduced brain volume is observed from the outset of illness (Zipursky *et al.* 1998; Rapoport *et al.* 1999) and, in particular, has been reported in neuroleptic-naïve first episode patients (Gur *et al.* 1999).

Twin and sibling studies also provide information about familial/genetic contributions to structural abnormalities identified. Thus, results from a recent twin study (Baaré *et al.* 2001) suggested that smaller ICV may be a genetically determined vulnerability to schizophrenia, while WBV may have both genetic and environmental determinants. In this context, it is of interest that the Edinburgh study of individuals at high risk for schizophrenia on account of having at least two affected family members found that the patients developing psychosis had smaller WBV (Lawrie *et al.* 2001).

Longitudinal follow-up studies of brain volume provide the most important means to assess the issue of progression of brain structural abnormalities in schizophrenia (Velakoulis *et al.* 2000b). DeLisi *et al.* (1997) identified reduction in hemispheric volume over a 4-year follow-up period in 50 first episode schizophrenia patients compared with 20 controls. More recently, Wood *et al.* (2001) followed 30 first episode psychosis patients, 12 patients with chronic schizophrenia and 26 control subjects with repeated MRI scans. There were no differences between first episode patients and controls in ICV or WBV at initial assessment; however, there was progressive loss of WBV over the 2- to 4-year follow-up period. Taken together with the twin and sibling studies, these studies confirm that WBV is reduced in schizophrenia, and also indicate that these changes are progressive.

Ventricular and sulcal cerebrospinal fluid spaces

There is a more consistent literature demonstrating enlarged ventricles in schizophrenia, particularly involving lateral and third ventricles (Shenton *et al.* 2001). However, it should be noted that such changes may not be specific to schizophrenia as they have also been noted in depressed patients (Elkis *et al.* 1995). Several studies have reported ventricular enlargement, predominantly in non-familial rather than familial cases (Cannon *et al.* 1998; Baaré *et al.* 2001), which is consistent with the observed association with obstetric complications (McNeil *et al.* 2000). Nevertheless, there is evidence that genetic factors also contribute to ventricular enlargement. Sharma *et al.* (1998) found that unaffected family members, whose position within the family indicated that they were obligate carriers of the predisposition to schizophrenia, had enlarged left lateral ventricles. Furthermore, there is substantial evidence that third ventricular enlargement may be genetically determined (Staal *et al.* 2000), consistent with the findings from the Edinburgh high-risk study in which high-risk individuals had abnormally enlarged third ventricles (Lawrie *et al.* 2001). Regionally specific CSF abnormalities include left temporal horn enlargement (for discussion see Shenton *et al.* 2001), which is consistent with left temporal structural abnormalities discussed below.

Recent longitudinal studies have also provided evidence for progressive ventricular and sulcal enlargement in schizophrenia from illness onset (Giedd *et al.* 1999; Mathalon *et al.* 2001). Further, in at least some studies, ventricular enlargement has been associated with poor outcome (Staal *et al.* 1999) and with duration of untreated psychosis (Madsen *et al.* 1999).

Brain regions implicated in schizophrenia

Frontal neocortex

Grey matter volume in frontal cortex and subregions

Both manual and automated or semiautomated techniques have been used to segment the brain into grey and white matter and CSF compartments. A number of studies have variously defined prefrontal subregions to assess whether abnormalities are widespread or regionally specific. The results from the majority of the published studies suggest that the volumetric differences in prefrontal cortex in schizophrenia result from selective loss of grey matter in heteromodal dorsolateral prefrontal cortex (Schlaepfer *et al.* 1994; Goldstein *et al.* 1999; Gur *et al.* 2000a). This is associated with grey matter volume reduction in other heteromodal association cortical regions in schizophrenia. It is not observed in patients with bipolar disorder (Schlaepfer *et al.* 1994). These studies suggest that structural abnormalities are apparent in a region consistently implicated by functional imaging studies (see below).

Other studies have also identified structural abnormalities in inferior frontal regions, including the orbitofrontal cortex, in treated (Szeszko *et al.* 1999) and drug-naïve patients (Crespo-Facorro *et al.* 2000; Gur *et al.* 2000a). In the large study by Gur *et al.* (2000a), comparing neuroleptic-naïve and chronic patients with schizophrenia with healthy controls, gender-related differences were found. While both males and females had reduced grey matter in dorsolateral prefrontal cortex, only males had smaller dorsomedial prefrontal cortex. In contrast, only women had smaller orbitofrontal regions. These latter abnormalities were associated with negative symptoms, depression and poorer premorbid functioning. While these findings demonstrate that involvement of the dorsal prefrontal cortex is a consistent feature of schizophrenia, there may be gender differences for orbitofrontal cortex, which may be related to a greater degree of affective disturbance in females. Further, these frontal abnormalities are observed early in the course of illness.

Evidence for frontal involvement from *in vivo* neurochemistry (MRS)

The findings from ^{31}P-MRS in the prefrontal cortex have been summarized elsewhere (Keshavan *et al.* 2000; Vance *et al.* 2000). Although there are some inconsistencies between studies, several studies have identified reduced PMEs in first- and multi-episode patients. In contrast, PDEs are elevated mainly in first episode patients, suggesting an increased membrane turnover at the onset of illness. These findings may reflect abnormal synaptic pruning in schizophrenia (Keshavan *et al.* 2000). Recent interest in phosphorus MRS has centred on the role of fatty acids as possible treatments for schizophrenia (Berger *et al.* 2002).

The findings from proton (^{1}H) MRS of prefrontal cortex suggest that there are reductions in NAA and NAA/Cr ratio in schizophrenia, including first episode neuroleptic-naïve patients, and in schizophrenia spectrum disorders (Vance *et al.* 2000). These findings are consistent with the volumetric studies described above, and indicate that prefrontal cortical volume reduction is caused by deficits in neuronal number or in neuronal integrity. While many of these studies strongly implicate the dorsolateral prefrontal region in schizophrenia, few MRS studies have examined other prefrontal areas such as the orbitofrontal cortex.

Staging of frontal cortical structural abnormalities

While it remains unclear at what stage in neurodevelopment the changes occur in schizophrenia, the studies that can inform this question include: those examining genetic vs. environmental influences on brain structural abnormalities; studies that assess ICV (as discussed earlier); studies assessing gyral and fissural morphology; and longitudinal investigations. Woods *et al.* (1996), in their tissue segmentation study in chronic schizophrenia, found reduced ICV in the frontal region while tissue/ICV ratios were lower in frontal, temporal and parietal regions, suggesting that frontal abnormalities occurred early in life before brain growth was complete, and generalized changes in the brain occurred later after brain growth had occurred. These findings are consistent with data showing that frontal abnormalities are apparent in first episode patients (Shenton *et al.* 2001) as well as with preliminary data in premorbid high-risk individuals (Lawrie *et al.* 2001; Pantelis *et al.* 2002). Further, twin and sibling studies provide evidence that there is a genetic effect on frontal lobe volumes in schizophrenia.

While these data suggest that frontal abnormalities are apparent premorbidly in schizophrenia, the few available follow-up studies provide evidence that there is further progression of abnormalities in frontal regions (Gur *et al.* 1998; Madsen *et al.* 1999), particularly on the left. Decreases in both frontal and temporal regions were also observed in a study of childhood-onset schizophrenia (Rapoport *et al.* 1999). Further, such changes have been associated with symptom severity, including an association of prefrontal and temporal lobe grey matter decline and greater negative symptoms (Mathalon *et al.* 2001).

Associations have been found between reduced grey matter volume and neuropsychological tests of memory and executive function (Baaré *et al.* 1999). More recently, studies using both ^{1}H-MRS together with functional imaging (PET and fMRI) have identified relationships between decreased NAA in dorsolateral prefrontal cortex and impaired function of the neuronal network for working memory (Callicott *et al.* 2000).

The available data from these studies indicate that frontal grey matter abnormalities are present from illness onset, may be apparent premorbidly and that further progressive changes occur following illness onset. Further, they are associated particularly with negative symptoms and with neuropsychological deficits.

Function of prefrontal cortex

The demonstration by Weinberger *et al.* (1986) that schizophrenic patients produce less activation of the frontal cortex than healthy controls during performance of the WCST has been replicated many times, with various tests of executive function (Weinberger & Berman 1996). Unfortunately, in many studies employing complex tasks, it is difficult to rule out the possibility that the patients were not as engaged in the task as the healthy controls. However, Weinberger and Berman (1996) have demonstrated that even when patients are matched with controls for performance, the schizophrenic patients exhibit less activation of frontal cortex during performance of the WCST.

Nevertheless, the relationship between diminished activation and task performance remains a vexed question. Fletcher *et al.* (1998) demonstrated that during a word learning task, frontal activation was only diminished under circumstances where the processing load was high and performance was impaired. Similarly, Carter *et al.* (1998) and Perlstein *et al.* (2001), using the *N*-back working memory task, in which the participant is required to respond when a presented item matches the previous *N* item presented, found that schizophrenic patients only exhibited a deficit in frontal activation when memory load was high and performance was impaired.

In contrast to the evidence for hypofrontality, several studies have reported that schizophrenic patients exhibit greater activation of frontal cortex than healthy subjects during working memory tasks (Callicott *et al.* 2000; Manoach *et al.* 2000). A potential clue to understanding why frontal activation is low under some circumstances and increased under others is provided by the observation that in some of the studies reporting diminished frontal activation in patients during executive tasks the diminished activation could be attributed partly to excessive activity in the less demanding baseline comparison condition. Mendrek (2001) found that acutely ill first episode patients failed to activate lateral frontal cortex during the 2-back working memory task, relative to a baseline 0-back task that placed little demand on working memory. This failure of activation was attributable both to excessive activity in lateral frontal cortex during the baseline 0-back task and to diminished activity during the 2-back task. After 6 weeks' antipsychotic treatment, the activation in the 2-back condition relative to the 0-back condition had improved greatly, mainly because of resolution of the previously excessive activation in the 0-back condition. Thus, in acute first episode schizophrenia, diminished frontal activation can be attributed to two abnormalities: excessive activation during the low-load baseline task, and a reduced activation during more demanding tasks. The former abnormality resolves during treatment, while the latter is an enduring feature.

One of the roles of the dorsolateral prefrontal cortex is the resolution of conflict between competing responses (MacDonald *et al.* 2000). A possible explanation for the complex relationship between processing load and lateral frontal activation in acute schizophrenia is that an externally specified task must compete with abnormal self-generated mental activity, associated with psychotic symptoms. When the externally specified task entails only a low load, this competition leads to excessive dorsolateral frontal activation. However, when the externally specified task entails a higher processing load, the lateral prefrontal cortex is unable to meet the demand, resulting in both defective performance and less activation than occurs in healthy subjects.

Substantial evidence indicates that reduced dopaminergic activity contributes to impaired frontal lobe function in schizophrenia. Weinberger *et al.* (1988) demonstrated that diminished activation during the WCST was correlated with low levels of the dopamine metabolite homovanillic acid in cerebrospinal fluid. The indirect dopaminergic agonist amphetamine can partially ameliorate the failure to activate frontal cortex during the WCST (Daniel *et al.* 1991). Furthermore, using fMRI, Egan *et al.* (2001) demonstrated that individuals with a tendency to slower degradation of dopamine by virtue of genetically determined variation in function of the enzyme catechol-O-methyltransferase (COMT) exhibited a more efficient physiological response in prefrontal cortex. It is probable that neurotransmitters other than dopamine also modulate frontal function. Honey *et al.* (1999) demonstrated that the atypical antipsychotic risperidone, which blocks serotonin 5-HT_2 receptors in addition to dopamine D_2 receptors, produced enhancement of frontal function compared with that seen during treatment with typical antipsychotics, which block mainly D_2 receptors.

Temporal neocortex

Structure of temporal neocortex

The available evidence suggests that the whole of the temporal lobe may be smaller in patients with schizophrenia (for review see Shenton *et al.* 2001), most likely resulting from reduced volume of grey matter (Gur *et al.* 2000b). However, like the situation in frontal cortex, the volumetric defects may differ in its various gyri. Particularly implicated in schizophrenia is the posterior part of superior temporal gyrus that includes the planum temporale, an area specialized for the processing of language (Shapleske *et al.* 1999). However, there is also structural imaging evidence for reduced volume of parahippocampal gyrus (Wright *et al.* 2000) and more recent evidence that the fusiform gyrus is smaller (Paillere-Martinot *et al.* 2001) and may show progressive change during the early phase of the illness (Pantelis *et al.* 2002). Studies also report abnormalities in the sulcal and gyral pattern of the temporal lobe (Kikinis *et al.* 1994), suggestive of developmental abnormalities.

Longitudinal studies of the whole temporal lobe have generally not found progressive loss of volume (DeLisi *et al.* 1995; Wood *et al.* 2001), or the change in schizophrenia has been similar to normals (Gur *et al.* 1998). However, this may depend on the neurodevelopmental stage at which patients are assessed, as data from childhood-onset schizophrenia indicate progressive loss of volume (Rapoport *et al.* 1999).

Superior temporal gyrus

The temporal lobe region most consistently implicated in schizophrenia is the superior temporal gyrus (STG), including the planum temporale. While in the review by Shenton *et al.* (2001) 67% of studies examining volume of the whole STG (including grey and white matter) show reduced volume, 100% of studies examining grey matter of STG demonstrate reduced volume, indicating remarkable consistency. This abnormality is observed in first episode patients and appears to be specific to schizophrenia rather than affective psychosis (Hirayasu *et al.* 1998).

In a meta-analysis of studies examining the planum temporale, patients with schizophrenia showed a reduction in the normal pattern of leftward asymmetry as a result of a relatively larger right planum than in normal controls (Shapleske *et al.* 1999). However, because of the variable methodologies used to measure this structure, the findings have been variable between studies and include reversal of asymmetry and reduced volume in left planum temporale (for discussion see Shenton *et al.* 2001). Abnormalities in STG and planum temporale have been associated with positive symptoms (Kwon *et al.* 1999) and with thought disorder (Petty *et al.* 1995).

Symptom expression and the superior temporal gyrus

The role of the STG in auditory processing, particularly in processing of language, suggests that it is likely to have a role in the expression of symptoms such as auditory hallucinations. To test the hypothesis that impaired ability to monitor the source of internally generated mental activity might be involved in the generation of hallucinations, McGuire *et al.* (1995) used PET to assess cerebral activity while the participants imagined hearing a stranger's voice completing sentences in schizophrenic patients prone to hallucinations and two control groups: non-hallucinating patients and healthy subjects. The healthy subjects and the non-hallucinating patients exhibited activation in the STG, but this activation was significantly diminished in the patients prone to hallucinations.

The evidence that abnormal structure of the superior temporal gyrus is associated with formal thought disorder (Petty *et al.* 1995) suggests that abnormal function of the STG might also have a role in formal thought disorder. Using PET to examine cerebral activity while patients produced speech in response to presented pictures, McGuire *et al.* (1998) demonstrated that severity of positive formal thought disorder was correlated inversely with amount of activity in the left STG. This finding was subsequently confirmed by Kircher *et al.* (2001) using fMRI.

Parietal cortex

Structural abnormalities of parietal cortex

While the parietal lobe has not been the focus of many structural imaging studies, there is evidence for its involvement structurally in schizophrenia (for review see Shenton *et al.* 2001), in line with the notion that heteromodal association cortex is especially affected in schizophrenia (Ross & Pearlson 1996). A number of studies have found structural abnormalities in heteromodal regions, including parietal regions (Schlaepfer *et al.* 1994; Goldstein *et al.* 1999). Niznikiewicz *et al.* (2000) have undertaken the most comprehensive study of the various gyri of the parietal lobe to date, although the sample consisted of only 15 male patients with chronic schizophrenia and 15 male control subjects. These authors identified a reversal of the normal left greater than right asymmetry in patients with schizophrenia, particularly in the angular gyrus of the inferior parietal lobule, consistent with involvement of the semantic–lexical network. They also reported correlations between the volumes of inferior parietal lobule and regions in prefrontal and temporal cortex, consistent with the notion of an interconnected network involving these regions.

Parietal lobe and symptom expression

Underactivity of the parietal lobe has been implicated in several classes of schizophrenic symptoms. In particular, parietal underactivity is correlated with severity of psychomotor poverty symptoms (Liddle *et al.* 1992) and with severity of disorganization symptoms (Liddle *et al.* 1992; Kaplan *et al.* 1993). The association with disorganization is consistent with the evidence that formal thought disorder is associated with reduced volume of temporoparietal language areas (Niznikiewicz *et al.* 2000). In addition, patients who exhibit delusions of control exhibit decreased ability to activate parietal cortex during the selection of motor activity (Spence *et al.* 1997). This is supported by a preliminary finding of reduced volume of parietal cortex in patients with passivity delusions compared with those not having these phenomena (Velakoulis *et al.* 2000).

Cingulate cortex

Structural abnormalities of the cingulate cortex

There are few published structural imaging studies of the cingulate, despite evidence for its involvement from neuropathology and functional imaging studies. Volumetric studies are limited by difficulties in delineating the boundaries of this structure, which has led to inconsistent findings, including those of recent studies using parcellation methods. Two studies in first episode schizophreniform patients did not identify abnormalities in cingulate volume (Hirayasu *et al.* 1999; Szeszko *et al.* 1999), although Hirayasu *et al.* (1999) found reduced volume of subgenual cingulate in affective psychosis patients with a family history of affective disorder. These findings contrast with those of Goldstein *et al.* (1999), who found reduced volume in cingulate and paracingulate gyri in schizophrenia.

Because of the difficulties defining the boundaries of the cingulate, automated methods of analysis using voxel-based morphometry (VBM) may be advantageous. In contrast to the manual tracing studies, these recent VBM investigations have identified cingulate abnormalities in chronic schizophrenia (Sigmundsson *et al.* 2001) and in childhood onset schizophrenia (Sowell *et al.* 2000). However, because these techniques rely on the accuracy of the coregistration method used, morphological anomalies in cingulate surface anatomy in patients compared with controls may masquerade as volumetric differences.

Using ^{1}H-MRS, Deicken *et al.* (1997) found lower NAA bilaterally in anterior cingulate regions, which was not associated with duration of illness or medication dosage, suggesting that neuronal integrity or function of the cingulate is impaired in schizophrenia. However, other studies have not found abnormality of NAA in the anterior cingulate cortex (Bertolino *et al.* 1998).

Abnormal cingulate gyrification

Yücel *et al.* (2002b) provide a detailed examination of the degree of fissurization of the cingulate and paracingulate in normal subjects and in patients with chronic schizophrenia. Patients had reduced cingulate fissurization in the left hemisphere, and manifested a relative absence of the paracingulate sulcus compared with normal subjects. Future studies assessing the volume of the cingulate cortex will need to control for such differences in gross surface anatomy.

Selective attention and response competition

An extensive body of evidence indicates that the dorsal part of the anterior cingulate cortex and adjacent medial frontal cortex are involved in selective attention and in the identification of conflict between competing responses (MacDonald *et al.* 2000). Schizophrenic patients exhibit less activation of anterior cingulate cortex than healthy subjects during the Stroop task, which entails competition between competing responses (Carter *et al.* 1997), and which has been related to cingulate morphology (Yücel *et al.* 2002a).

Cingulate cortex and disorganization symptoms

Disorganization symptoms, such as formal thought disorder and inappropriate affect, are associated with impairment in tasks that entail selection between competing responses. Several studies have demonstrated that the severity of disorganization symptoms is significantly correlated with increased rCBF in the anterior cingulate and adjacent medial frontal cortex (Liddle *et al.* 1992; Ebmeier *et al.* 1993; Yuasa *et al.* 1995). While this excessive activity might reflect pathological overactivity of the anterior cingulate, it is also possible that it reflects an appropriate response to the intrusion of irrelevant material into current mental processing, arising from a defect elsewhere in the brain. It should be noted that the evidence indicating a tendency for excessive activity in the anterior cingulate in the resting (but symptomatic) state in schizophrenia might explain, at least in part, the diminished activation relative to baseline of this brain region during the Stroop task, reported by Carter *et al.* (1997).

Hippocampus and amygdala

Structural abnormalities of the hippocampal formation and amygdala

With the introduction of improved MRI methodologies in recent years, providing higher image resolution, studies have consistently identified abnormalities in the hippocampus or the amygdalo–hippocampal complex in patients with schizophrenia, particularly affecting the left side (Nelson *et al.* 1998; Wright *et al.* 2000). In their meta-analysis of hippocampal and amygdala volumes in schizophrenia, Nelson *et al.* (1998) found significant mean effect sizes for left (0.37) and right hippocampus (0.39), corresponding to a bilateral reduction of 4%. In a second meta-analysis of studies measuring the amygdalo–hippocampal complex, the effect sizes rose to 0.67 and 0.72 respectively. No left–right differences were identified and there was no effect of duration of illness identified in this study. Similarly, Wright *et al.* (2000) identified significant volume reductions for studies assessing the amygdala alone (6% bilaterally), a similar magnitude in those assessing the amygdalo–hippocampal complex, while smaller reductions of around 3% bilaterally were found in studies assessing the hippocampus separately. However, these studies did not contrast first episode and chronic patients, and could not assess the effects of handedness or gender, as most studies were of right-handed males.

Investigations in first episode schizophrenia suggest that hippocampal volume reduction is apparent at illness onset, and is predominantly left-sided (Hirayasu *et al.* 1998; Velakoulis *et al.* 1999), while patients with established schizophrenia show bilateral hippocampal volume reduction (Velakoulis *et al.* 1999). Velakoulis *et al.* (1999) identified similar changes in both first episode schizophreniform and affective psychosis patients, suggesting that these findings may not be specific to schizophrenia, while the results from Hirayasu *et al.* (1998) suggested a similar pattern but were not significant. While the former investigators separated the hippocampus from the amygdala, the latter measured the amygdalo–hippocampal complex. Future studies need to separate these structures as they may be differentially affected in these disorders, because there is evidence that the amygdala is larger in affective psychosis (Altshuler *et al.* 2000), so that combining these structures would confound the assessment of diagnostic specificity.

In a study of monozygotic twins discordant for schizophrenia, Suddath *et al.* (1990) demonstrated that the affected twin almost invariably has a smaller hippocampal volume than the unaffected cotwin, even though in many cases for both twins the volume was in the normal range. This finding not only indicates that in most cases of schizophrenia hippocampal volume is probably decreased, compared with what it might have been in the absence of schizophrenia, but also suggests that environmental factors contribute to the decrease. In the Edinburgh study of individuals with multiply affected family members there was no identified genetic contribution to the observed hippocampal volume reduction (Lawrie *et al.* 2001). Two studies identified a specific effect of perinatal birth complications in causing the smaller hippocampi observed in schizophrenia (Stefanis *et al.* 1999; McNeil *et al.* 2000). This is consistent with the notion that neurochemical (e.g. glutamate) or hormonal effects (e.g. cortisol) can reduce hippocampal volume, and supports the view that hippocampal volume reduction is not specific to psychotic disorders. Despite the evidence that environmental factors contribute to the reduction in hippocampal volume reported in schizophrenia, there is also evidence that genes have a role. For example, Seidman *et al.* (1999) found significant volume reductions bilaterally in the amygdalo–hippocampal region and thalamus in first-degree relatives.

The question of whether or not there are progressive changes specific to the hippocampus after the onset of schizophrenia remains controversial. Longitudinal studies using manual tracing to measure the hippocampus have generally not identified changes during the course of the illness (Lieberman *et al.* 2001; Wood *et al.* 2001), but some cross-sectional studies have reported relationships between the volume of medial temporal lobe structures and the duration of illness (Matsumoto *et al.*

2001; Velakoulis *et al.* 2001). Data from childhood-onset schizophrenia suggests that changes may occur during adolescence (Giedd *et al.* 1999).

MRS abnormalities of the hippocampal formation

Studies of the hippocampus–amygdala using ^{1}H-MRS, including the more recent ones (Bertolino *et al.* 1998), are reasonably consistent in finding reduction of intraneuronal NAA in the hippocampus (Vance *et al.* 2000). Callicot *et al.* (1998) found reduced hippocampal NAA in a large sample of healthy siblings. However, to date there have been no longitudinal studies using MRS in high-risk populations.

Hippocampal formation and symptom expression

While the evidence from structural studies indicates that the volume of medial temporal structures is decreased in schizophrenia, the majority of the evidence from functional imaging studies suggests that positive psychotic symptoms, especially hallucinations, are associated with overactivity of medial temporal lobe structures. Liddle *et al.* (1992) found that severity of reality distortion (delusions and hallucinations) was positively correlated with rCBF in the hippocampal formation and parahippocampal gyrus. Subsequently, Silbersweig *et al.* (1995) and Shergil *et al.* (2000) demonstrated overactivity of the hippocampus and other medial temporal lobe structures during the occurrence of auditory hallucinations. It should be noted that all of these studies reported that positive symptoms were associated with activation in a distributed network of frontal, temporal and subcortical sites. None the less, the observation by Liddle *et al.* (2000) that the reduction in hippocampal metabolism produced by the first dose of risperidone in previously unmedicated first episode schizophrenic patients was strongly predictive of the subsequent decrease in severity of reality distortion symptoms supports the hypothesis that hippocampal overactivity plays a primary part in reality distortion.

Hippocampal activation during memory tasks

In a PET study designed to determine whether memory impairment in schizophrenia is more strongly associated with malfunction of frontal cortex or of temporal cortex, Heckers *et al.* (1998) found that schizophrenic patients exhibited reduced hippocampal activation, relative to baseline, during conscious recollection of studied words, but robust activation of the lateral frontal cortex during the effort to retrieve poorly encoded material. It should be noted that the reduced hippocampal activation during conscious recollection was accounted for by increased activity in the baseline state.

Function of the amygdala

During a study of the induction of sad mood, Schneider *et al.* (1998) found that schizophrenic patients exhibited less activation of the amygdala than healthy controls, despite a similar severity of induced negative affect. In contrast, in an fMRI study of the processing of facial expressions, Phillips *et al.* (1999) found that a small group of non-paranoid schizophrenic patients exhibited excessive activation of the amygdala while processing expressions of disgust, associated with the misperception of disgust as fear.

Subcortical structures

Basal ganglia

The basal ganglia have a cardinal role in the regulation of cortical activity by virtue of their involvement in the corticostriatal–thalamic loops that provide feedback to frontal cortex. Several studies have demonstrated that overactivity of the ventral striatum is associated with the production of delusions and/or hallucinations (Liddle *et al.* 1992; Silbersweig *et al.* 1995). Furthermore, antipsychotic treatment is associated with reduction in activity in the corticostriatal–thalamic loops (Holcomb *et al.* 1996; Liddle *et al.* 2000).

The feedback provided by the corticostriatal–thalamic loops is modulated by dopaminergic input from the midbrain. Blockade of D_2 receptors in the striatum has long been regarded as a potentially crucial aspect of the action of antipsychotic medication. Using either SPECT or PET, it is possible to measure the displacement of labelled D_2 ligands, such as iodobenzamide or [^{11}C]raclopride, from striatal receptors, following procedures that promote dopamine release. Several studies have shown that the amount of displacement of D_2 ligands following the administration of amphetamine is increased in schizophrenia (Laruelle *et al.* 1996; Breier *et al.* 1997), implying excessive release of endogenous dopamine. Furthermore Laruelle *et al.* (1996) demonstrated that the amount of ligand displacement was correlated with the severity of transient positive symptoms induced by the amphetamine.

By measuring the D_2 receptor availability before and after pharmacological depletion of endogenous dopamine, it is possible to estimate the level of endogenous dopamine in striatal synapses and, in addition, to measure the total density of D_2 receptors. Using this technique, Abi-Dargham *et al.* (2000) demonstrated that schizophrenic patients have higher levels of intrasynaptic dopamine than healthy subjects and, furthermore, after removing endogenous dopamine, the number of available D_2 receptors was greater than in healthy controls. Overall, these studies indicate that the dopamine system is over-responsive in schizophrenia, leading to increased levels of intrasynaptic dopamine at baseline and also to excessive release following procedures such as administration of amphetamine yet, paradoxically, D_2 receptors appear to be increased rather than downregulated. One explanation of these findings is that there is excessive phasic release of dopamine, together with a diminished level of tonic dopaminergic activity leading to D_2 receptor upregulation.

Thalamus

Although reliable assessment of the volume of the thalamus is difficult, the evidence indicates that the volume of the thalamus is decreased in schizophrenia. In a meta-analysis, Konick and Friedman (2001) found that the effect size for differences between patients and controls was – 0.29, although the magnitude of the effect size increased to – 0.41 when outliers were removed. Gilbert *et al.* (2001) reported that thalamic volume is reduced even in first episode cases. Lawrie *et al.* (1999) reported reduced thalamic volume in individuals at risk for schizophrenia, with multiply affected family members.

Functional imaging studies reveal reduced thalamic activation in schizophrenic patients in a variety of tasks that engage association cortex (Andreasen *et al.* 1996; Kiehl & Liddle 2001). Despite the evidence for diminished thalamic volume and diminished activation during cognitive tasks, there is substantial evidence that the thalamus is overactive during the occurrence of symptoms such as hallucinations (Silbersweig *et al.* 1995) and disorganization symptoms (Liddle *et al.* 1992), consistent with the hypothesis that psychotic symptoms entail excessive feedback via corticostriatal–thalamic circuits.

Cerebellum

The cerebellum receives input from most areas of association cortex via the midbrain, and sends reciprocal projections back to association cortex via the thalamus. Consistent with these connections, reduced activation of the cerebellum is often observed in schizophrenia during tasks that normally engage association cortex, particularly the frontal cortex (Andreasen *et al.* 1996; Kiehl & Liddle 2001; Mendrek 2001). Furthermore, MRI studies provide some evidence for a reduction in the volume of the cerebellar vermis (Ichimiya *et al.* 2001).

Schizophrenia as a disorder of connectivity

The evidence indicating structural and functional abnormalities in distributed brain systems suggests that the core abnormality in schizophrenia is unlikely to be a focal abnormality at a single cerebral location. Furthermore, the evidence that a particular brain region, such as the prefrontal cortex or the hippocampus, can be either under- or overactive in different circumstances indicates that the core abnormality is dynamic in nature. Taken together, these observations suggest that the core problem might be an abnormality of the connections between neurones, rather than a loss of neural cell bodies. Such a disturbance of connectivity might arise from an abnormality of the myelinated axons that make up white matter, or from an abnormality of the synapses and/or dendrites that are a major component of the neuropil surrounding cell bodies in grey matter.

There are several approaches to testing the hypothesis of abnormal connectivity. The first strategy is to measure the relationship between measurements of brain structure or function in separate brain areas. The demonstration that abnormalities in one area are correlated with abnormalities measured in another area indicates that the pathophysiology of schizophrenia involves pathological influence that is exerted at a distance, but does not directly demonstrate that the connections between the areas are abnormal. The second approach compares the patterns of correlation between physiological activity at spatially remote cerebral sites in patients with that in healthy individuals. The term functional connectivity is used to describe such correlations between cerebral activity at spatially remote sites (Friston *et al.* 1993). While correlated cerebral activity does not necessarily imply a direct anatomical connection between the sites involved, it nevertheless provides an index of the coordination of cerebral activity at distant sites. The third approach entails direct assessment of structural features that are indicative of intracerebral connections, such as the assessment of white matter tracts using diffusion tensor imaging. In this section we review functional imaging studies that illustrate these three different approaches to assessing connectivity in schizophrenia.

Correlations between abnormalities at separate sites

In a study of monozygotic twins discordant for schizophrenia, Weinberger *et al.* (1992) found that hippocampal volume, measured using MRI, predicted prefrontal rCBF activation during the WCST. This finding suggests that prefrontal malfunction is secondary to hippocampal structural abnormality. However, more recent studies have pointed to microstructural abnormality in the prefrontal cortex itself. Bertolino *et al.* (2000a) found that NAA in dorsolateral prefrontal cortex, measured with MRS, selectively predicted amphetamine-induced displacement of [^{11}C]raclopride from dopamine D_2 receptors in the striatum, implying that prefrontal cellular abnormality was associated with excessive endogenous dopamine levels in the striatum. Furthermore, in two separate studies, Bertolino *et al.* (2000b) found that NAA level in the dorsolateral prefrontal cortex was correlated with activation of the distributed working memory network, including the dorsolateral prefrontal, temporal and inferior parietal cortices, during performance of working memory tasks.

Abnormal correlation between cerebral activity at spatially remote sites

Several PET studies have focused on the question of whether or not schizophrenia is characterized by an abnormal correlation between the activity in the frontal and temporal lobes. Frith *et al.* (1995) observed that activation of frontal cortex during paced word generation (relative to a baseline measured during word repetition) was accompanied by suppression of activity in the superior temporal gyrus in healthy subjects. In patients with severe persistent illness, the magnitude of frontal activation was normal, but there was an aberrant increase in activity in the superior temporal gyrus. This observation was confirmed by Fletcher *et al.* (1996) in a study of medication-naïve first episode cases, raising the possibility that it is a characteristic feature of schizophrenia at all phases of the illness. Neither Frith *et al.* (1995) nor Fletcher *et al.* (1996) directly computed the correlation between activity in frontal and temporal cortex, but in a subsequent reanalysis of the data of Frith *et al.*, Liddle (2000) demonstrated that there was indeed a negative correlation in healthy controls and a positive correlation in patients, indicating aberrant functional connectivity. Furthermore, Liddle (2000) demonstrated abnormal connectivity between frontal cortex and a range of other cerebral sites including thalamus, cingulate cortex and precuneus.

To test the hypothesis that abnormal frontotemporal connectivity is a trait marker for schizophrenia, Spence *et al.* (2000) performed a similar study of word generation in remitted patients with minimal symptoms, and also in obligate carriers of the predisposition to schizophrenia. They found that neither the remitted patients nor obligate carriers had abnormal frontotemporal connectivity. Thus, this anomaly appears to be a state marker, characteristic of symptomatic cases. None the less, Spence *et al.* (2000) did observe that the remitted patients had decreased connectivity between lateral prefrontal cortex and anterior cingulate cortex.

Consistent with the evidence for abnormal connectivity between frontal cortex and diverse cerebral sites, Josin and Liddle (2001) demonstrated that chronic schizophrenic patients could be distinguished from healthy controls with 100% reliability using data regarding functional connectivity between prefrontal cortex and 11 other cerebral sites. Similarly, Meyer-Lindenberg *et al.* (2001) achieved 94% success in the diagnosis of schizophrenia on the basis of abnormal patterns of connectivity during both 2-back and 0-back conditions of an *N*-back working memory task in a comparison between medication-free patients and healthy controls. In particular, the patients did not exhibit the normal connectivity between dorsolateral prefrontal cortex and anterior cingulate. Overall, there is strong evidence for abnormal functional connectivity between lateral frontal cortex and other brain regions in schizophrenia. The question of whether or not any of these abnormalities might be a trait marker remains a subject of debate. The current evidence points towards an abnormality of functional connectivity between lateral prefrontal cortex and anterior cingulate cortex in all phases of the illness.

When reporting correlations as evidence of functional connectivity, no assumptions are made about the causal influence of one cerebral area on another. The strength of the causal influence that activity in one area has on activity in the other area is known as the effective connectivity between those areas. Deductions about effective connectivity can only be drawn from functional imaging data if assumptions are made a priori about the connections that exist between cerebral areas. The technique of path analysis or structural equation modelling can be employed to test the plausibility of a priori models in which the direction of the connections between a set of cerebral areas are specified. As an illustration of such an approach, Jennings *et al.* (1998) demonstrated abnormal connectivity between frontal cortex and temporal cortex and also between lateral frontal cortex and anterior cingulate cortex in schizophrenia during semantic processing. Similarly, Fletcher *et al.* (1999) used path analysis to demonstrate a disruption of the normal modulation of prefrontal–temporal interactions by the anterior cingulate cortex in schizophrenic patients during word generation.

Assessment of connectivity using structural imaging

The majority of the evidence for reduced cerebral tissue volume in schizophrenia indicates that the reduction in grey matter exceeds that in white matter. Futhermore, despite some reports from postmortem studies of decreased cell numbers in grey matter, the balance of evidence indicates no widespread decrease in numbers of neurones in neocortex (Pakkenberg 1993). Thus, it is plausible that the diminution of cerebral tissue in schizophrenia might largely reflect a diminution of neurophil as a result of diminished volume of the synapses and dendrites that constitute the connections between neurones. Because the development of connections reflects usage during the period of development, the correlations between grey matter volume in different regions provide an indirect index of the connectivity between those areas during development. Woodruff *et al.* (1997) observed that the correlation between frontal and temporal lobe volumes was significantly reduced in a group of schizophrenic patients compared with healthy controls. They interpreted this as evidence for frontal–temporal dissociation during development.

While the evidence for grey matter abnormality points towards a possible abnormality of dendrites and synapses, preliminary studies using diffusion tensor imaging also provide evidence of abnormality of the myelinated axons that constitute white matter. Buchsbaum *et al.* (1998) found abnormality of frontal–striatal connections, while Lim *et al.* (1999) reported abnormalities extending across much of the brain. Foong *et al.* (2000) found abnormality of white fibres in the splenium of the corpus callosum, suggesting a specific abnormality of interhemispheric connectivity.

Conclusions

The evidence indicates subtle diminution of cerebral tissue volume in diverse brain areas in schizophrenia. Features such as abnormal gyrification suggest that the primary abnormality arises early in development. On the other hand, there is some evidence from longitudinal studies for progression of abnormalities during the course of the illness. Consistent with the widespread abnormalities of brain structure, there are also widespread abnormalities of function. In some areas, such as frontal lobes, medial temporal lobe, basal ganglia and thalamus, both abnormal increases and decreases in activity have been reported, indicating that the core problem is dynamic in nature.

Preliminary evidence points to a disorder of the development of connections between cerebral areas, which might entail abnormality of long myelinated axons, and of synapses and dendrites. However, despite the fact that a substantial number of imaging findings in schizophrenia have been replicated, there are also many inconsistencies between studies. These inconsistencies probably arise from a variety of sources, including the heterogeneity of schizophrenia, the sensitivity of brain function to subtle variations in circumstances, and the evolving nature of imaging technology. Therefore, the findings of individual studies should be interpreted with caution.

Acknowledgements

We thank Dr Stephen Wood for commenting on various drafts of the chapter. Dr Pantelis' imaging work was supported by the National Health and Medical Research Council (grant numbers 145737, 145627, 114253, 981112, 970598) and grants from the Ian Potter and Stanley Foundations.

References

Abi-Dargham, A., Rodenhiser, J., Printz, D. *et al.* (2000) From the cover: increased baseline occupancy of D_2 receptors by dopamine in schizophrenia. *Proceedings of the National Academy of Sciences of the USA* **97**, 8104–8109.

Altshuler, L.L., Bartzokis, G., Grieder, T. *et al.* (2000) An MRI study of temporal lobe structures in men with bipolar disorder or schizophrenia. *Biological Psychiatry* **48**, 147–162.

Andreasen, N.C., Rezai, K., Alliger, R. *et al.* (1992) Hypofrontality in neuroleptic-naive patients and in patients with chronic schizophrenia: assessment with xenon-133 single photon emission computed tomography and the Tower of London. *Archives of General Psychiatry* **49**, 943–958.

Andreasen, N.C., O'Leary, D.S., Cizadlo, T. *et al.* (1996) Schizophrenia and cognitive dysmetria: a positron emission tomography study of dysfunctional prefrontothalamic–cerebellar circuitry. *Proceedings of the National Academy of Sciences of the USA* **93**, 9985–9990.

Baaré, W.F., Hulshoff Pol, H.E., Hijman, R. *et al.* (1999) Volumetric analysis of frontal lobe regions in schizophrenia: relation to cognitive function and symptomatology. *Biological Psychiatry* **45**, 1597–1605.

Baaré, W.F., van Oel, C.J., Hulshoff Pol, H.E. *et al.* (2001) Volumes of brain structures in twins discordant for schizophrenia. *Archives of General Psychiatry* **58**, 33–40.

Berger, G.E., Wood, S.J., Pantelis, C. *et al.* (2002) Implications of lipid biology for the pathogenesis of schizophrenia. *Australian & New Zealand Journal of Psychiatry* **36**, 355–366.

Bertolino, A., Nawroz, S., Mattay, V.S. *et al.* (1996) Regionally specific pattern of neurochemical pathology in schizophrenia as assessed by multislice proton magnetic resonance spectroscopic imaging. *American Journal of Psychiatry* **153**, 1554–1563.

Bertolino, A., Callicott, J.H., Elman, I. *et al.* (1998) Regionally specific neuronal pathology in untreated patients with schizophrenia: a proton magnetic resonance spectroscopic imaging study. *Biological Psychiatry* **43**, 641–648.

Bertolino, A., Breier, A., Callicott, J.H. *et al.* (2000a) The relationship between dorsolateral prefrontal neuronal *N*-acetylaspartate and evoked release of striatal dopamine in schizophrenia. *Neuropsychopharmacology* **22**, 125–132.

Bertolino, A., Esposito, G., Callicott, J.H.*et al.* (2000b) Specific relationship between prefrontal neuronal *N*-acetylaspartate and activation of the working memory cortical network in schizophrenia. *American Journal of Psychiatry* **157**, 26–33.

Breier, A., Buchanan, R.W., Elkashef, A. *et al.* (1992) Brain morphology and schizophrenia: a magnetic resonance imaging study of limbic, prefrontal cortex, and caudate structures. *Archives of General Psychiatry* **49**, 921–926.

Breier, A., Su, T.P., Saunders, R. *et al.* (1997) Schizophrenia is associated with elevated amphetamine-induced synaptic dopamine concentrations: evidence from a novel positron emission tomography method. *Proceedings of the National Academy of Sciences of the USA* **94**, 2569–2574.

Buchsbaum, M.S., Tang, C.Y., Peled, S. *et al.* (1998) MRI white matter diffusion anisotropy and PET metabolic rate in schizophrenia. *Neuroreport* **9**, 425–430.

Callicott, J.H., Egan, M.F., Bertolino, A. *et al.* (1998) Hippocampal *N*-acetyl aspartate in unaffected siblings of patients with schizophrenia: a possible intermediate neurobiological phenotype. *Biological Psychiatry* **44**, 941–950.

Callicott, J.H., Bertolino, A., Mattay, V.S. *et al.* (2000) Physiological dysfunction of the dorsolateral prefrontal cortex in schizophrenia revisited. *Cerebral Cortex* **10**, 1078–1092.

Cannon, T.D., van Erp, T.G., Huttunen, M. *et al.* (1998) Regional gray matter, white matter, and cerebrospinal fluid distributions in schizophrenic patients, their siblings, and controls. *Archives of General Psychiatry* **55**, 1084–1091.

Carter, C.S., Mintun, M., Nichols, T. & Cohen, J.D. (1997) Anterior cingulate gyrus dysfunction and selective attention deficits in schizophrenia: $[^{15}O]H_2O$ PET study during single-trial Stroop task performance. *American Journal of Psychiatry* **154**, 1670–1675.

Carter, C.S., Perlstein, W., Ganguli, R. *et al.* (1998) Functional hypofrontality and working memory dysfunction in schizophrenia. *American Journal of Psychiatry* **155**, 1285–1287.

Crespo-Facorro, B., Kim, J., Andreasen, N.C., O'Leary, D.S. & Magnotta, V. (2000) Regional frontal abnormalities in schizophrenia: a quantitative gray matter volume and cortical surface size study. *Biological Psychiatry* **48**, 110–119.

Daniel, D.G., Weinberger, D.R., Jones, D.W. *et al.* (1991) The effect of amphetamine on regional cerebral blood flow during cognitive activation in schizophrenia. *Journal of Neuroscience* **11**, 1907–1917.

Deicken, R.F., Zhou, L., Schuff, N. & Weiner, M.W. (1997) Proton magnetic resonance spectroscopy of the anterior cingulate region in schizophrenia. *Schizophrenia Research* **27**, 65–71.

DeLisi, L.E., Tew, W., Xie, S. *et al.* (1995) A prospective follow-up study of brain morphology and cognition in first-episode schizophrenic patients: preliminary findings. *Biological Psychiatry* **38**, 349–360.

DeLisi, L.E., Sakuma, M., Tew, W. *et al.* (1997) Schizophrenia as a chronic active brain process: a study of progressive brain structural change subsequent to the onset of schizophrenia. *Psychiatry Research* **74**, 129–140.

Ebmeier, K.P., Blackwood, D.H.R., Murray, C. *et al.* (1993) Single photon emission tomography with ^{99m}Tc-exametazime in unmedicated schizophrenic patients. *Biological Psychiatry* **33**, 487–495.

Egan, M.F., Goldberg, T.E. & Kolachana, B.S. (2001) Effect of COMT Val108/158 Met genotype on frontal lobe function and risk for schizophrenia. *Proceedings of the National Academy of Sciences of the USA* **98**, 6917–6922.

Elkis, H., Friedman, L., Wise, A. & Meltzer, H.Y. (1995) Meta-analyses of studies of ventricular enlargement and cortical sulcal prominence in mood disorders: comparisons with controls or patients with schizophrenia. *Archives of General Psychiatry* **52**, 735–746.

Erkwoh, R., Sabri, O., Steinmeyer, E.M. *et al.* (1997) Psychopathological and SPET findings in never-treated schizophrenia. *Acta Psychiatrica Scandinavica* **96**, 51–57.

Fletcher, P.C., Frith, C.D., Grasby, P.M. *et al.* (1996) Local and distributed effects of apomorphine on fronto-temporal function in acute unmedicated schizophrenia. *Journal of Neuroscience* **16**, 7055–7062.

Fletcher, P.C., McKenna, P.J., Frith, C.D. *et al.* (1998) Brain activations in schizophrenia during a graded memory task studied with functional neuroimaging. *Archives of General Psychiatry* **55**, 1001–1008.

Fletcher, P., McKenna, P.J., Friston, K.J., Frith, C.D. & Dolan, R.J. (1999) Abnormal cingulate modulation of fronto-temporal connectivity in schizophrenia. *Neuroimage* **9**, 337–342.

Foong, J., Maier, M., Clark, C.A. *et al.* (2000) Neuropathological abnormalities of the corpus callosum in schizophrenia: a diffusion tensor imaging study. *Journal of Neurology, Neurosurgery and Psychiatry* **68**, 242–244.

Foong, J., Symms, M.R., Barker, G.J. *et al.* (2001) Neuropathological abnormalities in schizophrenia: evidence from magnetization transfer imaging. *Brain* **124**, 882–892.

Friston, K.J., Liddle, P.F., Frith, C.D. & Frackowiak, R.S.J. (1993) Functional connectivity: the principal component analysis of large (PET) data sets. *Journal of Cerebral Blood Flow and Metabolism* **13**, 5–14.

Frith, C.D., Friston, K.J., Herold, S. *et al.* (1995) Regional brain activity in chronic schizophrenic patients during the performance of a verbal fluency task. *British Journal of Psychiatry* **167**, 343–349.

Giedd, J.N., Jeffries, N.O., Blumenthal, J. *et al.* (1999) Childhood-onset schizophrenia: progressive brain changes during adolescence. *Biological Psychiatry* **46**, 892–898.

Gilbert, A.R., Rosenberg, D.R., Harenski, K. *et al.* (2001) Thalamic volumes in patients with first-episode schizophrenia. *American Journal of Psychiatry* **158**, 618–224.

Goldstein, J.M., Goodman, J.M., Seidman, L.J. *et al.* (1999) Cortical abnormalities in schizophrenia identified by structural magnetic resonance imaging. *Archives of General Psychiatry* **56**, 537–547.

Gur, R.E., Cowell, P., Turetsky, B.I. *et al.* (1998) A follow-up magnetic resonance imaging study of schizophrenia: relationship of neuroanatomical changes to clinical and neurobehavioral measures. *Archives of General Psychiatry* **55**, 145–152.

Gur, R.E., Turetsky, B.I., Bilker, W.B. & Gur, R.C. (1999) Reduced gray matter volume in schizophrenia. *Archives of General Psychiatry* **56**, 905–911.

Gur, R.E., Cowell, P.E., Latshaw, A. *et al.* (2000a) Reduced dorsal and orbital prefrontal gray matter volumes in schizophrenia. *Archives of General Psychiatry* **57**, 761–768.

Gur, R.E., Turetsky, B.I., Cowell, P.E. *et al.* (2000b) Temporolimbic volume reductions in schizophrenia. *Archives of General Psychiatry* **57**, 769–775.

Heckers, S., Rauch, S.L., Goff, D. *et al.* (1998) Impaired recruitment of the hippocampus during conscious recollection in schizophrenia. *Nature Neuroscience* **1**, 318–323.

Hirayasu, Y., Shenton, M.E., Salisbury, D.F. *et al.* (1998) Lower left temporal lobe MRI volumes in patients with first-episode schizophrenia compared with psychotic patients with first-episode affective disorder and normal subjects. *American Journal of Psychiatry* **155**, 1384–1391.

Hirayasu, Y., Shenton, M.E., Salisbury, D.F. *et al.* (1999) Subgenual cingulate cortex volume in first-episode psychosis. *American Journal of Psychiatry* **156**, 1091–1093.

Holcomb, H.H., Cascella, N.G., Thakur, G.K. *et al.* (1996) Functional sites of neuroleptic action in the human brain: PET/FDG studies with and without haloperidol. *American Journal of Psychiatry* **153**, 41–49.

Honey, G.D., Bullmore, E.T., Soni, W. *et al.* (1999) Differences in frontal cortical activation by a working memory task after substitution of risperidone for typical antipsychotic drugs in patients with schizophrenia. *Proceedings of the National Academy of Sciences of the USA* **96**, 13432–13437.

Huber, G. (1964) Neuroradiologie und Psychiatrie. In: *Psychiatrie der Gegenwart, Forschung und Praxis*, Vol. 1 *Grundlagenforschung Zur Psychiatrie* Part B. (eds H.W. Gruhle, R. Jung, W. Mayer-Gross & M. Muller), pp. 253–290. Springer-Verlag, Berlin.

Ichimiya, T., Okubo, Y., Suhara, T. & Sudo, Y. (2001) Reduced volume of the cerebellar vermis in neuroleptic-naive schizophrenia. *Biological Psychiatry* **49**, 20–27.

Ingvar, D.H. & Franzen, G. (1974) Anomalies of cerebral blood flow distribution in patients with chronic schizophrenia. *Acta Psychiatrica Scandinavica* **50**, 425–462.

Jennings, J.M., McIntosh, A.R., Kapur, S., Zipursky, R.B. & Houle, S. (1998) Functional network differences in schizophrenia: an rCBF study of semantic processing. *Neuroreport* **9**, 1697–1700.

Johnstone, E.C., Crow, T.J., Frith, C.D., Husband, J. & Kreel, L. (1976) Cerebral ventricular size and cognitive impairment in chronic schizophrenia. *Lancet* **2**, 924–926.

Josin, G.M. & Liddle, P.F. (2001) Neural network analysis of the pattern of functional connectivity between cerebral areas in schizophrenia. *Biological Cybernetics* **884**, 117–122.

Kaplan, R.D., Szechtman, H., Franco, S. *et al.* (1993) Three clinical syndromes of schizophrenia in untreated subjects: relation to brain glucose activity measured by positron emission tomography (PET). *Schizophrenia Research* **11**, 47–54.

Keshavan, M.S., Stanley, J.A. & Pettegrew, J.W. (2000) Magnetic resonance spectroscopy in schizophrenia: methodological issues and findings. II. *Biological Psychiatry* **48**, 369–380.

Kiehl, K.A. & Liddle, P.F. (2001) An event-related functional magnetic resonance imaging study of an auditory oddball task in schizophrenia. *Schizophrenia Research* **48**, 159–171.

Kikinis, R., Shenton, M.E., Gerig, G. *et al.* (1994) Temporal lobe sulco gyral pattern anomalies in schizophrenia: an *in vivo* MR three-dimensional surface rendering study. *Neuroscience Letters* **182**, 7–12.

Kircher, T.J., Liddle, P.F., Brammer, M.J. *et al.* (2001) Patterns of brain activation and formal thought disorder in schizophrenia. *Archives of General Psychiatry* **58**, 769–774.

Konick, L.C. & Friedman, L. (2001) Meta-analysis of thalamic size in schizophrenia. *Biological Psychiatry* **49**, 28–38.

Kwon, J.S., McCarley, R.W., Hirayasu, Y. *et al.* (1999) Left planum temporale volume reduction in schizophrenia. *Archives of General Psychiatry* **56**, 142–148.

Laruelle, M., Abi-Dargham, A., van Dyck, C.H. *et al.* (1996) Single photon emission computerized tomography imaging of amphetamine-induced dopamine release in drug free schizophrenic subjects. *Proceedings of the National Academy of Sciences of the USA* **93**, 9235–9240.

Lawrie, S.M., Whalley, H., Kestelman, J.N. *et al.* (1999) Magnetic resonance imaging of brain in people at high risk of developing schizophrenia. *Lancet* **353**, 30–33.

Lawrie, S.M., Whalley, H.C., Abukmeil, S.S. *et al.* (2001) Brain structure, genetic liability, and psychotic symptoms in subjects at high risk of developing schizophrenia. *Biological Psychiatry* **49**, 811–823.

Liddle, P.F. (2000) Functional brain imaging of schizophrenia. In: *The Psychopharmacology of Schizophrenia* (eds M. Reveley & W. Deakin), pp. 109–130. Arnold, London.

Liddle, P.F., Friston, K.J., Frith, C.D. *et al.* (1992) Patterns of cerebral blood flow in schizophrenia. *British Journal of Psychiatry* **160**, 179–186.

Liddle, P.F., Lane, C.M.J. & Ngan, E.T.C. (2000) Immediate effects of risperidone on cortico-striato-thalamic loops and the hippocampus. *British Journal of Psychiatry* **177**, 402–407.

Lieberman, J., Chakos, M., Wu, H. *et al.* (2001) Longitudinal study of brain morphology in first episode schizophrenia. *Biological Psychiatry* **49**, 487–499.

Lim, K.O., Hedehus, M., Moseley, M. *et al.* (1999) Compromised white matter tract integrity in schizophrenia inferred from diffusion tensor imaging. *Archives of General Psychiatry* **56**, 367–374.

MacDonald, A.W. III, Cohen, J.D., Stenger, V.A. & Carter, C.S. (2000) Dissociating the role of the dorsolateral prefrontal and anterior cingulate cortex in cognitive control. *Science* **288**, 1835–1838.

McGuire, P.K., Silbersweig, D.A., Wright, I. *et al.* (1995) Abnormal monitoring of inner speech: a physiological basis for auditory hallucinations. *Lancet* **346**, 596–600.

McGuire, P.K., Quested, D., Spence, S. *et al.* (1998) Pathophysiology of 'positive' thought disorder in schizophrenia. *British Journal of Psychiatry* **173**, 231–235.

McNeil, T.F., Cantor-Graae, E. & Weinberger, D.R. (2000) Relationship of obstetric complications and differences in size of brain structures in monozygotic twin pairs discordant for schizophrenia. *American Journal of Psychiatry* **157**, 203–212.

Madsen, A.L., Karle, A., Rubin, P. *et al.* (1999) Progressive atrophy of the frontal lobes in first-episode schizophrenia: interaction with clinical course and neuroleptic treatment. *Acta Psychiatrica Scandinavica* **100**, 367–374.

Manoach, D.S., Gollub, R.L., Benson, E.S.*et al.* (2000) Schizophrenic subjects show aberrant fMRI activation of dorsolateral prefrontal cortex and basal ganglia during working memory performance. *Biological Psychiatry* **48**, 99–109.

Mathalon, D.H., Sullivan, E.V., Lim, K.O. & Pfefferbaum, A. (2001) Progressive brain volume changes and the clinical course of schizophrenia in men: a longitudinal magnetic resonance imaging study. *Archives of General Psychiatry* **58**, 148–157.

Matsumoto, H., Simmons, A., Williams, S. *et al.* (2001) Structural magnetic imaging of the hippocampus in early onset schizophrenia. *Biological Psychiatry* **49**, 824–831.

Mendrek, A. (2001) *An fMRI study of state and trait abnormalities in schizophrenia.* PhD thesis, University of British Columbia.

Meyer-Lindenberg, A., Poline, J.B., Kohn, P.D. *et al.* (2001) Evidence for abnormal cortical functional connectivity during working memory in schizophrenia. *American Journal of Psychiatry* **158**, 1809–1817.

Nelson, M.D., Saykin, A.J., Flashman, L.A. & Riordan, H.J. (1998) Hippocampal volume reduction in schizophrenia as assessed by magnetic resonance imaging: a meta-analytic study. *Archives of General Psychiatry* **55**, 433–440.

Ngan, T.C., Lane, C.M.J., Ruth, T.J. *et al.* (2002) Immediate and delayed effects of risperidone on cerebral metabolism: correlations with symptom change. *Journal of Neurosurgery, Neurology and Psychiatry* **72**, 106–110.

Niznikiewicz, M., Donnino, R., McCarley, R.W. *et al.* (2000) Abnormal angular gyrus asymmetry in schizophrenia. *American Journal of Psychiatry* **157**, 428–437.

Paillere-Martinot, M., Caclin, A. *et al.* (2001) Cerebral gray and white matter reductions and clinical correlates in patients with early onset schizophrenia. *Schizophrenia Research* **50**, 19–26.

Pakkenberg, B. (1993) Total nerve cell numbers in neocortex in chronic schizophrenics and controls using optical dissectors. *Biological Psychiatry* **34**, 786–772.

Pantelis, C., Velaloukis, D. McGorry, P.D. *et al.* (2002) Neuroanatomical abnormalities in people who devleop psychosis. *Lancet* (in press).

Perlstein, W.M., Carter, C.S., Noll, D.C. & Cohen, J.D. (2001) Relation of prefrontal cortex dysfunction to working memory and symptoms in schizophrenia. *Amercian Journal of Psychiatry* **158**, 1105–1113.

Petty, R.G., Barta, P.E., Pearlson, G.D. *et al.* (1995) Reversal of asymmetry of the planum temporale in schizophrenia. *American Journal of Psychiatry* **152**, 715–721.

Phillips, M.L., Williams, L., Senior, C. *et al.* (1999) A differential neural response to threatening and non-threatening negative facial expressions in paranoid and non-paranoid schizophrenics. *Psychiatry Research* **92**, 11–31.

Rapoport, J.L., Giedd, J.N., Blumenthal, J. *et al.* (1999) Progressive cortical change during adolescence in childhood-onset schizophrenia: a longitudinal magnetic resonance imaging study. *Archives of General Psychiatry* **56**, 649–654.

Raz, S. & Raz, N. (1990) Structural brain abnormalities in the major psychoses: a quantitative review of the evidence from computerized imaging. *Psychological Bulletin* **108**, 93–108.

Ross, C.A. & Pearlson, G.D. (1996) Schizophrenia, the heteromodal association neocortex and development: potential for a neurogenetic approach. *Trends in Neuroscience* **19**, 171–176.

Schlaepfer, T.E., Harris, G.J., Tien, A.Y. *et al.* (1994) Decreased regional cortical gray matter volume in schizophrenia. *American Journal of Psychiatry* **151**, 842–848.

Schneider, F., Weiss, U., Kessler, C. *et al.* (1998) Differential amygdala activation in schizophrenia during sadness. *Schizophrenia Research* **34**, 133–142.

Seidman, L.J., Faraone, S.V., Goldstein, J.M. *et al.* (1999) Thalamic and amygdala–hippocampal volume reductions in first-degree relatives of patients with schizophrenia: an MRI-based morphometric analysis. *Biological Psychiatry* **46**, 941–954.

Shapleske, J., Rossell, S.L., Woodruff, P.W. & David, A.S. (1999) The planum temporale: a systematic, quantitative review of its structural, functional and clinical significance. *Brain Research Reviews* **29**, 26–49.

Sharma, T., Lancaster, E., Lee, D. *et al.* (1998) Brain changes in schizophrenia: volumetric MRI study of families multiply affected with schizophrenia – the Maudsley Family Study 5. *British Journal of Psychiatry* **173**, 132–138.

Shenton, M.E., Dickey, C.C., Frumin, M. & McCarley, R.W. (2001) A review of MRI findings in schizophrenia. *Schizophrenia Research* **49**, 1–52.

Sheppard, G., Gruzelier, J., Manchanda, R. *et al.* (1983) ^{15}O positron emission tomographic scanning of predominantly never-treated acute schizophrenic patients. *Lancet* **ii**, 1448–1452.

Shergill, S.S., Brammer, M.J., Williams, S.C., Murray, R.M. & McGuire, P.K. (2000) Mapping auditory hallucinations in schizophrenia using functional magnetic resonance imaging. *Archives of General Psychiatry* **57**, 1033–1038.

Sigmundsson, T., Suckling, J., Maier, M. *et al.* (2001) Structural abnormalities in frontal, temporal, and limbic regions and interconnecting white matter tracts in schizophrenic patients with prominent negative symptoms. *American Journal of Psychiatry* **158**, 234–243.

Silbersweig, D.A., Stern, E., Frith, C. *et al.* (1995) A functional neuroanatomy of hallucinations in schizophrenia. *Nature* **378**, 176–179.

Sowell, E.R., Levitt, J., Thompson, P.M. *et al.* (2000) Brain abnormalities in early-onset schizophrenia spectrum disorder observed with statistical parametric mapping of structural magnetic resonance images. *American Journal of Psychiatry* **157**, 1475–1484.

Spence, S.A., Brooks, D.J., Hirsch, S.R. *et al.* (1997) A PET study of voluntary movement in schizophrenic patients experiencing passivity phenomena (delusions of alien control). *Brain* **120**, 1997–2011.

Spence, S.A., Liddle, P.F., Stefan, M.D. *et al.* (2000) Functional anatomy of verbal fluency in people with schizophrenia and those at genetic risk. *British Journal of Psychiatry* **176**, 52–60.

Staal, W.G., Hulshoff Pol, H.E. & Kahn, R.S. (1999) Outcome of schizophrenia in relation to brain abnormalities. *Schizophrenia Bulletin* **25**, 337–348.

Staal, W.G., Hulshoff Pol, H.E., Schnack, H.G. *et al.* (2000) Structural brain abnormalities in patients with schizophrenia and their healthy siblings. *American Journal of Psychiatry* **157**, 416–421.

Stefanis, N., Frangou, S., Yakeley, J. *et al.* (1999) Hippocampal volume reduction in schizophrenia: effects of genetic risk and pregnancy and birth complications. *Biological Psychiatry* **46**, 697–702.

Suddath, R.L., Christison, G.W., Torrey, E.F., Casanova, M.F. & Weinberger, D.R. (1990) Anatomical abnormalities in the brains of monozygotic twins discordant for schizophrenia. *New England Journal of Medicine* **322**, 789–794.

Szeszko, P.R., Bilder, R.M., Lencz, T. *et al.* (1999) Investigation of frontal lobe subregions in first-episode schizophrenia. *Psychiatric Research and Neuroimaging* **90**, 1–15.

Vance, A.L., Velakoulis, D., Maruff, P. *et al.* (2000) Magnetic resonance spectroscopy and schizophrenia: what have we learnt? *Australian and New Zealand Journal of Psychiatry* **34**, 14–25.

Velakoulis, D., Pantelis, C., McGorry, P.D. *et al.* (1999) Hippocampal volume in first-episode psychoses and chronic schizophrenia: a high-resolution magnetic resonance imaging study. *Archives of General Psychiatry* **56**, 133–141.

Velakoulis, D., Maruff, P., Suckling, J. *et al.* (2000a) Reduced volume of inferior parietal lobe in chronic schizophrenia patients with delusions. *Schizophrenia Research* **41**, 118.

Velakoulis, D., Wood, S.J., McGorry, P.D. & Pantelis, C. (2000b) Evidence for progression of brain structural abnormalities in schizophrenia: beyond the neurodevelopmental model. *Australian and New Zealand Journal of Psychiatry* **34**, S113–S126.

Velakoulis, D., Wood, S.J., Smith, D.J. *et al.* (2002) Increased duration of illness is associated with reduced volume in right medial temporal/anterior cingulate grey matter in patients with chronic schizophrenia. *Schizophrenia Research* **57**, 43–49.

Vogeley, K., Tepest, R., Pfeiffer, U. *et al.* (2001) Right frontal hypergyria differentiation in affected and unaffected siblings from families multiply affected with schizophrenia: a morphometric MRI study. *American Journal of Psychiatry* **158**, 494–496.

Ward, K.E., Friedman, L., Wise, A. & Schulz, S.C. (1996) Meta-analysis of brain and cranial size in schizophrenia. *Schizophrenia Research* **22**, 197–213.

Weinberger, D.R. & Berman, K.F. (1996) Prefrontal function in schizophrenia: confounds and controversies. *Philosophical Transactions of the Royal Society of London B, Biological Science* **351**, 1495–1503.

Weinberger, D.R., Berman, K.F. & Zec, R.F. (1986) Physiologic dysfunction of dorsolateral prefrontal cortex in schizophrenia. I. Regional cerebral blood flow evidence. *Archives of General Psychiatry* **43**, 114–124.

Weinberger, D.R., Berman, K.F. & Illowsky, B.P. (1988) Physiologic dysfunction of dorsolateral prefrontal cortex in schizophrenia. III. A new cohort and evidence for a monoaminergic mechanism. *Archives of General Psychiatry* **45**, 609–615.

Weinberger, D.R., Berman, K.F., Suddath, R. *et al.* (1992) Evidence of dysfunction of a prefrontal–limbic network in schizophrenia: a magnetic resonance imaging and regional cerebral blood flow study of discordant monozygotic twins. *American Journal of Psychiatry* **149**, 890–897.

Williamson, P., Pelz, D., Merskey, H. *et al.* (1992) Frontal, temporal, and striatal proton relaxation times in schizophrenic patients and normal comparison subjects. *American Journal of Psychiatry* **149**, 549–551.

Wood, S.J., Velakoulis, D., Smith, D.J. *et al.* (2001) A longitudinal study of hippocampal volume in first episode psychosis and chronic schizophrenia. *Schizophrenia Research* **52**, 37–46.

Woodruff, P.W.R., Wright, I.C., Shurique, N. *et al.* (1997) Structural brain abnormalities in male schizophrenics reflect frontotemporal dissociation. *Psychological Medicine* **27**, 1257–1263.

Woods, B.T. (1998) Is schizophrenia a progressive neurodevelopmental disorder? Toward a unitary pathogenetic mechanism. *American Journal of Psychiatry* **155**, 1661–1670.

Woods, B.T., Yurgelun-Todd, D., Goldstein, J.M., Seidman, L.J. & Tsuang, M.T. (1996) MRI brain abnormalities in chronic schizophrenia: one process or more? *Biological Psychiatry* **40**, 585–596.

Wright, I.C., Rabe-Hesketh, S., Woodruff, P.W.R. *et al.* (2000) Meta-analysis of regional brain volumes in schizophrenia. *American Journal of Psychiatry* **157**, 16–25.

Yuasa, S., Kurachi, M., Suzuki, M. *et al.* (1995) Clinical symptoms and regional cerebral blood flow in schizophrenia. *European Archives of Psychiatry and Clinical Neuroscience* **246**, 7–12.

Yücel, M., Pantelis, C., Stuart, G.W. *et al.* (2002a) Anterior cingulate activation during Stroop task performance: a PET to MRI coregistration study of individual patients with schizophrenia. *American Journal of Psychiatry* **159**, 251–254.

Yücel, M., Stuart, G.W., Maruff, P. *et al.* (2002b) Paracingulate morphologic differences in males with established schizophrenia: a maynetic resonance imaging morplometic study. *Biological Psychiatry* **52**, 15–23.

Zipursky, R.B., Lambe, E.K., Kapur, S. & Mikulis, D.J. (1998) Cerebral gray matter volume deficits in first episode psychosis. *Archives of General Psychiatry* **55**, 540–546.